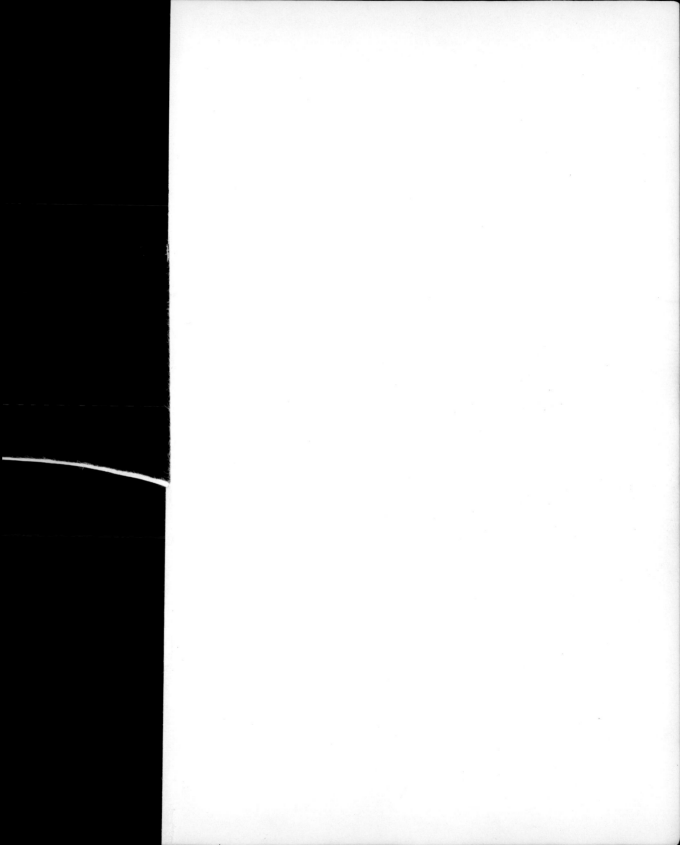

QUANTUM MECHANICS

VOLUME II

FROM THE SERIES IN PHYSICS

General Editors:

J. DE BOER, Professor of Physics, University of Amsterdam
H. BRINKMAN, Professor of Physics, University of Groningen
H. B. G. CASIMIR, Director of the Philips' Research Laboratories, Eindhoven

Monographs:

B. BAK, Elementary Introduction to Molecular Spectra
V. L. BONCH–BRUEVICH and S. V. TYABLIKOV, The Green Function Method in Statistical Mechanics
V. L. GINZBURG, Propagation of Electromagnetic Waves in Plasma
S. R. DE GROOT and P. MAZUR, Non-Equilibrium Thermodynamics
R. HOSEMANN and S. N. BAGCHI, Direct Analysis of Diffraction by Matter
H. J. LIPKIN, Beta Decay for Pedestrians
P. H. E. MEYER and E. BAUER, Group Theory. The Application to Quantum Mechanics
S. RAIMES, The Wave Mechanics of Electrons in Metals
D. TER HAAR, Elements of Hamiltonian Mechanics
S. TOMONAGA, Quantum Mechanics

Edited Volumes:

J. DE BOER and G. E. UHLENBECK (editors), Studies in Statistical Mechanics, Vol. I
FUNDAMENTAL PROBLEMS IN STATISTICAL MECHANICS. Proceedings of the NUFFIC International Summer Course in Science (Nijenrode, 1961)
G. M. GRAHAM and A. C. HOLLIS HALLETT (editors), Proceedings of the 7th International Conference on Low Temperature Physics (Toronto, 1960)
H. C. VAN DE HULST, C. DE JAGER and A. F. MOORE (editors), Space Research II. Proceedings of the Second International Space Science Symposium (Florence, 1961)
H. KALLMANN–BIJL (editor), Space Research, Proceedings of the 1st International Space Science Symposium (Nice, 1960)
H. MAECKER (editor), Proceedings of the 5th International Conference on Ionization Phenomena in Gases (Munich, 1961)
S. F. SINGER (editor), Progress in the Astronautical Sciences, Vol. I
E. WOLF (editor), Progress in Optics, Vol. I

QUANTUM MECHANICS

VOLUME II

ALBERT MESSIAH

Saclay, France

1962

NORTH-HOLLAND PUBLISHING COMPANY–AMSTERDAM

JOHN WILEY & SONS, INC. – NEW YORK

ORIGINAL TITLE: MÉCANIQUE QUANTIQUE, VOL. II

TRANSLATED FROM THE FRENCH

BY

J. POTTER

Orsay (S.-et-O.), France

MÉCANIQUE QUANTIQUE I AND II WERE PUBLISHED BY

DUNOD, PARIS

PUBLISHERS:

NORTH-HOLLAND PUBLISHING COMPANY, AMSTERDAM

JOHN WILEY & SONS, INC. – NEW YORK

Printed in the United States of America

Fluctuat nec mergitur

CONTENTS

OF VOLUME II

PART THREE

SYMMETRIES AND INVARIANCE

CHAPTER XIII

ANGULAR MOMENTUM IN QUANTUM MECHANICS

CHAPTER XIV

SYSTEMS OF IDENTICAL PARTICLES. PAULI EXCLUSION PRINCIPLE

CHAPTER XV

INVARIANCE AND CONSERVATION THEOREMS. TIME REVERSAL

PART FOUR

METHODS OF APPROXIMATION

CHAPTER XVI

STATIONARY PERTURBATIONS

CHAPTER XVII

APPROXIMATE SOLUTIONS OF THE TIME-DEPENDENT SCHRÖDINGER EQUATION

CHAPTER XVIII

THE VARIATIONAL METHOD AND ASSOCIATED PROBLEMS

CHAPTER XIX

COLLISION THEORY

PART FIVE

ELEMENTS OF RELATIVISTIC QUANTUM MECHANICS

CHAPTER XX

THE DIRAC EQUATION

CHAPTER XXI

FIELD QUANTIZATION. RADIATION THEORY

Mon Dieu! ma chère, que ton père
a la forme enfoncée dans la matière!
(*Les Précieuses Ridicules*, VI).

PART THREE

SYMMETRIES AND INVARIANCE

CHAPTER XIII

ANGULAR MOMENTUM IN QUANTUM MECHANICS

1. Introduction

Symmetry properties of the equations of motion play a large role in Quantum Mechanics as in Classical Mechanics. A systematic and general examination of symmetries and of their consequences will be made in Chapter XV. The present chapter is devoted to symmetries with respect to rotations—one of the most important types. In Quantum Mechanics, as in Classical Mechanics, the rotation of a system brings in its angular momentum, and the rotational invariance of the equations of motion is reflected in the angular momentum being a constant of the motion. Differences with Classical Mechanics arise because the angular momentum is not an ordinary vector but a vector operator, whose three components do not commute.

In section I, we define the angular momentum by the commutation rules for its components J_x, J_y, J_z [relations (XIII.3)] and solve the eigenvalue problem for $\mathbf{J}^2$ and J_z using only these rules and the fact that these three components are observables. The method, due to Dirac, is analogous in many ways to the treatment of the harmonic oscillator in Chapter XII.

Section II is devoted to a special case, the orbital angular momentum of a particle and the construction of the corresponding eigenfunctions (the spherical harmonics).

In section III we establish the connection between rotations and angular momentum. The rotation of a physical system is effected by a certain operator which depends on the components of the total angular momentum, and whose form is given by equation (XIII.60). We show that invariance of the equations of motion under rotation is equivalent to the condition that the Hamiltonian commute with the three angular momentum components, whence the law of conservation of angular momentum.

Experiment shows that most particles possess an intrinsic angular momentum, the spin. The notion of spin is examined in section IV.

Section V is devoted to the important problem of the addition of angular momenta.

The different operators of Quantum Mechanics may be characterized by their law of transformation under rotations. In particular, there are scalar operators (invariant under rotation), vector operators, and more generally, irreducible tensor operators, whose transformation properties are especially simple. These operators are characterized as well by their very simple commutation rules with the components of angular momentum, from which follow certain noteworthy properties of their representations (Wigner–Eckart theorem). These are treated, with their principal applications, in the sixth and last section of this chapter.

Appendix C is a complement to the present chapter in which are assembled the most important formulae and the principal properties of the different coefficients associated with rotations and with the addition of angular momenta.

I. EIGENVALUES AND EIGENFUNCTIONS OF ANGULAR MOMENTUM

2. Definition of Angular Momentum

We have already encountered the angular momentum operator in the treatment of single particle quantum systems. By definition, the angular momentum $\boldsymbol{l}$ of the particle is given by

$$\boldsymbol{l} \equiv \boldsymbol{r} \times \boldsymbol{p}, \qquad \text{(XIII.1)}$$

$\boldsymbol{r}$ and $\boldsymbol{p}$ being respectively the position and momentum vectors of the given particle. In Wave Mechanics, $\boldsymbol{l}$ is represented by the vector operator [1] $(-\mathrm{i})\, \boldsymbol{r} \times \nabla$ whose three components are differential operators satisfying the commutation rules

$$[l_x, l_y] = \mathrm{i}\, l_z, \qquad [l_y, l_z] = \mathrm{i}\, l_x, \qquad [l_z, l_x] = \mathrm{i}\, l_y. \qquad \text{(XIII.2)}$$

Each of them commutes with the square of the angular momentum

$$\boldsymbol{l}^2 \equiv l_x^2 + l_y^2 + l_z^2,$$

i.e.

$$[\boldsymbol{l}, \boldsymbol{l}^2] = 0.$$

These properties have already been derived in § V.18. Recall that the last of them is a simple consequence of relations (XIII.2).

[1]) In the present chapter the units are chosen so as to have $\hbar = 1$.

$\mathbf{r}$, $\mathbf{p}$, and $\mathbf{l}$ are *vector operators*. A vector operator $\mathbf{B}$ is defined by its components B_x, B_y, B_z along three orthogonal axes, where B_x, B_y, B_z are operators in the ordinary sense of the term. Given these three particular components, we can define the component B_u of $\mathbf{B}$ in an arbitrary direction $\mathbf{u}$ defined by the unit vector $\mathbf{u}(u_x, u_y, u_z)$:

$$B_u \equiv (\mathbf{u} \cdot \mathbf{B}) = u_x B_x + u_y B_y + u_z B_z.$$

We may thus define the components of $\mathbf{B}$ along any other system of orthogonal axes. The different manipulations of vector algebra (sum, scalar product, vector product, etc.) apply without change to vector operators if we observe a few precautions regarding the order of the operators involved (cf. § IX.2).

Consider now a quantum system of N particles. As above, we can define the angular momentum of the nth particle $\mathbf{l}^{(n)} = \mathbf{r}^{(n)} \times \mathbf{p}^{(n)}$. The total angular momentum of the system is the vector sum of the angular momenta of the N particles,

$$\mathbf{L} = \sum_{n=1}^{N} \mathbf{l}^{(n)}.$$

Since each individual angular momentum satisfies the commutation relations (XIII.2), and since the components of any one of them commute with those of any other, we have

$$[L_x, L_y] = \sum_n \sum_{n'} [l_x^{(n)}, l_y^{(n')}] = \sum_n [l_x^{(n)}, l_y^{(n)}] = \mathrm{i} \sum_n l_z^{(n)} = \mathrm{i}\, L_z.$$

We similarly obtain the two relations resulting from circular permutation of the indices. Thus the components of total angular momentum have the same commutation rules as those of the individual angular momenta themselves.

We are thus led to the following definition of angular momentum: *A vector operator $\mathbf{J}$ is an angular momentum if its components are observables satisfying the commutation relations*:

$$[J_x, J_y] = \mathrm{i}\, J_z, \qquad [J_y, J_z] = \mathrm{i}\, J_x, \qquad [J_z, J_x] = \mathrm{i}\, J_y. \tag{XIII.3}$$

From these three relations we can deduce analogous relations for the components of $\mathbf{J}$ along any other system of axis. Let J_u, J_v, J_w be the components of $\mathbf{J}$ along three orthogonal axes whose unit vectors $\mathbf{u}$, $\mathbf{v}$, $\mathbf{w}$ are so oriented that $\mathbf{w} = \mathbf{u} \times \mathbf{v}$. We can easily prove the relation

$[J_u, J_v] = \mathrm{i}\, J_w$ and the two relations resulting from circular permutation of the indices [1]). More generally, if $\boldsymbol{a}$ and $\boldsymbol{b}$ are any two vectors (or two vector operators that commute with each other and also with $\boldsymbol{J}$), we have

$$[\boldsymbol{a}\cdot\boldsymbol{J}, \boldsymbol{b}\cdot\boldsymbol{J}] = \mathrm{i}\,((\boldsymbol{a}\times\boldsymbol{b})\cdot\boldsymbol{J}). \tag{XIII.4}$$

3. Characteristic Algebraic Relations

The square of the angular momentum,

$$\boldsymbol{J}^2 \equiv J_x^2 + J_y^2 + J_z^2,$$

commutes with J_x, J_y and J_z. This property is a consequence of commutation relations (XIII.3), and can be deduced in the same way as the analogous property for the angular momentum $\boldsymbol{l}$ introduced in § 2. We write symbolically,

$$[\boldsymbol{J}, \boldsymbol{J}^2] = 0 \tag{XIII.5}$$

In consequence, $\boldsymbol{J}^2$ commutes with any function of the components of $\boldsymbol{J}$.

Let us introduce the two Hermitean conjugate operators

$$J_+ = J_x + \mathrm{i}\, J_y, \qquad J_- = J_x - \mathrm{i}\, J_y. \tag{XIII.6}$$

The three operators J_+, J_-, and J_z completely define the vector operator $\boldsymbol{J}$ and turn out to be more convenient for algebraic manipulations than J_x, J_y, and J_z. Their commutation relations can be deduced from relations (XIII.3):

$$[J_z, J_+] = J_+ \tag{XIII.7a}$$

$$[J_z, J_-] = -J_- \tag{XIII.7b}$$

$$[J_+, J_-] = 2J_z. \tag{XIII.7c}$$

---

1) These relations can also be written in the condensed form ($i, j, k = u$, v or w)

$$[J_i, J_j] = \mathrm{i} \sum_k \varepsilon_{ijk} J_k \quad \text{or} \quad \sum_{ij} \varepsilon_{ijk} J_i J_j = \mathrm{i}\, J_k,$$

where ε_{ijk} is the completely antisymmetrical tensor with three indices:

$$\varepsilon_{ijk} = \begin{cases} 0 \text{ if two indices are equal.} \\ +1 \text{ if } i, j, k \text{ are obtained by even permutation of } u, v, w. \\ -1 \text{ if } i, j, k \text{ are obtained by odd permutation of } u, v, w. \end{cases}$$

The second form is equivalent to the equation between vector operators,

$$\boldsymbol{J} \times \boldsymbol{J} = \mathrm{i}\, \boldsymbol{J}.$$

Also, from equation (XIII.5), we have

$$[\boldsymbol{J}^2, J_+] = [\boldsymbol{J}^2, J_-] = [\boldsymbol{J}^2, J_z] = 0. \qquad \text{(XIII.8)}$$

$\boldsymbol{J}^2$ is given by the expression

$$\boldsymbol{J}^2 = \tfrac{1}{2}(J_+ J_- + J_- J_+) + J_z^2$$

from which we deduce, with the aid of (XIII.7*c*), the two identities

$$J_- J_+ = \boldsymbol{J}^2 - J_z (J_z + 1) \qquad \text{(XIII.9}a\text{)}$$

$$J_+ J_- = \boldsymbol{J}^2 - J_z (J_z - 1). \qquad \text{(XIII.9}b\text{)}$$

4. Spectrum of $\boldsymbol{J}^2$ and J_z

Since $\boldsymbol{J}^2$ commutes with each of the components of $\boldsymbol{J}$, one can form a complete set of common eigenfunctions of $\boldsymbol{J}^2$ and one of its components, J_z for example. The fact that J_x, J_y, and J_z are *Hermitean* and obey *commutation relations* (XIII.3) imposes severe limitations on the eigenvalue spectrum.

$\boldsymbol{J}^2$ is a positive-definite Hermitean operator since it is the sum of positive-definite Hermitean operators [1]). Its eigenvalues are necessarily positive (or zero). They shall henceforth be written in the form $j(j+1)$, and labelled with the real quantum number $j(\geqslant 0)$.

Let $|jm\rangle$ be an eigenvector of $\boldsymbol{J}^2$ and J_z corresponding to the eigenvalues $j(j+1)$ and m respectively. We shall say that $|jm\rangle$ represents the state of angular momentum (jm). If $\boldsymbol{J}^2$ and J_z do not form a complete set of commuting observables, there may exist several linearly independent states (jm). In this case, $|jm\rangle$ is a particular ket vector chosen once and for all in the subspace of angular momentum (jm). The following argument is valid for any vector thus chosen. The only conditions imposed on $|jm\rangle$ are:

$$\boldsymbol{J}^2 |jm\rangle = j\,(j+1)\,|jm\rangle,$$
$$J_z\,|jm\rangle = m\,|jm\rangle.$$

Consider the vectors $J_+|jm\rangle$ and $J_-|jm\rangle$.

---

1) This is a consequence of the Hermitean character of J_x, J_y and J_z. For any $|u\rangle$, $\langle u|J_x{}^2|u\rangle$ is the norm of the vector $J_x|u\rangle$ and it is therefore $\geqslant 0$. Since $J_y{}^2$ and $J_z{}^2$ have the same property, $\langle u|\boldsymbol{J}^2|u\rangle \geqslant 0$ for any $|u\rangle$.

From identities (XIII.9*a*) and (XIII.9*b*),

$$J_- J_+ |jm\rangle = [j(j+1) - m(m+1)] |jm\rangle \equiv (j-m)(j+m+1) |jm\rangle \tag{XIII.10a}$$

$$J_+ J_- |jm\rangle = [j(j+1) - m(m-1)] |jm\rangle \equiv (j+m)(j-m+1) |jm\rangle. \tag{XIII.10b}$$

Thus the norms of the vectors $J_+ |jm\rangle$ and $J_- |jm\rangle$ are respectively

$$\langle jm | J_- J_+ | jm\rangle = (j-m)(j+m+1) \langle jm | jm\rangle$$
$$\langle jm | J_+ J_- | jm\rangle = (j+m)(j-m+1) \langle jm | jm\rangle.$$

By a fundamental axiom of Hilbert space these norms cannot be negative, and therefore

$$(j-m)(j+m+1) \geqslant 0, \qquad (j+m)(j-m+1) \geqslant 0,$$

from which

$$-j \leqslant m \leqslant j.$$

Moreover, since the vanishing of its norm is a necessary and sufficient condition for the vanishing of a vector,

$$J_+ |jm\rangle = 0 \text{ if, and only if } (j-m)(j+m+1) = 0;$$

similarly,

$$J_- |jm\rangle = 0 \text{ if, and only if } (j+m)(j-m+1) = 0.$$

Since m is necessarily in the interval $(-j, +j)$, these vanishing conditions reduce to $m=j$ and $m=-j$ respectively.

If $m \neq j$, the (non-null) vector $J_+ |jm\rangle$ is a vector of angular momentum $(j, m+1)$; i.e. following rule (XIII.8):

$$\boldsymbol{J}^2 J_+ |jm\rangle = J_+ \boldsymbol{J}^2 |jm\rangle = j(j+1) J_+ |jm\rangle$$

and, since from (XIII.7*a*)

$$J_z J_+ = J_+ (J_z + 1) \tag{XIII.11a}$$

we have

$$J_z J_+ |jm\rangle = J_+ (J_z + 1) |jm\rangle = (m+1) J_+ |jm\rangle.$$

Using the fact that J_- commutes with $\boldsymbol{J}^2$ and that, from (XIII.7*b*),

$$J_z J_- = J_- (J_z - 1) \tag{XIII.11b}$$

we obtain an analogous result for $J_- |jm\rangle$.

Summarizing, we have the important theorem:
If $|jm\rangle$ *is a vector of angular momentum* (jm) *and of norm* N:

(i) *necessarily*

$$-j \leqslant m \leqslant j; \qquad \text{(XIII.12)}$$

(ii) *if* $m=j, J_+|jm\rangle = 0$;
if $m \neq j, J_+|jm\rangle$ *is necessarily a vector of angular momentum* $(j, m+1)$ *and of norm* $[j(j+1)-m(m+1)]N$;

(iii) *if* $m=-j, J_-|jm\rangle = 0$;
if $m \neq -j, J_-|jm\rangle$ *is necessarily a vector of angular momentum* $(j, m-1)$ *and of norm* $[j(j+1)-m(m+1)]N$.

We now consider the vectors obtained by repeated application of the operator J_+ to $|jm\rangle$:

$$J_+|jm\rangle, J_+^2|jm\rangle, \ldots, J_+^p|jm\rangle, \ldots \qquad \text{(XIII.13)}$$

We know that $-j \leqslant m \leqslant j$. If $m=j, J_+|jm\rangle=0$. If $m<j$, $J_+|jm\rangle$ is a non-null vector of angular momentum $(j, m+1)$. It therefore has the properties (i)–(iii) characteristic of any common eigenvector of $\boldsymbol{J}^2$ and J_z: necessarily $m+1 \leqslant j$. If $m+1=j$, $J_+^2|jm\rangle=0$. If $m+1<j$, $J_+^2|jm\rangle$ is a non-null vector of angular momentum $(j, m+2)$ and therefore it too has the properties (i)–(iii). One may thus, step-by-step, continue the analysis of the properties of the vectors (XIII.13). Clearly this sequence must terminate somewhere; otherwise we could form eigenvectors of J_z having eigenvalues larger than any given number, in contradiction with (XIII.12) according to which the eigenvalues of J_z cannot be larger than j. Therefore, there exists an integer $p(\geqslant 0)$ such that $J_+^p|jm\rangle$ is a non-null vector of angular momentum $(j, m+p)$ and upon which the action of J_+ gives 0; we therefore have $m+p=j$. Thus we have shown that $j-m$ is integral $(\geqslant 0)$ and that the p vectors

$$J_+|jm\rangle, J_+^2|jm\rangle, \ldots, J_+^p|jm\rangle \qquad \text{(XIII.14)}$$

represent states of well-defined angular momentum, corresponding all to the same eigenvalue $j(j+1)$ of $\boldsymbol{J}^2$ and to the eigenvalues

$$m+1, m+2, \ldots, m+p=j,$$

of J_z respectively.

A similar examination of the vectors obtained by repeated application of J_- to $|jm\rangle$ shows that $j+m \equiv q$ is also an integer $\geqslant 0$, and that the q vectors

$$J_-|jm\rangle, J_-^2|jm\rangle, \ldots, J_-^q|jm\rangle \tag{XIII.15}$$

represent states of well-defined angular momentum all corresponding to the same eigenvalue $j(j+1)$ of $\boldsymbol{J}^2$, and to the eigenvalues

$$m-1, m-2, \ldots, m-q=-j,$$

of J_z respectively. Since p and q are both non-negative integers, their sum $p+q=2j$ is also a non-negative integer.

Bringing together these results, we have the following fundamental theorem:

(A) *The only possible eigenvalues of $\boldsymbol{J}^2$ are of the form $j(j+1)$, where j is a non-negative, integral or half-integral* [1]) *number*:

$$j=0, \tfrac{1}{2}, 1, \tfrac{3}{2}, 2, \ldots, \infty.$$

(B) *The only possible eigenvalues of J_z are the integral and half-integral numbers*:

$$m=0, \pm\tfrac{1}{2}, \pm 1, \pm\tfrac{3}{2}, \pm 2, \ldots, \pm\infty.$$

(C) *If $j(j+1)$ and m are the respective eigenvalues of $\boldsymbol{J}^2$ and J_z corresponding to a common eigenstate of these two operators*—that is, to a state of angular momentum (jm)—*the only possible values of m are the $(2j+1)$ quantities*

$$-j, -j+1, \ldots, +j.$$

5. Eigenvectors of $\boldsymbol{J}^2$ and J_z. Construction of the Invariant Subspaces $\mathscr{E}^{(j)}$

Starting from a vector $|j\,m\rangle$ of well-defined angular momentum one can construct in all $2j+1$ vectors of well-defined angular momentum by repeated application of the operators J_+ and J_-. In general these vectors are not normalized to unity but by proceeding in the following way one may easily construct eigenvectors which are.

---

[1]) Throughout this book "half-integral" will be understood to mean "half-odd-integral" i.e. the values $\frac{1}{2}, \frac{3}{2}, \frac{5}{2}, \ldots$.

Suppose that the norm of $|j\,m\rangle$ is equal to one. $J_+|j\,m\rangle$ is zero if $m=j$; if $m<j$ it is a vector of angular momentum $(j, m+1)$. Denote by $|j\,m+1\rangle$ the vector of norm 1 defined by

$$J_+|j\,m\rangle = c_m\,|j\,m+1\rangle.$$

From the expression given above for the norm of $J_+|j\,m\rangle$ it follows that

$$|c_m|^2 = [j\,(j+1) - m\,(m+1)].$$

We fix the phase of $|j\,m+1\rangle$ so that c_m is both real and positive. Thus:

$$J_+|j\,m\rangle = \sqrt{j\,(j+1) - m\,(m+1)}\,|j\,m+1\rangle.$$

Multiplying both sides by J_- and using (XIII.10a), we have

$$J_-|j\,m+1\rangle = \sqrt{j\,(j+1) - m\,(m+1)}\,|j\,m\rangle.$$

The vector $|j\,m+1\rangle$ may be treated in the same way. It suffices to replace everywhere m by $m+1$. If $m+1=j$, $J_+|j\,m+1\rangle=0$. If $m+1\neq j$ we form the vector $|j\,m+2\rangle$, of angular momentum $(j, m+2)$ and of norm 1 with its phase fixed by a convention identical to the one above. And so forth until we obtain $|j\,j\rangle$.

In the same way, by repeated application of J_-, we successively form the vectors $|j\,m-1\rangle, \ldots, |j\,-j\rangle$ of norm 1 and of angular momentum $(j, m-1), \ldots, (j, -j)$ respectively; their phase is fixed by an identical convention.

Thus, starting from $|j\,m\rangle$, we form a series of $(2\,j+1)$ orthonormal vectors

$$|j\,j\rangle\;|j\,j-1\rangle\;\ldots\;|j\,m\rangle\;\ldots\;|j\,-j\rangle \qquad \text{(XIII.16)}$$

satisfying the eigenvalue equations

$$\boldsymbol{J}^2\,|j\,\mu\rangle = j\,(j+1)\,|j\,\mu\rangle \qquad \text{(XIII.17)}$$

$$J_z\,|j\,\mu\rangle = \mu\,|j\,\mu\rangle \qquad \text{(XIII.18)}$$

and whose relative phases have been chosen in such a way that they are obtained one from another by the relations

$$J_+|j\,\mu\rangle = \sqrt{j\,(j+1) - \mu\,(\mu+1)}\,|j\,\mu+1\rangle \qquad \text{(XIII.19)}$$

$$J_-|j\,\mu\rangle = \sqrt{j\,(j+1) - \mu\,(\mu-1)}\,|j\,\mu-1\rangle. \qquad \text{(XIII.20)}$$

In particular

$$J_+ |j\,j\rangle = J_- |j\,-j\rangle = 0. \tag{XIII.21}$$

These $(2j+1)$ vectors span a certain subspace $\mathscr{E}^{(j)}$. Since the operators J_+, J_-, J_z transform these vectors one into another, they transform any vector of $\mathscr{E}^{(j)}$ into a vector of $\mathscr{E}^{(j)}$; in other words, they leave $\mathscr{E}^{(j)}$ invariant. Any function $F(\boldsymbol{J})$ of the components of $\boldsymbol{J}$, being a function only of the operators J_+, J_-, J_z also leaves $\mathscr{E}^{(j)}$ invariant. In section III we shall see that an overall rotation of the quantum system corresponds to the application of an operator of the type $F(\boldsymbol{J})$ to the state vector; therefore, any rotation of the whole system leaves $\mathscr{E}^{(j)}$ invariant.

6. Standard Representation $\{\boldsymbol{J}^2\, J_z\}$

If $\boldsymbol{J}^2$ and J_z do not form a complete set of commuting observables, there will be many systems of basis vectors common to these two operators. Even when they do form a complete set, the phase of each basis vector may be arbitrarily fixed.

Among the representations with $\boldsymbol{J}^2$ and J_z diagonal there are certain in which manipulations of the angular momentum are particularly simple, and which are therefore preferable. They will be called *standard representations* $\{\boldsymbol{J}^2\, J_z\}$. They are those representations in which the basis vectors corresponding to a specified value of the quantum number j can be grouped in one or several series of $(2j+1)$ vectors connected by relations (XIII.19–20). To each series there corresponds a subspace $\mathscr{E}^{(j)}$ and the entire Hilbert space is the direct sum of such subspaces.

To set up a standard representation we may proceed in the following way. Among the eigenvectors of $\boldsymbol{J}^2$ belonging to the eigenvalue $j\,(j+1)$ we consider those for which $J_z = j$. They form a certain subspace $\mathscr{F}^{(j)}$ of Hilbert space which according to the case can have one, several or an infinite number of dimensions. It is always possible to choose a complete set of orthonormal vectors $|\tau\, j\, j\rangle$ in $\mathscr{F}^{(j)}$. The index τ distinguishes these vectors of angular momentum $(j\,j)$ one from another; it can, according to the case, take one, several or an infinite number of values (discrete or continuous; we shall suppose them discrete). We have by hypothesis

$$\langle \tau\, j\, j | \tau'\, j\, j\rangle = \delta_{\tau\tau'}.$$

With each of these vectors $|\tau\, j\, j\rangle$ we can associate the $2j$ vectors obtained by repeated application of J_- according to the method of the preceding paragraph, thus forming a $(2j+1)$-dimensional subspace $\mathscr{E}^{(j)}$; to distinguish these subspaces one from another we shall denote them $\mathscr{E}(\tau\, j)$. Thus the $(2j+1)$ basis vectors of the subspace $\mathscr{E}(\tau\, j)$ are

$$|\tau\, j\, j\rangle, |\tau\, j\, j-1\rangle, \ldots, |\tau\, j\, -j\rangle.$$

These vectors are orthonormal and satisfy the fundamental relations

$$\boldsymbol{J}^2\, |\tau\, j\, \mu\rangle = j\,(j+1)\, |\tau\, j\, \mu\rangle \tag{XIII.22}$$

$$J_z\, |\tau\, j\, \mu\rangle = \mu\, |\tau\, j\, \mu\rangle \tag{XIII.23}$$

$$J_+\, |\tau\, j\, \mu\rangle = \sqrt{j\,(j+1) - \mu\,(\mu+1)}\, |\tau\, j\, \mu+1\rangle \tag{XIII.24}$$

$$J_-\, |\tau\, j\, \mu\rangle = \sqrt{j\,(j+1) - \mu\,(\mu-1)}\, |\tau\, j\, \mu-1\rangle. \tag{XIII.25}$$

From (XIII.24) and (XIII.25) we easily deduce the following important relations (Problem XIII.1):

$$|\tau\, j\, \pm\mu\rangle = \sqrt{\frac{(j+\mu)!}{(2\,j)!\,(j-\mu)!}}\, J_{\mp}^{j-\mu}\, |\tau\, j\, \pm j\rangle \tag{XIII.26}$$

$$|\tau\, j\, \pm j\rangle = \sqrt{\frac{(j+\mu)!}{(2\,j)!\,(j-\mu)!}}\, J_{\pm}^{j-\mu}\, |\tau\, j\, \pm\mu\rangle. \tag{XIII.27}$$

It is easily shown that the subspaces $\mathscr{E}(\tau\, j)$ (given j, variable τ) are mutually orthogonal and that together they form the subspace $\mathscr{E}_j$ for the eigenvalue $j\,(j+1)$ of $\boldsymbol{J}^2$. The demonstration is as follows.

The basis vectors $|\tau\, j\, \mu\rangle$ and $|\tau'\, j\, \mu'\rangle$ of subspaces $\mathscr{E}(\tau\, j)$ and $\mathscr{E}(\tau'\, j)$ $(\tau \neq \tau')$ are certainly orthogonal if $\mu \neq \mu'$, as they correspond to different eigenvalues of J_z; the same is true if $\mu = \mu'$ since by repeated application of (XIII.24)

$$\langle\tau'\, j\, \mu\, |\tau\, j\, \mu\rangle = \langle\tau'\, j\, \mu+1\, |\tau\, j\, \mu+1\rangle = \ldots = \langle\tau'\, j\, j\, |\tau\, j\, j\rangle = \delta_{\tau\tau'}.$$

To show that any eigenvector of $\boldsymbol{J}^2$ corresponding to the eigenvalue $j\,(j+1)$ is a linear combination of the $|\tau\, j\, \mu\rangle$ (τ and μ variable, j fixed) it suffices to show that any vector $|\varpi\, j\, \mu\rangle$ of angular momentum $(j\, \mu)$ is a linear combination of the basis vectors $|\tau\, j\, \mu\rangle$ of the same angular momentum. If $\mu = j$ this is true by our initial hypothesis. If $\mu \neq j$ we can reduce the problem to this case by applying the operator $J_+^{j-\mu}$ to the vector $|\varpi\, j\, \mu\rangle$ and using relations (XIII.26) and (XIII.27).

Thus, starting from a complete set of orthonormal vectors of angular momentum $(j\,j)$, we have constructed the basis vectors of a standard representation $\{J^2\,J_z\}$ in the subspace $\mathscr{E}_j$ corresponding to the eigenvalue $j\,(j+1)$ of J^2. Repeating the same operation for all possible eigenvalues of J^2 we obtain a standard basis for the entire Hilbert space.

Note the particularly simple form of the matrices representing the components of J in such a representation (cf. Problem XIII.2). From (XIII.23), (XIII.24) and (XIII.25),

$$\begin{aligned} \langle \tau\, j\, \mu\, | J_z\, | \tau'\, j'\, \mu' \rangle &= \mu\, \delta_{\tau\tau'}\, \delta_{jj'}\, \delta_{\mu\mu'} \\ \langle \tau\, j\, \mu\, | J_\pm\, | \tau'\, j'\, \mu' \rangle &= \sqrt{j\,(j+1) - \mu\mu'}\; \delta_{\tau\tau'}\, \delta_{jj'}\, \delta_{\mu\mu'\pm 1}. \end{aligned} \qquad \text{(XIII.28)}$$

7. Conclusion

The preceding study of the properties of angular momentum is exclusively based on the commutation relations of the latter and on the fact that its components are Hermitean operators in a Hilbert space. From this alone we have been able to show that the quantum number j can take only integral or half-integral values and that to each eigenvalue $j(j+1)$ of J^2 there corresponds one or several series of $(2j+1)$ linearly independent vectors; the vectors of a series are obtained one from another by application of the operators J_- and J_+ and correspond to the $(2j+1)$ possible values of the quantum number m:

$$-j, -j+1, \ldots, +j.$$

However, these hypotheses are not sufficient for the complete solution of the eigenvalue problem. It remains to determine:

(i) Which of the integral and half-integral numbers actually make up the spectrum of j;

(ii) How many series of $(2j+1)$ linearly independent vectors correspond to each of these values of j.

The answer to these questions depends on the problem considered. From the commutation relations alone one cannot *a priori* exclude the case in which j takes a single value (integral or half-integral) and in which there is just one set of $(2j+1)$ linearly independent vectors corresponding to this eigenvalue; the state vector space is then $(2j+1)$-dimensional. We have an example of this in section IV, in connection with spin.

Another important special case is that of the angular momentum $\boldsymbol{l}$ of a particle, as defined in equation (1). We shall see in section II, where this case is examined in detail, that the spectrum of j is then formed of all the integers from 0 to ∞, all half-integral values being excluded.[1]

II. ORBITAL ANGULAR MOMENTUM AND THE SPHERICAL HARMONICS

8. The Spectrum of $\boldsymbol{l}^2$ and l_z

Let us return to the one-particle quantum system first considered in § 2. Choosing the z axis as the polar direction, we can express the operator $\boldsymbol{l}^2$ and the components of $\boldsymbol{l}$ as functions of the polar angles (θ, φ) and of their derivatives [eqs. (B.82–84)]. In what follows the radial variable may be ignored. We wish to find the function $F_l^m(\theta, \varphi)$ that satisfies the two eigenvalue equations

$$\boldsymbol{l}^2 F_l^m(\theta, \varphi) = l(l+1)\, F_l^m(\theta, \varphi) \tag{XIII.29}$$

$$l_z\, F_l^m(\theta, \varphi) = m F_l^m(\theta, \varphi). \tag{XIII.30}$$

Since any wave function is a single-valued function of $\mathbf{r}$, $F_l^m(\theta, \varphi)$ must remain unchanged when φ is replaced by $\varphi + 2\pi$ [2]). Equation (XIII.30) has already been studied in § V.12. Since $l_z = -\mathrm{i}\partial/\partial\varphi$, $F_l^m(\theta, \varphi)$ is necessarily of the form $f_l^m(\theta)\mathrm{e}^{\mathrm{i}m\varphi}$ with m integral. Since m is integral, l must also be integral: *there is no half-integral orbital angular momentum.*

In order to determine among the integers $(\geqslant 0)$ the eigenvalues of $\boldsymbol{l}$ and their degeneracy, we form the eigenfunctions $F_l^l(\theta, \varphi)$

---

[1]) Problem XIII.15 treats another case in which $\boldsymbol{J}^2$ and J_z form a complete set of commuting observables (a single series of $(2j+1)$ vectors for each value of j) and in which j can take all integral or half-integral values. Due to the simultaneous presence of integral and half-integral values in this spectrum, the treatment of $\boldsymbol{J}$ as an angular momentum imposes certain qualifications as to the physical significance of the different observables of the system (cf. § 15).

[2]) Also, $F_l^m(0, \varphi)$ and $F_l^m(\pi, \varphi)$ do not depend on φ, conditions automatically satisfied by the eigenfunctions found below.

corresponding to angular momentum (l, l). Such a function is defined by the equations

$$l_z\ F_l^l\ (\theta, \varphi) = l\ F_l^l\ (\theta, \varphi) \tag{XIII.31}$$

$$l_+\ F_l^l\ (\theta, \varphi) = 0. \tag{XIII.32}$$

These equations correspond to the system (XIII.29–30) for the case $m=l$ since from (XIII.9a)

$$\boldsymbol{l}^2 = l_z\ (l_z + 1) + l_-\ l_+$$

and therefore (XIII.32) and (XIII.31) lead to (XIII.29) and vice versa. The system of first-order partial differential equations (XIII. 31–32) is easily solved once given the differential operators l_z and l_+ [eqs. (B.82–83)]. From (XIII.31),

$$F_l^l\ (\theta, \varphi) = f_l\ (\theta)\ \mathrm{e}^{\mathrm{i}l\varphi}.$$

Substituting this expression in (XIII.32), we obtain the differential equation

$$\left(\frac{\mathrm{d}}{\mathrm{d}\theta} - l \cot\theta\right) f_l\ (\theta) = 0,$$

whose solution is $\sin^l\theta$ to within a constant. For each integral value of l ($\geqslant 0$) there exists one, and only one, eigenfunction of angular momentum (l, l) (defined up to an arbitrary constant), namely

$$\sin^l\theta\ \mathrm{e}^{\mathrm{i}l\varphi}.$$

Thus, the spectrum of $\boldsymbol{l}^2$ is the sequence of numbers $l\ (l+1)$, where *l takes all integral values from 0 to $+\infty$*. To each eigenvalue $l\ (l+1)$ there correspond $(2l+1)$ eigenvalues m of l_z – the $(2l+1)$ integers in the interval $(-l, +l)$. To each such pair (lm) there corresponds *one, and only one eigenstate* (if we limit ourselves to functions of the angles θ and φ): the spectrum of $\boldsymbol{l}^2$ and l_z is entirely non-degenerate.

9. Definition and Construction of the Spherical Harmonics

The common eigenfunction of $\boldsymbol{l}^2$ and l_z corresponding to the eigenvalues $(l\ m)$ is undefined to the extent of an arbitrary constant. We shall fix this constant by normalizing to unity and adopting a suitable phase convention. We thus obtain the spherical harmonic of order $(l\ m)$, $Y_l^m\ (\theta, \varphi)$.

The $Y_l^m(\theta, \varphi)$ form an *orthonormal set* of functions of θ and φ (the volume element in the scalar-product integral being $d\Omega = \sin\theta \, d\theta \, d\varphi$). It is also a *complete* set. The proof of completeness will not be given here.

The phases are fixed in the following way [1]. We first require that the Y_l^m form a standard basis. For this it is sufficient that they satisfy equations (XIII.24–25) written in the $\{\theta\, \varphi\}$ representation [eq. (B.89)]. The relative phases of the $(2l+1)$ spherical harmonics corresponding to the same value of l are thus determined and it remains but to fix the phase of one of them, $Y_l^0(\theta, \varphi)$ say. This we do by requiring that $Y_l^0(0, 0)$ be real and positive.

If we denote by $|l\, m\rangle$ the vectors represented by the spherical harmonic $Y_l^m(\theta, \varphi)$ in the $\{\theta\, \varphi\}$ representation, the different vectors thus defined satisfy equations (XIII.24–25); and therefore, [eq. (XIII.26)],

$$|l\, m\rangle = \sqrt{\frac{(l+m)!}{(2l)!\,(l-m)!}}\, l_-^{\,l-m}\, |l\, l\rangle$$

$$= \sqrt{\frac{(l-m)!}{(2l)!\,(l+m)!}}\, l_+^{\,l+m}\, |l\, {-l}\rangle.$$

In other words

$$Y_l^m(\theta, \varphi) = \sqrt{\frac{(l+m)!}{(2l)!\,(l-m)!}}\, l_-^{\,l-m}\, Y_l^l(\theta, \varphi) \qquad \text{(XIII.33)}$$

$$= \sqrt{\frac{(l-m)!}{(2l)!\,(l+m)!}}\, l_+^{\,l+m}\, Y_l^{-l}(\theta, \varphi). \qquad \text{(XIII.34)}$$

The differential operators l_- and l_+ are explicitly given in the appendix [eq. (B.83)]. From the expression given there, we deduce that

$$l_\pm\, e^{i\mu\varphi} f(\theta) = \mp\, e^{i(\mu\pm1)\varphi} \left(\sin^{1\pm\mu}\theta \frac{d}{d(\cos\theta)} \sin^{\mp\mu}\theta \right) f(\theta).$$

For any $f(\theta)$ the expression in brackets on the right-hand side must be considered as an operator acting on the function $f(\theta)$ to the right

---

[1] This particularly convenient convention is the one adopted by most authors. However, for discussions involving invariance under time reversal, it is preferable to use the functions $\mathscr{Y}_l^m(\theta,\varphi) \equiv i^l\, Y_l^m(\theta, \varphi)$ when dealing with wave functions in configuration space (cf. § XV.22).

of it. Therefore, the repeated application of l_+ or l_- to the function $e^{i\mu\varphi} f(\theta)$ gives (μ and s integral)

$$l_\pm{}^s \, e^{i\mu\varphi} f(\theta) = (\mp)^s \, e^{i(\mu\pm s)\varphi} \left(\sin^{s\pm\mu}\theta \frac{d^s}{d(\cos\theta)^s} \sin^{\mp\mu}\theta \right) f(\theta). \quad \text{(XIII.35)}$$

From the discussion of § 8, we know that

$$Y_l{}^l(\theta, \varphi) = c_l \sin^l\theta \, e^{il\varphi},$$

where c_l is a constant whose modulus is determined by the normalization condition on $Y_l{}^l$, which gives

$$|c_l| = (4\pi)^{-\frac{1}{2}} \frac{\sqrt{(2l+1)!}}{2^l \, l!}, \quad \text{(XIII.36)}$$

and whose phase remains to be determined in agreement with the convention adopted above.

Substituting this expression for $Y_l{}^l$ in equation (XIII.33) we obtain, with the aid of identity (XIII.35)

$$Y_l{}^m(\theta, \varphi) = c_l \sqrt{\frac{(l+m)!}{(2l)!\,(l-m)!}} \, e^{im\varphi} \sin^{-m}\theta \frac{d^{l-m}}{d(\cos\theta)^{l-m}} \sin^{2l}\theta. \quad \text{(XIII.37)}$$

When $m = -l$, this formula gives

$$Y_l{}^{-l}(\theta, \varphi) = (-)^l \, c_l \, e^{-il\varphi} \sin^l\theta. \quad \text{(XIII.38)}$$

Substituting this expression for $Y_l{}^{-l}$ in equation (XIII.34) and again using (XIII.35), we obtain a new expression for $Y_l{}^m$ equivalent to the preceding one:

$$Y_l{}^m(\theta, \varphi) = (-)^m \, c_l \sqrt{\frac{(l-m)!}{(2l)!\,(l+m)!}} \, e^{im\varphi} \sin^m\theta \frac{d^{l+m}}{d(\cos\theta)^{l+m}} \sin^{2l}\theta.$$
$$\text{(XIII.39)}$$

When $m = 0$, these two expressions are identical

$$Y_l{}^0(\theta, \varphi) = c_l \sqrt{\frac{1}{(2l)!}} \frac{d^l}{d(\cos\theta)^l} (1 - \cos^2\theta)^l.$$

To within a multiplicative constant, this is just the Legendre polynomial P_l (cos θ) [eq. (B.71)]:

$$Y_l^0(\theta, \varphi) = (-)^l \frac{c_l\, 2^l\, l!}{\sqrt{(2l)!}} P_l(\cos\theta)$$

$$= (-)^l \frac{c_l}{|c_l|} \sqrt{\frac{2l+1}{4\pi}} P_l(\cos\theta).$$

The condition that $Y_l^0(0, 0)$ be real and positive imposes the choice of phase

$$\frac{c_l}{|c_l|} = (-)^l.$$

Expressions (XIII.37) and (XIII.38) for $Y_l^m(\theta, \varphi)$ are thus completely specified.

Most of the properties of spherical harmonics given in Appendix B can be read directly from the condensed forms (XIII.37) and (XIII.38). Note in particular that

$$Y_l^{-m}(\theta, \varphi) = (-)^m\, Y_l^{m*}(\theta, \varphi),$$

that Y_l^m is the product of $e^{im\varphi} \sin^{|m|}\theta$ by a polynomial of degree $l - |m|$ and of parity $(-)^{l-|m|}$ in cos θ, and that the *parity* of Y_l^m (Problem XIII. 4) is $(-)^l$, i.e.

$$Y_l^m(\pi - \theta, \varphi + \pi) = (-)^l\, Y_l^m(\theta, \varphi).$$

III. ANGULAR MOMENTUM AND ROTATIONS

10. Definition of Rotation. Euler Angles

In this paragraph we review certain properties of rotations in ordinary space.

By definition, a rotation about a given point O is an overall displacement of the points of space in which the point O remains fixed. In such a displacement, each point P takes up a new position P′ and there is a one-to-one correspondence between P and P′. One could also define a rotation about O as a one-to-one correspondence between the points of space in which the point O corresponds to itself and which conserves both distances (and therefore angles) and the sense of coordinate axes [1]).

A unit vector $\boldsymbol{u}$ and an angle φ define a particular rotation $\mathscr{R}_{\boldsymbol{u}}(\varphi)$, of angle φ about the oriented axis defined by $\boldsymbol{u}$ (the positive sense of rotation being defined in the usual way). There are an infinite number of ways of thus specifying the same rotation. $\mathscr{R}_{\boldsymbol{u}}(\varphi)$ is equal to $\mathscr{R}_{\boldsymbol{u}_1}(\varphi)$ if

$$\begin{matrix} \boldsymbol{u}_1 = \boldsymbol{u} \\ \varphi_1 = \varphi + 2n\pi \end{matrix} \quad \text{or} \quad \begin{matrix} \boldsymbol{u}_1 = -\boldsymbol{u} \\ \varphi_1 = -\varphi + 2n\pi \end{matrix} \qquad (n \text{ any integer}).$$

We say that the rotation is *infinitesimal* if $\varphi = \varepsilon$ is an infinitesimal. It is easy to write down the transform $\boldsymbol{V}'$, of a vector $\boldsymbol{V}$ in an infinitesimal rotation $\mathscr{R}_{\boldsymbol{u}}(\varepsilon)$:

$$\boldsymbol{V}' \simeq \boldsymbol{V} + \varepsilon(\boldsymbol{u} \times \boldsymbol{V}) \qquad (\varepsilon \ll 1). \tag{XIII.40}$$

Another method of specifying a rotation consists in giving its Euler angles α, β, γ. Let Oxyz be the system obtained by the rotation of the Cartesian system OXYZ, and Ou one of the two *directed* axes perpendicular to OzZ (Fig. XIII.1). The Euler angles are [2])

$$\alpha = (\mathrm{O}y, \mathrm{O}u), \qquad \beta = (\mathrm{O}z, \mathrm{O}Z), \qquad \gamma = (\mathrm{O}u, \mathrm{O}Y).$$

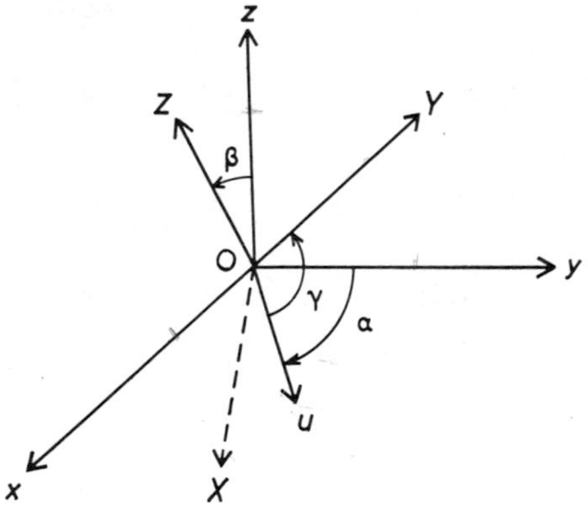

Fig. XIII.1. Definition of the Euler angles.

---

[1]) In contrast with reflections which conserve distances but change the sense of coordinate axes.

[2]) The definition adopted here differs slightly from the one generally adopted in the theory of the gyroscope.

The rotation is the result of the following sequence of three rotations:

(i) a rotation of angle α about Oz, $\mathscr{R}_Z(\alpha)$ (Oy goes into Ou)
(ii) a rotation of angle β about Ou, $\mathscr{R}_u(\beta)$ (Oz goes into OZ)
(iii) a rotation of angle γ about OZ, $\mathscr{R}_Z(\gamma)$ (Ou goes into OY)

We denote the resulting rotation by $\mathscr{R}(\alpha\,\beta\,\gamma)$ and write

$$\mathscr{R}(\alpha\,\beta\,\gamma) = \mathscr{R}_Z(\gamma)\,\mathscr{R}_u(\beta)\,\mathscr{R}_z(\alpha). \tag{XIII.41}$$

The angles α, β, γ are algebraic quantities with a positive or negative sign according as the corresponding rotations about the axes Oz, Ou, OZ are positive or negative. The system Oxyz being chosen once and for all, the same rotation can be defined by several different sets of Euler angles. A necessary and sufficient condition for

$$\mathscr{R}(\alpha\,\beta\,\gamma) = \mathscr{R}(\alpha_1\,\beta_1\,\gamma_1)$$

is that:

$$\begin{array}{lcl} \alpha_1 = \alpha + 2\pi n_\alpha & & \alpha_1 = \alpha + \pi + 2\pi n_\alpha \\ \beta_1 = \beta + 2\pi n_\beta & \text{or} & \beta_1 = -\beta + 2\pi n_\beta \\ \gamma_1 = \gamma + 2\pi n_\gamma & & \gamma_1 = \gamma - \pi + 2\pi n_\gamma \end{array} \tag{XIII.42}$$

$$(n_\alpha,\ n_\beta,\ n_\gamma \text{ any integers}).$$

With each rotation $\mathscr{R}$ can be associated a certain 3×3 matrix defined in the following way. We choose, once and for all, a right-handed Cartesian system Oxyz with unit vectors $\boldsymbol{a}_1$, $\boldsymbol{a}_2$, $\boldsymbol{a}_3$ in the directions Ox, Oy, Oz respectively. Under rotation these transform respectively into 3 new vectors, $\mathbf{A}_1$, $\mathbf{A}_2$, $\mathbf{A}_3$ forming a new right-handed Cartesian system OXYZ. Each of the vectors $\mathbf{A}_j$ is a linear combination of the vectors $\boldsymbol{a}_1$, $\boldsymbol{a}_2$, $\boldsymbol{a}_3$ [1]:

$$\mathbf{A}_j \equiv \mathscr{R}[\boldsymbol{a}_j] = \boldsymbol{a}_i\,\mathscr{R}_{ij}, \qquad \mathscr{R}_{ij} = (\boldsymbol{a}_i \cdot \mathbf{A}_j).$$

The coefficients $\mathscr{R}_{ij}$ of these three linear combinations are the elements of a 3×3 matrix which we denote by the same letter $\mathscr{R}$ as the rotation itself. The rotation is completely defined by this matrix, i.e. if $\mathbf{V} \equiv \boldsymbol{a}_j V_j$ is any vector in space defined by its coordinates (V_1, V_2, V_3) along

---

[1] In this entire section we shall systematically adopt the convention of summing over repeated indices; thus:

$$\boldsymbol{a}_i\,\mathscr{R}_{ij} = \boldsymbol{a}_1\,\mathscr{R}_{1j} + \boldsymbol{a}_2\,\mathscr{R}_{2j} + \boldsymbol{a}_3\,\mathscr{R}_{3j}.$$

the axis $Oxyz$, it is transformed by the rotation into the vector

$$\mathbf{V}' \equiv \mathscr{R}[\mathbf{V}] = \mathbf{A}_j \, V_j = \mathbf{a}_i \, \mathscr{R}_{ij} \, V_j. \qquad \vec{V} = \overleftrightarrow{R} \cdot \vec{V}$$

The components of $\mathbf{V}'$ along the axes $Oxyz$ are

$$V'_i = \mathscr{R}_{ij} \, V_j. \tag{XIII.43}$$

They are obtained from those of $\mathbf{V}$ by application of the matrix $\mathscr{R}$.

Since the $\mathbf{A}_i$ form a Cartesian system, the real matrix $\mathscr{R}$ is orthogonal and unimodular:

$$\mathscr{R} = \mathscr{R}^*, \qquad \tilde{\mathscr{R}} = \mathscr{R}^{-1}, \qquad \det \mathscr{R} = 1.$$

The system of axes $Oxyz$ having been chosen once and for all, the matrix associated with a rotation is uniquely defined. Conversely, to each real, orthogonal, unimodular matrix there corresponds one, and only one rotation.

The elements of the matrix associated with the rotation $\mathscr{R}\,(\alpha\,\beta\,\gamma)$ are given explicitly as functions of its Euler angles in Appendix C [formula (C.45)]. As an example we give the transformation law for the coordinates of the above-mentioned vector $\mathbf{V}$ in a rotation $\mathscr{R}_z\,(\alpha)$ of angle α about Oz:

$$\vec{V} = V_1 \hat{a}_1 + V_2 \hat{a}_2 + V_z \hat{a}_z =$$
$$= V_1' \hat{A}_1 + V_2' \hat{A}_2 + V_3' \hat{A}_3$$
$$V_1' = \left(\hat{A}_1 \cdot \vec{V} \right)$$

$$V'_1 = V_1 \cos \alpha - V_2 \sin \alpha$$
$$V'_2 = V_1 \sin \alpha + V_2 \cos \alpha \tag{XIII.44}$$
$$V'_3 = V_3.$$

The product of two rotations $\mathscr{R}_1$ and $\mathscr{R}_2$, namely the transformation $\mathscr{R} \equiv \mathscr{R}_2 \mathscr{R}_1$ obtained by successively effecting $\mathscr{R}_1$ and then $\mathscr{R}_2$, is also a rotation. Relation (XIII.41) is an example of such a product. It is not easy to write the Euler angles of $\mathscr{R}$ as a function of those of $\mathscr{R}_1$ and $\mathscr{R}_2$ but its associated matrix is easily obtained being the product of the matrices associated with $\mathscr{R}_1$ and $\mathscr{R}_2$:

$$\mathscr{R} = \mathscr{R}_2 \, \mathscr{R}_1.$$

11. Rotation of a Physical System. Rotation Operator

In discussing a given rotation in relation to a physical problem — what follows is also true for any spatial transformation — one can adopt two points of view which must be clearly distinguished. The first (sometimes called passive) consists in rotating the reference axis, keeping fixed each point P of space and the physical quantities attached to it. The second (sometimes called active) consists in keeping the axes fixed and rotating the physical system itself. The two points of view are equivalent. That we rotate the coordinate axes, or that we rotate the physical system itself in the opposite direction, amounts to exactly the same thing. Unless otherwise specified, in what follows we shall adopt the second of these viewpoints (rotation of the physical system).

In Quantum Mechanics, more care is required in defining the "rotation of a physical system" than in Classical Mechanics due to the relation between dynamical variables and dynamical states being much less direct. For simplicity, we first consider the case of a single particle. Denote by a a possible dynamical state of the particle and by $\psi(\boldsymbol{r})$ the corresponding wave function. Denote by a' the state obtained by subjecting the particle to a certain rotation $\mathscr{R}$, and by $\psi'(\boldsymbol{r})$ the wave-function corresponding to a':

$$a' \equiv \mathscr{R}[a], \qquad \psi'(\boldsymbol{r}) \equiv \mathscr{R}[\psi(\boldsymbol{r})].$$

When we say that the state a goes over into the state a' in the rotation $\mathscr{R}$, we mean that whatever observations we make upon the system in state a', the results of these observations can be deduced by a rotation $\mathscr{R}$ from the results that the same observation would yield if made upon the system in state a. Consider, for example, a position measurement. The probability distributions for states a and a' are $|\psi(\boldsymbol{r})|^2$ and $|\psi'(\boldsymbol{r})|^2$ respectively. The above statement asserts that the latter is obtained from the former by a rotation $\mathscr{R}$, i.e. *the value of the second function at a given point* $\boldsymbol{r}$ *is equal to the value of the first at the point* $\boldsymbol{r}_1$, *which transforms into* $\boldsymbol{r}$ *in the rotation* $\mathscr{R}$;

$$|\psi'(\boldsymbol{r})|^2 = |\psi(\boldsymbol{r}_1)|^2, \qquad \boldsymbol{r}_1 = \mathscr{R}^{-1}\boldsymbol{r}. \tag{XIII.45}$$

Similarly, if $\varphi(\boldsymbol{p})$ and $\varphi'(\boldsymbol{p})$ are the momentum space wave functions corresponding respectively to ψ and ψ', we must have

$$|\varphi'(\boldsymbol{p})|^2 = |\varphi(\boldsymbol{p}_1)|^2, \qquad \boldsymbol{p}_1 = \mathscr{R}^{-1}\boldsymbol{p}. \tag{XIII.46}$$

In order to satisfy all these conditions it is clearly sufficient that the value of the function ψ' at $\boldsymbol{r}$ equal the value of the function ψ at $\boldsymbol{r}_1$, i.e.

$$\psi'(\boldsymbol{r}) \equiv \mathscr{R}[\psi(\boldsymbol{r})] = \psi(\mathscr{R}^{-1}\boldsymbol{r}). \tag{XIII.47}$$

It can be shown that this is also a necessary condition [1]; the wave function is therefore unambiguously defined.

Relation (XIII.47) sets up a one-to-one correspondence between ψ and ψ'. It is clear that this correspondence is linear. In other words there exists an operator R such that

$$\psi' = R\,\psi.$$

R is unitary since the norms of ψ and ψ' are equal:

$$\int |\psi'(\boldsymbol{r})|^2\,\mathrm{d}\boldsymbol{r} = \int |\psi(\mathscr{R}^{-1}\boldsymbol{r})|^2\,\mathrm{d}\boldsymbol{r} = \int |\psi(\boldsymbol{r}_1)|^2\,\mathrm{d}\boldsymbol{r}_1$$

(to obtain the last integral we have made the change of variable $\boldsymbol{r}_1 = \mathscr{R}^{-1}\boldsymbol{r}$ and used the fact that the volume element $\mathrm{d}\boldsymbol{r}$ is conserved in the rotation $\mathscr{R}^{-1}$).

All of this may easily be generalized to a system of N particles, the wave function $\psi(\boldsymbol{r}^{(1)}, \boldsymbol{r}^{(2)}, \ldots, \boldsymbol{r}^{(N)})$ transforming in the rotation $\mathscr{R}$ into

$$\mathscr{R}[\psi(\boldsymbol{r}^{(1)}, \ldots, \boldsymbol{r}^{(N)})] = \psi(\mathscr{R}^{-1}\boldsymbol{r}^{(1)}, \ldots, \mathscr{R}^{-1}\boldsymbol{r}^{(N)}) = R\,\psi(\boldsymbol{r}^{(1)}, \ldots, \boldsymbol{r}^{(N)}). \tag{XIII.48}$$

The rotation operator R is, as above, linear and unitary.

In all generality, a unitary operator R is associated with each rotation $\mathscr{R}$ of a given physical system; the application of R to the vector $|a\rangle$ representing the dynamical state of the system before rotation gives the vector $|a'\rangle$ representing its dynamical state after rotation:

$$R\,R^\dagger = R^\dagger\,R = 1 \tag{XIII.49}$$

$$|a'\rangle = R\,|a\rangle. \tag{XIII.50}$$

From (XIII.50) we can easily deduce the law for the transformation of the density operator by referring directly to its definition. Let ϱ be the density operator representing a certain (pure or mixed)

[1] The general proof will be given in § XV.6. The function ψ' is actually defined by these conditions only to within a phase factor. This factor is fixed if we require that the operators R defined below form a group isomorphic with the rotations; this is what is done here.

state of the system, ϱ' the one representing the state resulting from the rotation $\mathscr{R}$. We have

$$\varrho' \equiv \mathscr{R}\,[\varrho] = R\,\varrho\,R^{\dagger}. \tag{XIII.51}$$

12. Rotation of Observables

Besides rotating the system itself, we can also rotate the instruments with which we observe it. Having defined the law for the transformation of state vectors, we must now define the law for the transformation of the observables representing the various measuring operations that can be made on the system.

Let Q be an observable and $Q' = \mathscr{R}\,[Q]$ its transform in the rotation $\mathscr{R}$. Physically, the observable Q represents a measuring operation and the transformation of Q into Q' represents an overall rotation of the measuring instrument. Therefore, the average value of measurements of Q made on the system in state $|a\rangle$ is equal to the average value of measurements of Q' made on the system in state $|a'\rangle \equiv \mathscr{R}\,[|a\rangle]$, i.e.,

$$\langle a\,|Q\,|a\rangle = \langle a'\,|Q'\,|a'\rangle.$$

Since $|a'\rangle = R\,|a\rangle$, this may be written

$$\langle a\,|Q\,|a\rangle = \langle a\,|R^{\dagger}\,Q'\,R\,|a\rangle.$$

Since this must hold for every $|a\rangle$, we have (cf. § VII.5)

$$Q = R^{\dagger}\,Q'\,R,$$

i.e.,

$$Q' = R\,Q\,R^{\dagger}. \tag{XIII.52}$$

Thus, in a rotation $\mathscr{R}$, the observables undergo the same unitary transformation as the state vectors.

In particular, if an observable S represents a *scalar* quantity—that is, invariant under rotation [1])—then for any R,

$$S' \equiv R\,S\,R^{\dagger} = S.$$

[1]) This definition of a scalar will be adopted throughout the present chapter. Later on quantities invariant under rotation will be classed as scalars and pseudo-scalars. The first are unchanged in a reflection, the second are multiplied by -1.

Since R is unitary, this may be written

$$[R, S]=0. \tag{XIII.53}$$

Thus an observable invariant under rotation commutes with all of the rotation operators.

Vector operators provide another particularly interesting case. We follow the notation of § 10 and denote the vector operator with components $K_i=(\mathbf{K}\cdot\mathbf{a}_i)$ by $\mathbf{K}$. If we apply the rotation $\mathscr{R}$ to the operator K_1, the component of $\mathbf{K}$ along Ox, the operator obtained, K_1', is the component of $\mathbf{K}$ along OX. In general $\mathscr{R}\,[\mathbf{K}\cdot\mathbf{a}]=\mathbf{K}\cdot\mathbf{a}'$, where $\mathbf{a}'=\mathscr{R}\,[\mathbf{a}]$; thus

$$K_i' \equiv \mathscr{R}\,[K_i]=\mathbf{K}\cdot\mathbf{A}_i=K_j\,\mathscr{R}_{ji}.$$

Hence the transformation law for the Cartesian components of $\mathbf{K}$ is

$$K_i' \equiv R\,K_i\,R^{\dagger}=\tilde{\mathscr{R}}_{ij}\,K_j. \tag{XIII.54}$$

Note that $\tilde{\mathscr{R}}$, the inverse of $\mathscr{R}$, appears here rather than $\mathscr{R}$ itself as in (XIII.43): the components of $\mathbf{K}$ transform in the rotation $\mathscr{R}$ like those of a vector in the rotation $\mathscr{R}^{-1}$.

13. Angular Momentum and Infinitesimal Rotations

We are now in a position to establish the fundamental relation between the angular momentum of a system and its infinitesimal rotation operators.

We first consider the case of the single particle of § 11. According to transformation law (XIII.47), the rotation $\mathscr{R}_z(\alpha)$ of angle α about Oz, transforms the function $\psi(x, y, z)$ [cf. eq. (XIII.44)] into

$$\mathscr{R}_z(\alpha)\,[\psi(x, y, z)]=\psi(x\cos\alpha+y\sin\alpha, -x\sin\alpha+y\cos\alpha, z).$$

In particular the infinitesimal rotation $\mathscr{R}_z(\varepsilon)$ gives, taking only terms of the first order in ε in the Taylor expansion of the right-hand side about the point (x, y, z),

$$\begin{aligned}
R_z(\varepsilon)\,[\psi(x, y, z)] &\simeq \psi(x+y\varepsilon, -x\varepsilon+y, z)\\
&\simeq \psi(x, y, z)+\varepsilon\left(y\frac{\partial\psi}{\partial x}-x\frac{\partial\psi}{\partial y}\right)\\
&\simeq (1-\mathrm{i}\varepsilon l_z)\,\psi(x, y, z).
\end{aligned}$$

The last line follows from the definition of the differential operator l_z ($\hbar = 1$). The infinitesimal rotation operator is therefore of the form:

$$R_z(\varepsilon) \simeq 1 - \mathrm{i}\varepsilon l_z.$$

The same argument applied to the infinitesimal rotation about $\boldsymbol{u}$ gives

$$R_{\boldsymbol{u}}(\varepsilon) = 1 - \mathrm{i}\varepsilon\,(\boldsymbol{l}\cdot\boldsymbol{u}).$$

For a system of N particles we have a similar result. Starting from (XIII.48) rather than (XIII.47) as above, an analogous treatment gives

$$\mathscr{R}_z(\varepsilon) \simeq 1 - \mathrm{i}\varepsilon L_z,$$

and more generally

$$R_{\boldsymbol{u}}(\varepsilon) \simeq 1 - \mathrm{i}\varepsilon\,(\boldsymbol{L}\cdot\boldsymbol{u}),$$

where $\boldsymbol{L}$ is the total angular momentum of the system.

In summary:

If $\boldsymbol{J}$ *is the total angular momentum of a system, its component along any axis* $\boldsymbol{u}$ *is related to the operator of infinitesimal rotation about that axis by the relation*

$$\boxed{R_{u}(\varepsilon) \simeq 1 - \mathrm{i}\varepsilon\,(\boldsymbol{J}\cdot\boldsymbol{u})} \qquad \text{(XIII.55)}$$

When the system has no classical analogue this fundamental relation serves as the definition of total angular momentum.

For this definition to be coherent we must be sure that the operator $(\boldsymbol{J}\cdot\boldsymbol{u})$ is the component along $\boldsymbol{u}$ of a certain vector operator $\boldsymbol{J}$. It is sufficient [1], for this, that to each *infinitesimal* rotation $\mathscr{R}_{\boldsymbol{u}}(\varepsilon)$ there corresponds *one, and only one* infinitesimal-rotation operator $R_{\boldsymbol{u}}(\varepsilon)$. By the transformation law for vectors (XIII.40), the operation $\mathscr{R}_{\boldsymbol{u}}(\varepsilon)$ is equivalent, to first order in ε, to the product of operations $\mathscr{R}_x(\varepsilon u_x)\,\mathscr{R}_y(\varepsilon u_y)\,\mathscr{R}_z(\varepsilon u_z)$, so that

$$\begin{aligned} R_{\boldsymbol{u}}(\varepsilon) &\simeq R_x(\varepsilon u_x)\,R_y(\varepsilon u_y)\,R_z(\varepsilon u_z) \\ &\simeq 1 - \mathrm{i}\varepsilon\,(u_x J_x + u_y J_y + u_z J_z). \end{aligned}$$

It follows from this definition that any scalar operator S commutes

---

[1]) This amounts to supposing that the rotation operators form a group.

with the components of $\boldsymbol{J}$ [eq. (XIII.53)]:

$$[(\boldsymbol{u}\cdot\boldsymbol{J}), S]=0. \tag{XIII.56}$$

Relation (XIII.55) also provides the commutation rules for the components of $\boldsymbol{J}$ with those of a general vector operator $\boldsymbol{K}$. Let $K_a \equiv \boldsymbol{K}\cdot\boldsymbol{a}$ be the component of $\boldsymbol{K}$ along a given unit vector $\boldsymbol{a}$. By definition, its transform in the rotation $\mathscr{R}_{\boldsymbol{u}}(\varepsilon)$ is

$$K_a' \equiv R_{\boldsymbol{u}}(\varepsilon)\, K_a\, R_{\boldsymbol{u}}^{\dagger}(\varepsilon) \simeq K_a - \mathrm{i}\varepsilon\, [J_u, K_a].$$

However, by the law for the transformation of the vector $\boldsymbol{a}$ [eq. (XIII.40)],

$$K_a' = \boldsymbol{K}\cdot\boldsymbol{a}' \simeq \boldsymbol{K}\cdot[\boldsymbol{a}+\varepsilon\, (\boldsymbol{u}\times\boldsymbol{a})].$$

Equating the terms of first order in ε in these two expressions, we find

$$[J_u, K_a] = \mathrm{i}\boldsymbol{K}\cdot(\boldsymbol{u}\times\boldsymbol{a}),$$

i.e.,

$$\boxed{[(\boldsymbol{u}\cdot\boldsymbol{J}), (\boldsymbol{a}\cdot\boldsymbol{K})] = \mathrm{i}((\boldsymbol{u}\times\boldsymbol{a})\cdot\boldsymbol{K})} \tag{XIII.57}$$

Substitution of the operator $\boldsymbol{J}$ for $\boldsymbol{K}$ gives us back the commutation relations characteristic of angular momentum [eq. (XIII.4)].

The following definition of the *total* angular momentum is equivalent to the one given above:

If the fundamental observables of a system are the scalar operators S_1, S_2, ... and the components of the vector operators $\boldsymbol{K}_1$, $\boldsymbol{K}_2$, ..., the *total* angular momentum of the system is by definition a *vector operator* $\boldsymbol{J}$ whose components commute with all of the S and satisfy the commutation relations (XIII.57) with the components of the $\boldsymbol{K}$.

If relations (XIII.57) are not satisfied by all of the vectors $\boldsymbol{K}_1$, $\boldsymbol{K}_2$,..., $\boldsymbol{J}$ is not the total angular momentum of the system, even if it satisfies the commutation rules (XIII.4) characteristic of an angular momentum operator. Thus, in the N particle case considered in § 11, any vector operator formed by summing a certain number of individual angular momenta $\boldsymbol{l}^{(i)}$ will verify relations (XIII.4), but only the sum $\boldsymbol{L}$ of *all* the $\boldsymbol{l}^{(i)}$ corresponds to the definition of total angular momentum.

14. Construction of the Operator $R\ (\alpha\ \beta\ \gamma)$

Any finite rotation can be looked upon as a succession of infinitesimal rotations. The corresponding rotation operator is the product of the corresponding infinitesimal rotation operators. Since these are well-defined functions of the total angular momentum [eq. (XIII.55)], any finite rotation operator can also be expressed as a function of the total angular momentum.

The rotation $\mathscr{R}_{\boldsymbol{u}}\ (\varphi)$ is a succession of infinitesimal rotations about the $\boldsymbol{u}$ axis. In particular,

$$\mathscr{R}_{\boldsymbol{u}}\ (\varphi+\mathrm{d}\varphi)=\mathscr{R}_{\boldsymbol{u}}\ (\mathrm{d}\varphi)\ \mathscr{R}_{\boldsymbol{u}}\ (\varphi).$$

Putting $J_u \equiv (\boldsymbol{J}\cdot\boldsymbol{u})$ and applying formula (XIII.55), this gives

$$\begin{aligned} R_{\boldsymbol{u}}\ (\varphi+\mathrm{d}\varphi) &= R_{\boldsymbol{u}}\ (\mathrm{d}\varphi)\ R_{\boldsymbol{u}}\ (\varphi) \\ &= (1-\mathrm{i}J_u\ \mathrm{d}\varphi)\ R_{\boldsymbol{u}}\ (\varphi), \end{aligned}$$

or again

$$\frac{\mathrm{d}}{\mathrm{d}\varphi} R_{\boldsymbol{u}}\ (\varphi) = -\mathrm{i}J_u\ R_{\boldsymbol{u}}\ (\varphi) \qquad (R_{\boldsymbol{u}}\ (0)=1).$$

This differential equation is easily integrated to give

$$R_u\ (\varphi)=\mathrm{e}^{-\mathrm{i}\varphi J_u}. \tag{XIII.58}$$

Consider now the rotation $\mathscr{R}\ (\alpha\ \beta\ \gamma)$ defined by its Euler angles (α, β, γ). It was seen in § 10 that it may be looked upon as a succession of rotations of angles α, β, γ about axes Oz, Ou, OZ respectively (Fig. XIII.1). We therefore have

$$R\ (\alpha\ \beta\ \gamma)=R_Z\ (\gamma)\ R_u\ (\beta)\ R_z\ (\alpha).$$

With the aid of (XIII.58), the three rotations on the right-hand side can be expressed in terms of the angular momentum components J_Z, J_u, and J_z:

$$R\ (\alpha\ \beta\ \gamma)=\mathrm{e}^{-\mathrm{i}\gamma J_Z}\ \mathrm{e}^{-\mathrm{i}\beta J_u}\ \mathrm{e}^{-\mathrm{i}\alpha J_z}. \tag{XIII.59}$$

Note the order of the three exponentials on the right-hand side.

We shall put this expression in a form where only the components of angular momentum along the coordinate axes appear. The rotation $\mathscr{R}_z\ (\alpha)$ takes the operator J_y over into the operator J_u and so, by the law for the transformation of operators (XIII.52),

$$J_u = R_z(\alpha)\, J_y\, R_z^\dagger(\alpha) = e^{-i\alpha J_z}\, J_y\, e^{+i\alpha J_z}.$$

Thus

$$e^{-i\beta J_u} = e^{-i\alpha J_z}\, e^{-i\beta J_y}\, e^{+i\alpha J_z}.$$

Substituting this expression into the right-hand side of (XIII.59), we get

$$R(\alpha\,\beta\,\gamma) = e^{-i\gamma J_Z}\, e^{-i\alpha J_z}\, e^{-i\beta J_y}.$$

Similarly, J_Z is obtained from J_z by successive application of the rotations $\mathscr{R}_z(\alpha)$ and $\mathscr{R}_u(\beta)$ and can thus be eliminated like J_u above to give finally:

$$\boxed{R(\alpha\,\beta\,\gamma) = e^{-i\alpha J_z}\, e^{-i\beta J_y}\, e^{-i\gamma J_z}} \qquad \text{(XIII.60)}$$

15. Rotation through an Angle 2π and Half-integral Angular Momenta

From equation (XIII.58)

$$R_{\mathbf{u}}(2\pi) = e^{-2\pi i J_u}.$$

Although *a rotation through* 2π *about an axis* $\mathbf{u}$ brings us back to our starting point, the corresponding rotation operator is not necessarily equal to 1. It is diagonal in the representation in which J_u is diagonal and its diagonal elements are $+1$ or -1 according as the corresponding eigenvalue of J_u is integral or half-integral.

Call D the function of J^2, with eigenvalue $+1$ for j integral and -1 for j half-integral. D is an observable, and has the following characteristic properties:

(i) $\frac{1}{2}(1+D)$ is the projector onto the subspace of integral j;

(ii) $\frac{1}{2}(1-D)$ is the projector onto the subspace of half-integral j;

(iii) $D^2 = 1$;

(iv) D commutes with all of the rotation operators:

$$[D, R] = 0.$$

Clearly

$$R_{\mathbf{u}}(2\pi) = D. \qquad \text{(XIII.61)}$$

In order to have $R_{\mathbf{u}}(2\pi) = 1$, it is necessary that the angular momentum take only integral values. On the other hand, we shall always have:

$$R_u\,(4\pi) = D^2 = 1.$$

The existence of a one-to-one correspondence between the infinitesimal rotations and the infinitesimal R operators [definition (XIII.55)] in no way implies that there is a similar correspondence for finite rotations. There are infinitely many ways of writing a finite rotation as a product of infinitesimal rotations, the operators $R_u\,(\varphi)$ and $R\,(\alpha\,\beta\,\gamma)$ discussed above correspond each to one of these ways. There is no *a priori* reason to suppose that another way would give the same operator.

It can be shown (the proof will not be given here) that to each finite rotation $\mathscr{R}$ there corresponds in all two operators, R' and R'', differing by a "rotation through 2π",

$$R'' = DR'. \tag{XIII.62}$$

In the physical systems hitherto encountered, the total angular momentum could take only integral values, in which case $D = 1$, $R' = R''$, so that to each rotation $\mathscr{R}$ there corresponds one, and only one operator for the rotation of ket vectors. If the system has half-integral angular momentum states, the operators R' and R'' are not identical.

The occurrence of two different operators to describe the same rotation requires some discussion. That the rotation of a ket through 2π does not give the same ket raises no difficulty of principle so long as no observable effect is produced. Clearly the results of an experiment are not modified if beforehand one rotates some of the instruments of observation through an angle 2π; two identical counters occupying the same position will necessarily give the same answers. Therefore, if an observable Q represents a measureable quantity, it must be invariant under a rotation through 2π; more generally, if we effect a certain rotation $\mathscr{R}$ upon Q, the observable obtained must not depend on the particular path followed in so doing:

$$R'\,Q\,R'^{\dagger} = R''\,Q\,R''^{\dagger}.$$

The invariance under "rotation through 2π" is sufficient to guarantee this more general property. Formally it may be written

$$[D, Q]=0. \tag{XIII.63}$$

By definition, an observable is a Hermitean operator having a complete set of eigenvectors. Any operator representing a physical quantity must be an observable – a necessary condition for the self-consistence of Quantum Mechanics. However, the converse is by no means necessarily true. We will give the name of *physical observable* to an observable associated with a physically measurable quantity. The foregoing analysis shows that any physical observable must obey relation (XIII.63) [1]. In studying a physical system, one usually implicitly assumes that all the observables of the system are physical observables; although this hypothesis often facilitates discussion, it is not essential. More restrictive conditions may hold without any serious modification of the interpretation of the theory. Relation (XIII.63) is just one of these restrictions; we shall encounter others in the discussion of identical particles [2].

In view of the foregoing discussion, no principle of Quantum Mechanics opposes the existence of half-integral angular momenta. Indeed, they are observed in nature.

16. Irreducible Invariant Subspaces. Rotation Matrices $R^{(J)}$

Expression (XIII.60) shows that any rotation operator is a function of the components of total angular momentum, as stated at the end of § 5. The vectors of a space $\mathscr{E}^{(J)}$ of the type constructed in that paragraph are therefore carried over in a rotation into vectors of $\mathscr{E}^{(J)}$ i.e., *the space* $\mathscr{E}^{(J)}$ *is invariant under rotation* [3].

Better, if $|u\rangle$ is an arbitrarily chosen vector of that space, then the set of vectors $R\,|u\rangle$ obtained from $|u\rangle$ by rotation span the whole of $\mathscr{E}^{(J)}$. We say of a space having this property that it is *irreducible*

---

[1] The observables of all the physical systems studied in this book (including angular momenta with half-integral eigenvalues) will all satisfy XIII.63. The distinction between observable and physical observable is then purely academic. However, one can imagine systems for which the observables do not all satisfy (XIII.53); Problem XIII.15 provides an example.

[2] For a general discussion of relations of the type (XIII.63) and their consequences (superselection rules) cf. Wick, Wightman and Wigner, Phys. Rev. **88** (1952) 101.

[3] We shall henceforth use the capitals J, M to denote the quantum numbers of total angular momentum.

with respect to rotations. If, on the other hand, there existed in $\mathscr{E}^{(J)}$ at least one vector $|v\rangle$ such that the set of vectors $R\,|v\rangle$ only partially spanned $\mathscr{E}^{(J)}$, then $\mathscr{E}^{(J)}$ would be reducible with respect to rotations.

The irreducibility of $\mathscr{E}^{(J)}$ can be demonstrated as follows. Let the space spanned by the vectors $R\,|u\rangle$ be denoted by $\mathscr{E}_1{}^{(J)}$. $J_+\,|u\rangle$ belongs to $\mathscr{E}_1{}^{(J)}$ for we have

$$J_+\,|u\rangle \equiv (J_x + \mathrm{i}J_y)\,|u\rangle = \frac{1}{\varepsilon}\,(1 - \mathrm{i} + \mathrm{i}R_x\,(\varepsilon) - R_y\,(\varepsilon))\,|u\rangle.$$

The same is true for $J_-\,|u\rangle$. More generally, any vector obtained by application of J_+ or J_- to a vector of $\mathscr{E}_1{}^{(J)}$ belongs to $\mathscr{E}_1{}^{(J)}$. Consider now the expansion $|u\rangle = \sum_M |JM\rangle\,\langle JM\,|u\rangle$ and denote by m the smallest value of M for which $\langle J\,M\,|u\rangle \neq 0$. Following the methods of § 5, the vector $J_+{}^{J-m}\,|u\rangle$ is a non-null vector proportional to $|J\,J\rangle$; thus $|J\,J\rangle$ belongs to $\mathscr{E}_1{}^{(J)}$, and since by repeated application of J_- to $|J\,J\rangle$ we form all of the $|J\,M\rangle$, they too belong to $\mathscr{E}_1{}^{(J)}$. Therefore, $\mathscr{E}_1{}^{(J)}$ contains a complete set of basis vectors for $\mathscr{E}^{(J)}$; the two spaces are therefore identical. Q.E.D.

As pointed out in § 6, the ket-vector space of a physical system is formed by the direct sum of a certain number of $(2\,J+1)$-dimensional subspaces $\mathscr{E}\,(\tau\,J)$, where τ represents the set of quantum numbers which distinguish between those corresponding to the same eigenvalue of $\boldsymbol{J}^2$. Each of the $\mathscr{E}\,(\tau\,J)$ is an *irreducible invariant subspace with respect to rotations*. In a standard representation $\{\boldsymbol{J}^2\,J_z\}$, the components of $\boldsymbol{J}$ are represented in each of these subspaces by very simple τ-independent matrices. Similarly, each rotation operator $R\,(\alpha\,\beta\,\gamma)$ is represented in each of the $\mathscr{E}\,(\tau\,J)$ by a certain $(2J+1)$-dimensional matrix, $R^{(J)}\,(\alpha\,\beta\,\gamma)$, *depending on* $\boldsymbol{J}$ *but independent of the quantum numbers* τ. By definition:

$$\begin{aligned} R^{(J)}_{MM'}\,(\alpha\,\beta\,\gamma) &\equiv \langle\tau\,J\,M\,|R\,(\alpha\,\beta\,\gamma)\,|\tau\,J\,M'\rangle \\ &\equiv \langle J\,M\,|\mathrm{e}^{-\mathrm{i}\alpha J_z}\,\mathrm{e}^{-\mathrm{i}\beta J_y}\,\mathrm{e}^{-\mathrm{i}\gamma J_z}\,|J\,M'\rangle. \end{aligned} \tag{XIII.64}$$

These matrices constitute a particularly convenient representation of the operators $R\,(\alpha\,\beta\,\gamma)$ and are commonly used each time it is necessary to change the orientation of the state vectors or observables. They are called *rotation matrices*. Their principal properties and the explicit expressions for some of them are given in Appendix C (Section IV).

From the very definition of these matrices it follows that the $(2j+1)$

basis vectors of a subspace $\mathscr{E}(\tau J)$ transform in a given rotation $\mathscr{R}(\alpha\,\beta\,\gamma)$ according to the law

$$R(\alpha\,\beta\,\gamma)\,|\tau\,J\,M\rangle = \sum_{M'} |\tau\,J\,M'\rangle\, R^{(J)}_{M'M}(\alpha\,\beta\,\gamma). \qquad \text{(XIII.65)}$$

One can easily demonstrate the converse, namely: if $(2J+1)$ vectors $|u_M\rangle$ $(M=-J, -J+1, \ldots, +J)$ transform one into another by rotation according to the law

$$R(\alpha\,\beta\,\gamma)\,|u_M\rangle = \sum_{M'} |u_{M'}\rangle\, R^{(J)}_{M'M}(\alpha\,\beta\,\gamma) \qquad \text{(XIII.66)}$$

then they satisfy the eigenvalue equations

$$\boldsymbol{J}^2\,|u_M\rangle = J(J+1)\,|u_M\rangle, \qquad J_z\,|u_M\rangle = M\,|u_M\rangle,$$

and are obtained one from another by application of J_+ and J_- in accordance with the relations (XIII.24–25).

17. Rotational Invariance and Conservation of Angular Momentum. Rotational Degeneracy

The invariance of a quantity under rotation can always be expressed as a special property of angular momentum. This is because any rotation can be expressed as a product of infinitesimal rotations and therefore if a quantity is invariant under these, it is invariant under any rotation whatever. Through relations (XIII.55) the angular momentum appears in the condition of invariance under infinitesimal rotations.

Thus, for a wave function or for a ket $|\rangle$ to be rotationally invariant, a necessary and sufficient condition is that the application of an arbitrary component of the total angular momentum give zero:

$$\boldsymbol{J}\,|\rangle = 0.$$

In fact, it is sufficient that

$$\boldsymbol{J}^2\,|\rangle = 0. \qquad \text{(XIII.67)}$$

Such is the case for the wave functions of a particle in the s-state; functions of this type depend only on the variable r. It is also the case for wave functions for several particles depending only on the distances between the particles and on the angles of the position vectors with respect to one another [1]).

---

[1]) This is to be compared with the property $(\boldsymbol{l} + \boldsymbol{l}')\,P_l(\cos\alpha) = 0$ which appears in the proof of the addition theorem (Problem XIII.5).

Similarly, for an observable S to be invariant under rotation [condition (XIII.53)], a necessary and sufficient condition is that it commute with the components of angular momentum.

$$[\boldsymbol{J}, S]=0. \tag{XIII.68}$$

The invariance of the Hamiltonian under rotation deserves particular attention. If we have

$$[R, H]=0 \text{ for any } R \tag{XIII.69}$$

then *the equations of motion are invariant under rotation*: two state vectors that are the transforms one of the other in a given rotation at time t_0, will continue to be so related throughout the course of time. This is obvious, for if $|\psi(t)\rangle$ satisfies the Schrödinger equation, we have, whatever R,

$$\left(i\hbar\frac{\partial}{\partial t}-H\right) R\,|\psi(t)\rangle = R\left(i\hbar\frac{\partial}{\partial t}-H\right)|\psi(t)\rangle = 0$$

and therefore $R\,|\psi(t)\rangle$ is also a solution of the Schrödinger equation.

Similarly, if $|\rangle$ is an eigenvector of H, all the vectors $R\,|\rangle$ that can be obtained by rotation are also eigenvectors of H belonging to the same eigenvalue i.e., the subspace of each eigenvalue of H is invariant with respect to rotations.

All of the consequences of invariance under rotation of the equations of motion are contained in the relations

$$[\boldsymbol{J}, H]=0 \tag{XIII.70}$$

which express the invariance of H with respect to infinitesimal rotations.

When these relations are satisfied the operators $\boldsymbol{J}^2$, J_z and H commute, and the solving of the eigenvalue problem for H is considerably simplified – we may seek the eigenfunctions of H among the common eigenfunctions of $\boldsymbol{J}^2$ and J_z. Moreover, the energy spectra corresponding to the same value of J are the same, the eigenfunctions belonging to the $(2J+1)$ possible values of M being obtained one from another by repeated application of J_+ or J_-. In other words, the energy eigenvalues are independent of M. To each eigenvalue E_J corresponding to a given value of J there corresponds one or several series of $(2J+1)$ eigenvectors; the eigenvectors of a given series are obtained one from another by repeated application of J_+ or J_- and span an irreducible invariant subspace with respect to rotations. This type of degeneracy is called *rotational degeneracy.*

The case of a particle in a central field (Ch. IX) is a good illustration of the present discussion. The Hamiltonian of a particle in a central field must obviously be invariant under rotation; one verifies directly that it commutes with the three components of the angular momentum $\boldsymbol{l}$. The method of Chapter IX consists precisely in seeking the eigenfunctions of H among the common eigenfunctions of $\boldsymbol{l}^2$ and l_z belonging to the eigenvalues $l\,(l+1)$ and m respectively, i.e., among the functions of form

$$\chi_l\,(r)\;Y_l^m\,(\theta,\,\varphi).$$

Such a problem reduces to solving a second-order differential equation in r. Moreover, since m does not appear in that equation, we can form from each of the radial functions thus determined in all $(2l+1)$ eigenfunctions of H belonging to the same eigenvalue.

As previously stated, we have here a striking analogy between Classical Mechanics and Quantum Mechanics. When the equations of motion of a classical system are invariant under rotations of the coordinate axes, the total angular momentum of the system is conserved, a property which permits us to obtain first integrals of the motion and which simplifies considerably the solving of the equations. In the same way, the invariance under rotation of the equations of motion in Quantum Mechanics leads to the conservation of the total angular momentum; however, here the conservation laws are not so simply expressed due to the fact that the components of angular momentum do not commute.

IV. SPIN

18. The Hypothesis of Electron Spin

The Schrödinger theory as it results from the simple application of the correspondence principle cannot explain the properties of complex atoms, even leaving relativistic corrections aside. Two important modifications are required. Neither have any analogue in classical mechanics that would have permitted their existence to be foreseen. The one consists in retaining only those solutions of the Schrödinger theory that have certain well-defined symmetry properties in a permutation of the coordinates of the electrons. It is known as the Pauli principle and will be studied in Chapter XIV. It may be ignored for the purpose of the present discussion. The other is the hypothesis of electron spin.

The principal evidence supporting this hypothesis comes from the study of the behavior of complex atoms in a magnetic field (Zeeman effect, Stern–Gerlach experiment).

The Schrödinger equation for an atom of Z (spinless) electrons has already been written down [eq. (II.30)]. If we suppose the nucleus to be infinitely heavy its position will coincide with the center of mass, and the Hamiltonian in the center of mass system is simply

$$H_0 = \sum_{i=1}^{Z} \left(\frac{\boldsymbol{p}_i^{\,2}}{2m} - \frac{Ze^2}{r_i} \right) + \sum_{i<j} \frac{e^2}{|\boldsymbol{r}_i - \boldsymbol{r}_j|} . \qquad \text{(XIII.71)}$$

To obtain the Hamiltonian of the same atom placed in the static magnetic field described by the potential $\boldsymbol{A}(\boldsymbol{r})$ we need only to replace each $\boldsymbol{p}_i$ by $\boldsymbol{p}_i - e\boldsymbol{A}(\boldsymbol{r}_i)/c$. In particular, for a constant magnetic field $\mathscr{H}$, $\boldsymbol{A} = \frac{1}{2}(\mathscr{H} \times \boldsymbol{r})$ and

$$\left(\boldsymbol{p} - \frac{e}{c}\boldsymbol{A} \right)^2 = \boldsymbol{p}^2 - \frac{e}{c}(\boldsymbol{A}\cdot\boldsymbol{p} + \boldsymbol{p}\cdot\boldsymbol{A}) + \frac{e^2}{c^2}\boldsymbol{A}^2$$

$$= \boldsymbol{p}^2 - \frac{e}{c}(\mathscr{H}\cdot\boldsymbol{l}) + \frac{e^2}{4c^2}\mathscr{H}^2 r_\perp^{\,2},$$

where $r_\perp^{\,2}$ is the square of the projection of $\boldsymbol{r}$ on the plane perpendicular to the field $\mathscr{H}$. The Hamiltonian becomes

$$H = H_0 - \frac{e}{2mc}\mathscr{H}\cdot\boldsymbol{L} + \frac{e^2}{8mc^2}\mathscr{H}^2 \sum_{i=1}^{Z} r_{i\perp}^2 ;$$

$\boldsymbol{L}$ is the total angular momentum of the Z electrons: $\boldsymbol{L} \equiv \sum_i (\boldsymbol{r}_i \times \boldsymbol{p}_i)$. In the phenomena that we shall study, the contribution of the third term in the above expression is entirely negligible [1]). Thus we have,

---

[1]) This term is the main factor in atomic diamagnetism. Knowing that $\langle r^2 \rangle \simeq 10^{-16}\,\text{cm}^2$, we can evaluate its order of magnitude $(Ze^2/12\,mc^2)\,\mathscr{H}^2\langle r^2\rangle$. The ratio of this to the level distance $e\hbar\mathscr{H}/2\,mc$ found below is about $10^{-9}Z\mathscr{H}$ (gauss), a negligibly small quantity, even for a very strong field and a very heavy atom. Thus its neglect can in no way be held responsible for the conflicts which appear further along.

to a very good approximation

$$H = H_0 - \frac{e}{2mc}(\mathscr{H} \cdot \mathbf{L}). \tag{XIII.72}$$

This is just what we would have if each electron in circulating in its orbit induced a magnetic moment

$$\mu = \frac{e}{2mc}\boldsymbol{l}$$

proportional to its angular momentum, the constant of proportionality (the gyromagnetic ratio) being precisely equal to the value given by the classical theory of this effect, namely $e/2mc$. In this interpretation the total magnetic moment of the atom is equal to the sum of the Z individual magnetic moments, i.e.

$$\mathscr{M} = \frac{e}{2mc}\mathbf{L},$$

and the energy of the atom placed in the field $\mathscr{H}$ differs from the energy in the absence of the field by the magnetic energy term $-(\mathscr{M} \cdot \mathscr{H})$.

A certain number of important properties can be deduced simply by inspection of expression (XIII.72) if we take into account that H_0, being invariant under rotation, commutes with the three components of $\mathbf{L}$.

Let us take the direction of $\mathscr{H}$ as the z axis. H_0, $\mathbf{L}^2$ and L_z have a common set of eigenvectors $|n\,L\,M\rangle$ and the corresponding eigenvalues of H_0, E_0^{nL}, are independent of M and are $(2L+1)$-fold degenerate [1]).

H is a function of H_0 and L_z [eq. (XIII.72)] and therefore has the same set of eigenfunctions, the eigenvalue of the vector $|nLM\rangle$ being

$$E^{nLM} = E_0^{nL} - M\mu_B\,\mathscr{H}, \tag{XIII.73}$$

[1]) If several of these eigenvalues accidentally coincide (as in the hydrogen atom) the degeneracy is higher. Suppose $E_0^{nL} = E_0^{n'L'}$; the degeneracy is then of order $(2L + 1) + (2L' + 1)$. In this case the argument that follows above needs some modification of detail. However, the conclusions drawn are valid if we everywhere replace L by the larger of L and L'. In particular the result that each Zeeman "multiplet" has an odd number of equidistant levels is not modified.

where

$$\mu_{\mathrm{B}} = \frac{e\hbar}{2mc} \qquad \text{(Bohr magneton).} \qquad \text{(XIII.74)}$$

Since M can take all integral values from $-L$ to $+L$, each level $E_0{}^{nL}$ gets split under the effect of the field $\mathscr{H}$ into $(2L+1)$ distinct, equidistant levels distributed according to (XIII.73). We therefore have the following theoretical predictions:

(i) Each level $E_0{}^{nL}$ of the atomic spectrum is split by the field $\mathscr{H}$ into a "multiplet" of $(2L+1)$ equidistant levels;

(ii) These levels are distributed on either side of $E_0{}^{nL}$ in such a way that their distance from $E_0{}^{nL}$ averages to zero;

(iii) The distance between two neighboring levels is a quantity $\mu_{\mathrm{B}}\mathscr{H}$ that is independent of the atom considered and proportional to $\mathscr{H}$.

These theoretical predictions are only partially confirmed by experiment. There are two important discrepancies:

(a) in atoms of odd Z, the multiplets are all even, which is just what one would have if **L** were half-integral;

(b) the distance between neighbors in the same multiplet is found to be $g\mu_{\mathrm{B}}\mathscr{H}$, the factor g (the Landé factor) varying from one multiplet to another within rather large limits.

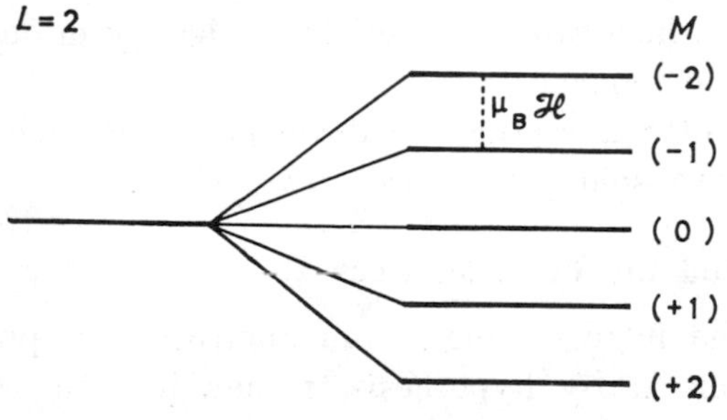

Fig. XIII.2. Zeeman effect for a D state ($L = 2$). On the left, energy level in absence of field; on the right, corresponding levels when $\mathscr{H} \neq 0$.

The existence of half-integral angular momenta is directly established by the Stern–Gerlach experiment (§ I.10). As the atoms making up the beam are almost all in their ground state, the number of spots observed on the screen is equal to the multiplicity of the ground state.

With silver atoms we observe in all two spots, hence the ground state of the silver atom has angular momentum $\frac{1}{2}$. More generally, atoms having odd Z invariably give an even number of spots, result characteristic of a half-integral angular momentum.

Points (a) and (b) show up simultaneously in the study of the anomalous Zeeman effect. The spectral results in general permit the simultaneous determination of the multiplicity of the states between which the optical transitions are effected, and their respective Landé g-factors.

To surmount these difficulties it is necessary to introduce half-integral angular momenta and gyromagnetic ratios differing from $e/2mc$. This is what is very simply done by the hypothesis of electron spin (Uehlenbeck and Goudsmit, 1925):

Each electron has an intrinsic angular momentum or spin **s**, *of magnitude* $\frac{1}{2}\hbar$ *(spin* $\frac{1}{2}$*) with which is associated the magnetic moment*

$$\mu_s = g_s \frac{e}{2mc} \mathbf{s}. \tag{XIII.75}$$

g_s is an adjustable constant. The theory is in excellent agreement with experiment if we take

$$g_s \simeq 2. \tag{XIII.76}$$

This value for g_s is explained by the relativistic theory of the electron (Ch. XX).

Experiment shows that the nucleons (protons and neutrons) also have a spin $\frac{1}{2}$, which can be directly revealed by measuring the associated magnetic moment [1]).

In the rest of this section we develop the non-relativistic theory of particles with spin $\frac{1}{2}$ (*the Pauli Theory*).

19. Spin $\frac{1}{2}$ and the Pauli Matrices

Let **s** be the intrinsic angular momentum (or spin vector) of a particle of spin $\frac{1}{2}$. By hypothesis, $\mathbf{s}^2$ has just the one eigenvalue

---

[1]) If $\boldsymbol{\mu}_p$, $\mathbf{s}_p$, M_p denote respectively the magnetic moment, the spin and the mass of the proton, one has [cf. eq. (XIII.75)]:

$$\mu_p = g_p \frac{e}{2 M_p c} \mathbf{s}_p.$$

There is an analogous formula for the neutron. Experiment gives $g_p = 5.59$ and $g_n = -3.83$.

$s(s+1)=\frac{1}{2}\times\frac{3}{2}=\frac{3}{4}$. Each component, for example s_z, can take one or the other of the values $\pm\frac{1}{2}$. We suppose these to be non-degenerate. Consequently the components of **s** are operators acting in a two-dimensional space in which a possible basis is constituted by the two eigenvectors

$$|+\rangle \equiv |\tfrac{1}{2}\ +\tfrac{1}{2}\rangle, \qquad |-\rangle \equiv |\tfrac{1}{2}\ -\tfrac{1}{2}\rangle$$

of $\mathbf{s}^2$ and s_z.

If we adopt this basis we can easily write down the matrices representing the operators s_x, s_y, s_z. They are particular J_x, J_y, J_z matrices with elements given by equations (XIII.28).

In addition to the commutation relations characteristic of angular momenta, the components of **s** verify the special relations

$$s_x{}^2=s_y{}^2=s_z{}^2=\tfrac{1}{4}, \qquad s_+{}^2=s_-{}^2=0.$$

Since

$$s_+{}^2=(s_x+\mathrm{i}\,s_y)^2=(s_x{}^2-s_y{}^2)+\mathrm{i}\,(s_x\,s_y+s_y\,s_x),$$

we can deduce that

$$s_x\,s_y+s_y\,s_x=0,$$

i.e. that the operators s_x, s_y, s_z anticommute [1]).

It is convenient to introduce the *Pauli matrices* $\boldsymbol{\sigma}\equiv(\sigma_x, \sigma_y, \sigma_z)$ defined by the equation

$$\mathbf{s}=\tfrac{1}{2}\boldsymbol{\sigma}. \qquad \text{(XIII.77)}$$

They are given explicitly by

$$\sigma_x=\begin{pmatrix}0 & 1\\ 1 & 0\end{pmatrix}, \quad \sigma_y=\begin{pmatrix}0 & -\mathrm{i}\\ \mathrm{i} & 0\end{pmatrix}, \quad \sigma_z=\begin{pmatrix}1 & 0\\ 0 & -1\end{pmatrix}.$$

Their principal properties, which can be deduced from their definition and which can easily be verified in their explicit form, are summarized by the following equations:

$$\sigma_x{}^2=\sigma_y{}^2=\sigma_z{}^2=1. \qquad \text{(XIII.78)}$$

$$\sigma_x\,\sigma_y=-\sigma_y\,\sigma_x=\mathrm{i}\sigma_z. \qquad \text{(XIII.79}a\text{)}$$

$$\sigma_y\,\sigma_z=-\sigma_z\,\sigma_y=\mathrm{i}\sigma_x. \qquad \text{(XIII.79}b\text{)}$$

$$\sigma_z\,\sigma_x=-\sigma_x\,\sigma_z=\mathrm{i}\sigma_y. \qquad \text{(XIII.79}c\text{)}$$

$$\sigma_x\,\sigma_y\,\sigma_z=\mathrm{i}. \qquad \text{(XIII.80)}$$

$$\mathrm{Tr}\,\sigma_x=\mathrm{Tr}\,\sigma_y=\mathrm{Tr}\,\sigma_z=0. \qquad \text{(XIII.81)}$$

$$\det\sigma_x=\det\sigma_y=\det\sigma_z=-1. \qquad \text{(XIII.82)}$$

---

1) Two operators A, B anticommute if $AB+BA=0$

From these we can deduce the important identity (Problem XIII.9)

$$(\boldsymbol{\sigma}\cdot\boldsymbol{A})\,(\boldsymbol{\sigma}\cdot\boldsymbol{B})=(\boldsymbol{A}\cdot\boldsymbol{B})+\mathrm{i}\boldsymbol{\sigma}\cdot(\boldsymbol{A}\times\boldsymbol{B}), \qquad \text{(XIII.83)}$$

$\boldsymbol{A}$ and $\boldsymbol{B}$ being any two vectors [1]).

Since $\boldsymbol{s}$ is the angular momentum, the rotation operator $R_{\boldsymbol{u}}{}^{(s)}(\varphi)$ effecting the transformation of vectors of that space in the rotation $\mathscr{R}_{\boldsymbol{u}}(\varphi)$ is, from (XIII.58)

$$R_{\boldsymbol{u}}{}^{(s)}(\varphi)\equiv \mathrm{e}^{-\frac{1}{2}\mathrm{i}\varphi\sigma_u},$$

where $\sigma_u \equiv (\boldsymbol{u}\cdot\boldsymbol{\sigma})$. Expanding the exponential and separately summing the terms even and odd in σ_u with the aid of the relations

$$\sigma_u{}^{2p}=1, \qquad \sigma_u{}^{2p+1}=\sigma_u$$

[cf. eq. (XIII.83)] we obtain the very simple expression

$$R_{\boldsymbol{u}}{}^{(s)}(\varphi)=\cos\tfrac{1}{2}\varphi-\mathrm{i}\sigma_u\sin\tfrac{1}{2}\varphi. \qquad \text{(XIII.84)}$$

Observe that the operator of rotation through 2π is equal to -1, in agreement with the results of § 15.

The operator representing the rotation $\mathscr{R}(\alpha\,\beta\,\gamma)$ is, from (XIII.60)

$$R^{(s)}(\alpha\,\beta\,\gamma)=\mathrm{e}^{-\frac{1}{2}\mathrm{i}\alpha\sigma_z}\,\mathrm{e}^{-\frac{1}{2}\mathrm{i}\beta\sigma_y}\,\mathrm{e}^{-\frac{1}{2}\mathrm{i}\gamma\sigma_z}. \qquad \text{(XIII.85)}$$

Its explicit form can be calculated in the same way as that of $\mathscr{R}_{\boldsymbol{u}}(\varphi)$ and is given in the Appendix [formula (C.74)].

The vectors of the space considered here bear some analogy to those of ordinary space. The latter are geometric entities with three components and which under rotation transform one into another following a well-determined law. Such is also the case with those considered here [transformation law (XIII.85)] except that they have two components instead of three. They are called *spinors*.

20. Observables and Wave Functions of a Spin ½ Particle. Spinor Fields

Consider a particle of spin ½.

Its fundamental variables may be put into two categories, the

---

1) or two vector operators providing their components commute with those of $\boldsymbol{\sigma}$. In this case the order of $\boldsymbol{A}$ and $\boldsymbol{B}$ in the two sides of the identity must be respected. Example:

$$(\boldsymbol{\sigma}\cdot\boldsymbol{r})\,(\boldsymbol{\sigma}\cdot\boldsymbol{p})=(\boldsymbol{r}\cdot\boldsymbol{p})+\mathrm{i}\,\boldsymbol{\sigma}\cdot(\boldsymbol{r}\times\boldsymbol{p}).$$

orbital variables and the intrinsic, or spin, variables. The first are the components of position $\boldsymbol{r}$ and momentum $\boldsymbol{p}$; they verify the fundamental commutation relations ($\hbar=1$)

$$[r_i, p_j] = \mathrm{i}\delta_{ij}.$$

The second are the components of the spin $\boldsymbol{s}$; they verify the commutation relations

$$[s_i, s_j] = \mathrm{i}\varepsilon_{ijk}\, s_k,$$

and in addition must satisfy the supplementary condition $\boldsymbol{s}^2 = \frac{3}{4}$.

As the orbital variables commute with the spin variables, the space $\mathscr{E}$ of the state vectors of the particle is the tensor product

$$\mathscr{E} = \mathscr{E}^{(0)} \otimes \mathscr{E}^{(s)}$$

of the orbital space $\mathscr{E}^{(0)}$ and of the spin space $\mathscr{E}^{(s)}$ (cf. § VIII.7). $\mathscr{E}^{(0)}$ is the state space of a particle without spin, $\mathscr{E}^{(s)}$ is the two-dimensional space constructed in the preceding paragraph.

To represent the vectors of $\mathscr{E}$, one usually chooses the representation with $\boldsymbol{r}$ and s_z diagonal; each vector $|\psi\rangle$ is then represented by the wave function

$$\psi(\boldsymbol{r}, \mu) \equiv \langle \boldsymbol{r}\, \mu | \psi \rangle, \qquad \text{(XIII.86)}$$

a function of the continuous variables $\boldsymbol{r} \equiv (x, y, z)$, and of the discrete variable μ representing the eigenvalue of s_z and taking the two values $\pm\frac{1}{2}$.

The total angular momentum of the particle is

$$\boldsymbol{j} \equiv \boldsymbol{l} + \boldsymbol{s}. \qquad \text{(XIII.87)}$$

The fundamental variables of the system are the components of the three vector-operators $\boldsymbol{r}$, $\boldsymbol{p}$, $\boldsymbol{s}$. Clearly $\boldsymbol{j}$ verifies with each of these the commutation relations (XIII.57) characterizing the total angular momentum, for $\boldsymbol{l} \equiv \boldsymbol{r} \times \boldsymbol{p}$ verifies these relations with $\boldsymbol{r}$ and $\boldsymbol{p}$ and commutes with $\boldsymbol{s}$, and $\boldsymbol{s}$ verifies these relations with itself and commutes with $\boldsymbol{r}$ and $\boldsymbol{p}$.

The rotation operator $R(\alpha\,\beta\,\gamma)$ can now be deduced [eq. (XIII.60)]. Since $\boldsymbol{l}$ and $\boldsymbol{s}$ commute, it takes the form of a product of two commuting operators:

$$R(\alpha\,\beta\,\gamma) = R^{(s)}(\alpha\,\beta\,\gamma)\, R^{(0)}(\alpha\,\beta\,\gamma) \qquad \text{(XIII.88)}$$

$R^{(s)}(\alpha\,\beta\,\gamma)$, defined by equation (XIII.85), *rotates the spin*, while $R^{(0)}(\alpha\,\beta\,\gamma)$, defined by

$$R^{(0)}(\alpha\,\beta\,\gamma) = e^{-i\alpha l_z}\, e^{-i\beta l_y}\, e^{-i\gamma l_z}$$

rotates the orbital variables.

In a rotation through 2π, $R^{(0)} = 1$ and $R^{(s)} = -1$, and therefore all kets change sign in such a rotation. However, all of the fundamental observables are invariant in a rotation through 2π and therefore, following the discussion of § 15, their physical interpretation raises no difficulty.

It is often convenient to put

$$\psi(\mathbf{r}, \pm \tfrac{1}{2}) = \psi_{\pm}(\mathbf{r})$$

and to write the wave function $\psi(\mathbf{r}, \mu)$ in the form of a *two component wave function*:

$$\psi \equiv \begin{pmatrix} \psi_+(\mathbf{r}) \\ \psi_-(\mathbf{r}) \end{pmatrix}.$$

For each value of $\mathbf{r}$, ψ represents a ket vector of the space $\mathscr{E}^{(s)}$, namely

$$\langle \mathbf{r} | \psi \rangle \equiv \psi_+(\mathbf{r})\,|+\rangle + \psi_-(\mathbf{r})\,|-\rangle. \qquad \text{(XIII.89)}$$

In other words, the wave function may be regarded as a spinor field [1].

The extension of these considerations to a system containing Z particles of spin $\frac{1}{2}$ is straightforward. The state space for the whole system is the tensor product of the state spaces for each individual particle. In particular, the total spin space has 2^Z dimensions and is the tensor product of the Z individual spin spaces. A system of Pauli matrices, $\boldsymbol{\sigma}^{(i)}$, is then introduced for each individual spin. An

---

[1]) In a rotation $\mathscr{R}(\alpha\beta\gamma)$, the spinor field ψ transforms into

$$\mathscr{R}[\psi] = R\,\psi = R^{(\frac{1}{2})} \begin{pmatrix} \psi_+(\mathscr{R}^{-1}\,\mathbf{r}) \\ \psi_-(\mathscr{R}^{-1}\,\mathbf{r}) \end{pmatrix}.$$

This is a direct result of (XIII.88); $R^{(\frac{1}{2})}$ is the rotation matrix corresponding to $J = \frac{1}{2}$. We may compare this transformation law to formula XIII.47 for a scalar field. We have an analogous formula for a vector field, with $R^{(1)}$ in place of $R^{(\frac{1}{2})}$ (cf. § 21).

overall rotation of the spins can be expressed with the aid of the total spin:

$$\mathbf{S} = \tfrac{1}{2} \sum_{i=1}^{Z} \boldsymbol{\sigma}^{(i)}. \tag{XIII.90}$$

An overall rotation through 2π of the spins is represented by the operator $(-)^Z$.

21. Vector Fields and Particles of Spin 1

It is well to stress the parallel between the concept of a spinor field and the more familiar concept of a vector field.

Let $\mathbf{A}(\mathbf{r})$ be a vector field associated with a physical system. It might, for example, be a magnetic or electric field or, as we shall see, the wave function of a particle of spin 1.

Let us examine how $\mathbf{A}(\mathbf{r})$ transforms under rotation. Let $A'(\mathbf{r})$ be the rotated field resulting from an overall rotation $\mathscr{R}$ of the physical system:

$$\mathbf{A}' \equiv \mathscr{R}\,[\mathbf{A}].$$

The field $\mathbf{A}'$ at the point $\mathbf{r}$ is obtained by applying the rotation $\mathscr{R}$ to the vector $A(\mathbf{r}_1)$ representing the field $\mathbf{A}$ at the point $\mathbf{r}_1 \equiv \mathscr{R}^{-1}\,\mathbf{r}$, i.e. [cf. eq. (XIII.43) and (XIII.47)]:

$$A_i'(\mathbf{r}) = \mathscr{R}_{ij}\, A_j\,(\mathscr{R}^{-1}\,\mathbf{r}) \qquad (i = x, y, z).$$

Thus for a rotation α about Oz we find [cf. eq. (XIII.44)]

$$\mathbf{A}' \equiv \mathscr{R}_z(\alpha)\,[\mathbf{A}] \qquad \mathbf{r}_1 \equiv (x\cos\alpha + y\sin\alpha, -x\sin\alpha + y\cos\alpha, z)$$

$$A'_x(\mathbf{r}) = A_x(\mathbf{r}_1)\cos\alpha - A_y(\mathbf{r}_1)\sin\alpha$$

$$A'_y(\mathbf{r}) = A_x(\mathbf{r}_1)\sin\alpha + A_y(\mathbf{r}_1)\cos\alpha$$

$$A'_z(\mathbf{r}) = A_z(\mathbf{r}_1).$$

In particular, the infinitesimal rotation ε about Oz gives

$$\mathscr{R}_z(\varepsilon)\,[\mathbf{A}] = (1 - \mathrm{i}\varepsilon\,(l_z + s_z))\,\mathbf{A}, \tag{XIII.91}$$

where l_z is the above-defined differential operator and s_z the operator defined by

$$s_z \begin{pmatrix} A_x(\mathbf{r}) \\ A_y(\mathbf{r}) \\ A_z(\mathbf{r}) \end{pmatrix} = \begin{pmatrix} -\mathrm{i}A_y(\mathbf{r}) \\ \mathrm{i}A_x(\mathbf{r}) \\ 0 \end{pmatrix}.$$

s_z transforms each component of the field at a given point into a particular linear combination of the three components of the field at the same point. $\mathbf{A}$ being defined by its three Cartesian components A_x, A_y and A_z, s_z is represented by the matrix

$$s_z = \begin{pmatrix} 0 & -\mathrm{i} & 0 \\ \mathrm{i} & 0 & 0 \\ 0 & 0 & 0 \end{pmatrix}.$$

One similarly defines the operators s_x and s_y; their representative matrices are

$$s_x = \begin{pmatrix} 0 & 0 & 0 \\ 0 & 0 & -\mathrm{i} \\ 0 & \mathrm{i} & 0 \end{pmatrix} \qquad s_y = \begin{pmatrix} 0 & 0 & \mathrm{i} \\ 0 & 0 & 0 \\ -\mathrm{i} & 0 & 0 \end{pmatrix}.$$

We easily show that s_x, s_y, s_z verify the commutation relations characteristic of the components of an angular momentum. We denote this angular momentum by $\mathbf{s}$; the calculation of its square gives:

$$\mathbf{s}^2 = 2$$

which corresponds to an angular momentum $s = 1$. By definition, we shall say that $\mathbf{s}$ is the intrinsic angular momentum, or spin, of the vector field.

A field such as $\mathbf{A}(\mathbf{r})$ can describe a particle of spin 1. Put:

$$A_i(\mathbf{r}) \equiv A(\mathbf{r}, i) \qquad (i = x, y \text{ or } z),$$

$A(\mathbf{r}, i)$ is a wave function which depends not only on the position variables but also on an index i which may take 3 values and which constitutes an internal variable describing the orientation of the particle. The scalar product of two wave functions of this type is:

$$\langle B, A \rangle \equiv \sum_i \int B^*(\mathbf{r}, i)\, A(\mathbf{r}, i)\, \mathrm{d}\mathbf{r} = \int (\mathbf{B}^* \cdot \mathbf{A})\, \mathrm{d}\mathbf{r}. \qquad \text{(XIII.92)}$$

An operator such as $\boldsymbol{l}$ acts on the position variables alone, while $\mathbf{s}$ acts on the internal variable i. Clearly $\boldsymbol{l}$ and $\mathbf{s}$ commute since they act on different variables. The operator of infinitesimal rotation about the z axis is defined by equation (XIII.91); we likewise obtain the operator of infinitesimal rotation about any other axis; applying definition (XIII.55) we find the total angular momentum of the particle:

$$\mathbf{j} \equiv \boldsymbol{l} + \mathbf{s}$$

[cf. eq. (XIII.87)].

More generally, any linear transformation of a vector field may be looked upon as the action of a certain linear operator that can be expressed as a function of the three fundamental vector operators:

$$\boldsymbol{r}, \quad \boldsymbol{p} \equiv -\mathrm{i}\nabla, \quad \boldsymbol{s}.$$

In particular, we have the important identity

$$\text{curl} \equiv \boldsymbol{s} \cdot \boldsymbol{p} \tag{XIII.93}$$

which may easily be verified from the definition of the curl and the explicit form of the matrices s_x, s_y, s_z given above.

The concepts of scalar product, of rotation, and more generally, of linear transformation, are independent of the representation chosen. The wave function $\boldsymbol{A}(\boldsymbol{r}, i)$ represents the dynamical state of the particle in a representation in which the basis vectors for the internal variable correspond to unit vectors along each of the three axes Ox, Oy, Oz; these basis vectors, $|x\rangle$, $|y\rangle$, $|z\rangle$ are respectively eigenvectors of s_x, s_y, s_z belonging to the eigenvalue 0. (cf. Problem XIII.10.) It is often more convenient to choose the representation where the basis vectors are the eigenvectors of s_z, $|+\rangle$, $|0\rangle$, $|-\rangle$, belonging respectively to the eigenvalues $+1$, 0, -1. These are obtained one from another by the standard law defined in § 6. In this new representation, s_x, s_y and s_z are represented by matrices verifying relations (XIII.28) (with $j = j' = 1$) and the ket $|A\rangle$ associated with the vector field $\boldsymbol{A}$ is represented by the wave function

$$A(\boldsymbol{r}, \mu) \equiv A_\mu(\boldsymbol{r}) \qquad (\mu = +, 0, -),$$

from the definition [cf. eq. (XIII.89)]

$$\langle \boldsymbol{r} | A \rangle \equiv A_+(\boldsymbol{r})\,|+\rangle + A_0(\boldsymbol{r})\,|0\rangle + A_-(\boldsymbol{r})\,|-\rangle.$$

We have:

$$\begin{aligned} A_+ &= -\frac{\sqrt{2}}{2}(A_x - \mathrm{i}A_y) \\ A_0 &= \quad A_z \\ A_- &= \quad \frac{\sqrt{2}}{2}(A_x + \mathrm{i}A_y). \end{aligned} \tag{XIII.94}$$

22. Spin-dependent Interactions in Atoms

The existence of intrinsic magnetic moment leads to spin-dependent terms in the Hamiltonian of *an electron in an electromagnetic field*.

In particular, in the presence of a magnetic field $\mathscr{H}(\boldsymbol{r})$ we have the *direct coupling* term suggested by the correspondence principle:

$$-\boldsymbol{\mu}\cdot\mathscr{H}(\mathbf{r}) \equiv -\mu_{\mathrm{B}}\boldsymbol{\sigma}\cdot\mathscr{H},$$

where $\boldsymbol{\mu}$ is the intrinsic magnetic moment defined by equations (XIII.75–76).

This is not the only additional term. Even with a purely electrostatic potential it is clear that terms due to *spin-orbit coupling* will appear, for an electron moving in such a potential "sees" a magnetic field, which field can interact with $\boldsymbol{\mu}$. This argument from Classical Mechanics can be used as a guide for the empirical determination of the spin-orbit coupling. However, since we are dealing here with a relativistic effect (tending to zero in the limit $v \ll c$), it is preferable that it be derived from the relativistic equation of the electron. This can be done by making an expansion in v/c and retaining non-zero terms of the lowest order. This problem will be studied in Chapter XX. In a spherically symmetrical potential $V(r)$, the spin-orbit interaction is obviously invariant under rotation, and therefore commutes with all three components of the total angular momentum $\boldsymbol{j}$. The expression given by the relativistic theory is

$$\frac{\hbar^2}{2m^2c^2}(\boldsymbol{l}\cdot\boldsymbol{s})\frac{1}{r}\frac{\mathrm{d}V}{\mathrm{d}r}. \qquad \text{(XIII.95)}$$

For the same reasons, the Hamiltonian H_0 of the Z electrons of a complex atom contains spin-orbit terms in addition to the Coulomb terms shown in eq. (XIII.71). These additional terms commute with the total angular momentum

$$\boldsymbol{J} = \boldsymbol{L} + \boldsymbol{S}$$

but, unlike the rest of H_0, they do not commute with $\boldsymbol{L}$ and $\boldsymbol{S}$ separately. Moreover, although their contribution to the total energy is relatively very small (except for the heaviest atoms), their presence results in a qualitative modification in the atomic spectrum – removal of the degeneracy – and therefore can never be ignored [1]).

The Hamiltonian H of an atom in a constant magnetic field $\mathscr{H}$ is obtained by applying the treatment of § 18 to the Hamiltonian without external field, H_0, and adding the direct magnetic interaction

[1]) For completeness, one should also mention the modifications due to the existence of the magnetic moment of the nucleus (hyperfine structure).

terms $-\sum_i \boldsymbol{\mu}^{(i)} \cdot \mathscr{H}$. If we neglect the "diamagnetic term" in $\mathscr{H}^2$, as we did in equation (XIII.72), we find

$$H = H_0 - \frac{e}{2mc}\,[\mathscr{H} \cdot (\mathbf{L} + 2\mathbf{S})]. \tag{XIII.96}$$

23. Spin-dependent Nucleon-Nucleon Interactions

As a further example of spin-dependent interactions, we consider the interaction of two nucleons. Let M_0 be the mass of the nucleons, $\mathbf{r} = \mathbf{r}_1 - \mathbf{r}_2$ their relative position, $\mathbf{p} = \frac{1}{2}(\mathbf{p}_1 - \mathbf{p}_2)$ their relative momentum, $\frac{1}{2}\boldsymbol{\sigma}_1$ and $\frac{1}{2}\boldsymbol{\sigma}_2$ their respective spins. The motion of the center of mass separates completely from the relative motion; the dynamical variables and dynamical states considered below refer exclusively to the relative motion. The orbital angular momentum is

$$\mathbf{L} = \mathbf{r} \times \mathbf{p},$$

the total spin

$$\mathbf{S} = \tfrac{1}{2}(\boldsymbol{\sigma}_1 + \boldsymbol{\sigma}_2) \tag{XIII.97}$$

and the total angular momentum

$$\mathbf{J} = \mathbf{L} + \mathbf{S}. \tag{XIII.98}$$

The Hamiltonian is of the form

$$H = \frac{\mathbf{p}^2}{M_0} + V.$$

The four types of rotationally-invariant interaction most commonly proposed are

$$V_1(r) \tag{XIII.99a}$$

$$V_2(r)\,(\boldsymbol{\sigma}_1 \cdot \boldsymbol{\sigma}_2) \tag{XIII.99b}$$

$$V_3(r)\,(\mathbf{L} \cdot \mathbf{S}) \tag{XIII.99c}$$

$$V_4(r)\left[3\,\frac{(\boldsymbol{\sigma}_1 \cdot \mathbf{r})\,(\boldsymbol{\sigma}_2 \cdot \mathbf{r})}{r^2} - \boldsymbol{\sigma}_1 \cdot \boldsymbol{\sigma}_2\right]. \tag{XIII.99d}$$

The spin-dependent operators appearing in the last three expressions are written in their traditional form. They can be expressed differently. Thus, squaring both sides of (XIII.97) and using the identity

$$\boldsymbol{\sigma}_1{}^2 = \boldsymbol{\sigma}_2{}^2 = 3$$

we get

$$\boldsymbol{\sigma}_1 \cdot \boldsymbol{\sigma}_2 = 2\boldsymbol{S}^2 - 3, \tag{XIII.100}$$

and squaring both sides of eq. (XIII.98) we get

$$\boldsymbol{L} \cdot \boldsymbol{S} = \tfrac{1}{2}(\boldsymbol{J}^2 - \boldsymbol{L}^2 - \boldsymbol{S}^2). \tag{XIII.101}$$

Finally, from eq. (XIII.97)

$$\begin{aligned}(\boldsymbol{S} \cdot \boldsymbol{r})^2 &= \tfrac{1}{4}[(\boldsymbol{\sigma}_1 \cdot \boldsymbol{r}) + (\boldsymbol{\sigma}_2 \cdot \boldsymbol{r})]^2 = \tfrac{1}{4}[(\boldsymbol{\sigma}_1 \cdot \boldsymbol{r})^2 + (\boldsymbol{\sigma}_2 \cdot \boldsymbol{r})^2 + 2(\boldsymbol{\sigma}_1 \cdot \boldsymbol{r})\,(\boldsymbol{\sigma}_2 \cdot \boldsymbol{r})] \\ &= \tfrac{1}{2}[(\boldsymbol{\sigma}_1 \cdot \boldsymbol{r})\,(\boldsymbol{\sigma}_2 \cdot \boldsymbol{r}) + r^2].\end{aligned}$$

Therefore

$$(\boldsymbol{\sigma}_1 \cdot \boldsymbol{r})\,(\boldsymbol{\sigma}_2 \cdot \boldsymbol{r}) = 2(\boldsymbol{S} \cdot \boldsymbol{r})^2 - r^2,$$

and consequently

$$S_{12} \equiv 3\,\frac{(\boldsymbol{\sigma}_1 \cdot \boldsymbol{r})\,(\boldsymbol{\sigma}_2 \cdot \boldsymbol{r})}{r^2} - \boldsymbol{\sigma}_1 \cdot \boldsymbol{\sigma}_2 \tag{XIII.102}$$

$$= 2\left[3\,\frac{(\boldsymbol{S} \cdot \boldsymbol{r})^2}{r^2} - \boldsymbol{S}^2\right]. \tag{XIII.102$'$}$$

The operator S_{12} is called the "tensor operator" and the interaction (XIII.99*d*) the "tensor force".

If V is a linear combination of interactions of type (XIII.99), the Hamiltonian will be invariant both under rotation and under reflection (in a reflection, $\boldsymbol{r}$ and $\boldsymbol{p}$ become respectively $-\boldsymbol{r}$ and $-\boldsymbol{p}$; spin operators remain unchanged). This second invariance property will be discussed later. For the present we mention only the following. Call P the operator which operating on $\psi(\boldsymbol{r})$ gives $\psi(-\boldsymbol{r})$. The eigenfunctions of P are functions of well-defined parity. Invariance under reflection signifies that $[H, P] = 0$. If the Hamiltonian has this property we may look for its eigenfunctions among the functions of well-defined parity.

Interactions (XIII.99) are arranged in order of decreasing symmetry.

The first is independent of spin.

The second commutes with $\boldsymbol{L}$ and $\boldsymbol{S}$ separately: it is invariant not only in an overall rotation but also in a rotation of the orbital variables alone and in a rotation of the spins alone. If V contains only terms of the form (XIII.99*a*) and (XIII.99*b*), then the eigenfunctions of H may be sought among the common eigenfunctions of $\boldsymbol{L}^2$, $\boldsymbol{S}^2$, L_z, S_z and the corresponding eigenvalues will have a rotational degeneracy of order $(2L+1)\,(2S+1)$ and will be independent of the eigenvalues of L_z and S_z.

If V also contains a term of the form (XIII.99c), then H will still commute with $\mathbf{L}^2$ and $\mathbf{S}^2$ but will cease to be separately invariant under rotations of space and rotations of the spins. Its eigenfunctions may be sought among the common eigenfunctions of $\mathbf{L}^2$, $\mathbf{S}^2$, $\mathbf{J}^2$ and J_z and its eigenvalues will have a rotational degeneracy of order $(2J+1)$ only.

Interaction (XIII.99d) is the least symmetrical of the four. It still commutes with $\mathbf{S}^2$ (from (102′), $[\mathbf{S}^2, S_{12}]=0$), but not with $\mathbf{L}^2$. If V contains a term of the form (XIII.99d), the eigenfunctions of H may be sought among the common eigenfunctions of P, $\mathbf{S}^2$, $\mathbf{J}^2$, and J_z.

V. ADDITION OF ANGULAR MOMENTA

24. The Addition Problem

In many problems, the Hamiltonian is invariant under rotation and therefore commutes with the components of the total angular momentum $\mathbf{J}$. We then seek the eigenfunctions of the Hamiltonian among the simultaneous eigenfunctions of $\mathbf{J}^2$ and J_z. It is therefore important to be able to enumerate, and to form, the vectors of angular momentum $(J\ M)$.

In the simple case of a spinless particle in a central field (Ch. IX) the total angular momentum is simply the orbital angular momentum $\mathbf{l}$, and the eigenfunctions of total angular momentum have the form $\chi(r)\ Y_l^m(\theta, \varphi)$. In the general case, $\mathbf{J}$ is a sum of individual angular momenta

$$\mathbf{J}=\sum_i \mathbf{j}_i,$$

i.e., of the orbital angular momenta and of the spins of the particles constituting the system. In general we know how to construct the eigenvectors of the individual angular momenta. Thus, in the case of the two-nucleon system considered in § 13 we have

$$\mathbf{J}=\mathbf{L}+\tfrac{1}{2}\boldsymbol{\sigma}_1+\tfrac{1}{2}\boldsymbol{\sigma}_2 \tag{XIII.103}$$

and the eigenfunctions of the individual angular momenta are of the form $\psi(r)\ Y_l^m(\theta, \varphi)\,|\mu_1\rangle\,|\mu_2\rangle$, where μ_1 and μ_2 may take the values $+\frac{1}{2}$ or $-\frac{1}{2}$ according as nucleons 1 and 2 have their spins up or down respectively. The addition problem consists in forming linear combinations of these to obtain a complete set of eigenfunctions of the total angular momentum.

25. Addition Theorem for Two Angular Momenta

The simplest problem is that of adding *two* angular momenta. Suppose that

$$\boldsymbol{J} = \boldsymbol{j}_1 + \boldsymbol{j}_2,$$

where $\boldsymbol{j}_1$ and $\boldsymbol{j}_2$ are respectively the angular momenta of the separate systems 1 and 2 which together form the system under study, and suppose that we have constructed a complete set of common eigenvectors

$$|\alpha\, j_1\, j_2\, m_1\, m_2\rangle \qquad \text{(XIII.104)}$$

of $\boldsymbol{j}_1^2$, $\boldsymbol{j}_2^2$, j_{1z} and j_{2z}. α represents the additional quantum numbers necessary to specify the dynamical state completely or, if one prefers, the eigenvalues of the observables A which with $\boldsymbol{j}_1^2$, $\boldsymbol{j}_2^2$, j_{1z} and j_{2z} form a complete set of commuting observables, and which commute as well with the components of $\boldsymbol{j}_1$ and of $\boldsymbol{j}_2$. In addition we suppose that the vectors (XIII.104) form a standard basis with respect to the angular momenta 1 and 2. To each set of quantum numbers $(\alpha\, j_1\, j_2)$ there correspond as many vectors as there are distinct pairs $(m_1\, m_2)$; these vectors are obtained one from another by repeated application of $j_{1\pm}$ or $j_{2\pm}$, as set forth in §6, and span a subspace $\mathscr{E}\,(\alpha\, j_1\, j_2)$ of $(2j_1+1)\;(2j_2+1)$ dimensions.

Note that A, $\boldsymbol{j}_1^2$ and $\boldsymbol{j}_2^2$ commute with $\boldsymbol{J}$. We therefore look for the eigenvectors of $\boldsymbol{J}^2$ and J_z among the eigenvectors of these operators and in doing so each subspace $\mathscr{E}\,(\alpha\, j_1\, j_2)$ may be treated separately. We consider a particular $\mathscr{E}$ and to simplify notation we represent the vectors $|\alpha\, j_1\, j_2\, m_1\, m_2\rangle$ of this subspace by $|m_1\, m_2\rangle$ and the eigenvectors of total angular momentum situated in this space by $|J\, M\rangle$ (which supposes J and M suffice to define them, which we shall show to be the case).

In this paragraph, we shall determine the possible values of the pair $(J\, M)$ and their respective orders of degeneracy. The construction of the eigenvectors will be discussed in § 27.

The solution to our problem is based on the following two observations:

(a) Each vector $|m_1\, m_2\rangle$ is an eigenvector of J_z belonging to the eigenvalue

$$M = m_1 + m_2.$$

Proof: since $J_z = j_{1z} + j_{2z}$, $J_z \, |m_1 \, m_2\rangle = (m_1 + m_2) \, |m_1 \, m_2\rangle$.

(b) To each value of J there corresponds a certain number $N(J)$ of linearly independent series of $(2J+1)$ eigenvectors of total angular momentum, the vectors of a given series being obtained one from another by repeated application of J_+ or J_-, and corresponding respectively to the $(2J+1)$ possible values for M: $-J, -J+1, \ldots, +J$.

It follows [1]) that if $n(M)$ denotes the order of degeneracy of the eigenvalue M,

$$n(M) = \sum_{J \geqslant |M|} N(J)$$

and consequently

$$N(J) = n(J) - n(J+1). \qquad \text{(XIII.105)}$$

To obtain $N(J)$, it is therefore sufficient to determine $n(M)$ for each possible value of M. From (a) it is seen that $n(M)$ is simply the number of pairs $(m_1 \, m_2)$ such that

$$M = m_1 + m_2.$$

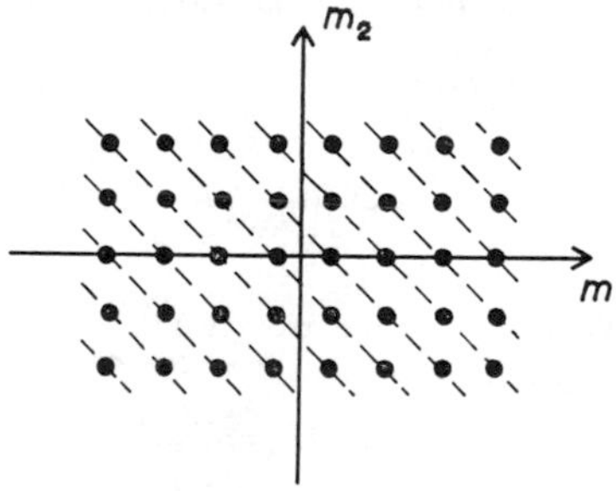

Fig. XIII.3. Finding the possible values of $M = m_1 + m_2$ and the frequency of their occurrence $n(M)$ ($j_1 = \frac{7}{2}$; $j_2 = 2$).

To find this number, it is convenient to use the diagram of Fig. XIII.3 in which each pair $(m_1 + m_2)$ is represented by a point of abscissa m_1 and ordinate m_2. $n(M)$ is the number of points situated on the diagonal $x + y = M$. In the case when $j_1 > j_2$, we find

$$n(M) = \begin{cases} 0 & \text{if } \; |M| > j_1 + j_2 \\ j_1 + j_2 + 1 - |M| & \text{if } \; j_1 + j_2 \geqslant |M| \geqslant |j_1 - j_2| \\ 2j_2 + 1 & \text{if } \; |j_1 - j_2| \geqslant |M| \geqslant 0. \end{cases}$$

---

[1]) The same argument has already been used in the three-dimensional harmonic oscillator problem (§ XII.15).

Substituting these numbers in (XIII.105), we find

$$N(J) = 1 \text{ for } J = j_1 + j_2,\ j_1 + j_2 - 1,\ \ldots,\ |j_1 - j_2|.$$

Whence the FUNDAMENTAL ADDITION THEOREM: *In the* $(2j_1+1)$ $(2j_2+1)$*-dimensional space spanned by the vectors* $|\alpha\, j_1\, j_2\, m_1\, m_2\rangle$ (α, j_1, j_2 *fixed*; m_1, m_2 *variable*)

(i) *the possible values of* **J** *are* [1])

$$j_1 + j_2,\ j_1 + j_2 - 1,\ \ldots,\ |j_1 - j_2|;$$

(ii) *To each of these values there corresponds one, and only one series of* $(2J+1)$ *eigenvectors* $|J\,M\rangle$ *of the total angular momentum.*

26. Applications and Examples

We first note an obvious consequence of the addition theorem:

The total angular momentum resulting from the addition of any number of angular momenta is integral or half-integral according as the number of individual half-integral angular momenta is even or odd.

It will be seen that this property is verified in all the examples to follow.

As a first example, consider the *addition of two spins* $\frac{1}{2}$.

State space here has 4 dimensions. The total spin S can take two values: 0 and 1.

To $S=0$ there corresponds just one vector $|00\rangle$: we say that the spin is in the *singlet* state.

To $S=1$ there correspond the three vectors $|11\rangle$, $|10\rangle$, $|1\,-1\rangle$; these are the three vectors of the *triplet* state.

It is easy to write down the projectors P_0 and P_1 onto the singlet and triplet states respectively as functions of S^2 or of $\boldsymbol{\sigma}_1 \cdot \boldsymbol{\sigma}_2$. Since $\mathbf{S}^2 = S(S+1)$, $\mathbf{S}^2$ has the eigenvalues 0 in the singlet state and 2 in the triplet state, whence [cf. identity (XIII.100)]:

$$P_0 = 1 - \tfrac{1}{2}\mathbf{S}^2 = \tfrac{1}{4}(1 - \boldsymbol{\sigma}_1 \cdot \boldsymbol{\sigma}_2)$$
$$P_1 = \tfrac{1}{2}\mathbf{S}^2 = \tfrac{1}{4}(3 + \boldsymbol{\sigma}_1 \cdot \boldsymbol{\sigma}_2).$$

Note that

$$\boldsymbol{\sigma}_1 \cdot \boldsymbol{\sigma}_2 = P_1 - 3P_0. \tag{XIII.106}$$

As a second example we consider *a particle of spin* $\frac{1}{2}$. Its orbital

---

[1]) In other words, J takes all values such that $j_1 + j_2 + J$ is an integer with j_1, j_2 and J forming the sides of a triangle.

angular momentum l and its spin are coupled to give the total angular momentum j which can take the two values

$$j=l+\tfrac{1}{2}, \qquad j=l-\tfrac{1}{2},$$

except if $l=0$ (s-state) in which case j takes only the one value $j=\frac{1}{2}$. Thus j can take all the half-integral values from $\frac{1}{2}$ to ∞, and to each of them there correspond two terms (and two series of $(2j+1)$ vectors) of *opposite parity.*

As a final example we consider the *two-nucleon system* of § 23. Here we must couple three angular momenta – the orbital angular momentum and the two spins [eq. (XIII.98)]. We first couple the spins to give the total spin $\mathbf{S}$, which has the two possible values 0 and 1. $\mathbf{S}$ is then coupled with the angular momentum $\mathbf{L}$ of the relative coordinate, which may take all positive or zero integral values. To each pair of values (LS) there correspond $(2S+1)(2L+1)$ vectors that can be linearly combined to get the eigenvectors of total angular momentum. From the addition theorem, we have the following values for J:

$$\text{singlet state: } S=0 \qquad J=L$$

$$\text{triplet state: } S=1 \quad \begin{cases} J=L-1,\, L,\, L+1 & \text{if} \quad L\neq 0 \\ J=1 & \text{if} \quad L=0. \end{cases}$$

We employ the following spectroscopic notation to denote the terms thus formed:

The value of L is given by a capital letter with the same convention as in § IX–6; it has a superscript on the left equal to $2S+1$ (the multiplicity of the total spin) and a subscript on the right equal to J. For example, ${}^3D_2$ is the term with $L=2$, triplet spin, and total angular momentum $J=2$. To each value of J there correspond 4 terms [and in all $4(2J+1)$ vectors] except for $J=0$ which only has 2. We list below the various terms corresponding to the first 4 values of J:

$J=0$		${}^3P_0$		${}^1S_0$
$J=1$	${}^3S_1$	${}^3D_1$	${}^3P_1$	${}^1P_1$
$J=2$	${}^3P_2$	${}^3F_2$	${}^3D_2$	${}^1D_2$
$J=3$	${}^3D_3$	${}^3G_3$	${}^3F_3$	${}^1F_3$

The same notation is currently used for the particle of spin $\frac{1}{2}$ considered above. In this case the orbital angular momentum is denoted by a small letter – capitals being reserved for the total angular momentum of a system of several particles – and the superscript on the left is simply omitted. The terms corresponding to the first four values of j are:

$$\begin{array}{ccccc} j= & \frac{1}{2} & \frac{3}{2} & \frac{5}{2} & \frac{7}{2} \\ & \mathrm{s}_{\frac{1}{2}}\mathrm{p}_{\frac{1}{2}} & \mathrm{p}_{\frac{3}{2}}\mathrm{d}_{\frac{3}{2}} & \mathrm{d}_{\frac{5}{2}}\mathrm{f}_{\frac{5}{2}} & \mathrm{f}_{\frac{7}{2}}\mathrm{g}_{\frac{7}{2}} \end{array}$$

27. Eigenvectors of the Total Angular Momentum. Clebsch–Gordon Coefficients

To each pair $(J\ M)$ given by the addition theorem there corresponds an eigenvector $|\alpha\, j_1\, j_2\, J\, M\rangle$ of the total angular momentum. To define this vector unambiguously, we take it to be of norm 1, and we fix its phase by an appropriate convention to which we return below. Like the $|\alpha\, j_1\, j_2\, m_1\, m_2\rangle$, the vectors $|\alpha\, j_1\, j_2\, J\, M\rangle$ form an orthonormal basis in the subspace $\mathscr{E}\,(\alpha\, j_1\, j_2)$. We pass from the one basis to the other by the unitary transformation:

$$|\alpha\, j_1\, j_2\, J\, M\rangle = \sum_{m_1 m_2} |\alpha\, j_1\, j_2\, m_1\, m_2\rangle\, \langle \alpha\, j_1\, j_2\, m_1\, m_2\,|\alpha\, j_1\, j_2\, J\, M\rangle. \tag{XIII.107}$$

The coefficients of this transformation have an important property: *they are independent of* α, *depending only on the quantities* j_1, j_2, J, m_1, m_2, M. In the subspace $\mathscr{E}\,(\alpha\, j_1\, j_2)$ the $|\alpha\, j_1\, j_2\, m_1\, m_2\rangle$ are the basis vectors of a standard representation; a representation in which the components of $\boldsymbol{j}_1$ and $\boldsymbol{j}_2$ are represented by matrices independent of α [cf. eq. (XIII.28)]; it follows that the matrices representing $\boldsymbol{J}^2$ and J_z are also independent of α and that the components

$$\langle \alpha\, j_1\, j_2\, m_1\, m_2\,|\alpha\, j_1\, j_2\, J\, M\rangle$$

of their common eigenvectors have the same property. These therefore have a purely geometrical character and depend only upon the angular momenta in question and their orientation, and not upon the physical nature of the dynamical variables 1 and 2 from which the angular momenta are constructed. They are called *Clebsch–Gordon* (C.–G.) *coefficients* or vector-addition coefficients, and will be written

$\langle j_1\, j_2\, m_1\, m_2\, | J\, M\rangle$. With this notation, (XIII.107) becomes

$$|\alpha\, j_1\, j_2\, J\, M\rangle = \sum_{m_1 m_2} |\alpha\, j_1\, j_2\, m_1\, m_2\rangle \langle j_1\, j_2\, m_1\, m_2\, | J\, M\rangle. \qquad \text{(XIII.108)}$$

To completely define the C.–G. coefficients it remains to fix the phases of the vectors $|\alpha\, j_1\, j_2\, J\, M\rangle$. For the relative phases of the $(2J+1)$ vectors corresponding to a given J we adopt the "standard" convention of § 6. The $|\alpha\, j_1\, j_2\, J\, M\rangle$ are then defined up to a phase depending on J. This we specify by requiring that the component of $|\alpha\, j_1\, j_2\, J\, J\rangle$ along $|\alpha\, j_1\, j_2\, j_1\, J-j_1\rangle$ be real and positive

$$\langle j_1\, j_2\, j_1\, m_2\, | J\, J\rangle \text{ real } \geqslant 0. \qquad \text{(XIII.109)}$$

Many properties of the C.–G. coefficients follow directly from their definition.

From the Addition Theorem, in order for $\langle j_1\, j_2\, m_1\, m_2\, | J\, M\rangle$ not to be zero we must simultaneously have (*selection rules*)

$$m_1 + m_2 = M, \qquad |j_1 - j_2| \leqslant J \leqslant j_1 + j_2.$$

We show below that the C.–G. coefficients relating to a given value of J can all be obtained from the coefficient $\langle j_1\, j_2\, j_1\, J-j_1\, | J\, J\rangle$ by applying recursion relations with real coefficients. Since this one is real, all of the others are real.

Moreover, since they are the coefficients of a unitary transformation, they obey the *orthogonality relations*

$$\sum_{m_1 m_2} \langle j_1\, j_2\, m_1\, m_2\, | J\, M\rangle \langle j_1\, j_2\, m_1\, m_2\, | J'\, M'\rangle = \delta_{JJ'}\, \delta_{MM'} \qquad \text{(XIII.110}a\text{)}$$

$$\sum_{JM} \langle j_1\, j_2\, m_1\, m_2\, | J\, M\rangle \langle j_1\, j_2\, m_1'\, m_2'\, | J\, M\rangle = \delta_{m_1 m_1'} \delta_{m_2 m_2'}\, . \qquad \text{(XIII.110}b\text{)}$$

In the simplest cases we can determine the linear combinations (XIII.108) directly. For $J = j_1 + j_2$ and $M = J$, we have

$$|\alpha\, j_1\, j_2\, j_1 + j_2\, j_1 + j_2\rangle = |\alpha\, j_1\, j_2\, j_1\, j_2\rangle.$$

By repeated application of $J_- \equiv j_{1-} + j_{2-}$ to both sides of this equation we construct all the $|\alpha\, j_1\, j_2\, J\, M\rangle$ corresponding to $J = j_1 + j_2$. Following this, we construct all the vectors of the series $J = j_1 + j_2 - 1$, beginning with the one corresponding to $M = J$, which is unambiguously defined by the phase condition (XIII.109) and its property of being orthogonal to $|\alpha\, j_1\, j_2\, j_1 + j_2\, j_1 + j_2 - 1\rangle$, and forming all the others by repeated application of J_-. And so on.

In the case of the addition of two spins $\frac{1}{2}$, the eigenvectors of total spin are built up in this way from the eigenvectors $|++\rangle$, $|+-\rangle$, $|-+\rangle$ and $|--\rangle$ of the individual spins. The results are given in the following table:

	$S=1$	$S=0$
$M=1$	$\|11\rangle=\|++\rangle$	
$M=0$	$\|10\rangle=\dfrac{\|+-\rangle+\|-+\rangle}{\sqrt{2}}$	$\|00\rangle=\dfrac{\|+-\rangle-\|-+\rangle}{\sqrt{2}}$
$M=-1$	$\|1-1\rangle=\|--\rangle.$	

When larger angular momenta are to be added one must turn to more elaborate methods of calculation. Various recursion relations may be established [eq. (C.18–20)]. As an example, the application of J_+ or J_- to both sides of (XIII.108) gives [eqs. (C.19) and (C.18)]:

$$\begin{aligned}\sqrt{J(J+1)-M(M+1)}\,&\langle j_1\, j_2\, m_1\, m_2\,|J\, M+1\rangle\\ &=\sqrt{j_1(j_1+1)-m_1(m_1-1)}\,\langle j_1\, j_2\, m_1-1\, m_2\,|J\, M\rangle\\ &+\sqrt{j_2(j_2+1)-m_2(m_2-1)}\,\langle j_1\, j_2\, m_1\, m_2-1\,|J\, M\rangle\end{aligned} \qquad \text{(XIII.111)}$$

$$\begin{aligned}\sqrt{J(J+1)-M(M-1)}\,&\langle j_1\, j_2\, m_1\, m_2\,|J\, M-1\rangle\\ &=\sqrt{j_1(j_1+1)-m_1(m_1+1)}\,\langle j_1\, j_2\, m_1+1\, m_2\,|J\, M\rangle\\ &+\sqrt{j_2(j_2+1)-m_2(m_2+1)}\,\langle j_1\, j_2\, m_1\, m_2+1\,|J\, M\rangle.\end{aligned} \qquad \text{(XIII.112)}$$

When $M=J$ the left-hand side of (XIII.111) vanishes. It may then be used to give all of the coefficients $\langle j_1\, j_2\, m_1\, m_2\,|J\, J\rangle$ as multiples of one of them, $\langle j_1\, j_2\, j_1\, J-j_1\,|J\, J\rangle$ say. With the normalization condition for the vector $|\alpha\, j_1\, j_2\, J\, J\rangle$ $(\sum_{m_1 m_2} \langle j_1\, j_2\, m_1\, m_2\,|J\, J\rangle^2=1)$ and the phase condition (XIII.109) they are completely determined. The other C.–G. coefficients may then all be derived by repeated application of the recursion relation (XIII.112). This method of calculating the C.–G. coefficients has been used by Racah to express them in the condensed form (C.21) [1]).

[1]) To carry this calculation through to the end, one must use the following identity, due to Racah:

$$\sum_s \frac{(a+s)!\,(b-s)!}{(c+s)!\,(d-s)!}=\frac{(a+b+1)!\,(a-c)!\,(b-d)!}{(c+d)!\,(a+b-c-d+1)!}$$

(a, b, c, d, integers such that $a \geqslant c \geqslant 0$, $b \geqslant d \geqslant 0$; s taking all integral values from $-c$ to $+d$).

In addition to the properties already mentioned, the C.–G. coefficients have important *symmetry properties*, which greatly facilitate tabulation. These are given, along with the principal properties of the C.–G. coefficients, in Appendix C (Section I), which also contains a table of the simpler coefficients.

28. Application: Two-Nucleon System

As an application of the addition of angular momenta to the treatment of rotationally invariant systems, we return to the two-nucleon system of § 23. We shall study the Schrödinger equation for various forms of spin dependent potentials. The discussion will be limited to potentials of type (XIII.99).

Suppose we have a potential of the form

$$V = V_1(r) + V_2(r)\,(\boldsymbol{\sigma}_1 \cdot \boldsymbol{\sigma}_2).$$

In this case the Hamiltonian commutes with $\mathbf{L}$ and $\mathbf{S}$ and the eigenfunctions are products of spin functions $|S\,\mu\rangle$ by functions of $\mathbf{r}$ of well-defined orbital angular momentum $(l\,m)$. From (XIII.106) we see that the potential is different according as $S=0$ or 1. The solving of the Schrödinger equation is thus equivalent to solving two Schrödinger equations for a spinless particle in a central potential, each corresponding to one of the two possible values of S. If $S=0$, the orbital part of the eigenfunction is that of a (spinless) particle in the potential $V_1 - 3V_2$; if $S=1$ that of a particle in the potential $V_1 + V_2$. The eigenvalue problem reduces to a radial equation for each pair of values $(L\,S)$.

If the potential is of the form

$$V = V_1(r) + V_2(r)\,(\boldsymbol{\sigma}_1 \cdot \boldsymbol{\sigma}_2) + V_3(r)\,(\mathbf{L} \cdot \mathbf{S}),$$

the Hamiltonian is no longer separately invariant under rotations of space and of the spins, but since it still commutes with $\mathbf{L}^2$ and $\mathbf{S}^2$ we can look for the simultaneous eigenfunctions of $\mathbf{L}^2$, $\mathbf{S}^2$, $\mathbf{J}^2$ and J_z. To each set $(L\,S\,J)$ there corresponds a type of function whose dependence on the angles θ, φ and on the spin variables is completely determined, and which is explicitly given with the aid of the C.–G. coefficients as follows:

$$\begin{aligned} \Psi^M_{LSJ} &\equiv F(r)\,\mathscr{Y}^M_{LSJ} \\ \mathscr{Y}^M_{L\,\prime} &= \sum Y_L{}^m(\theta, \varphi)\,|S\,\mu\rangle\,\langle L\,S\,m\,\mu\,|J\,M\rangle. \end{aligned} \qquad \text{(XIII.113)}$$

Thus the three functions of the state $^1\mathrm{P}_1$ have the "angular dependence" $\mathscr{Y}^M_{101} = Y^M_1 |00\rangle$ $(M = 0, \pm 1)$. The five functions of the state $^3\mathrm{D}_2$:

$$\mathscr{Y}^M_{212} = \sum_{m\mu} Y^m_2 |1\,\mu\rangle \langle 21\,m\,\mu|2\,M\rangle \qquad (M=0, \pm 1, \pm 2).$$

Following (XIII.100) and (XIII.101), the application of the Hamiltonian to a function of this type gives

$$H\Psi^M_{LSJ} = \left[-\frac{\hbar^2}{M_0}\frac{1}{r}\frac{\mathrm{d}^2}{\mathrm{d}r^2} r + \frac{\hbar^2}{M_0}\frac{L(L+1)}{r^2} + V_{LSJ} \right] \Psi^M_{LSJ},$$

with

$$V_{LSJ}(r) = V_1(r) + [2S(S+1) - 3]\, V_2(r) + \tfrac{1}{2}[J(J+1) - L(L+1) - S(S+1)]\, V_3(r).$$

The problem of solving the Schrödinger equation thus reduces to solving the radial equation

$$\left[-\frac{\hbar^2}{M_0}\frac{1}{r}\frac{\mathrm{d}^2}{\mathrm{d}r^2} r + \frac{\hbar^2}{M_0}\frac{L(L+1)}{r^2} + V_{LSJ}(r) \right] F(r) = E\,F(r).$$

Thus we have a problem resembling that of a (spinless) particle in a central potential, with the sole difference that the "effective central potential" $V_{LSJ}(r)$ differs from one triplet $(L\,S\,J)$ to another [1]).

As a final example we consider a potential of the form

$$V = V_C(r) + V_T(r)\, S_{12}.$$

Due to the presence of the "tensor" force, the Hamiltonian no longer commutes with $\boldsymbol{L}^2$, but it still commutes with $\boldsymbol{S}^2$, and also with the "parity" operator P introduced in § 23. Consequently we can look for the eigenfunctions of H among the simultaneous eigenfunctions of P, $\boldsymbol{S}^2$, $\boldsymbol{J}^2$, J_z; that is, among the functions of well-defined total angular momentum $(J\,M)$ having a well-defined parity and a well-defined value of S.

---

[1]) For $S = 0$, the spin-orbit force vanishes and we have, for any L and J,

$$V_{L0L} = V_1 - 3V_2.$$

Similarly, if $S = 1$ and $L = J$ the "effective potential" does not depend on L:

$$V_{L1L} = V_1 + V_2 - V_3.$$

If $S=0$, then necessarily $L=J$ (therefore $P=(-)^J$) and the eigenfunction is necessarily of the form $F(r)\,\mathscr{Y}^M_{J0J}$. Again, since $\mathbf{S}\,|00\rangle=0$, from (XIII.102′)

$$S_{12}\,\mathscr{Y}^M_{J0J}\equiv S_{12}\,Y^M_J(\theta,\varphi)\,|00\rangle=0.$$

Consequently, $F(r)$ satisfies the radial equation for a particle of angular momentum J in the potential $V_C(r)$.

If $S=1$ and $P=(-)^J$, necessarily $L=J$ and the "angular dependence" of the eigenfunction is, as before, completely defined:

$$\Psi^M_{J1J}=F(r)\,\mathscr{Y}^M_{J1J}.$$

One can show (Problem XIII.11) that $S_{12}\,\mathscr{Y}^M_{J1J}=2\mathscr{Y}^M_{J1J}$. Thus $F(r)$ satisfies the radial equation for a particle of angular momentum J in the potential $V_C(r)+2V_T(r)$.

If $S=1$ and $P=(-)^{J+1}$, the only possible values of L are $J+1$ and $J-1$ (unless $J=0$ in which case there is just the one value $L=1$) so that the eigenfunction is of the form

$$\Psi\equiv F_{J-1}(r)\,\mathscr{Y}_-+F_{J+1}(r)\,\mathscr{Y}_+,$$

where, to simplify the writing, we have put $\mathscr{Y}_\pm\equiv\mathscr{Y}^M_{J\pm 11J}$. Now S_{12} acting on $\mathscr{Y}_+$ or on $\mathscr{Y}_-$ gives a combination of these two functions (Problem 11); hence $(H-E)\,\Psi$ is also a linear combination of these two functions, the coefficients being functions of r. Writing $(H-E)\,\Psi=0$ amounts to making these two coefficients vanish and gives a system of two second-order differential equations in $F_{J-1}(r)$ and $F_{J+1}(r)$.

As an example we write the system of coupled radial equations for $J=1$. This case is encountered in the study of the deuteron. The wave function is a mixture of the states $^3S_1$ and $^3D_1$, and may be put in the form

$$\Psi\equiv\frac{1}{r}u_S(r)\,\mathscr{Y}^M_{011}+\frac{1}{r}u_D(r)\,\mathscr{Y}^M_{211}.$$

Since (Problem XIII.11)

$$\begin{aligned} &S_{12}\,\mathscr{Y}^M_{011}=\sqrt{8}\,\mathscr{Y}_{211} \qquad && S_{12}\,\mathscr{Y}^M_{211}=\sqrt{8}\,\mathscr{Y}^M_{011}-2\mathscr{Y}^M_{211},\\ &\mathbf{L}^2\,\mathscr{Y}^M_{011}=0 && \mathbf{L}^2\,\mathscr{Y}^M_{211}=6\mathscr{Y}^M_{211}\end{aligned} \qquad \text{(XIII.114)}$$

and since

$$H\equiv-\frac{\hbar^2}{M_0}\frac{1}{r}\frac{\mathrm{d}^2}{\mathrm{d}r^2}r+\frac{\hbar^2\mathbf{L}^2}{M_0r^2}+V_C(r)+V_T(r)\,S_{12},$$

the equation $(H-E)\,\Psi=0$ is equivalent to

$$\begin{aligned} \left[\frac{\hbar^2}{M_0}\frac{\mathrm{d}^2}{\mathrm{d}r^2}+E-V_C(r)\right]u_{\mathrm{S}} &= \sqrt{8}\,V_T(r)\,u_{\mathrm{D}} \\ \left[\frac{\hbar^2}{M_0}\left(\frac{\mathrm{d}^2}{\mathrm{d}r^2}-\frac{6}{r^2}\right)+E+2\,V_T(r)-V_C(r)\right]u_{\mathrm{D}} &= \sqrt{8}\,V_T(r)\,u_{\mathrm{S}}. \end{aligned} \qquad \text{(XIII.115)}$$

29. Addition of Three or More Angular Momenta. Racah Coefficients. "3sj" Symbols

The two-nucleon system studied in § 28 provides an example of a system where the total angular momentum is the sum of three individual angular momenta [eq. (XIII.103)]. We were able to study this specially simple example without having recourse to elaborate techniques. We now examine the addition of three angular momenta in the general case.

We suppose our system to be made up of three distinct systems 1, 2, and 3 with angular momenta $\boldsymbol{j}_1$, $\boldsymbol{j}_2$, and $\boldsymbol{j}_3$ respectively. The total angular momentum is then

$$\boldsymbol{J}=\boldsymbol{j}_1+\boldsymbol{j}_2+\boldsymbol{j}_3.$$

The addition problem consists in forming the eigenvectors of the total angular momentum in the space spanned by the $(2j_1+1)\,(2j_2+1)\,(2j_3+1)$ eigenvectors

$$|\alpha\, j_1\, j_2\, j_3\, m_1\, m_2\, m_3\rangle$$

of individual angular momenta corresponding to well-defined values of the quantum numbers α, j_1, j_2 and j_3. α, defined here as in § 25, plays no role in what follows and will simply be omitted. There are several ways of constructing the vectors of angular momentum $(J\,M)$.

(i) We can couple $\boldsymbol{j}_1$ and $\boldsymbol{j}_2$ (Fig. XIII.4a) to form the angular momentum $\boldsymbol{J}_{12}=\boldsymbol{j}_1+\boldsymbol{j}_2$, and then couple $\boldsymbol{J}_{12}$ and $\boldsymbol{j}_3$ to form $\boldsymbol{J}$. We obtain in this way the eigenvectors

$$\begin{aligned} &|(j_1\, j_2)\, J_{12},\, j_3\,;\, J\, M\rangle \\ &= \sum_{\substack{m_1\, m_2 \\ M_{12}\, m_3}} |j_1\, j_2\, j_3\, m_1\, m_2\, m_3\rangle\, \langle j_1\, j_2\, m_1\, m_2\,|J_{12}\, M_{12}\rangle\, \langle J_{12}\, j_3\, M_{12}\, m_3\,|J\, M\rangle \end{aligned} \qquad \text{(XIII.116)}$$

common to $\boldsymbol{j}_1^2$, $\boldsymbol{j}_2^2$, $\boldsymbol{j}_3^2$, $\boldsymbol{J}_{12}^2$, $\boldsymbol{J}^2$ and J_z;

(ii) We can couple $\mathbf{j}_2$ and $\mathbf{j}_3$ (Fig. XIII.4*b*) to form the angular momentum $\mathbf{J}_{23}=\mathbf{j}_2+\mathbf{j}_3$, and then couple $\mathbf{j}_1$ and $\mathbf{J}_{23}$ to form $\mathbf{J}$. We obtain in this way the eigenvectors

$$|j_1, (j_2\, j_3)\, J_{23}; J\, M\rangle$$
$$= \sum_{\substack{m_2 m_3 \\ m_1 M_{23}}} |j_1\, j_2\, j_3\, m_1\, m_2\, m_3\rangle \langle j_2\, j_3\, m_2\, m_3\, |J_{23}\, M_{23}\rangle \langle j_1\, J_{23}\, m_1\, M_{23}\, |J\, M\rangle \tag{XIII.117}$$

common to $\mathbf{j}_1^2$, $\mathbf{j}_2^2$, $\mathbf{j}_3^2$, $\mathbf{J}_{23}^2$, $\mathbf{J}^2$ and J_z;

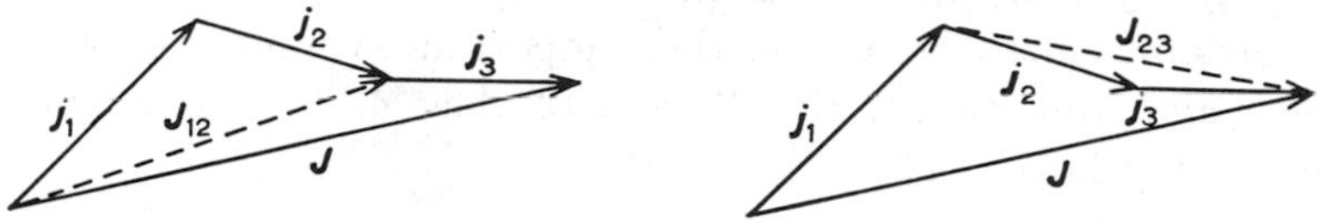

a) $\mathbf{j}_1+\mathbf{j}_2=\mathbf{J}_{12}$
$\mathbf{J}_{12}+\mathbf{j}_3=\mathbf{J}$

b) $\mathbf{j}_2+\mathbf{j}_3=\mathbf{J}_{23}$
$\mathbf{j}_1+\mathbf{J}_{23}=\mathbf{J}$

Fig. XIII.4. Different ways of coupling three angular momenta.

(iii) We can couple $\mathbf{j}_1$ and $\mathbf{j}_3$ to form $\mathbf{J}_{13}$ and then $\mathbf{J}_{13}$ and $\mathbf{j}_2$ to form $\mathbf{J}$.

Thus we have the choice between three different sets of basis vectors for the total angular momentum. In many problems it is useful to be able to pass from one set to another. The transformation involved is a unitary transformation. We have for example

$$|j_1, (j_2\, j_3)\, J_{23}; J\, M\rangle$$
$$= \sum_{J_{12}} |\, (j_1\, j_2)\, J_{12}, j_3; J\, M\rangle \langle (j_1\, j_2)\, J_{12}, j_3\, J\, |j_1, (j_2\, j_3)\, J_{23}\, J\rangle. \tag{XIII.118}$$

Obviously the coefficients of this unitary transformation are independent of α, for the same reason that the C.–G. coefficients are independent of α. Applying J_+ or J_- to both sides of (XIII.118) it is easily seen that they are also independent of M, and so depend only on the six angular momenta j_1, j_2, j_3, J_{12}, J_{23} and J.

Rather than directly make use of these coefficients it is more convenient to use either the Racah W coefficients or the Wigner "6*j*" symbols, which are defined as follows:

$$\langle (j_1 j_2) J_{12}, j_3 J\, | j_1, (j_2 j_3) J_{23} J\rangle = \sqrt{(2J_{12}+1)\,(2J_{23}+1)}\; W\,(j_1 j_2\, J j_3; J_{12}\, J_{23})$$
$$= (-)^{j_1+j_2+j_3+J} \sqrt{(2J_{12}+1)(2J_{23}+1)} \begin{Bmatrix} j_1 & j_2 & J_{12} \\ j_3 & J & J_{23} \end{Bmatrix}.$$

It is clear, just from their definition, that the W coefficients are simply the sum over the "m" indices of four C.–G. coefficients. Except for the simplest arguments, the direct calculation of these coefficients is very tedious: it consists in calculating first a great many C.–G. coefficients, and then a complicated expression built up from these coefficients. Racah has succeeded in obtaining a workable expression for W [formula (C.36)]. There exist tables of the W coefficients for the most common arguments.

The "$6j$" symbols differ from the W only through their sign. They are interesting chiefly because of their important symmetry properties.

The main properties of the W and of the "$6j$" are assembled in Appendix C (Section II).

The treatment given above for the case of three angular momenta can be generalized to the addition of a greater number n of angular momenta:

$$\boldsymbol{J}=\boldsymbol{j}_1+\boldsymbol{j}_2+\ldots+\boldsymbol{j}_n. \tag{XIII.119}$$

By coupling two of the individual angular momenta: $\boldsymbol{j}_i+\boldsymbol{j}_k=\boldsymbol{J}_{ik}$, we reduce the problem to the addition of $(n-1)$ angular momenta, the vectors $\boldsymbol{j}_i$ and $\boldsymbol{j}_k$ being replaced in the right-hand side of (XIII.119) by their sum $\boldsymbol{J}_{ik}$. By repeating this operation we reduce the problem to the addition of $(n-2)$ angular momenta, and so on. We thus achieve the addition of the n angular momenta through the introduction of all $(n-2)$ intermediate angular momenta, and form in this way a set of basis vectors for the total angular momentum.

In this fashion one can form several distinct sets of basis vectors. We have seen that when $n=3$ there are three of them. It can be shown that in the general case there are $\frac{1}{2}n!$. One passes from one set to another by a unitary transformation (with real coefficients). One can easily convince oneself that the coefficients of that transformation depend neither upon α nor upon the eigenvalue M of the component J_z of $\boldsymbol{J}$. Thus they depend only on the quantum numbers J, j_1, j_2, ..., j_n and on the two series of $(n-2)$ quantum numbers such as J_{ik} giving the length of the intermediate angular momenta characterising each of the sets of basis vectors: in all, $1+n+2(n-2)=3(n-1)$ quantum numbers "j". The coefficients may be put in the form of "$3(n-1)\ j$" symbols, generalizations of the "$6j$" symbols introduced in the addition of three angular momenta. The "$3(n-1)\ j$" symbols are sums over the "m" indices of $2(n-1)$ C.–G. coefficients. The principal properties of the "$9j$" symbols (symbols for the addition of four angular momenta) are given in Appendix C (Section III).

VI. IRREDUCIBLE TENSOR OPERATORS [1]

30. Representation of Scalar Operators

If an observable is invariant under rotation, the subspace of each of its eigenvalues is invariant under rotation. This important property has already been mentioned in § 17. The observable treated there was the Hamiltonian, but clearly the property in question holds for any scalar observable.

More generally, even if not diagonal, a scalar observable is represented in a given standard representation by a particularly simple matrix, as will now be shown.

Let $|\tau\, J\, M\rangle$ be the basis vectors of a standard representation $\{\boldsymbol{J}^2\, J_z\}$ (notation of § 6) and let S be a scalar operator (not necessarily an observable). By hypothesis

$$[\boldsymbol{J}, S]=0.$$

It follows that the vector $S\,|\tau'\, J'\, M'\rangle$, like $|\tau'\, J'\, M'\rangle$, is a vector of angular momentum $(J'\, M')$ orthogonal to any vector of different angular momentum. Therefore, the matrix element $\langle\tau\, J\, M\,|S\,|\tau'\, J'\, M'\rangle$ is zero if $J\neq J'$ or $M\neq M'$. Furthermore, since J_+ commutes with S, when $J=J'$ and $M=M'$ we have

$$\begin{aligned}\langle\tau\, J\, M\,|S\,|\tau'\, J\, M\rangle &\\ &=[J\,(J+1)-M\,(M-1)]^{-\frac{1}{2}}\,\langle\tau\, J\, M\,|S\,J_+\,|\tau'\, J\, M-1\rangle\\ &=[J\,(J+1)-M\,(M-1)]^{-\frac{1}{2}}\,\langle\tau\, J\, M\,|J_+\,S\,|\tau'\, J\, M-1\rangle\\ &=\langle\tau\, J\, M-1\,|S\,|\tau'\, J\, M-1\rangle.\end{aligned}$$

This shows that the matrix element is independent of M. The two properties are summarized in the relation

$$\langle\tau\, J\, M\,|S\,|\tau'\, J'\, M'\rangle=\delta_{JJ'}\,\delta_{MM'}\,S^{(J)}_{\tau\tau'}, \qquad \text{(XIII.120)}$$

---

[1] For a systematic account of the algebra of irreducible tensors and its applications in the theory of angular momentum in Quantum Mechanics, see U. Fano and G. Racah, *Irreducible Tensorial Sets* (Academic Press Inc., New York, 1959).

where $S^{(J)}_{\tau\tau'}$ is a quantity depending only on J, τ and τ'. In the case when S is an observable, the matrix $S^{(J)}_{\tau\tau'}$ is Hermitean and can be diagonalized.

31. Irreducible Tensor Operators. Definition

We now generalize (XIII.120) to a class of operators, called irreducible tensor operators, which are not rotationally invariant, but nevertheless have specially simple laws of transformation under rotation.

The concept of a tensor operator is a generalization of the concept of a vector operator.

We begin with the definition of a *tensor*. Suppose we have an n-dimensional space $\mathscr{E}_n$ such that in a rotation the vectors of $\mathscr{E}_n$ transform linearly into vectors of $\mathscr{E}_n$: with each rotation is associated a linear operator of $\mathscr{E}_n$. By definition, the vectors of $\mathscr{E}_n$ are n-component tensors. Thus the spinors and the vectors of ordinary space are respectively 2- and 3-component tensors; vectors of a subspace $\mathscr{E}(\tau J)$ of the type defined in § 6 are $(2J+1)$-component tensors, and kets of the ket-vector space of a quantum system are tensors of an infinite number of components.

If we choose a set of basis vectors in $\mathscr{E}_n$, each of the above defined tensors is represented by its n components, and the rotation is represented by the action of an $n \times n$ matrix on these n components. Thus the rotation of a vector of ordinary space, represented by its Cartesian coordinates, is given by the matrix $\mathscr{R}$ defined in § 10. Similarly, if we set up a standard representation in $\mathscr{E}(\tau J)$, any tensor $|u\rangle$ of $\mathscr{E}(\tau J)$ is represented by its $(2J+1)$ components $u_M \equiv \langle \tau J M | u \rangle$ and the components u'_M of its transform in the rotation $\mathscr{R}(\alpha \beta \gamma)$ are obtained by application of the rotation matrix $R^{(J)}(\alpha \beta \gamma)$ (§ 16):

$$u'_M = \sum_{M'} R^{(J)}_{MM'}(\alpha \beta \gamma)\, u_{M'}. \tag{XIII.121}$$

As a further example we consider the nine quantities $V_i W_j$ $(i, j = 1, 2, 3)$ obtained by multiplying each component of the vector $\mathbf{V}$ by each component of the vector $\mathbf{W}$. These are the nine components of a tensor which we denote by $\mathbf{V} \otimes \mathbf{W}$. The components of its transform in a rotation $\mathscr{R}$ are given by

$$\begin{aligned}[\mathbf{V} \otimes \mathbf{W}]'_{ij} \equiv V_i{}' W_j{}' &= \mathscr{R}_{ik} \mathscr{R}_{jl} V_k V_l \\ &= \mathscr{R}_{ik} \mathscr{R}_{jl} [\mathbf{V} \otimes \mathbf{W}]_{kl}.\end{aligned}$$

Among the large variety of tensors that can be formed, the *irreducible tensors* enjoy a privileged position. By definition, a tensor is irreducible, if the space $\mathscr{E}_n$ in which it is defined is irreducible with respect to rotations.

The vectors of ordinary space, the spinors, the vectors of a space $\mathscr{E}(\tau J)$, are irreducible tensors.

On the other hand, the tensor $\mathbf{V} \otimes \mathbf{W}$ is reducible. The nine-dimensional space in which it is defined is the direct sum of three irreducible invariant subspaces (with respect to rotations), having respectively 1, 3 and 5 dimensions. The projections of $\mathbf{V} \otimes \mathbf{W}$ onto each of these subspaces are therefore irreducible tensors; they are, to within a constant, the scalar product $\mathbf{V} \cdot \mathbf{W}$, the vector $\mathbf{V} \times \mathbf{W}$, and an irreducible 5-component tensor which transforms under rotation like the harmonic polynomials of second degree (cf. § B.10)[1]).

Similarly, the vectors of the $(2j_1+1)(2j_2+1)$-dimensional space of § 25 are reducible $(2j_1+1)(2j_2+1)$-component tensors whose decomposition into irreducible parts is given by the Addition Theorem.

One passes from the concept of a tensor to that of a tensor operator in the same way as one passes from the concept of a vector to that of a vector operator.

If n operators transform linearly one into another in a rotation like n linearly independent vectors of a space $\mathscr{E}_n$, then they are the components of an n-dimensional *tensor operator* [2]). A linear transformation of these n components will furnish n new operators, which may be regarded as the components of the same tensor operator in another representation. If the space $\mathscr{E}_n$ is irreducible the *tensor operator* is said to be *irreducible*.

Vector operators constitute a special class of irreducible tensor operators.

If $\mathbf{V}$ and $\mathbf{W}$ are two vector operators, the nine operators $V_i W_j$ are the components of a reducible tensor operator which is the direct sum of three irreducible tensor operators, the scalar $\mathbf{V} \cdot \mathbf{W}$, the vector $\mathbf{V} \times \mathbf{W}$ and the tensor operator defined, for example, by the five components given in note 1 below.

---

[1]) The rotation matrices obviously depend upon the representation chosen for this tensor. In the representation where its components are:

$$\tfrac{1}{2}(V_1 W_2 + V_2 W_1), \quad \tfrac{1}{2}(V_2 W_3 + V_3 W_2), \quad \tfrac{1}{2}(V_3 W_1 + V_1 W_3),$$
$$V_1 W_1 - V_2 W_2, \quad 2V_3 W_3 - V_1 W_1 - V_2 W_2.$$

These transform among themselves like the linearly independent polynomials

$$xy, \quad yz, \quad zx, \quad x^2 - y^2, \quad 2z^2 - x^2 - y^2.$$

[2]) Thus this transformation law is not the same as that for the *components of a vector* of $\mathscr{E}_n$ along its n basis vectors. In the same way the transformation law (XIII.54) for the components of a vector operator $\mathbf{K}$ is not the same as the transformation law (XIII.43) for the components of a vector $\mathbf{V}$ along the same set of basis vectors. Note in particular the difference between the law (XIII.122) below and the law (XIII.121).

A tensor operator is unambiguously defined by the law of transformation under rotation of its components in a given representation:

By definition, the $(2k+1)$ *operators* $T_q^{(k)}$ $(q=-k, -k+1, \dots, +k)$ *are the standard components of an irreducible* k^{th}*-order tensor operator,* $\mathsf{T}^{(k)}$, *if they transform in a rotation according to the law*

$$R T_q^{(k)} R^{-1} = \sum_{q'} T_{q'}^{(k)} R_{q'q}^{(k)}. \qquad \text{(XIII.122)}$$

This transformation law is the same as the one for the basis vectors $|k\, q\rangle$ of a standard representation for a $(2k+1)$-dimensional space irreducible with respect to rotations:

$$R\, |k\, q\rangle = \sum_{q'} |k\, q'\rangle\, R_{q'q}^{(k)}.$$

If (XIII.122) is satisfied for any infinitesimal rotation it will be satisfied for any rotation whatever. For an infinitesimal rotation, R is given by (XIII.55), the matrices $R^{(k)}$ are easily obtained from their definition (XIII.64) and the law (XIII.122) is equivalent to the following commutation relations for the $T_q^{(k)}$ with the components of total angular momentum

$$[J_\pm, T_q^{(k)}] = \sqrt{k\,(k+1) - q\,(q\pm 1)}\; T_{q\pm 1}^{(k)} \qquad \text{(XIII.123}a\text{)}$$

$$[J_z, T_q^{(k)}] = q\, T_q^{(k)}. \qquad \text{(XIII.123}b\text{)}$$

Relations (XIII.123), which may be compared with (XIII.23–25), provide another definition of the irreducible tensor operator $\mathsf{T}^{(k)}$ (strictly equivalent to the one given above).

If the $T_q^{(k)}$ represent physical quantities, they are necessarily invariant in a rotation through 2π (cf. § 15), and k *is therefore an integer*. In what follows we shall consider only irreducible tensor operators of integral order.

It can easily be shown that the $(2k+1)$ operators

$$S_q^{(k)} \equiv (-)^q\, T_{-q}^{(k)\dagger}$$

satisfy relations (XIII.123) (Problem XIII.16), and are therefore the standard components of an irreducible tensor operator of order k, $\mathsf{S}^{(k)}$. By definition, $\mathsf{S}^{(k)}$ and $\mathsf{T}^{(k)}$ are *Hermitean conjugates one of the other*:

$$\mathsf{S}^{(k)} = \mathsf{T}^{(k)\dagger}$$

(since k is an integer it is clear that Hermitean conjugation is a reciprocal operation).

Scalars are irreducible tensor operators of the zeroth order. Vector operators are irreducible tensor operators of order 1: if K_x, K_y, K_z are the Cartesian components of a vector operator, its standard components are

$$K_1^{(1)} = -\frac{1}{\sqrt{2}}(K_x + iK_y), \quad K_0^{(1)} = K_z, \quad K_{-1}^{(1)} = \frac{1}{\sqrt{2}}(K_x - iK_y). \qquad \text{(XIII.124)}$$

[It will be observed that the coefficients here differ from those of (XIII.94).]

The $(2k+1)$ spherical harmonics $Y_k^q(\theta, \varphi)$ $(q = -k, \ldots, +k)$ considered as operators, are the standard components of an irreducible tensor operator of order k, $\mathsf{Y}^{(k)}$.

32. Representation of Irreducible Tensor Operators. Wigner–Eckart Theorem

The most important property of irreducible tensor operators is given by the WIGNER–ECKART THEOREM:

In a standard representation $\{\mathbf{J}^2 J_z\}$ whose basis vectors are denoted by $|\tau J M\rangle$, the matrix element $\langle \tau J M | T_q^{(k)} | \tau' J' M' \rangle$ of the qth standard component of a given k^{th}-order irreducible tensor operator, $\mathsf{T}^{(k)}$, is equal to the product of the Clebsch–Gordon coefficient

$$\langle J' \, k \, M' \, q | J \, M \rangle$$

by a quantity independent of M, M' and q.

Thus:

$$\langle \tau J M | T_q^{(k)} | \tau' J' M' \rangle = \frac{1}{\sqrt{2J+1}} \langle \tau J \| \mathsf{T}^{(k)} \| \tau' J' \rangle \langle J' \, k \, M' \, q | J \, M \rangle, \qquad \text{(XIII.125)}$$

where $\langle \tau J \| \mathsf{T}^{(k)} \| \tau' J' \rangle$ is a quantity called the *reduced matrix element*, which varies from one tensor operator to another and depends on the indices τ, J and τ', J' (the factor $1/\sqrt{2J+1}$ is introduced simply for convenience).

To prove this theorem we consider the $(2k+1)(2J'+1)$ vectors

$$T_q^{(k)} |\tau' J' M' \rangle \qquad (q = -k, \ldots, +k; \; M' = -J', \ldots, +J'),$$

and the following linear combinations of these vectors:

$$|\sigma J'' M''\rangle = \sum_{M'q} T_q^{(k)} |\tau' J' M'\rangle \langle J' k M' q | J'' M''\rangle.$$

Application of the orthogonality relations for the C.–G. coefficients [eq. (XIII.110*b*)] gives

$$T_q^{(k)} |\tau' J' M'\rangle = \sum_{J''M''} |\sigma J'' M''\rangle \langle J' k M' q | J'' M''\rangle. \qquad \text{(XIII.126)}$$

Note that the vectors $T_q^{(k)} |\tau' J' M'\rangle$ are not necessarily linearly independent, and that therefore certain of the $|\sigma J'' M''\rangle$ may vanish.

From (XIII.123*a*) and (XIII.124):

$$\begin{aligned} J_+ T_q^{(k)} |\tau' J' M'\rangle &= [J_+, T_q^{(k)}] |\tau' J' M'\rangle + T_q^{(k)} J_+ |\tau' J' M'\rangle \\ &= \sqrt{k(k+1) - q(q+1)}\, T_{q+1}^{(k)} |\tau' J' M'\rangle \\ &\quad + \sqrt{J'(J'+1) - M'(M'+1)}\, T_q^{(k)} |\tau' J' M'+1\rangle, \end{aligned}$$

and consequently

$$\begin{aligned} J_+ &|\sigma J'' M''\rangle \\ &= \sum_{M'q} T_q^{(k)} |\tau' J' M'\rangle \{\sqrt{k(k+1) - q(q-1)}\, \langle J' k M' q-1 | J'' M''\rangle \\ &\qquad + \sqrt{J'(J'+1) - M'(M'-1)}\, \langle J' k M'-1\, q | J'' M''\rangle\}. \end{aligned}$$

From the recursion relation (XIII.111) for the Clebsch–Gordon coefficients, the bracket on the right-hand side is equal to

$$\sqrt{J''(J''+1) - M''(M''+1)}\, \langle J' k M' q | J'' M''+1\rangle,$$

so that we have the vector $|\sigma J'' M''+1\rangle$ appearing there:

$$J_+ |\sigma J'' M''\rangle = \sqrt{J''(J''+1) - M''(M''+1)}\, |\sigma J'' M''+1\rangle.$$

We can show in the same way that

$$\begin{aligned} J_- |\sigma J'' M''\rangle &= \sqrt{J''(J''+1) - M''(M''-1)}\, |\sigma J'' M-1\rangle \\ J_z |\sigma J'' M''\rangle &= M'' |\sigma J'' M''\rangle. \end{aligned}$$

From these three relations, we can conclude that the $(2J''+1)$ vectors $|\sigma J'' M''\rangle$ corresponding to the same value of J'',

(i) are either all zero, or

(ii) are (un-normalized) eigenfunctions of angular momentum $(J'' M'')$ obtained one from another in accordance with the standard convention.

Therefore, the scalar products $\langle \tau\, J\, M\, |\sigma\, J''\, M''\rangle$ are all zero, except those, if they exist, for which $J''=J$ and $M''=M$, i.e. the $(2J+1)$ products $\langle \tau\, J\, M\, |\sigma\, J\, M\rangle$, and these are independent of M.

The theorem then follows, for by (XIII.126) the matrix element $\langle \tau\, J\, M\, |T_q{}^{(k)}\, |\tau'\, J'\, M'\rangle$ is given by

$$\langle \tau\, J\, M\, |T_q{}^{(k)}\, |\tau'\, J'\, M'\rangle = \sum_{J''M''} \langle \tau\, J\, M\, |\sigma\, J''\, M''\rangle\, \langle J'\, k\, M'\, q\, |J''\, M''\rangle.$$

Q.E.D.

Among the most important consequences of the Wigner–Eckart theorem are the *selection rules* for the operator $T_q{}^{(k)}$.

For the matrix element $\langle \tau\, J\, M\, |\, T_q{}^{(k)}\, |\tau'\, J'\, M'\rangle$ *to be non-zero we must simultaneously have*:

$$q = M - M' \tag{XIII.127}$$

$$|J - J'\,| \leqslant k \leqslant J + J'. \tag{XIII.128}$$

These two rules are an immediate consequence of the presence of the Clebsch–Gordon coefficient in the right-hand side of (XIII.125). In practice, it is the second of these rules that is the most useful. It is usually expressed in the form of the following corollary [1]).

If $A^{(k)}$ *is a component of a* k^{th}*-order irreducible tensor operator, the matrix element of* $A^{(k)}$ *between two vectors of angular momentum* J, J' *are necessarily zero if* k *violates the inequalities*: $|J-J'\,| \leqslant k \leqslant J+J'$.

33. Applications

The Wigner–Eckart theorem has many applications in atomic and nuclear physics, notably in β-decay, in electromagnetic radiation and in angular correlation problems in general.

Let us take the emission of electromagnetic radiation from a nucleus (γ-emission) as an example. Suppose that in going from the excited state $\mathcal{N}^*$ to its ground state $\mathcal{N}$, an atom emits a γ-ray:

$$\mathcal{N}^* \to \mathcal{N} + \gamma.$$

Let J and J' be the spins (i.e. total angular momenta) of the nuclei $\mathcal{N}$ and $\mathcal{N}^*$ respectively. In the theory of γ-emission it is shown that

---

[1]) The component $A^{(k)}$ appearing in this corollary is not necessarily a standard component; any other, i.e. any linear combination of standard components, has the same property.

the probability *amplitude* for emission of a γ-ray of polarization ν in the direction $\Omega=(\theta, \varphi)$ is proportional to the matrix element

$$\langle \tau\, J\, M\, | H\, (\Omega, \nu)\, | \tau'\, J'\, M' \rangle$$

of a certain operator $H\,(\Omega, \nu)$ between the state vectors for the initial and final states [1]. $H\,(\Omega, \nu)$ may be expanded into spherical harmonics. The details will not be gone into here [2]; it takes the form of a series of irreducible tensor operators of two types (of opposite parities): the electric and magnetic multipole moments. The electric 2^l-pole moment $\mathsf{Q}^{(l)}$ is an irreducible tensor operator of order l and of parity $(-)^l$; the magnetic 2^l-pole moment $\mathsf{M}^{(l)}$ is an irreducible tensor operator of order l and of parity $(-)^{l+1}$. Among the more familiar multipole moments we have:

(i) the magnetic moment (in the ordinary sense of the term) which is the magnetic dipole moment $\mathsf{M}^{(1)}$;

(ii) the quadrupole moment (in the ordinary sense of the term), which is the electric quadrupole moment $\mathsf{Q}^{(2)}$.

In accordance with the selection rules for tensor operators, the only non-zero contributions are from moments with multipolarity within the limits

$$|J-J'| \leqslant l \leqslant J+J' \tag{XIII.129}$$

(there is also a parity selection rule that we do not consider here). Also, the contributions of the components $Q_m{}^{(l)}$ of a moment satisfying (XIII.129) are proportional, by the Wigner–Eckart theorem, to the Clebsch–Gordon coefficient $\langle J'\, l\, M'\, m\, | J\, M \rangle$; to obtain them we need only to know the proportionality coefficient, i.e. the reduced matrix element $\langle \tau\, J\, \| \mathsf{Q}^{(l)} \| \tau'\, J' \rangle$.

Thus we have the transition probability once the reduced matrix elements for the multipole moments obeying the selection rules are known. In practice the multipole expansion converges rapidly and significant contributions come only from the one or two multipoles of lowest order.

The even multipole moments ($\mathsf{M}^{(1)}$, $\mathsf{Q}^{(2)}$, ...) are also involved where one calculates the level shifts in an atom or nucleus in a static

---

[1] Cf. § XXI.31.

[2] Cf. J. Blatt and V. Weisskopf, *Theoretical Nuclear Physics* (Wiley, New York, 1952), Ch. XII and Appendix B.

electromagnetic field. Thus, the coupling of an atom with a constant magnetic field permits a measurement of its magnetic moment, and its coupling with an inhomogeneous electric field permits a measurement of its quadrupole moment. Actually what one measures is the average value of these operators for the state of the nucleus considered, that is, the matrix elements

$$\langle \tau\, J\, M \,|M_m{}^{(1)}\,|\tau\, J\, M'\rangle, \qquad \langle \tau\, J\, M \,|Q_m{}^{(2)}\,|\tau\, J\, M'\rangle, \text{ etc.}$$

or, what amounts to the same, the reduced diagonal matrix elements

$$\langle \tau\, J \,\|\mathsf{M}^{(1)}\,\|\tau\, J\rangle, \qquad \langle \tau\, J \,\|\mathsf{Q}^{(2)}\,\|\tau\, J\rangle, \text{ etc.}$$

Note that the magnetic moment necessarily vanishes if $J=0$, the quadrupole moment if $J=0$ or $\frac{1}{2}$. More generally, the 2^l-pole moment of a nucleus of spin J necessarily vanishes if $2\,J<l$.

EXERCISES AND PROBLEMS

1. Starting from relations (XIII.24) and (XIII.25) between the $(2j+1)$ vectors

$$|\tau\, j\, \mu\rangle \qquad (\mu=-j, -j+1, \ldots, +j),$$

prove relations (XIII.26) and (XIII.27).

2. Show that in any representation where J_x and J_z are real matrices (therefore symmetrical), J_y is a pure imaginary matrix (therefore antisymmetrical).
[N.B. Standard representations fall into this category.]

3. Show that if any operator commutes with *two* of the components of an angular momentum vector, it commutes with the third.

4. Let $\boldsymbol{l}$ be the orbital angular momentum of a particle, θ and φ its polar angles and P the "parity operator". P is the operator effecting a reflection in the origin; its action on a function $F(\theta, \varphi)$ is defined by:

$$PF(\theta, \varphi) = F(\pi - \theta, \varphi + \pi).$$

Show that $[P, \boldsymbol{l}] = 0$, and from this that the spherical harmonics have a well-defined parity depending only on the quantum number l. Determine it.

5. Let $\boldsymbol{r}$, $\boldsymbol{r}'$ be two vectors in ordinary space, $\Omega \equiv (\theta, \varphi)$, $\Omega' \equiv (\theta', \varphi')$ their respective polar angles, $\boldsymbol{l}$, $\boldsymbol{l}'$ the corresponding angular momentum operators; let α $(0 \leqslant \alpha \leqslant \pi)$ be the angle between them: $\boldsymbol{r}\cdot\boldsymbol{r}' = rr' \cos\alpha$. The Legendre polynomial $P_l(\cos\alpha)$ is, through $\cos\alpha$, a function of the polar angles of $\boldsymbol{r}$ and $\boldsymbol{r}'$. Show that it satisfies the partial differential equations

$$\begin{aligned} \boldsymbol{l}^2\, P_l(\cos\alpha) = \boldsymbol{l}'^2\, P_l(\cos\alpha) = l\,(l+1)\, P_l(\cos\alpha) \\ (l_i + l_i')\, P_l(\cos\alpha) = 0 \end{aligned} \qquad (i=x, y \text{ or } z).$$

Deduce from these the Addition Theorem:

$$\frac{2l+1}{4\pi} P_l(\cos\alpha) \equiv Y_l^0(\alpha)\, Y_l^0(0) = \sum_{m=-l}^{+l} (-)^m\, Y_l^m(\Omega)\, Y_l^{-m}(\Omega').$$

6. Let $\boldsymbol{u}$, $\boldsymbol{v}$, $\boldsymbol{w}$ be three unit vectors forming a right-handed Cartesian system. Show that the infinitesimal rotation

$$\hat{\mathscr{R}} \equiv \mathscr{R}_v^{-1}(\varepsilon)\, \mathscr{R}_u^{-1}(\varepsilon)\, \mathscr{R}_v(\varepsilon)\, \mathscr{R}_u(\varepsilon)$$

(notation of section III) differs from $\mathscr{R}_w(-\varepsilon^2)$ only by terms of higher order than ε^2. Starting from the defining equation (XIII.58), calculate directly the infinitesimal rotation operator $\hat{R}$ up to order ε^2 and verify the commutation relation $[J_u, J_v] = \mathrm{i}\, J_w$.

7. With the aid of the commutation relations (XIII.56), verify that the scalar product of two vector operators, $\boldsymbol{A}$ and $\boldsymbol{B}$, $\boldsymbol{A}\cdot\boldsymbol{B} \equiv A_x B_x + A_y B_y + A_z B_z$, commutes with the components of total angular momentum.

8. Show that

$$\exp(-\mathrm{i}\beta J_y) = \exp(\tfrac{1}{2}\mathrm{i}\pi J_x)\, \exp(-\mathrm{i}\beta J_z)\, \exp(-\tfrac{1}{2}\mathrm{i}\pi J_x).$$

Deduce from this that the matrix elements $\langle JM \mid \exp(-\mathrm{i}\beta J_y) \mid JM' \rangle$ are polynomials of degree $2J$ with respect to the variables $\sin\frac{1}{2}\beta$ and $\cos\frac{1}{2}\beta$.

9. Prove the identity $(\boldsymbol{\sigma}\cdot\boldsymbol{A})(\boldsymbol{\sigma}\cdot\boldsymbol{B}) = (\boldsymbol{A}\cdot\boldsymbol{B}) + \mathrm{i}\boldsymbol{\sigma}\cdot(\boldsymbol{A}\times\boldsymbol{B})$.
[$\boldsymbol{\sigma} \equiv (\sigma_x\ \sigma_y\ \sigma_z)$ Pauli matrices, $\boldsymbol{A}$ and $\boldsymbol{B}$ vector operators commuting with $\boldsymbol{\sigma}$ but not necessarily with each other.]

10. Let $\boldsymbol{s}$ be the intrinsic angular momentum of a particle of spin 1 ($\boldsymbol{s}^2 = s(s+1) = 2$).

(i) Show that for any component $s_u \equiv (\boldsymbol{s}\cdot\boldsymbol{u})$ one has

$$s_u^3 = s_u \qquad \exp(-\mathrm{i}\varphi s_u) = 1 - \mathrm{i}\sin\varphi\, s_u - (1-\cos\varphi)\, s_u^2,$$

and give an explicit expression for the rotation matrix $R^{(1)}(\alpha\beta\gamma)$.

(ii) Let $|z\rangle$ be a vector of norm 1 such that $s_z\,|z\rangle = 0$, and let $|x\rangle$ and $|y\rangle$ be the vectors obtained from it by rotations of $+\frac{1}{2}\pi$ about Oy and $-\frac{1}{2}\pi$ about Ox respectively. Prove the following relations, as well as those resulting from circular permutation of x, y and z:

$$s_x\,|x\rangle = 0 \qquad s_x\,|y\rangle = \mathrm{i}\,|z\rangle \qquad s_x^2\,|y\rangle = |y\rangle$$
$$s_x\,|z\rangle = -\mathrm{i}\,|y\rangle \qquad s_x^2\,|z\rangle = |z\rangle.$$

Use these to show that $|x\rangle$, $|y\rangle$, $|z\rangle$ form an orthonormal basis and that the matrices representing s_x, s_y and s_z in that basis are those given in § 21.

(iii) Show that $\langle i \mid R(\alpha\beta\gamma) \mid j\rangle = \mathscr{R}_{ij}(\alpha\beta\gamma) \qquad (i, j = x, y \text{ or } z)$
(notation of § 10 and 14).

11. Let $\boldsymbol{S}$ be the total spin of a system of two nucleons. Show that the operator $Q \equiv (\boldsymbol{S}\cdot\boldsymbol{r})^2/r^2$ is a projector. Show that the tensor operator $S_{12} \equiv 2[3Q - \boldsymbol{S}^2]$ satisfies the identity: $S_{12}{}^2 = 4\boldsymbol{S}^2 - 2S_{12}$ and that its only possible eigenvalues are 0, 2, and -4. Determine the action of Q, and that of S_{12}, on the functions of the angular variables and spins $\mathscr{Y}^M_{LSJ}$ introduced in § 28.

[If one adopts the condensed notation

$$\mathscr{Y}^{(0)} \equiv \mathscr{Y}^M_{J0J},\ \mathscr{Y}_0{}^{(1)} \equiv \mathscr{Y}^M_{J1J},\ \mathscr{Y}_\pm{}^{(1)} \equiv \mathscr{Y}^M_{J\pm1\,1J},$$

one finds

$$Q\,\mathscr{Y}^{(0)} = 0 \qquad (2J+1)\,Q\,\mathscr{Y}_+{}^{(1)} = J\,\mathscr{Y}_+{}^{(1)} + \sqrt{J\,(J+1)}\,\mathscr{Y}_-{}^{(1)}$$

$$Q\,\mathscr{Y}_0{}^{(1)} = \mathscr{Y}_0{}^{(1)} \qquad (2J+1)\,Q\,\mathscr{Y}_-{}^{(1)} = \sqrt{J\,(J+1)}\,\mathscr{Y}_+{}^{(1)} + (J+1)\,\mathscr{Y}_-{}^{(1)}.\ ]$$

12. Consider a spin $\frac{1}{2}$ particle. Show that in the space of states of a given orbital angular momentum l, the operators

$$\frac{l+1+\boldsymbol{l}\cdot\boldsymbol{\sigma}}{2l+1} \quad \text{and} \quad \frac{l-\boldsymbol{l}\cdot\boldsymbol{\sigma}}{2l+1}$$

are projectors onto the states of total angular momentum $j = l+\frac{1}{2}$ and $j = l-\frac{1}{2}$ respectively.

13. We add two equal angular momenta $j_1 = j_2 = j$. Without using the symmetry properties of the C.–G. coefficients show that in a permutation of m_1 and m_2 the eigenfunctions of the total angular momentum are either symmetrical (invariant) or antisymmetrical (multiplied by -1), and that this symmetry property depends only on J. Show that they are symmetrical or antisymmetrical according as $(-)^{2j+J}$ is equal to $+1$ or -1.

14. We denote by $\boldsymbol{J}^2\{A\}$ the following function of the operator A and the components of angular momentum:

$$\boldsymbol{J}^2\{A\} \equiv [J_x, [J_x, A]] + [J_y, [J_y, A]] + [J_z, [J_z, A]].$$

Show that if $\mathsf{T}^{(k)}$ is a kth-order irreducible tensor operator, its components verify the relation

$$\boldsymbol{J}^2\{T_q{}^{(k)}\} = k\,(k+1)\,T_q{}^{(k)}.$$

15. Let $a_r, a_r{}^\dagger$ ($r = 1,2$) be the annihilation and creation operators of a two-dimensional, isotropic, harmonic oscillator:

$$[a_r, a_s] = [a_r{}^\dagger, a_s{}^\dagger] = 0 \qquad [a_r, a_s{}^\dagger] = \delta_{rs}.$$

We write

$$S = \tfrac{1}{2}[a_1{}^\dagger a_1 + a_2{}^\dagger a_2]$$

$$J_1 = \tfrac{1}{2}[a_2{}^\dagger a_1 + a_1{}^\dagger a_2] \qquad J_2 = \tfrac{1}{2}\mathrm{i}\,[a_2{}^\dagger a_1 - a_1{}^\dagger a_2] \qquad J_3 = \tfrac{1}{2}[a_1{}^\dagger a_1 - a_2{}^\dagger a_2].$$

J_1, J_2, J_3 may be considered as the Cartesian coordinates of a certain vector operator $\boldsymbol{J}$.

[N.B. Following the notations of § XII.14, $L = 2J_2$.]

(i) Show that the components of $\boldsymbol{J}$ verify the commutation relations $\boldsymbol{J}\times\boldsymbol{J}=\mathrm{i}\,\boldsymbol{J}$ characteristic of an angular momentum, and that one has:

$$\boldsymbol{J}^2=S(S+1) \qquad \text{(therefore } [S,\boldsymbol{J}]=0).$$

(ii) $\boldsymbol{J}$ will henceforth be considered to be the angular momentum of the system, and we denote the eigenvalues of $\boldsymbol{J}^2$ and J_3 by $j(j+1)$ and m respectively. Show that $\boldsymbol{J}^2$ and J_3 form a complete set of commuting observables, and that j may take all *integral* and *half-integral* values $\geqslant 0$ i.e.

$$j=0,\ \tfrac{1}{2},\ 1,\ \tfrac{3}{2},\ 2,\ \ldots,\ \infty.$$

Show that the vectors $[(j+m)!\,(j-m)!]^{-\frac{1}{2}}\, a_1^{\dagger j+m}\, a_2^{\dagger j-m}\,|\,0\rangle$ form the basis of a standard representation $\{\boldsymbol{J}^2, J_3\}$.

(iii) Show that $a_1{}^{\dagger}$ and $a_2{}^{\dagger}$ are respectively the $+\frac{1}{2}$ and $-\frac{1}{2}$ components of an irreducible tensor operator of order $\frac{1}{2}$, and that it follows that the expressions $R\,a_r{}^{\dagger}\,R^{-1}$ $(r=1,2)$, where R denotes the rotation operator

$$R=\exp\,(-\,\mathrm{i}\alpha J_3)\,\exp\,(-\,\mathrm{i}\beta J_2)\,\exp\,(-\,\mathrm{i}\gamma J_3),$$

are linear combinations of $a_1{}^{\dagger}$ and $a_2{}^{\dagger}$. Determine the coefficients.

(iv) Use the preceding results to demonstrate the Wigner formula (C.72) and the principal properties of the $R^{(j)}$ matrices set forth in Appendix C (except for the formulas of composition and reduction).

16. Show that if the $(2k+1)$ operators $T_q{}^{(k)}$ $(q=-\,k,\ldots,+\,k)$ verify the commutation relations (XIII.123), the $(2k+1)$ operators $S_q^{(k)}\equiv(-)^q\,T_{-q}^{(k)\dagger}$ have the same property.

17. Show that the integral

$$\int Y_{l_1}^{m_1}(\theta,\varphi)\,Y_{l_2}^{m_2}(\theta,\varphi)\,Y_{l_3}^{m_3}(\theta,\varphi)\,\mathrm{d}\Omega$$

is proportional to $(-)^{m_3}\langle l_1\,l_2\,m_1\,m_2\,|\,l_3-m_3\rangle$, the coefficient of proportionality being independent of m_1, m_2 and m_3. Determine this coefficient. [Use the addition theorem of Problem XIII.5.]

18. Show that the "tensor" operator

$$S_{12}\equiv 2\left[3\,\frac{(\boldsymbol{S}\cdot\boldsymbol{r})^2}{r^2}-\boldsymbol{S}^2\right]$$

considered as a function of $\boldsymbol{r}$ depends only on the angles θ and φ, and this through *spherical harmonics of order* 2.

[We find

$$S_{12}=\left(\frac{24\pi}{5}\right)^{\frac{1}{2}}\{S_-{}^2\,Y_2{}^2-(S_-\,S_z+S_z\,S_-)\,Y_2{}^1+\sqrt{\frac{2}{3}}\,(3S_z{}^2-\boldsymbol{S}^2)\,Y_2{}^0$$
$$+(S_+\,S_z+S_z\,S_+)\,Y_2{}^{-1}+S_+{}^2\,Y_2{}^{-2}\}$$
$$=\left(\frac{24\pi}{5}\right)^{\frac{1}{2}}(\mathsf{S}^{(2)}\cdot\mathsf{Y}^{(2)}).$$

S_{12} is the scalar product [in the sense of definition (C.87)] of the second-order irreducible tensor operators $\mathbf{S}^{(2)}$ and $\mathbf{Y}^{(2)}$, which depend respectively on the spin and orbital variables.]

19. Let K_u denote the component of a vector operator $\mathbf{K}$ in a given direction, J_u the component of the total angular momentum $\mathbf{J}$ in the same direction, and let $|\tau Ja\rangle, |\tau Jb\rangle$ be two ket vectors belonging to the *same* subspace $\mathscr{E}(\tau J)$ (definition of § 16). Show that:

$$\langle \tau\, J\, a\, |K_u\, |\tau\, J\, b\rangle = \langle \tau\, J\, a\, |J_u\, |\tau\, J\, b\rangle \frac{\langle \mathbf{J}\cdot\mathbf{K}\rangle}{J\,(J+1)},$$

where $\langle \mathbf{J}\cdot\mathbf{K}\rangle$ denotes the average value of the scalar operator $\mathbf{J}\cdot\mathbf{K}$ in this subspace:

$$\langle \mathbf{J}\cdot\mathbf{K}\rangle = \langle \tau\, J\, a\, |\mathbf{J}\cdot\mathbf{K}\, |\tau\, J\, a\rangle$$

[i.e. the elements of the matrices of $\mathbf{K}$ in $\mathscr{E}(\tau J)$ are the same as those of its "projection" $\mathbf{J}(\mathbf{J}\cdot\mathbf{K})/J(J+1)$.]

CHAPTER XIV

SYSTEMS OF IDENTICAL PARTICLES. PAULI EXCLUSION PRINCIPLE

1. Identical Particles in Quantum Theory

Two particles are identical if their physical properties are exactly the same, this precluding the possibility of an observation that could distinguish between them. In Classical Mechanics this property of *indistinguishability of identical particles* plays a secondary role; in Quantum Mechanics it raises a serious problem.

As a definite example, let us consider the collision of two identical particles, and the extent to which their identity can affect the theory.

If the system obeys the laws of Classical Mechanics, its dynamical state is defined at any time by giving $\xi^{(1)} \equiv (\boldsymbol{r}^{(1)}, \boldsymbol{p}^{(1)})$, the position and momentum of particle 1, and $\xi^{(2)} \equiv (\boldsymbol{r}^{(2)}, \boldsymbol{p}^{(2)})$, the position and momentum of particle 2. The evolution of the system is determined by a certain Hamiltonian function depending on these 12 variables:

$$H(\xi^{(1)}, \xi^{(2)}) \equiv H(\boldsymbol{r}^{(1)}, \boldsymbol{p}^{(1)}, \boldsymbol{r}^{(2)}, \boldsymbol{p}^{(2)}).$$

If we have a potential $V(r)$ depending only on the distance between the two particles, and if m is their mass, then

$$H(\xi^{(1)}, \xi^{(2)}) = \frac{\boldsymbol{p}^{(1)2}}{2m} + \frac{\boldsymbol{p}^{(2)2}}{2m} + V(|\boldsymbol{r}^{(1)} - \boldsymbol{r}^{(2)}|). \qquad \text{(XIV.1)}$$

The particles being identical, there can be no modification of the dynamical properties of the system when they are permuted, i.e. when we ascribe the dynamical state of particle 1 to particle 2, and *vice versa*. In particular the function H is invariant in such a permutation:

$$H(\xi', \xi'') = H(\xi'', \xi'). \qquad \text{(XIV.2)}$$

On the other hand, the state of the system at any time can only be known to within a permutation of the variables 1 and 2; an observation of the system at a given time shows that one particle is in a certain state ξ' and the other in another state ξ'', but does not permit to determine which particle is in which state. This would seem to constitute a difficulty but, as we shall see, it is only an apparent one.

Suppose that at time t_0 we have one of the particles in state ξ_0' and the other in state ξ_0''. There are two possibilities; either it is particle 1 that occupies ξ_0' or it is particle 2. These correspond, however, to one and the same physical situation, for since H has the symmetry property (XIV.2), the laws of motion $\xi'(t)$ and $\xi''(t)$ of the particles in ξ_0' and ξ_0'' respectively at time t_0 are the same in the two cases. It is a simple matter of convention whether the particle starting from ξ_0' be called 1 and the one starting from ξ_0'' called 2, or inversely.

It is not so simple if the two-particle system is governed by the laws of Quantum Mechanics. The beginning of the foregoing analysis can be repeated word for word. Here again, the identity of the two particles finds its expression in the invariance of the Hamiltonian under permutation of their dynamical variables [eq. (XIV.2)], and more generally in the fact that any physical observable is invariant in such a permutation. As in Classical Mechanics, there results a certain ambiguity in the determination of the state of the system, but the ambiguity is now more profound, and its consequences more serious.

Let us suppose that an observation made on the system before the collision shows that one of the particles is in the state $\psi_0'(\boldsymbol{r})$, and that the other is in the state $\psi_0''(\boldsymbol{r})$ [1]). In practice, these functions represent wave packets localized in different regions of space; it follows that the functions

$$\begin{aligned} \psi_0(\boldsymbol{r}^{(1)}, \boldsymbol{r}^{(2)}) &\equiv \psi_0'(\boldsymbol{r}^{(1)})\, \psi_0''(\boldsymbol{r}^{(2)}) \\ \bar{\psi}_0(\boldsymbol{r}^{(1)}, \boldsymbol{r}^{(2)}) &\equiv \psi_0''(\boldsymbol{r}^{(1)})\, \psi_0'(\boldsymbol{r}^{(2)}) \end{aligned} \qquad \text{(XIV.3)}$$

are linearly independent. This initial observation does not permit to decide whether the system is in state ψ_0 or in state $\bar{\psi}_0$. More precisely, the observation consists in simultaneously measuring a certain set of compatible variables, and the functions ψ_0 and $\bar{\psi}_0$ are both eigenfunctions corresponding to the set of values given by that measuring operation. Since any linear combination of these functions $\lambda\psi_0 + \mu\bar{\psi}_0$ has the same property, the initial observation does not permit to decide which of these linear combinations represents the initial state of the system. We say that there is an *exchange degeneracy*.

We shall now examine the evolution of the system in the course

---

[1]) We suppose that the two identical particles are spinless, thus sharpening the parallel between Classical and Quantum Theory.

of time. Let $\psi(\boldsymbol{r}^{(1)}, \boldsymbol{r}^{(2)}, t)$ and $\bar{\psi}(\boldsymbol{r}^{(1)}, \boldsymbol{r}^{(2)}, t)$ denote the solutions of the Schrödinger equation corresponding respectively to the initial conditions ψ_0 and $\bar{\psi}_0$. Since the Hamiltonian has the symmetry property (XIV.2), they are obtained from one another by permutation of the arguments $\boldsymbol{r}^{(1)}$ and $\boldsymbol{r}^{(2)}$. It is convenient to introduce functions that are symmetrical and antisymmetrical in this permutation:

$$\psi^{(S)} = \frac{1}{\sqrt{2}}(\psi + \bar{\psi}) \qquad \psi^{(A)} = \frac{1}{\sqrt{2}}(\psi - \bar{\psi}).$$

These are the solutions of the Schrödinger equation corresponding respectively to the initial conditions:

$$\psi_0{}^{(S)} = \frac{1}{\sqrt{2}}(\psi_0 + \bar{\psi}_0) \qquad \psi_0{}^{(A)} = \frac{1}{\sqrt{2}}(\psi_0 - \bar{\psi}_0).$$

If initially the system is in the state

$$\Psi_0 = \alpha\psi_0{}^{(A)} + \beta\psi_0{}^{(S)} \qquad (|\alpha|^2 + |\beta|^2 = 1),$$

at a later time t it will be in the state

$$\Psi(\boldsymbol{r}^{(1)}, \boldsymbol{r}^{(2)}, t) = \alpha\psi^{(A)} + \beta\psi^{(S)}. \tag{XIV.4}$$

The probability density $P(\boldsymbol{r}', \boldsymbol{r}'')$ of finding one of the particles at $\boldsymbol{r}'$ and the other at $\boldsymbol{r}''$ is [1])

$$P(\boldsymbol{r}', \boldsymbol{r}'') = |\Psi(\boldsymbol{r}', \boldsymbol{r}'')|^2 + |\Psi(\boldsymbol{r}'', \boldsymbol{r}')|^2 \tag{XIV.5}$$

$$= 2[|\alpha|^2\,|\psi^{(A)}(\boldsymbol{r}', \boldsymbol{r}'')|^2 + |\beta|^2\,|\psi^{(S)}(\boldsymbol{r}', \boldsymbol{r}'')|^2]. \tag{XIV.6}$$

For this expression to be independent of α and β we must have

$$|\psi^{(A)}(\boldsymbol{r}', \boldsymbol{r}'')| = |\psi^{(S)}(\boldsymbol{r}', \boldsymbol{r}'')|.$$

This equality holds for all $\boldsymbol{r}'$ and $\boldsymbol{r}''$ so long as the two particles have not entered into interaction and the two wave packets $\psi'(\boldsymbol{r})$ and $\psi''(\boldsymbol{r})$ do not overlap. It ceases to be true, in general, when one or the other of these conditions is not fulfilled. One can easily convince oneself by considering a few particular cases. Suppose, for example, that the two particles do not interact ($V(|\boldsymbol{r}^{(1)} - \boldsymbol{r}^{(2)}|) = 0$), and that they are moving freely towards one another. ψ will then be a product

[1]) To obtain the second line we use the symmetry properties of the functions $\psi^{(A)}$ and $\psi^{(S)}$:

$$\Psi(\boldsymbol{r}'', \boldsymbol{r}') = -\,\alpha\psi^{(A)}(\boldsymbol{r}', \boldsymbol{r}'') + \beta\psi^{(S)}(\boldsymbol{r}', \boldsymbol{r}'').$$

of two free wave packets: $\psi = \psi'(\boldsymbol{r}^{(1)}, t)\, \psi''(\boldsymbol{r}^{(2)}, t)$. During a certain period of time the wave packets will overlap, i.e. there exists a region of space where the functions $\psi'(\boldsymbol{r})$ and $\psi''(\boldsymbol{r})$ are both different from zero; if $\boldsymbol{r}$ is a point in that region,

$$|\psi^{(S)}(\boldsymbol{r}, \boldsymbol{r})| = \sqrt{2}\, |\psi'(\boldsymbol{r})\, \psi''(\boldsymbol{r})| \neq 0,$$

while

$$|\psi^{(A)}(\boldsymbol{r}, \boldsymbol{r})| = 0 \qquad \text{(XIV.7)}$$

for any $\boldsymbol{r}$. Another interesting example is provided by the problem of scattering in a central potential. It is described in § 9, where we show that the scattering amplitude for $\psi^{(A)}$ is a superposition of odd-order spherical partial waves, and that of $\psi^{(S)}$ a superposition of even-order spherical partial waves; in general, these two amplitudes will not have the same absolute value, and consequently the differential cross section will depend crucially on the ratio $|\alpha|^2/|\beta|^2$.

Thus the existence of an exchange degeneracy is a source of real difficulty since it prevents us from making a precise theoretical prediction for the statistical distribution of results of measurements to be made on the system after the collision.

This difficulty is overcome by the introduction of the following *symmetrization postulate*, which fixes once and for all the coefficients α and β of the linear combination (XIV.3), and thus lends itself easily to experimental verification.

The dynamical states of a system of two identical particles are necessarily either all symmetrical ($\alpha=0$, $\beta=1$) *or all antisymmetrical* ($\alpha=1$, $\beta=0$) *in the permutation of the two particles.*

One or the other of these two possibilities actually occurs, depending on the nature of the particles considered. This postulate is easily extended to systems of any number of identical particles. It will be given in its general form and its principal consequences analysed in section I of this chapter. Section II is devoted to applications.

In the course of this work we shall be using certain elementary properties of permutations. These are given in § 14 of Appendix D [1]).

---

[1]) The elements of group theory brought together in Appendix D are not necessary for the understanding of the present chapter. The contents of § 14 of that Appendix form a whole independent of the rest; the only ideas of group theory used there are certain definitions relating to groups (group, class, invariant subgroup, etc.) which are set forth in § 2 of the Appendix.

I. SYMMETRIZATION POSTULATE

2. Similar Particles and the Symmetrical Representation

Consider a system of N particles. The dynamical variables describing the ith particle are functions of its position $\boldsymbol{r}^{(i)}$, of its momentum $\boldsymbol{p}^{(i)}$ and of its spin $\boldsymbol{s}^{(i)}$. These three vectors will henceforth collectively be denoted by $\xi^{(i)}$. Given the magnitude of the spin of the ith particle, we can construct the space of its dynamical states, $\mathscr{F}^{(i)}$. The space $\mathscr{E}$ of the dynamical states of the whole system is the tensor product

$$\mathscr{E} = \mathscr{F}^{(1)} \otimes \mathscr{F}^{(2)} \otimes \ldots \otimes \mathscr{F}^{(N)}. \tag{XIV.8}$$

By definition, two of these particles are *similar* if they have the same spin (similarity does not necessarily imply identity). The observables and state vectors of the one will then be in one-to-one correspondence with the observables and state vectors of the other, and consequently it is possible to exchange two similar particles. More generally, if n particles are similar, the $n!$ permutations of these n particles are well-defined operations, to each of which there corresponds a certain operator of the space $\mathscr{E}$. We now proceed to construct these permutation operators, and to simplify the discussion we suppose $n = N$.

Consider one of these N similar particles. ξ is the set of its fundamental observables, and $\mathscr{F}$ the space of its state vectors. Let q be a complete set of commuting observables of $\mathscr{F}$, and $|q_\varkappa\rangle$ the eigenvectors of a basis for q, with corresponding eigenvalues $q_\varkappa$ (the index or set of indices $\varkappa$ serves to distinguish the eigenvalues one from another). Then

$$\langle q_\varkappa | q_\mu \rangle = \delta_{\varkappa\mu}. \tag{XIV.9}$$

q might, for example, be the three components x, y, z of $\boldsymbol{r}$, taken together with the component of spin in the z direction, s_z. Each particle a ($a = 1, 2, \ldots, N$) of the system has its own set of commuting observables $q^{(a)}$. Clearly the set $Q \equiv (q^{(1)}, q^{(2)}, \ldots, q^{(N)})$ is a complete set of commuting observables for the space $\mathscr{E}$, and the vectors

$$|q_\alpha{}^{(1)}\, q_\beta{}^{(2)} \ldots q_\nu{}^{(N)}\rangle \equiv |q_\alpha\rangle^{(1)} |q_\beta\rangle^{(2)} \ldots |q_\nu\rangle^{(N)} \tag{XIV.10}$$

formed by taking the tensor product of the basis vectors of the spaces $\mathscr{F}^{(1)}, \mathscr{F}^{(2)}, \ldots, \mathscr{F}^{(N)}$ form the basis for a certain representation of the vectors and operators of $\mathscr{E}$ – the $\{Q\}$ representation. We shall call a representation of this type a *symmetrical representation.*

3. Permutation Operators

The state represented by vector (XIV.10) is obviously the one in which particle 1 is in state $|q_\alpha\rangle$, particle 2 in state $|q_\beta\rangle$, ..., particle N in state $|q_\nu\rangle$. A permutation of the N particles modifies their distribution among $|q_\alpha\rangle, |q_\beta\rangle, ..., |q_\nu\rangle$, and therefore replaces (XIV.10) by another, in general different [1]), vector of the basis $\{Q\}$. Thus such an operation establishes a one-to-one correspondence between the vectors of this orthonormal basis, and consequently defines a certain linear and unitary operator in state-vector space. In this way we associate with each permutation of the N particles a *permutation operator* P having the unitary property:

$$PP^\dagger = P^\dagger P = 1. \tag{XIV.11}$$

Thus, in the transposition (1 2) – interchange of particles 1 and 2 – the vector (XIV.10) transforms into a vector representing a state in which particle 1 is in $|q_\beta\rangle$, particle 2 in $|q_\alpha\rangle$, and the others in the same states as before; the associated permutation operator $P_{(12)}$ is defined by the equation

$$P_{(12)}\,|q_\alpha{}^{(1)}\,q_\beta{}^{(2)}\,q_\gamma{}^{(3)}\,\dots\,q_\nu{}^{(N)}\rangle = |q_\beta{}^{(1)}\,q_\alpha{}^{(2)}\,q_\gamma{}^{(3)}\,\dots\,q_\nu{}^{(N)}\rangle.$$

To simplify the writing, we continue our study of permutations for the case $N=3$. The principles enunciated will of course hold for any N. As an example let us define the operator $P_{(123)}$ associated with the permutation (1 2 3) in which 1 takes the place of 3, 2 that of 1, and 3 that of 2:

$$P_{(123)}\,|q_\alpha{}^{(1)}\,q_\beta{}^{(2)}\,q_\gamma{}^{(3)}\rangle = |q_\gamma{}^{(1)}\,q_\alpha{}^{(2)}\,q_\beta{}^{(3)}\rangle. \tag{XIV.12}$$

If $|\psi\rangle$ is a vector of $\mathscr{E}$,

$$\begin{aligned} P_{(123)}\,|\psi\rangle &= \sum_{\alpha\beta\gamma} P_{(123)}\,|q_\alpha{}^{(1)}\,q_\beta{}^{(2)}\,q_\gamma{}^{(3)}\rangle\,\langle q_\alpha{}^{(1)}\,q_\beta{}^{(2)}\,q_\gamma{}^{(3)}\,|\psi\rangle \\ &= \sum_{\alpha\beta\gamma} |q_\gamma{}^{(1)}\,q_\alpha{}^{(2)}\,q_\beta{}^{(3)}\rangle\,\langle q_\alpha{}^{(1)}\,q_\beta{}^{(2)}\,q_\gamma{}^{(3)}\,|\psi\rangle. \end{aligned}$$

---

[1]) When the N individual states $|q_\alpha\rangle, \dots, |q_\nu\rangle$ are not all different, certain permutations will leave vector (XIV.10) unchanged; if they are all identical, (XIV.10) will be unchanged by any permutation.

Re-naming the dummy indices in the last line, this becomes

$$P_{(123)}\,|\psi\rangle = \sum_{\alpha\beta\gamma} |q_\alpha^{(1)}\, q_\beta^{(2)}\, q_\gamma^{(3)}\rangle\, \langle q_\beta^{(1)}\, q_\gamma^{(2)}\, q_\alpha^{(3)}\,|\psi\rangle. \quad \text{(XIV.13)}$$

If $\psi(q_\alpha\, q_\beta\, q_\gamma)$ is the wave function of $|\psi\rangle$ in the $\{Q\}$ representation ($\psi(q_\alpha\, q_\beta\, q_\gamma)$ is the probability amplitude for finding particle 1 in $|q_\alpha\rangle$, 2 in $|q_\beta\rangle$, 3 in $|q_\gamma\rangle$), then the wave function of $P_{(123)}\,|\psi\rangle$ is the function

$$P_{(123)}\,\psi(q_\alpha\, q_\beta\, q_\gamma) = \psi(q_\beta\, q_\gamma\, q_\alpha) \qquad \text{(XIV.14)}$$

obtained *by applying to the arguments of* $\psi(q_\alpha\, q_\beta\, q_\gamma)$ *the inverse of the permutation* (1 2 3).

The law for the transformation of vectors in a permutation is especially simple for vectors of the form

$$|u^{(1)}\, v^{(2)}\, w^{(3)}\rangle \equiv |u\rangle^{(1)}\, |v\rangle^{(2)}\, |w\rangle^{(3)};$$

it is the same as the law of transformation of the basis vectors of the $\{Q\}$ representation. The vector resulting from the action of P on such a vector is just the one obtained by applying the permutation p to the particles 1, 2, 3, in the individual states $|u\rangle$, $|v\rangle$, $|w\rangle$, i.e. [eq. (XIV.12)]

$$P_{(123)}\,|u^{(1)}\, v^{(2)}\, w^{(3)}\rangle = |w^{(1)}\, u^{(2)}\, v^{(3)}\rangle.$$

The demonstration is simple; equation (XIV.13) here reads

$$P_{(123)}\,|u^{(1)}\, v^{(2)}\, w^{(3)}\rangle = \sum_{\alpha\beta\gamma} |q_\alpha^{(1)}\, q_\beta^{(2)}\, q_\gamma^{(3)}\rangle\, \langle q_\alpha\,|w\rangle\, \langle q_\beta\,|u\rangle\, \langle q_\gamma\,|v\rangle$$

and the right-hand side is just the expansion of $|w^{(1)}\, u^{(2)}\, v^{(3)}\rangle$ in terms of the basis vectors of $\{Q\}$.

This property, verified here for a particular case, is a general one (Problem XIV.1). In consequence, the operator P associated with a given permutation is independent of the particular symmetrical representation chosen to define it.

Just as the action of P on a vector gives the vector obtained from the latter by the permutation p, the transformation of a given operator $F\,(\xi^{(1)}, \xi^{(2)}, \ldots, \xi^{(N)})$ of $\mathscr{E}$ by the unitary operator P gives the operator resulting from the application of p to the arguments of F. If we put

$$p = \begin{pmatrix} 1 & 2 & \ldots & N \\ \alpha_1 & \alpha_2 & \ldots & \alpha_N \end{pmatrix},$$

we have

$$P F(\xi^{(1)}, \xi^{(2)}, \ldots, \xi^{(N)})\, P^\dagger = F\,(\xi^{(\alpha_1)}, \xi^{(\alpha_2)}, \ldots, \xi^{(\alpha_N)}). \qquad \text{(XIV.15)}$$

In particular

$$P_{(123)}\, F(\xi^{(1)}, \xi^{(2)}, \xi^{(3)})\, P^\dagger_{(123)} = F(\xi^{(2)}, \xi^{(3)}, \xi^{(1)}) \qquad \text{(XIV.16)}$$

($\xi^{(2)}$ takes the place of $\xi^{(1)}$, $\xi^{(3)}$ that of $\xi^{(2)}$ and $\xi^{(1)}$ that of $\xi^{(3)}$).

To establish this rule it is sufficient to show that it holds when F is any one of the fundamental observables of the system. Consider one of these observables; one can always construct a symmetrical representation in which it is diagonal. Suppose, for example, that it is one of the $q^{(i)}$ of the $\{Q\}$ representation considered above. To show that $Pq^{(i)}\, P^\dagger = q^{(\alpha_i)}$, it suffices to show that the two sides have the same action on all of the basis vectors of $\{Q\}$. The demonstration is not difficult and we shall content ourselves here with carrying it through for the special case $N=3$, $i=1$, $p=(1\ 2\ 3)$:

$$\begin{aligned} P_{(123)}\, q^{(1)}\, P^\dagger_{(123)}\, |q_\alpha{}^{(1)}\, q_\beta{}^{(2)}\, q_\gamma{}^{(3)}\rangle &= P_{(123)}\, q^{(1)}\, |q_\beta{}^{(1)}\, q_\gamma{}^{(2)}\, q_\alpha{}^{(3)}\rangle \\ &= q_\beta\, P_{(123)}\, |q_\beta{}^{(1)}\, q_\gamma{}^{(2)}\, q_\alpha{}^{(3)}\rangle \\ &= q_\beta\, |q_\alpha{}^{(1)}\, q_\beta{}^{(2)}\, q_\gamma{}^{(3)}\rangle = q^{(2)}\, |q_\alpha{}^{(1)}\, q_\beta{}^{(2)}\, q_\gamma{}^{(3)}\rangle. \end{aligned}$$

As applied to observables, this definition of permutations answers well to one's intuitive idea of permutations of observables: the observable $PBP^\dagger$ resulting from the application of the permutation p to an observable B has the same eigenvalue spectrum as B, and the eigenvectors of $PBP^\dagger$ are obtained from the eigenvectors of B corresponding to the same eigenvalue by application of the permutation operator P.

In particular, B is invariant under permutations of the N particles if $PBP^\dagger = B$ for each of the $N!$ permutations of these particles, i.e. if

$$[P, B] = 0$$

for any P. If such is the case, we say that B is *symmetrical* with respect to the N particles.

4. Algebra of Permutation Operators. Symmetrizers and Antisymmetrizers

Two successive permutations p', p'' are equivalent to a single permutation $p = p''\, p'$. From the definition of a permutation operator it is clear that the same relation holds for the associated operators P, P', P'':

$$P = P'' P'. \tag{XIV.17}$$

Thus the permutation operators obey the same algebraic relations as the permutations to which they correspond [1]).

In particular, any P can be expressed as a product of transpositions. In general there are many such products for the same P, but all of these products will contain either an even or an odd number of transpositions. The *parity* of the permutation is + or − according as this number is even or odd, and is denoted $(-)^P$. If P, P' and P'' are related by XIV.17, then clearly $(-)^p = (-)^{p'+p''}$.

Certain permutations, notably transpositions, are equal to their own inverse. In such a case [cf. eq. (XIV.11)], the associated operator is an observable, whose possible eigenvalues are ± 1.

As an example consider the transposition (ij):

$$P_{(ij)}{}^2 = 1. \tag{XIV.18}$$

The eigenvectors of the eigenvalue $+1$ are invariant in the transposition (ij); they are by definition *symmetrical* in i and j. The projector onto the space of all vectors symmetrical in i and j is the *symmetrizing operator*

$$S_{[ij]} = \tfrac{1}{2}(1 + P_{(ij)}). \tag{XIV.19}$$

The eigenvectors of the eigenvalue -1 change sign in the transposition (ij); they are by definition *antisymmetrical* in i and j; the projector onto the space of vectors antisymmetrical in i and j is the *antisymmetrizing operator*

$$A_{[ij]} = \tfrac{1}{2}(1 - P_{(ij)}). \tag{XIV.20}$$

---

[1]) In particular, $P_{(123)} = P_{(12)}\, P_{(23)}$. Let us verify that the successive application of $P_{(23)}$ and $P_{(12)}$ to the wave function $\psi(q_\alpha\, q_\beta\, q_\gamma)$ does give back the result (XIV.14). Put

$$\psi_1(q_\alpha\, q_\beta\, q_\gamma) \equiv P_{(23)} \psi(q_\alpha\, q_\beta\, q_\gamma);$$

then

$$\psi_1(q_\alpha\, q_\beta\, q_\gamma) = \psi(q_\alpha\, q_\gamma\, q_\beta)$$

and

$$P_{(123)}\, \psi(q_\alpha\, q_\beta\, q_\gamma) = P_{(12)}\, \psi_1(q_\alpha\, q_\beta\, q_\gamma) = \psi_1(q_\beta\, q_\alpha\, q_\gamma) = \psi(q_\beta\, q_\gamma\, q_\alpha).$$

The same result is obtained by *first* applying the permutation (1 2), and *then* the permutation (2 3), to the arguments of the function $\psi(q_\alpha\, q_\beta\, q_\gamma)$.

We obviously have

$$\begin{aligned} &S_{[ij]}+A_{[ij]}=1 \qquad && P_{(ij)}\, S_{[ij]}=S_{[ij]}\; P_{(ij)}=S_{[ij]} \\ &S_{[ij]}-A_{[ij]}=P_{(ij)} \qquad && P_{(ij)}\, A_{[ij]}=A_{[ij]}\, P_{(ij)}=-A_{[ij]}. \end{aligned} \tag{XIV.21}$$

Any vector is the sum of a vector that is antisymmetrical in i and j and a vector that is symmetrical in i and j; a decomposition of this type was used in discussing the collision of two identical particles in § 1.

We next consider the extension of the notion of symmetry and antisymmetry of dynamical states, which so far has been defined only for the permutation $P_{(ij)}$, to the more general case of the $N!$ permutations P.

We take a vector $|u\rangle$ of $\mathscr{E}$ and denote by $\mathscr{E}_u$ the subspace spanned by $|u\rangle$ and all the vectors that can be obtained from it by permutation. The number of dimensions of $\mathscr{E}_u$ is equal or inferior to $N!$ according as the $N!$ vectors $P|u\rangle$ are linearly independent or not.

An extreme case is when the $P|u\rangle$ all represent the same state:

$$P|u\rangle = c_p|u\rangle \tag{XIV.22}$$

for any p. There are restricting conditions on the constants c_p. If P is a transposition we know that c_p can take only the values ± 1. Further, since any transposition (ij) is equal to the product $(1i)$ $(2j)$ $(1\,2)$ $(2j)$ $(1i)$,

$$P_{(ij)} = P_{(1i)}\, P_{(2j)}\, P_{(12)}\, P_{(2j)}\, P_{(1i)}$$

and therefore

$$c_{(ij)} = c_{(1i)}{}^2\, c_{(2j)}{}^2\, c_{(12)} = c_{(12)}. \tag{XIV.23}$$

Hence the constant c is the same for all the transpositions: either $c_{\text{tr}} = +1$ or $c_{\text{tr}} = -1$, and since any permutation p is a product of transpositions, the corresponding constant c_p is a certain power of c_{tr}, this power being even or odd according as p is even or odd.

Thus we can conclude that equation (XIV.22) is fulfilled only in the two following cases:

$$\text{(a) for any } p,\ c_p=1 \qquad P|u\rangle=|u\rangle, \tag{XIV.24}$$

$$\text{(b) for any } p,\ c_p=(-)^p \qquad P|u\rangle=(-)^p\,|u\rangle; \tag{XIV.25}$$

vector $|u\rangle$ is said to be *symmetrical* or *antisymmetrical* with respect to permutations of the N particles according as it is (a) or (b) that applies.

The symmetrical vectors form a subspace $\mathscr{E}^{(S)}$ of $\mathscr{E}$, and the anti-symmetrical vectors a second subspace $\mathscr{E}^{(A)}$ of $\mathscr{E}$, orthogonal to $\mathscr{E}^{(S)}$. We shall now show that the corresponding projectors are respectively given by

$$S = \frac{1}{N!} \sum_P P \qquad A = \frac{1}{N!} \sum_P (-)^p P \tag{XIV.26}$$

($\sum_P$ being extended over the $N!$ possible permutations). Consider the sequence obtained by arranging the permutations in some arbitrary order. Multiplication of each element on the right or on the left by a permutation operator P_1 can only modify their order in the sequence. Hence

$$P_1 S = S P_1 = S \qquad P_1 A = A P_1 = (-)^{p_1} A. \tag{XIV.27}$$

Replacing each element P by its inverse $P^\dagger$ also merely changes the order of the elements, and since the inverse of a permutation has the same parity as the permutation itself, we have

$$S = S^\dagger \qquad A = A^\dagger. \tag{XIV.28}$$

From equation (XIV.27) and definitions (XIV.26) we easily deduce the relations

$$S^2 = S \qquad A^2 = A \tag{XIV.29}$$

and

$$SA = AS = 0. \tag{XIV.30}$$

Relations (XIV.28–30) show that S and A are orthogonal projectors. Now if $|u\rangle$ is in $\mathscr{E}^{(S)}$, then from (XIV.24),

$$S|u\rangle = \frac{1}{N!} \sum_P P|u\rangle = \left(\frac{1}{N!} \sum_P\right)|u\rangle = |u\rangle$$

and, conversely, if $|\rangle$ is an arbitrary vector, then from (XIV.27),

$$PS|\rangle = S|\rangle;$$

hence S is indeed the projector onto $\mathscr{E}^{(S)}$. One can similarly show that A is the projector onto $\mathscr{E}^{(A)}$.

When $N=3$, S and A are explicitly given by

$$S = \tfrac{1}{6}(1 + P_{(12)} + P_{(23)} + P_{(31)} + P_{(123)} + P_{(321)})$$
$$A = \tfrac{1}{6}(1 - P_{(12)} - P_{(23)} - P_{(31)} + P_{(123)} + P_{(321)}).$$

As this example clearly shows, $S + A \neq 1$ if $N > 2$. In fact $S + A$

projects onto the space of states invariant under an even permutation of the N particles, a subspace of $\mathscr{E}$ when $N > 2$.

Returning to the space $\mathscr{E}_u$ defined above, we deduce from eq. (XIV.27) that for any P,

$$SP|u\rangle = S|u\rangle \qquad AP|u\rangle = (-)^p A|u\rangle.$$

Thus the vectors $P|u\rangle$ spanning $\mathscr{E}_u$ all have the same projection on $\mathscr{E}^{(S)}$, and to within a sign the same projection on $\mathscr{E}^{(A)}$. Therefore, according as $S|u\rangle$ is different to zero or not, $\mathscr{E}_u$ *contains one, and only one symmetrical vector or none whatever*; and similarly, according as $A|u\rangle$ is different to zero or not, $\mathscr{E}_u$ *contains one and only one antisymmetrical vector or none whatever* [1]).

5. Identical Particles and the Symmetrization Postulate

If the N particles of the system considered above are not only similar but identical, then none of the dynamical properties of the system are modified by a permutation of these particles. From this invariance property, important deductions can be made concerning the law of motion and the observables of the system.

If $|\psi_0\rangle$ is the state of the system at the initial time t_0, its state at a later time t is obtained by application of the evolution operator $U(t, t_0)$: $|\psi_t\rangle = U(t, t_0)\,|\psi\rangle$. If the initial state is $P|\psi_0\rangle$, the evolution of the system is exactly the same except for the permutation P and at time t it will be in the state $P|\psi_t\rangle$. Consequently

$$U(t, t_0)\,P|\psi_0\rangle = P|\psi_t\rangle = PU(t, t_0)\,|\psi_0\rangle$$

and, since this must hold whatever $|\psi_0\rangle$,

$$[P, U(t, t_0)] = 0. \tag{XIV.31}$$

If H is the Hamiltonian of the system, $U(t, t_0)$ is the solution of the Schrödinger equation

$$\mathrm{i}\hbar \frac{\mathrm{d}}{\mathrm{d}t}\, U(t, t_0) = HU(t, t_0)$$

defined by the initial condition: $U(t_0, t_0) = 1$. From (XIV.31), and

[1]) If the $N!$ vectors $P|u\rangle$ are linearly independent, the particular linear combinations of these vectors $S|a\rangle$ and $A|u\rangle$ are certainly non-zero; in this case, $\mathscr{E}_u$ contains one symmetrical vector and one antisymmetrical vector.

from the relation obtained by differentiating it with respect to t, we obtain

$$[P, H] = 0. \tag{XIV.32}$$

Conversely, if H and P commute, $U(t, t_0)$ and its transform under permutation $PUP^\dagger$ are equal since they satisfy the same Schrödinger equation with the same initial condition; and therefore U and P commute. Thus a necessary and sufficient condition that the equation of motion be invariant under permutation is that H satisfy (XIV.32) for all P.

Consider next a physical observable [1]) B of the system and let $|u\rangle$ be an eigenvector of B corresponding to the eigenvalue b. If the system is in the state $|u\rangle$, then a measurement of B is certain to give the result b, and if the system is in the state $P|u\rangle$ obtained by applying the permutation P to $|u\rangle$, a measurement of B must give the same result:

$$BP|u\rangle = bP|u\rangle$$

and this for any permutation P. In other words, each vector of the space $\mathscr{E}_u$, generated by applying all possible permutations of the N particles to $|u\rangle$, must also be an eigenvector of B corresponding to the same eigenvalue b (exchange degeneracy). A necessary and sufficient condition for this to be true for all eigenvalues of B is that (cf. § VII.15)

$$[B, P] = 0 \tag{XIV.33}$$

for any P.

Thus, the N particles are identical if the Hamiltonian H and all the physical observables of the system are symmetrical with respect to these particles.

In consequence, if we should wish to determine the state of the system by a simultaneous measurement of the variables q of each individual particle, such a determination can at best be made only to within an exchange degeneracy [2]); we can affirm that of the total

---

[1]) The meaning of the expression *physical observable* has been given in § XIII.15. The present analysis of invariance under permutation may be compared with the analysis of the invariance of physical observables under "rotation through 2π" given in that paragraph.

[2]) $q^{(1)}, q^{(2)}, \ldots, q^{(N)}$ form a complete set of commuting observables in the space $\mathscr{E}$, but only symmetrical functions of these can be physical observables,

number of particles N there are n_1 particles in the state $|q_1\rangle$, n_2 in the state $|q_2\rangle, \ldots, n_\varkappa$ in the state $|q_\varkappa\rangle, \ldots$ $(n_1+n_2+\ldots+n_\varkappa+\ldots=N)$, but the identity of the particles in each of these states will remain undetermined. There are $(N!/n_1!\, n_2! \ldots n_\varkappa! \ldots)$ basis vectors of the $\{Q\}$ representation having the desired property. Let $\mathscr{E}(n_1\, n_2 \ldots n_\varkappa \ldots)$ be the space spanned by these vectors (generated by the application of the $N!$ permutations to any one of them). The state of the system is certainly represented by one of the vectors of this space, but the above-mentioned observation does not permit to decide which one. However, as we have seen in the example of § 1, the predictions of the theory depend upon which one, and this ambiguity is therefore a source of real difficulty. It is removed by the introduction of the SYMMETRIZATION POSTULATE:

The states of a system containing N identical particles are necessarily either all symmetrical or all antisymmetrical with respect to permutations of the N particles.

Which of these prescriptions is to be applied depends upon the nature of the identical particles. Particles with symmetrical states are called *bosons*, those with antisymmetrical states, *fermions*. (The reasons for these names will become clear later on.) *Experiment shows* that the elementary particles of spin $\frac{1}{2}$ occurring in nature (electrons, protons, neutrons, etc.,) are fermions, while those of integral spin (photons, π mesons, etc.) are bosons.

The above-defined space $\mathscr{E}(n_1\, n_2 \ldots n_\varkappa)$ has no more than one symmetrical vector and no more than one antisymmetrical vector. Thus the symmetrization postulate completely removes the exchange degeneracy. It remains to show that it does not come into conflict with the fundamental postulates of Quantum Mechanics concerning the motion of physical systems and the measurement of physical quantities.

Let us consider the boson case (fermions may be treated in the same way). In the preceding paragraph we defined the projector onto

---

and these do not form a complete set in $\mathscr{E}$. The symmetrization postulate, to be introduced further along, will consist in limiting the state vector space to a certain subspace of $\mathscr{E}$ in which the physical observables in question form a complete set (and in which, therefore, the exchange degeneracy is completely removed).

the symmetrical states, S. It is a particular combination of permutation operators [eq. (XIV.26)], and therefore commutes with the evolution operator $U(t, t_0)$ for the system

$$[S, U(t, t_0)] = 0 \qquad \text{(XIV.34)}$$

and with the physical observables

$$[S, B] = 0. \qquad \text{(XIV.35)}$$

Eq. (XIV.34) shows that if the system is initially in a symmetrical state it will remain in a symmetrical state so long as it is left undisturbed. Let us now suppose that an ideal measurement of B is performed. From eq. (XIV.35), S and B have at least one common set of basis vectors; if the state of the system is symmetrical, the expansion of the state vector in terms of this basis contains only symmetrical eigenvectors of B. It is therefore certain that the operation of measuring B will leave the system in a symmetrical state.

6. Bosons and Bose–Einstein Statistics

Consider a system of N bosons. The states of the system span the subspace $\mathscr{E}^{(S)}$ of $\mathscr{E}$. We can form a basis in $\mathscr{E}^{(S)}$ from the vectors of the $\{Q\}$ representation by proceeding in the following way.

In each subspace $\mathscr{E}(n_1\, n_2 \,\ldots\, n_\varkappa \ldots)$ we can form one, and only one, normalized symmetrical vector (defined to within a phase), the vector

$$\left[\frac{N!}{n_1!\; n_2! \;\ldots\; n_\varkappa! \;\ldots}\right]^{\frac{1}{2}} S\,|q_1^{n_1}\, q_2^{n_2} \,\ldots\, q_\varkappa^{n_\varkappa} \ldots\rangle \qquad \text{(XIV.36)}$$

$|q_1^{n_1}\, q_2^{n_2} \ldots q_\varkappa^{n_\varkappa} \ldots\rangle$ being the basis vector of $\{Q\}$ for which the first n_1 particles are in state $|q_1\rangle$, the following n_2 in state $|q_2\rangle$, ..., the following $n_\varkappa$ in state $|q_\varkappa\rangle$, ...; S is the symmetrizing operator defined above [eq. (XIV.26)]; the constant in brackets is a normalization constant $(0! = 1)$. The proof is as follows. The interchange of two particles occupying the same state leaves $|q_1^{n_1}\, q_2^{n_2} \ldots q_\varkappa^{n_\varkappa} \ldots\rangle$ unchanged, while the interchange of two particles occupying different states gives another of the basis vectors of $\{Q\}$. More generally, this vector is invariant under any of the $\prod n_\varkappa! \equiv n_1!\; n_2! \ldots n_\varkappa! \ldots$ permutations not changing the distribution of the N particles among the individual states $|q_1\rangle, |q_2\rangle, \ldots |q_\varkappa\rangle, \ldots$; any other permutation changes it into another of the basis vectors of $\{Q\}$. Applying each of the $N!$

permutations to $|q_1^{n_1} q_2^{n_2} \dots q_\varkappa^{n_\varkappa} \dots\rangle$ we form the $[N!/\prod n_\varkappa!]$ basis vectors of $\mathscr{E}(n_1\, n_2 \dots n_\varkappa \dots)$, each of them being obtained $(\prod n_\varkappa!)$ times. The vector (XIV.36), being equal to $[\prod n_\varkappa!/N!]^{\frac{1}{2}}$ multiplied by the sum of these basis vectors, is therefore symmetrical and normalized to unity. Q.E.D.

Thus, to each sequence $n_1, n_2, \dots, n_\varkappa, \dots$ of non-negative integers such that

$$n_1 + n_2 + \dots + n_\varkappa + \dots = N,$$

there corresponds one and only one symmetrical state of the system, represented by the vector (XIV.36). The set of vectors so formed constitutes an orthonormal basis in $\mathscr{E}^{(S)}$.

Next we show that *a boson gas obeys Bose–Einstein statistics*. By boson gas is meant a system formed of a very large number N of bosons having mutual interactions weak enough to be neglected in a first approximation. The Hamiltonian H of the system can then be written as a sum of N individual Hamiltonians:

$$H = h^{(1)} + h^{(2)} + \dots + h^{(i)} + \dots + h^{(N)}. \qquad \text{(XIV.37)}$$

According to the Boltzmann theory, thermodynamical equilibrium is realized when the system is in the most probable "macroscopic state". A given "macroscopic state" is in fact a set of quantum states (or "microscopic states") sufficiently close to one another that it is impossible to differentiate between them at the macroscopic level. According to the ergodic hypothesis, microscopic states of the same energy are all equally probable. The probability of a given macroscopic state is therefore proportional to the number of distinct microscopic states composing it. The determination of the thermodynamical equilibrium of the system depends essentially on this number. Suppose that h is included in the set q of dynamical variables defining the representation $\{Q\}$. Each distribution

$$n_1, n_2, \dots, n_\varkappa, \dots$$

of the N particles among the different possible individual states

$$|q_1\rangle, |q_2\rangle, \dots, |q_\varkappa\rangle, \dots$$

defines one, and only one, microscopic state of the system [represented by (XIV.36)]. This is just the hypothesis of Bose–Einstein statistics, where the particles are supposed indistinguishable and where in consequence states of the system differing only in the identity of the particles occupying the various individual states count as one and the same microscopic state. In Maxwell–Boltzmann statistics, on the other hand, each particle is supposed distinguishable at the microscopic level, and the $[N!/\prod n_\varkappa!]$ states of the system corresponding to the same distribution $n_1, n_2, \ldots, n_\varkappa, \ldots$ are counted as separate microscopic states.

Important remark—The general expression for the density operator representing the state of a system in thermodynamical equilibrium

$$\varrho = \mathrm{e}^{-H/kT}/\mathrm{Tr}\, \mathrm{e}^{-H/kT} \tag{XIV.38}$$

and the expressions derived from it in § VIII.25 remain valid here. The profound difference introduced by the symmetrization postulate comes from the fact that ϱ is now an operator of $\mathscr{E}^{(S)}$ rather than of $\mathscr{E}$, and the different manipulations of quantum statistics, in particular the calculation of traces, must now be made in this more restricted space. Thus, when H is of the form (XIV.37), ϱ considered as an operator of the space $\mathscr{E}$ is a tensor product of operators defined in each of the individual spaces $\mathscr{F}^{(1)}, \mathscr{F}^{(2)} \ldots, \mathscr{F}^{(N)}$:

$$\varrho = \prod_{i=1}^{N} [\mathrm{e}^{-h^{(i)}/kT}/\mathrm{Tr}_i\, \mathrm{e}^{-h^{(i)}/kT}].$$

But this factorisation loses all significance if ϱ is an operator of $\mathscr{E}^{(S)}$, for the N factors taken separately are not operators of $\mathscr{E}^{(S)}$.

7. Fermions and Fermi–Dirac Statistics. Exclusion Principle

An analysis similar to the foregoing can be made of the N-fermion system. Its states span the subspace $\mathscr{E}^{(A)}$ of $\mathscr{E}$.

Starting from the $\{Q\}$ representation we obtain a complete set of orthonormal antisymmetrical vectors by taking a normalized antisymmetrical vector—if it exists—in each subspace $\mathscr{E}(n_1\, n_2 \ldots n_\varkappa \ldots)$. A necessary and sufficient condition that such a vector exist is that $A|q_1^{n_1}\, q_2^{n_2} \ldots q_\varkappa^{n_\varkappa} \ldots\rangle$ be different to zero. Let us suppose that we have at least one of the integers $n_1, n_2, \ldots, n_\varkappa, \ldots$ greater than 1. In the state represented by $|q_1^{n_1}\, q_2^{n_2} \ldots q_\varkappa^{n_\varkappa} \ldots\rangle$ at least two particles, the ith and the jth say, occupy the same individual state, so that this vector is symmetrical in the interchange of these two particles, i.e.

$$|q_1^{n_1} q_2^{n_2} \dots q_\varkappa^{n_\varkappa} \dots\rangle = \tfrac{1}{2}(1+P_{(ij)})\, |q_1^{n_1} q_2^{n_2} \dots q_\varkappa^{n_\varkappa} \dots\rangle.$$

But, from (XIV.27)

$$A(1+P_{(ij)}) = 0,$$

so that

$$A|q_1^{n_1} q_2^{n_2} \dots q_\varkappa^{n_\varkappa} \dots\rangle = 0. \qquad \text{(XIV.39)}$$

In other words, *two fermions cannot occupy the same individual quantum state*. This is the *Pauli exclusion principle* [1]).

Suppose now that at most one particle is in any individual state ($n_\varkappa=0$ or 1). The vector

$$A|q_1^{n_1} q_2^{n_2} \dots q_\varkappa^{n_\varkappa} \dots\rangle \equiv \frac{1}{N!} \sum_P (-)^p\, P|q_1^{n_1} q_2^{n_2} \dots q_\varkappa^{n_\varkappa} \dots\rangle$$

is the sum of $N!$ mutually orthogonal vectors and therefore is certainly non-zero. Its norm is $(1/N!)$. If $|q_\alpha\rangle, |q_\beta\rangle, \dots, |q_\nu\rangle$ are the N individual occupied states, the corresponding antisymmetrical state is represented by the vector of norm 1: $\sqrt{N!}\, A\, |q_\alpha^{(1)}\, q_\beta^{(2)} \dots q_\nu^{(N)}\rangle$. This vector can be written in the form of an $N\times N$ determinant (*the Slater determinant*)

$$\sqrt{N!}\, A|q_\alpha^{(1)}\, q_\beta^{(2)} \dots q_\nu^{(N)}\rangle \equiv \frac{1}{\sqrt{N!}} \begin{vmatrix} |q_\alpha\rangle^{(1)} & |q_\alpha\rangle^{(2)} & \dots & |q_\alpha\rangle^{(N)} \\ |q_\beta\rangle^{(1)} & |q_\beta\rangle^{(2)} & \dots & |q_\beta\rangle^{(N)} \\ \vdots & & & \\ |q_\nu\rangle^{(1)} & |q_\nu\rangle^{(2)} & \dots & |q_\nu\rangle^{(N)} \end{vmatrix} \qquad \text{(XIV.40)}$$

This identity can be directly verified from the definition of a determinant. Further, (XIV.40) is still valid when certain of the N individual states are identical, in which case two or more lines of the determinant are equal, giving back the Pauli exclusion principle.

Thus, to each set $|q_\alpha\rangle, |q_\beta\rangle, \dots, |q_\nu\rangle$ of N *different* states chosen from among the individual states $|q_1\rangle, |q_2\rangle, \dots, |q_\varkappa\rangle, \dots$, there corresponds one, and only one, antisymmetrical state, which is represented by vector (XIV.40). The set of vectors so constructed constitutes an orthonormal basis in $\mathscr{E}^{(A)}$.

---

[1]) The exclusion principle was formulated by Pauli in 1925 as a general property of electrons permitting one to explain the structure of complex atoms (cf. § 12).

A fermion gas is governed by Fermi–Dirac statistics. The demonstration is analogous to the one for the boson case. Only the numbering of microscopic states is different. Each set of N different individual states defines one, and only one, microscopic state of the fermion system [represented by vector (XIV.40)]. This is just the hypothesis of Fermi–Dirac statistics, which states that the N particles are indistinguishable and that there can be no more than one of them in any individual state.

The note at the end of the preceding paragraph also applies to fermions. The density operator for a fermion system in thermodynamic equilibrium is given by equation (XIV.38); here of course, it is an operator in $\mathscr{E}^{(A)}$.

Thus, the differences between the three types of identical particle statistics lie in the definition of the state-vector space as indicated by the following table.

Statistics	Maxwell–Boltzmann	Bose–Einstein	Fermi–Dirac
Character of the particles	distinguishable	indistinguishable	indistinguishable + exclusion
State-vector space	$\mathscr{E}$	$\mathscr{E}^{(S)}$	$\mathscr{E}^{(A)}$

8. Is it always Necessary to Symmetrize the Wave Function

We consider a system of n identical particles. If the particles are electrons the state of the system will be represented by an antisymmetrical wave function. These are not, however, the only electrons in the universe. To ignore the others, and to treat this system as an entity distinct from the rest, supposes that the dynamical properties of the n electrons are not affected by the presence of the others. The question arises whether such a hypothesis is well founded, or whether the symmetrization postulate, in establishing a certain correlation between these n electrons and the others, renders it invalid.

In practice, the electrons of a system are all inside a certain spatial domain D, and the dynamical properties in which we are interested all correspond to measurements to be made inside this domain. It turns out that the other electrons may simply be ignored so long as they remain outside D and so long as their interaction with the electrons of the system remains negligible. This is a general result and applies to bosons as well as to fermions. We shall prove it here for the special case of a system of two fermions.

If one ignores the existence of all other particles, the dynamical state of the two fermions is represented by a certain normalized antisymmetrical wave function, $\varphi(1, 2)$. 1 and 2 denote the coordinates and the spin components s_z of particles 1 and 2 respectively. In general, a given state of the system, χ say, is represented by a certain antisymmetrical wave function normalized to unity, $\chi(1, 2)$. If at a given time the system is in the state φ, its dynamical properties at that time are given by the set of probabilities

$$w = |\langle\chi|\varphi\rangle|^2. \tag{XIV.41}$$

In reality, the two fermions are part of a system of N fermions. Let us see if these dynamical properties are the same as those found if we correctly take into account the existence of the other $(N-2)$ fermions. Let $\Psi(3, 4, \ldots, N)$ be the normalized antisymmetrical wave function representing the dynamical state of the other $(N-2)$ fermions. If fermions 1 and 2 were not identical to fermions 3, 4, ..., N, the state of the whole system would be represented by

$$\varphi(1, 2)\,\Psi(3, 4, \ldots, N)$$

and would retain this factorisation property so long as the interaction between the first two fermions and the others remained negligible. Actually, the vector $|\Phi\rangle$, which correctly represents the state of the whole system, is proportional to the antisymmetrical vector $A|\varphi\Psi\rangle$, A being the antisymmetrizing operator for the N particles [definition (XIV.26)].

By hypothesis, the wave packets φ and Ψ do not overlap; more precisely, it is certain that the two fermions are inside a specified spatial domain D and that all the others are outside D. Moreover, we are concerned only with the dynamical properties of the two fermions inside D.

Denote by $\Theta(3, 4, \ldots, N)$ an antisymmetrical wave function of norm 1 that vanishes when any of the $(N-2)$ position vectors $\boldsymbol{r}^{(3)}, \ldots, \boldsymbol{r}^{(N)}$ are inside D. Θ represents the state of a system of $(N-2)$ fermions all situated outside D. By hypothesis, Ψ is a function of this type. If the functions $\Theta_1, \Theta_2, \ldots, \Theta_i, \ldots$ form a complete orthonormal set of such functions, then

$$\Psi = \sum_i \Theta_i \langle \Theta_i | \Psi \rangle.$$

We denote by $\chi(12)$ any normalized antisymmetrical wave function of 1 and 2 having the converse property, i.e. the property that χ vanishes if either of the vectors $\boldsymbol{r}^{(1)}$, $\boldsymbol{r}^{(2)}$ is outside D. χ represents, therefore, two fermions inside D. By hypothesis, φ is such a function.

The permutations of the N particles may be put into two categories depending upon their action on the vector $|\chi\Theta\rangle$. Those of the first category, which we denote by F, can at most change the sign of $|\chi\Theta\rangle$; they are the $2!(N-2)!$ permutations which exchange 1 and 2 and/or exchange 3, 4, ..., N among themselves. Thus,

$$F|\chi\Theta\rangle = (-)^f |\chi\Theta\rangle.$$

All other permutations, which we denote by G, exchange at least one of the particles 1, 2 with one of the $(N-2)$ others; hence, $G|\chi\Theta\rangle$ represents a state in which at least one of the particles 1, 2 is definitely outside D; it is orthogonal to any vector of the type $|\chi\Theta\rangle$:

$$\langle \chi'\Theta' | G | \chi\Theta \rangle = 0.$$

We can now deduce the following identity:

$$\begin{aligned} \langle \chi'\Theta' | A | \chi\Theta \rangle &= \frac{1}{N!} \sum_P (-)^p \langle \chi'\Theta' | P | \chi\Theta \rangle \\ &= \frac{1}{N!} \sum_F (-)^f \langle \chi'\Theta' | F | \chi\Theta \rangle \qquad \text{(XIV.42)} \\ &= \frac{2!\,(N-2)!}{N!} \langle \chi'\Theta' | \chi\Theta \rangle. \end{aligned}$$

Notice that the norm of $A|\chi\Theta\rangle$ is $\langle \chi\Theta | A | \chi\Theta \rangle$, i.e. $2!(N-2)!/N!$.

We now wish to know the probability w that the two fermions inside D are in the state χ. If the $(N-2)$ other fermions were distinguishable from these two, the state of the system would be represented by $|\varphi\Psi\rangle$ and the probabilities in question would be:

$$\sum_i |\langle \chi\Theta_i | \varphi\Psi \rangle|^2 = |\langle \chi | \varphi \rangle|^2 \left(\sum_i |\langle \Theta_i | \Psi \rangle|^2\right) = |\langle \chi | \varphi \rangle|^2. \qquad \text{(XIV.43)}$$

Since the N fermions are identical, the state of the system is

$$|\Phi\rangle = \sqrt{\binom{2}{N}}\, A|\varphi\Psi\rangle \qquad \left(\binom{2}{N} = \frac{N!}{2!\,(N-2)!}\right)$$

and the sought-for probability is that of finding the system in any one of the states represented by the orthonormal antisymmetrical vectors

$$|X_i\rangle = \sqrt{\binom{2}{N}}\, A|\chi\Theta_i\rangle,$$

namely

$$w = \sum_i |\langle X_i|\Phi\rangle|^2 = \binom{2}{N}^2 \sum_i |\langle\chi\Theta_i|A|\varphi\Psi\rangle|^2.$$

From (XIV.42) and (XIV.43),

$$w = \sum |\langle\chi\Theta_i|\varphi\Psi\rangle|^2 = |\langle\chi|\varphi\rangle|^2,$$

which is just (XIV.41).

Thus we can just ignore the existence of the $(N-2)$ other fermions and still obtain the correct result.

II. APPLICATIONS

9. Collision of two Spinless Identical Particles

Here we resume the discussion of the collision problem considered in § 1.

Let $(\mathbf{R}, \mathbf{P})$ and $(\mathbf{r}, \mathbf{p})$ be the dynamical variables for the center of mass and for the relative particle respectively:

$$\mathbf{R} = \tfrac{1}{2}(\mathbf{r}^{(1)} + \mathbf{r}^{(2)}), \qquad \mathbf{r} = \mathbf{r}^{(1)} - \mathbf{r}^{(2)}. \tag{XIV.44}$$

The Hamiltonian is

$$H = \frac{\mathbf{P}^2}{4m} + \frac{\mathbf{p}^2}{m} + V(\mathbf{r}) \tag{XIV.45}$$

and the dynamical state of the system at any given time is represented by a certain wave function $\Psi(\mathbf{R}, \mathbf{r})$ depending on $\mathbf{R}$ and $\mathbf{r}$.

In the interchange of the two particles, $\mathbf{R}$ is invariant, and $\mathbf{r}$ goes over into $-\boldsymbol{r}$. The wave function must satisfy the symmetrization postulate, so we have [1])

$$\Psi(\boldsymbol{R}, -\boldsymbol{r}) = \pm\, \Psi(\boldsymbol{R}, \boldsymbol{r}) \tag{XIV.46}$$

the upper sign corresponding to the case when the two particles are bosons, the lower to the case when they are fermions.

Let us first treat the same problem supposing the two particles distinguishable. The solution has been given in section I of Chapter X. We briefly recall it here, keeping the notation of § 4–7 of that chapter. Before collision ($t \ll 0$), the state of the system formed of the target particle and a given particle of the incident beam is characterized by the relative velocity $\boldsymbol{v} = \hbar \boldsymbol{k}/\frac{1}{2}m$ and by the impact parameter $\boldsymbol{b}$. It is represented by a product of the form $\Phi(\boldsymbol{R}, t)\ \varphi_{\boldsymbol{b}}(\boldsymbol{r}, t)$ where Φ and φ are two free wave packets of norm 1 [2]). If we work in the center-of-mass system, the group velocity of the wave $\Phi(\boldsymbol{R}, t)$ is zero and the wave $\varphi(\boldsymbol{r}, t)$ propagates with velocity $\boldsymbol{v}$. Under the conditions in which the cross sections are to be calculated, the spreading out of $\varphi(\boldsymbol{r}, t)$ is negligible; its form has been chosen once and for all and is given by [eq. (X.13)]

$$\varphi_{\boldsymbol{b}}(\boldsymbol{r}, t) = \mathrm{e}^{-\mathrm{i}\boldsymbol{k}\cdot\boldsymbol{b} - \mathrm{i}Et/\hbar}\, \chi(\boldsymbol{r} - \boldsymbol{v}t - \boldsymbol{b})\, \mathrm{e}^{\mathrm{i}\boldsymbol{k}\cdot\boldsymbol{r}}. \tag{XIV.47}$$

After the collision ($t \gg 0$) the wave function $\Psi_{\boldsymbol{b}}(\boldsymbol{R}, \boldsymbol{r}, t)$ defined by these initial conditions becomes

$$\Psi_{\boldsymbol{b}}(\boldsymbol{R}, \boldsymbol{r}, t) = \Phi(\boldsymbol{R}, t)\, [\varphi_{\boldsymbol{b}}(\boldsymbol{r}, t) + \psi_{\boldsymbol{b}}^{(d)}(\boldsymbol{r}, t)], \tag{XIV.48}$$

---

[1]) Permutation is an operation that differs from spatial reflection, in which $\boldsymbol{R}$ and $\boldsymbol{r}$ *both* change sign. In the present discussion, where the particles are spinless and where, as we shall see, the center of mass has no effective role, the two operations could easily be confused, as they have the same effect on the relative-particle wave function.

[2]) Rigorously speaking, the initial state should be represented by a product of the type (XIV.3), since there can be no correlation between the particles until they enter into collision. A product of the type $\Phi\varphi$ can be put in the form (XIV.3) only for particular types of waves Φ and φ. Example:

$$\Phi\varphi \propto \exp\, [\mathrm{i}(\boldsymbol{K}\cdot\boldsymbol{R} + \boldsymbol{k}\cdot\boldsymbol{r}) - a\, (4(\boldsymbol{R} - \boldsymbol{R}_0)^2 + (\boldsymbol{r} - \boldsymbol{r}_0)^2)].$$

However, the calculation of cross sections is independent of the particular form of the initial wave packets, and the error made in starting from a wave packet of the type $\Phi\varphi$ is negligible. This was implicitly assumed in the discussion of § X.7.

where $\psi_{\boldsymbol{b}}^{(d)}(\boldsymbol{r}, t)$ represents the divergent wave packet [eq. (X.20)]

$$\psi_{\boldsymbol{b}}^{(d)}(\boldsymbol{r}, t) \sim \mathrm{e}^{-\mathrm{i}\boldsymbol{k}\cdot\boldsymbol{b}-\mathrm{i}Et/\hbar}\,\chi[\boldsymbol{u}(r-vt)+\boldsymbol{s}-\boldsymbol{b}]\,f(\theta, \varphi)\,\frac{\mathrm{e}^{\mathrm{i}kr}}{r}. \quad \text{(XIV.49)}$$

Since we are working in the center-of-mass system, the wave packet $\Phi(\boldsymbol{R}, t)$ remains concentrated at the origin and the cross section $\sigma^{(1)}(\Omega)$ for the scattering of particle 1 in the direction $\Omega = (\theta, \varphi)$ is equal to the cross section for the scattering of the relative particle in the same direction, i.e. (§ X.6)

$$\sigma^{(1)}(\Omega) = |f(\theta, \varphi)|^2. \quad \text{(XIV.50)}$$

The cross section $\sigma^{(2)}(\Omega)$, for the scattering of particle 2 in the direction Ω is equal to the cross section for the scattering of the relative particle in the opposite direction, i.e.

$$\sigma^{(2)}(\Omega) = |f(\pi-\theta, \varphi+\pi)|^2. \quad \text{(XIV.51)}$$

When the two particles are identical, two important modifications of this treatment are required:

(a) the detectors no longer distinguish between particles 1 and 2, and consequently the cross section $\sigma(\Omega)$ must be redefined;

(b) the function $\Psi_{\boldsymbol{b}}$ must be properly symmetrized.

Modification (a) is not peculiar to Quantum Mechanics. Let us define $\sigma(\Omega)$ as the number of particles (1 and 2) emitted into the solid angle $(\Omega, \Omega+\mathrm{d}\Omega)$ per unit time and per unit incident flux, i.e. [cf. eq. (XIV.5)]

$$\sigma(\Omega) = \sigma^{(1)}(\Omega)+\sigma^{(2)}(\Omega). \quad \text{(XIV.52)}$$

Note that with this definition

$$\sigma^{(\mathrm{tot})} = \tfrac{1}{2}\int \sigma(\Omega)\,\mathrm{d}\Omega \quad \text{(XIV.53)}$$

if we retain the usual definition of the total cross section $\sigma^{(\mathrm{tot})}$, namely the number of particles eliminated from the incident beam per unit time and per unit incident flux.

Modification (b), on the other hand, is a specifically quantum effect. The properly symmetrized wave packet which reproduces the same initial conditions as $\Psi_{\boldsymbol{b}}(\boldsymbol{R}, \boldsymbol{r}, t)$ is, as will now be shown, given by the expression

$$\hat{\Psi}_{\boldsymbol{b}}(\boldsymbol{R}, \boldsymbol{r}, t) = \frac{1}{\sqrt{2}}[\Psi_{\boldsymbol{b}}(\boldsymbol{R}, \boldsymbol{r}, t) \pm \Psi_{\boldsymbol{b}}(\boldsymbol{R}, -\boldsymbol{r}, t)].$$

Before collision, i.e. for $t \ll 0$, this function $\hat{\Psi}_{\boldsymbol{b}}$ takes the form $\Phi(\mathbf{R}, t)\, \hat{\varphi}_{\boldsymbol{b}}(\boldsymbol{r}, t)$ where [eq. (XIV.47)]

$$\hat{\varphi}_{\boldsymbol{b}}(\boldsymbol{r}, t) = \mathrm{e}^{-\mathrm{i}\boldsymbol{k}\cdot\boldsymbol{b}-\mathrm{i}Et/\hbar} \frac{1}{\sqrt{2}} [\chi(\boldsymbol{r}-\boldsymbol{v}t-\boldsymbol{b})\, \mathrm{e}^{\mathrm{i}\boldsymbol{k}\cdot\boldsymbol{r}} \pm \chi(-\boldsymbol{r}-\boldsymbol{v}t-\boldsymbol{b})\, \mathrm{e}^{-\mathrm{i}\boldsymbol{k}\cdot\boldsymbol{r}}]$$

$\Phi\hat{\varphi}$ is thus the sum of two waves. The first represents the initial state of a collision in the center-of-mass system where particle 1 impinges upon particle 2 with the relative velocity $\boldsymbol{v}$ and the impact parameter $\boldsymbol{b}$; the second represents the state in which the roles of particles 1 and 2 are interchanged. Since these two waves do not overlap (since $t \ll 0$) and since both are of norm $\frac{1}{2}$, $\Phi\hat{\varphi}$ is a wave function of norm 1 representing, like $\Phi\varphi$, two particles impinging upon one another in their center-of-mass system with relative velocity $\boldsymbol{v}$ and impact parameter $\boldsymbol{b}$.

After collision $\hat{\Psi}_{\boldsymbol{b}}$, like $\Psi_{\boldsymbol{b}}$, takes the form of a sum of two terms [cf. eq. (XIV.48)]. The first, $\Phi\hat{\varphi}$, represents the transmitted wave and does not enter into the calculation of the cross section; the second, $\Phi\hat{\psi}^{(d)}$, represents the scattered wave and is obtained from $\Phi\psi^{(d)}$ by effecting upon $\psi^{(d)}$ the same operation of symmetrization as was used to pass from $\Psi_{\boldsymbol{b}}$ to $\hat{\Psi}_{\boldsymbol{b}}$:

$$\hat{\psi}_{\boldsymbol{b}}{}^{(d)}(\boldsymbol{r}, t) = \frac{1}{\sqrt{2}} [\psi_{\boldsymbol{b}}{}^{(d)}(\boldsymbol{r}, t) \pm \psi_{\boldsymbol{b}}{}^{(d)}(-\boldsymbol{r}, t)].$$

Going back to the asymptotic expression (XIV.49), we see that the passage from $\Phi\psi^{(d)}$ to $\Phi\hat{\psi}^{(d)}$ is accomplished by replacing the scattering amplitude $f(\theta, \varphi)$ by the symmetrized amplitude

$$\hat{f}(\theta, \varphi) = \frac{1}{\sqrt{2}} [f(\theta, \varphi) \pm f(\pi-\theta, \varphi+\pi)].$$

From the expression for the scattered wave packets we deduce the scattering cross section in the same way as when the particles are distinguishable. This gives

$$\sigma^{(1)}(\Omega) = |\hat{f}(\theta, \varphi)|^2 = \tfrac{1}{2} |f(\theta, \varphi) \pm f(\pi-\theta, \varphi+\pi)|^2$$
$$\sigma^{(2)}(\Omega) = |\hat{f}(\pi-\theta, \varphi+\pi)|^2 = \sigma^{(1)}(\Omega)$$

whence, in accordance with definition (XIV.52),

$$\sigma(\Omega) = 2\, |\hat{f}(\theta, \varphi)|^2 = |f(\theta, \varphi) \pm f(\pi-\theta, \varphi+\pi)|^2. \qquad \text{(XIV.54)}$$

Recall that the scattering amplitude is the coefficient of the outgoing wave in the stationary solution of the Schrödinger equation

$$\frac{\hbar^2}{m}(\triangle + k^2)\,\psi(\mathbf{r}) = V(\mathbf{r})\,\psi(\mathbf{r})$$

that has the asymptotic form

$$e^{i\mathbf{k}\cdot\mathbf{r}} + f(\theta, \varphi)\frac{e^{ikr}}{r}.$$

The symmetrized scattering amplitude $\hat{f}(\theta, \varphi)$ is equal to $\sqrt{2}$ times the even part of $f(\theta, \varphi)$ or to $\sqrt{2}$ times the odd part of $f(\theta, \varphi)$, according as the particles are bosons or fermions. If V is a central potential, the even part of $f(\theta)$ is the sum of contributions from partial waves of even order, the odd part the sum of contributions of partial waves of odd order. At energies sufficiently low that the only important contribution is from the s wave, two (spinless) fermions are hardly scattered by one another at all, while two bosons have a scattering cross section four times greater than if they were distinguishable (the scattering amplitude is multiplied by $\sqrt{2}$ and the cross section is equal to twice the squared modulus of this symmetrized amplitude; the combination of these two effects gives the factor 4).

10. Collision of two Protons

The treatment given in the preceding paragraph can easily be extended to the collision of two identical particles with spin. As an example we consider the collision of two protons, assuming a central interaction potential. The total spin is a constant of the motion, but the interaction may differ in the singlet and triplet states; let $f_s(\theta)$ and $f_t(\theta)$ denote the corresponding (un-symmetrized) scattering amplitudes.

Since protons are fermions, the wave function describing a two-proton system must be antisymmetrical in the interchange of the two particles. If this function represents a triplet state, it will be symmetrical in the exchange of the spins, hence antisymmetrical in the exchange of $\mathbf{r}^{(1)}$ and $\mathbf{r}^{(2)}$, and the symmetrized scattering amplitude is

$$\hat{f}_t(\theta) = \frac{1}{\sqrt{2}}\left[f_t(\theta) - f_t(\pi - \theta)\right].$$

The cross section for mutual scattering of protons in the triplet state is therefore

$$\sigma_t(\Omega) = 2\,|\hat{f}_t(\theta)|^2 = |f_t(\theta) - f_t(\pi-\theta)|^2.$$

If this function represents a singlet state, it will be antisymmetrical in the exchange of the spins, hence symmetrical in the exchange of the spatial coordinate, and the symmetrized scattering amplitude is

$$\hat{f}_s(\theta) = \frac{1}{\sqrt{2}}\,[f_s(\theta) + f_s(\pi-\theta)].$$

The cross section for mutual scattering of two protons in the singlet state is therefore

$$\sigma_s(\Omega) = 2\,|\hat{f}_s(\theta)|^2 = |f_s(\theta) + f_s(\pi-\theta)|^2.$$

If the target and the incoming beam are both composed of unpolarized protons, in each collision there will be a random distribution of the spins of the incident and struck particles. Since the space of the triplet states has three dimensions, and that of singlet states one, the total spin of the initial state has a probability $\frac{3}{4}$ of being triplet and $\frac{1}{4}$ of being singlet; therefore

$$\begin{aligned}\sigma(\Omega) &= \tfrac{3}{4}\sigma_t(\Omega) + \tfrac{1}{4}\sigma_s(\Omega)\\ &= \tfrac{3}{4}\,|f_t(\theta) - f_t(\pi-\theta)|^2 + \tfrac{1}{4}\,|f_s(\theta) + f_s(\pi-\theta)|^2.\end{aligned} \qquad \text{(XIV.55)}$$

If in addition the forces are independent of spin

$$f_s(\theta) = f_t(\theta) = f(\theta),$$

and we find:

$$\sigma(\Omega) = |f(\theta)|^2 + |f(\pi-\theta)|^2 - \tfrac{1}{2}\,[f^*(\theta)\,f(\pi-\theta) + f(\theta)\,f^*(\pi-\theta)]. \qquad \text{(XIV.56)}$$

In particular, if we are at sufficiently low energies that nuclear forces can be neglected and $V(r)$ treated as a repulsive Coulomb potential e^2/r, the amplitude $f(\theta)$ will be given by formula (XI.33) and the scattering cross section by the *Mott formula*

$$\sigma(\Omega) = \left(\frac{e^2}{4E}\right)^2 \left[\sin^{-4}\frac{\theta}{2} + \cos^{-4}\frac{\theta}{2} - \sin^{-2}\frac{\theta}{2}\cos^{-2}\frac{\theta}{2}\cos\left(\frac{e^2}{\hbar v}\ln\left(\tan^2\frac{\theta}{2}\right)\right)\right], \qquad \text{(XIV.57)}$$

in which E is the energy in the center-of-mass system and v the relative velocity of the two protons. It is instructive to compare this with the Rutherford formula [eq. (XI.36)].

A classical calculation would give only the first two terms of the Mott formula:

$$\sigma_{\mathrm{cl}}(\Omega) = \left(\frac{e^2}{4E}\right)^2 \left[\sin^{-4}\frac{\theta}{2} + \cos^{-4}\frac{\theta}{2}\right].$$

The third term is due to the purely quantum effect of interference between the scattering amplitudes $f(\theta)$ and $f(\pi-\theta)$. When $e^2/\hbar v \gg 1$ it oscillates rapidly about 0, the more rapidly as we move away from the angle $\theta = \frac{1}{2}\pi$ (in either direction). In the limit $\hbar \to 0$, these oscillations, while maintaining the same amplitude, become increasingly rapid, so that the average value of $\sigma(\Omega)$, taken over a small but non-zero solid angle $\varrho(\Omega)$, tends to the cross section $\sigma_{\mathrm{cl}}(\Omega)$.

11. Statistics of Atomic Nuclei

An atomic nucleus may in many problems be treated as a particle endowed with a certain spin j.

In the domain of atomic physics this is an excellent approximation. An atomic nucleus is an assembly of $\mathscr{N}$ nucleons: Z protons and N neutrons ($\mathscr{N} = Z + N$), whose dynamical variables are functions of the fundamental variables of its $\mathscr{N}$ constituents. Let $\mathbf{R}$ and $\mathbf{P}$ be the position and momentum of the center of mass (cf. § IX.13) and let ϱ denote the ensemble of the internal variables—nucleon spins and relative positions and momenta of nucleons with respect to one another. Among these we have notably the total angular momentum $\mathbf{j}$ of the internal variables, the so-called *spin of the nucleus*: $\mathbf{j}$ is the sum of the $\mathscr{N}$ individual nucleon spins and the $(\mathscr{N}-1)$ relative orbital angular momenta; according to the law for the addition of angular momenta, j may take integral or half-integral values according as $\mathscr{N}$ is even or odd.

In the absence of an external field, the motion of the center of mass separates out, and the Hamiltonian of the system becomes the sum of two terms: the kinetic energy of the center of mass $\mathbf{P}^2/2M$ (M is the total mass of the nucleus) and the internal energy $h(\varrho)$ comprising the kinetic energy of the nucleons and their energy of mutual interaction. h has a certain number of bound states. We denote by ε_0 the eigenvalue corresponding to the ground state. Since the forces between nucleons are invariant under rotation, $h(\varrho)$ commutes with the three components of $\mathbf{j}$ (cf. Ch. XIII). Each eigenvalue of its discrete spectrum corresponds to a definite value j of the spin and has a degeneracy of order $(2j+1)$. Henceforth,

j will denote the spin of the ground state, μ the possible values of j_z ($\mu = -j, -j+1, ..., +j$) and χ_μ the eigenfunction for the ground state of angular momentum $(j\mu)$:

$$h(\varrho)\,\chi_\mu = \varepsilon_0\,\chi_\mu \qquad j_z\,\chi_\mu = \mu\,\chi_\mu.$$

The $(2j+1)$ vectors χ_μ differ only in their orientation. They can be obtained one from another by repeated application of j_+ and j_-, and form a possible basis for the representation of the vector operator $\mathbf{j}$. Nuclear radii are of the order of 10^{-13} to 10^{-12} cm, and consequently the average inter-nucleon distance in a nucleus in the state χ_μ is a distance of that order. So long as the nucleus remains in its ground state the wave function of the system is of the form $\sum_\mu \psi(\mathbf{R}, \mu)\,\chi_\mu$ and we are able to treat it as a particle of spin j whose wave function in the $\{\mathbf{R}, j_z\}$ representation is $\psi(\mathbf{R}, \mu)$ since $h(\varrho)$ can be replaced in the Hamiltonian by the constant ε_0 and $\psi(\mathbf{R}, \mu)$ evolves in time like the wave function of a free particle of mass M (to within a constant phase factor without physical significance).

If the nucleus is placed in an external field, for example an electric field with potential $V(\mathbf{r})$, the Hamiltonian will include, in addition to the terms already mentioned, terms for the interaction of the Z protons with the external field. It may now be only approximately treated as a particle of spin j, for the Hamiltonian no longer commutes with $h(\varrho)$. It remains, however, an excellent approximation if the field varies little over distances of the order of a nuclear radius, since one can then replace the value of the field at each proton by its value at the center of mass; the external interaction then becomes $ZeV(\mathbf{R})$ and the Hamiltonian has eigenstates of the form $\sum_\mu \psi(\mathbf{R}, \mu)\,\chi_\mu$, where $\psi(\mathbf{R}, \mu)$ is a stationary state of a particle of mass M, spin j and charge Ze in the electric potential [1] $V(\mathbf{R})$.

Consider a system of n nuclei, all in their ground state. It is a perfectly justifiable approximation to treat each as a particle of given spin so long as they remain sufficiently far apart, as is the case in a molecule or a solid. If we denote by $\mathbf{R}^{(i)}$ the position of the ith nucleus and by $\mu^{(i)}$ the z-component of its spin, the wave function of the system is a certain function of the $\mathbf{R}^{(i)}$ and the $\mu^{(i)}$, whose motion is determined by a certain Hamiltonian that depends on the variables $\mathbf{R}^{(i)}$, $\mathbf{P}^{(i)}$ and $\mathbf{j}^{(i)}$.

---

[1] The first corrections to this approximation preserve this picture of the nucleus; they consist in attributing to it a quadrupole moment (if $j \geqslant 1$) which can be expressed as a function of the components of $\mathbf{j}$, thus leading to a coupling of the nuclear spin with the external field.

Let us examine to what extent this simplified description will be affected by the symmetrization postulate. We may expect that symmetrization will be involved only when some of the nuclei are identical. This can be proved by an argument analogous to the one of § 8. Two different nuclei are distinguishable particles in spite of the fact that their constituents, neutrons and protons, are identical.

Let us therefore consider a system of two identical nuclei of spin j. We describe the state of the system by the wave function

$$\psi(\mathbf{R}^{(1)}, \mu^{(1)};\ \mathbf{R}^{(2)}, \mu^{(2)}).$$

The interchange of the two nuclei is the operation P defined by

$$P\psi = \psi(\mathbf{R}^{(2)}, \mu^{(2)};\ \mathbf{R}^{(1)}, \mu^{(1)}).$$

In actual fact the system contains $2Z$ protons and $2N$ neutrons and its dynamical state is obtained by antisymmetrizing with respect to the protons and with respect to the neutrons the vector

$$\Psi = \sum_{\mu_1\mu_2} \psi(\mathbf{R}^{(1)}, \mu_1;\ \mathbf{R}^{(2)}, \mu_2)\, \chi^{(1)}_{\mu_1}\, \chi^{(2)}_{\mu_2}.$$

The operation P consists in interchanging the protons and the neutrons of the first nucleus with the protons and the neutrons of the second, in all $\mathcal{N}$ elementary interchanges; since in each of these the correctly antisymmetrized state vector changes sign, we can deduce that

$$P\Psi = (-)^{\mathcal{N}}\, \Psi,$$

and that therefore

$$P\psi = (-)^{\mathcal{N}}\, \psi.$$

This may easily be generalized to a system containing more than two identical nuclei. The wave function must be symmetrical or antisymmetrical with respect to permutations of the identical nuclei, according to whether these nuclei contain an even or an odd number of nucleons.

In other words, atomic nuclei are:

(a) *bosons* if they contain an *even* number of nucleons;

(b) *fermions* if they contain an *odd* number of nucleons.

These differences of statistics make a spectacular appearance in many phenomena where purely nuclear effects would seem to be unimportant. Such is the case with the remarkable properties of liquid helium (He^4) at very low temperatures. He^4 obeys Bose–Einstein statistics; the isotope He^3 obeys Fermi–Dirac statistics and behaves at these temperatures in a fundamentally different way.

Another example, to which we shall presently return (§ XVIII.17), is provided by the band spectrum of homonuclear diatomic molecules.

12. Complex Atoms. Central Field Approximation

The Pauli principle has a profound effect on the spectra of complex atoms.

In the absence of an external field, the Hamiltonian of an atom is independent of the spins of its Z electrons and is given by equation (XIII.71). To be exact, one should add terms for the spin-orbit interaction, but these can be neglected for the purpose of the present discussion. Except for the special case of the hydrogen atom ($Z=1$), the eigenvalue problem for such a Hamiltonian cannot be exactly solved.

For determining the stationary states of the atom, we often make use of the independent-particle or *central-field approximation*, according to which each electron moves independently of the others in a central potential $V(r)$ representing the attraction of the nucleus and the averaged repulsive effect of the other electrons. This last-mentioned effect clearly depends on the dynamical state of the electrons and thus a single potential $V(r)$ cannot, even approximately, account for the whole spectrum of the atom. However, if we restrict our study to the ground and first excited states, $V(r)$ can be fixed once and for all, and the more judicious the choice, the better the approximation. The overall effect of the electrons is to put up a screen about the nuclear Coulomb field, the effect becoming more appreciable as we move away from the nucleus: $V(r)$, which is of the form $-Ze^2/r$ near the origin, increasingly deviates from this pure Coulomb form with increasing r to become $-e^2/r$ in the asymptotic region. These semi-quantitative considerations suffice for the present. Further on we discuss two methods for systematically determining $V(r)$, the methods of Thomas–Fermi (§ 13), and Hartree–Fock (Ch. XVIII).

In the central field approximation, the Hamiltonian is written

$$H = h^{(1)} + h^{(2)} + \ldots + h^{(Z)}, \qquad \text{(XIV.58)}$$

where

$$h = \frac{\boldsymbol{p}^2}{2m} + V(r).$$

The eigenvectors of H are $Z \times Z$ Slater determinants which can be built up from a set of basis vectors for h. The eigenvalue of H corresponding to a given Slater determinant is equal to the sum of the energies of the Z individual states that appear in it. Thus the eigenvalue problem for H is easily solved once we have the solution of the eigenvalue problem for the individual Hamiltonian h.

h is the Hamiltonian of a particle of spin $\frac{1}{2}$ in a spin-independent central potential. The solution of the corresponding eigenvalue problem for a spinless particle has been given in Chapter IX. The only effect of the spin is to double the degeneracy of each level. h, $\boldsymbol{l}^2$, l_z and s_z constitute a complete set of commuting observables whose basis vectors $|n\, l\, m_l\, m_s\rangle$ are labelled with the four quantum numbers n, l, m_l, m_s: the spin quantum number, m_s, can take the values $\pm\,\frac{1}{2}$; n, the principle quantum number, has the same definition as in the hydrogen atom problem. (The number of nodes of the radial function is $n-l-1$.) Since the energy of each state, ε_{nl}, depends only on n and l, each individual level is $2(2l+1)$-fold degenerate.

The order of the levels ε_{nl} in the energy spectrum does not depend crucially on the form of the potential $V(r)$. For a given l they are in order of increasing n. If $V(r)$ was simply the Coulomb field of the nucleus, all the levels corresponding to a given value of n ($l=0$, 1, ..., $n-1$) would coincide (cf. Fig. XI.1, p. 418). The screening effect of the other electrons results in a raising of these levels that varies as the average distance of the electron from the nucleus, and which therefore increases with n and l. If we limit our study to the ground and first excited states, the order of succession of individual levels is nearly the same for all atoms, namely

1s	2s	2p	3s	3p	[4s, 3d]	4p	[5s, 4d]	5p	[6s, 4f, 5d]	6p	[7s, 5f, 6d]
2	2	6	2	6	2+10	6	2+10	6	2+14+10	6	2+14+10.

The bracketed levels nearly coincide and their order can vary from one atom to another. The number under each term is the degeneracy of the corresponding level.

To each set of Z different individual states there corresponds a Slater determinant, and therefore a stationary state of the atom. The energy of that state, being the sum of the energies of its constituent individual states, depends only on the number of electrons occupying each of the levels ε_{nl}. The specification of the occupation number of each individual level defines a *configuration*: with this definition, states belonging to the same configuration have the same energy.

Let ν_i be the number of electrons occupying the level ε_i. ν_i is at most equal to the degeneracy g_i of the level. If $\nu_i = g_i$, the electrons form a *closed shell*; if $\nu_i < g_i$, the shell is *incomplete*. There are

$$g_i!/\nu_i!\,(g_i - \nu_i)!$$

ways to distribute the ν_i electrons among the g_i individual states of the level, Therefore, nearly all configurations are degenerate – the only ones that are not are those formed exclusively of closed shells.

The ground state configuration is formed by putting the Z electrons in the lowest energy levels. They are thus distributed among a certain number h of shells, the first $(h-1)$ being filled, the last one generally not, except for very special values of Z ($Z = 2$, 4, 10, 12, 18 etc.).

Consider the carbon atom for example ($Z = 6$). In the ground state, shells 1s and 2s are closed, and the two remaining electrons are in the 2p shell. As there are $\binom{2}{6} = 15$ ways of distributing these 2 electrons among the 6 states available in that shell, the ground state of the carbon atom (in the independent particle approximation) is 15-fold degenerate. In the case of neon ($Z = 10$), the ground state is made up of the three closed shells 1s, 2s and 2p, and therefore is non-degenerate.

The electrons in the lowest shells are also those nearest the nucleus. The chemical properties of atoms are practically independent of the motion of these electrons. At the low energies involved in chemical reaction, the interactions between atoms depend essentially, if not exclusively, on the motion of the electrons in the outer shells, hence, two atoms having outside shells of similar electronic structure will have similar chemical properties. Thus the outside shell of each of the rare-air gases (Ne, A, Kr, Xe) is a closed p shell; that of each of the halogens (F, Cl, Br, I), a p shell lacking but one electron; and that of the alkalies, (Na, K, Rb, Cs), an s shell containing one electron with a closed p shell just below. Quite generally, the position of each chemical element in the Periodic Table can easily be predicted if we know the order of succession of the electronic shells [1]).

---

[1]) For further details of the quantum mechanical explanation of the chemical properties of atoms, see: M. Born, *Atomic Physics*, 6th ed. (Blackie, Glasgow, 1957); L. Pauling and E. B. Wilson, *Introduction to Quantum Mechanics* (McGraw-Hill, New York, 1935). On the general theory of atomic spectra, see: E. U.

13. The Thomas–Fermi Model of the Atom

When $Z \gg 1$, one can determine the ground state potential by applying a semi-classical method due to Thomas and Fermi.

Let $\varrho(\mathbf{r})$ be the probability density for finding an electron in the volume element $(\mathbf{r}, \mathbf{r}+\mathrm{d}\mathbf{r})$ when the atom is in its ground state. We suppose this function to be spherically symmetrical. It satisfies the normalization condition

$$4\pi \int_0^\infty \varrho(r)\, r^2\, \mathrm{d}r = Z. \qquad \text{(XIV.59)}$$

The Z electrons form about the nucleus a cloud of negative electricity of average density $-e\varrho(r)$. The charges in the atom thus give rise to an average electrical potential $\Phi(r)$ whose sources are:

(i) the point charge of the nucleus, situated at the origin and equal to Ze;

(ii) a continuous distribution of electricity of density $-e\varrho(r)$. In mathematical language, Φ is the solution of the Poisson equation

$$\Delta\Phi \equiv \frac{1}{r}\left(\frac{\mathrm{d}^2}{\mathrm{d}r^2}\, r\right)\Phi = 4\pi e\varrho \qquad \text{(XIV.60)}$$

that has the following behavior at the origin:

$$\lim_{r\to 0} r\Phi = Ze. \qquad \text{(XIV.61)}$$

In the limit $Z \gg 1$, the electric field due to an electron is small compared to that of all the others, and we can represent the potential acting on each electron in the independent particle approximation by $-e\Phi(r)$.

The ground state of the atom is the state in which the Z electrons occupy the Z lowest quantum states of a particle of mass m in the field $-e\Phi$. The density $\varrho(r)$ is thus the sum of the densities $|\psi|^2$ of the Z lowest levels. This implies that a functional relation exists between $\varrho(r)$ and the potential $-e\Phi$. To determine this relation, we turn to the following *"semi-classical" approximation.*

In the classical limit, the number of stationary states in the energy

---

Condon and G. H. Shortly, *The Theory of Atomic Spectra*, 4th ed. (Cambridge University Press, 1957); G. Racah, Phys. Rev. **62** (1942) 438 and **63** (1943) 367.

band $(\varepsilon, \varepsilon+\delta\varepsilon)$ is proportional to the volume occupied by this band in the phase space of the corresponding classical particle; the proportionality factor, $2/h^3$, is double that given in § VI.11, owing to the electron having two spin states. When the Z lowest quantum states are occupied, the energy distribution of the electrons in the atom is thus the same as that of a statistical mixture of Z classical electrons having a density in phase space $n(\mathbf{r}, \mathbf{p})$ equal to

$$n(\mathbf{r}, \mathbf{p}) = \begin{cases} \dfrac{2}{h^3} & \text{if} \quad \varepsilon \equiv \dfrac{p^2}{2m} - e\Phi < \varepsilon_0 \\ 0 & \text{if} \quad \varepsilon > \varepsilon_0 . \end{cases} \tag{XIV.62}$$

ε_0 is the energy of the highest level occupied. Since the zero of energy may be arbitrarily fixed, we put $\varepsilon_0 = 0$.

In the spirit of the classical approximation, we assume that the electrons have the same spatial distribution as this classical statistical mixture:

$$\varrho(r) = \int n(\mathbf{r}, \mathbf{p})\, \mathrm{d}\mathbf{p} = \frac{2}{h^3} \int_{\varepsilon<0} \mathrm{d}\mathbf{p}.$$

Replacing ε by its expression in terms of $\mathbf{p}$ and Φ, we find, after a simple integration,

$$\varrho(r) = \begin{cases} \dfrac{8\pi}{3h^3}\,(2me\Phi)^{3/2} & \text{if} \quad \Phi > 0 \\ 0 & \text{if} \quad \Phi < 0 . \end{cases} \tag{XIV.63}$$

Substitution of (XIV.63) into the right-hand side of (XIV.60) gives a second-order differential equation for Φ. With (XIV.59) and (XIV.61) the function is thereby completely defined. Relations (XIV.61), (XIV.63), (XIV.59), and (XIV.62) are the fundamental relations of the Thomas–Fermi model.

To deduce Φ and ϱ from these relations, it is convenient to make the following changes of variable and function:

$$r = Z^{-1/3}\, bx \qquad \Phi = \frac{Ze}{r}\,\chi, \tag{XIV.64}$$

where

$$b = \frac{1}{2}\left(\frac{3\pi}{4}\right)^{2/3} \frac{\hbar^2}{me^2} \simeq 0.5 \times 10^{-8} \text{ cm}. \tag{XIV.65}$$

From (XIV.63) we get ϱ as a function of the dimensionless quantities χ and x:

$$\varrho = \begin{cases} \dfrac{Z^2}{4\pi b^3}\left(\dfrac{\chi}{x}\right)^{3/2} & \text{if} \quad \chi > 0 \\ 0 & \text{if} \quad \chi < 0. \end{cases} \qquad \text{(XIV.66)}$$

The fundamental equation (XIV.60) is equivalent to the equation

$$\frac{d^2\chi}{dx^2} = \begin{cases} x^{-1/2}\,\chi^{3/2} & \text{if} \quad \chi > 0 \\ 0 & \text{if} \quad \chi < 0. \end{cases} \qquad \text{(XIV.67)}$$

Condition (XIV.61) gives $\chi(0)=1$. From eq. (XIV.67), $\chi(x)$ obviously has at most one zero in the interval $(0, \infty)$; if x_0 is the position of this zero, χ will be positive in the interval $(0, x_0)$ and negative in the interval (x_0, ∞). Hence, taking into account (XIV.64), (XIV.66) and (XIV.67), (XIV.59) becomes

$$1 = \int_0^{x_0} \sqrt{x}\,\chi^{3/2}\,dx = \int_0^{x_0} x\,\chi''\,dx = x\,\chi' - \chi\Big|_0^{x_0} = x_0\,\chi'(x_0) + 1.$$

This condition requires the derivative χ' to vanish at the same point as does χ itself, which means that the point in question must be at infinity.

Thus, $\chi(x)$ is the solution of

$$\chi'' = x^{-1/2}\,\chi^{3/2} \qquad \text{(XIV.68)}$$

that satisfies the conditions

$$\chi(0) = 1 \qquad \chi(\infty) = 0. \qquad \text{(XIV.69)}$$

$\chi(x)$ must be found by numerical integration, and is given in Fig. XIV.1. Knowing $\chi(x)$, we can find $\varrho(r)$ and $\Phi(r)$.

For the classical approximation to be justified, a large majority of the Z individual electron states must be in the "large quantum number region" i.e. $Z \gg 1$. For a given atom, the electron density $\varrho(r)$ and the electrostatic potential $\Phi(r)$ given by the Thomas–Fermi model are those which obtain in the limit when the quantum of action $\hbar$ and the charge $(-e)$ for each electron become infinitesimal while the number of electrons Z becomes infinite, the characteristic

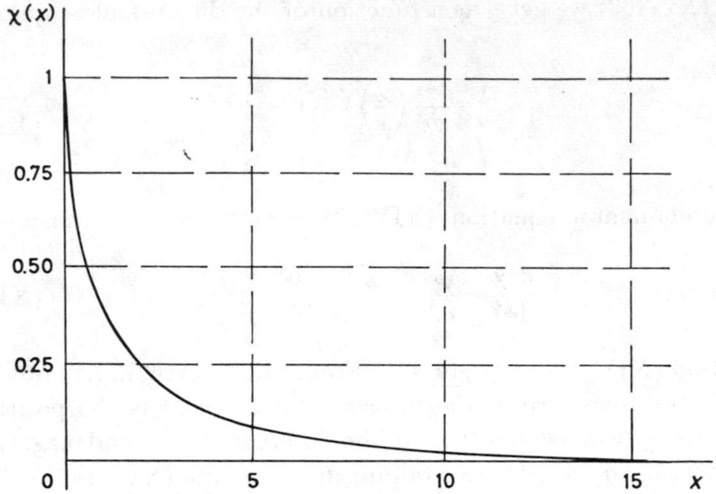

Fig. XIV.1. The Thomas–Fermi $\chi(x)$ function

$\chi'' = x^{-1/2}\chi^{3/2}, \qquad \chi(0) = 1, \qquad \chi(\infty) = 0$

for any value of Z, using eqs. (XIV.64–66).

length $\hbar^2/me^2$ and the total charge of the electronic cloud $(-Ze)$ remaining constant [1]).

The Thomas–Fermi model permits an estimation of the atomic radius. This quantity needs to be defined, since the electronic density becomes zero only at infinity and therefore the atom is not an object occupying a well-defined region in space. By atomic radius we shall mean the radius $R(\alpha)$ of the sphere centered at the origin and containing a given fraction $(1-\alpha)$ of the Z atomic electrons. Thus, according to this definition,

$$(1-\alpha)\,Z = 4\pi \int_0^R \varrho(r)\,r^2\,\mathrm{d}r.$$

We put

$$R(\alpha) = Z^{-1/3}\,b\,X(\alpha).$$

[1]) The Thomas–Fermi method over-estimates the electron density near the origin $(r \lesssim b/Z)$, and also in the asymptotic region $(r \gg b)$; at the origin $\varrho(r)$ diverges like $r^{-3/2}$ instead of remaining finite, at infinity it goes to zero like r^{-6}, rather than exponentially.

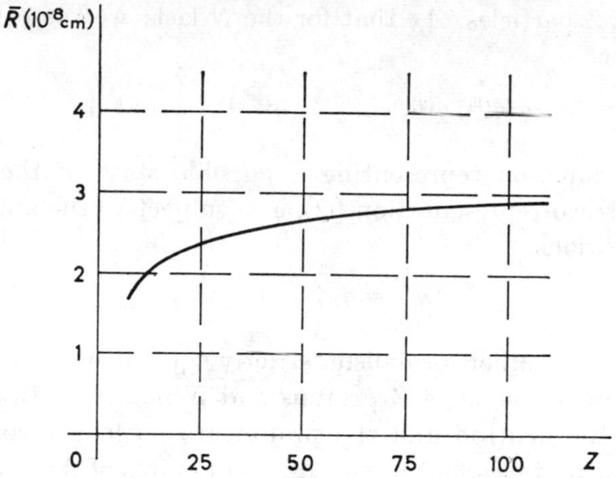

Fig. XIV.2. Z dependence of the radius $\bar{R}$ of the Thomas–Fermi atom:

$$4\pi \int_0^{\bar{R}} \varrho(R)\, r^2\, \mathrm{d}r = Z - 1.$$

A brief calculation, with use of (XIV.64), (XIV.66), and (XIV.68), results in the following equation for X:

$$\chi(X) - X\,\chi'(X) = \alpha.$$

This equation must be numerically solved.

If we adopt the same value of α for all atoms, X will be the same for them all, and the atomic radius will be proportional to $Z^{-1/3}$.

For $\alpha = 1/Z$, the corresponding radius

$$\bar{R} \equiv R\left(\frac{1}{Z}\right) = Z^{-1/3}\, b\, X\left(\frac{1}{Z}\right)$$

is the radius of the sphere containing all but one of the electrons. Figure XIV.2 gives $\bar{R}$ as a function of Z; observe that it is practically independent of Z ($\bar{R} \simeq 2$–3×10^{-8} cm).

14. Nucleon Systems and Isotopic Spin

Let us consider a system of Z protons and N neutrons. The motion of the system will be governed by a certain Hamiltonian H. Neutrons and protons are similar particles, and to distinguish between them we shall number the protons from 1 to Z and the neutrons from $Z+1$ to $Z+N \equiv \mathcal{N}$; A_Z will denote the antisymmetrizing operator for the first Z particles, A_N that for the N last; we keep the notation of § 2–4. Let

$$\varphi(q^{(1)}, q^{(2)}, \dots, q^{(Z)}, q^{(Z+1)}, \dots, q^{(\mathcal{N})})$$

be a wave function representing a possible state of the system in the symmetrical representation $\{Q\}$. φ is subject to the antisymmetrization conditions

$$A_N \varphi = \varphi \qquad A_Z \varphi = \varphi. \tag{XIV.70}$$

There exists another formalism, strictly equivalent to the foregoing, to describe this system of Z protons and N neutrons. In this second formalism, the neutron and the proton are no longer considered as two different particles, but as two different states of the same particle, the *nucleon*. The system in question is described as a system of $\mathcal{N}$ nucleons, of which Z are in the proton state and N in the neutron state; the $\mathcal{N}$ nucleons are then identical fermions and the states of the system are antisymmetrical with respect to permutations of these $\mathcal{N}$ identical fermions. The object of the present paragraph is to describe this new formalism and to prove its equivalence to the ordinary one.

To distinguish between the proton state and the neutron state, each nucleon must be assigned a new dynamical variable – its charge – admitting of two possible values; we shall denote the corresponding eigenstates by ϖ and ν, ϖ representing the proton state, ν the neutron state. The charge space of the nucleon is a two-dimensional space like spin-space. We can therefore define operators for it which are analogous to those introduced for spin-space and which have the same mathematical properties. Consider in particular the three Pauli matrices; in the representation where ϖ and ν are basis vectors, these matrices will represent a vector operator $\boldsymbol{\tau} \equiv (\tau_1, \tau_2, \tau_3)$ in charge space analogous to the vector $\boldsymbol{\sigma} \equiv (\sigma_x, \sigma_y, \sigma_z)$. The vector

$$\mathbf{t} = \tfrac{1}{2}\boldsymbol{\tau} \tag{XIV.71}$$

is the analogue of the spin $\mathbf{s}$, and is called the *isotopic spin* of the nucleon. We see that

$$t_3 \varpi = \tfrac{1}{2}\tau_3 \varpi = \tfrac{1}{2}\varpi \qquad t_3 \nu = \tfrac{1}{2}\tau_3 \nu = -\tfrac{1}{2}\nu.$$

The projectors Π_{ϖ} and Π_{ν}, onto the proton and neutron states respectively, are given by

$$\Pi_{\varpi} = \tfrac{1}{2}(1+\tau_3) \qquad \Pi_{\nu} = \tfrac{1}{2}(1-\tau_3) \tag{XIV.72}$$

and the operator representing the charge of the nucleon is given by

$$e\,\Pi_{\varpi} = \tfrac{1}{2}(1+\tau_3)\,e.$$

The product of the $\mathcal{N}$ individual charge spaces is the charge space $\mathscr{E}_{\mathrm{C}}$ for the system of $\mathcal{N}$ nucleons. The total charge of the system is represented by the operator

$$C \equiv \sum_{i=1}^{\mathcal{N}} e\,\Pi_{\varpi}^{(i)} = e(\tfrac{1}{2}\mathcal{N} + T_3), \tag{XIV.73}$$

T_3 being the third component of the *total isotopic spin*

$$\mathbf{T} = \sum_{i=1}^{\mathcal{N}} \mathbf{t}^{(i)}. \tag{XIV.74}$$

We obtain an orthonormal basis in $\mathscr{E}_{\mathrm{C}}$ by taking products of $\mathcal{N}$ ϖ- or ν-vectors. In particular the basis vector

$$\zeta = \varpi^{(1)}\,\varpi^{(2)} \dots \varpi^{(Z)}\,\nu^{(Z+1)} \dots \nu^{(\mathcal{N})}$$

represents the charge state in which the first Z particles are protons and the last N neutrons. In what follows we shall deal only with states of charge $C = Ze$, i.e. with

$$T_3 = \tfrac{1}{2}(Z-N).$$

We can construct $(\mathcal{N}!/Z!\,N!)$ basis vectors corresponding to this eigenvalue. A typical one of these,

$$\zeta_{\alpha} = \varpi^{(\alpha_1)}\,\varpi^{(\alpha_2)} \dots \varpi^{(\alpha_Z)}\,\nu^{(\alpha_{Z+1})} \dots \nu^{(\alpha_{\mathcal{N}})},$$

represents the state in which the Z particles $\alpha_1, \alpha_2, \dots, \alpha_Z$ are protons, and the others neutrons.

The ket vectors for the system of $\mathcal{N}$ nucleons are the vectors of the space formed by taking the tensor product of $\mathscr{E}_{\mathrm{C}}$ with the space $\mathscr{E}_0$ of the other dynamical variables. When we permute these $\mathcal{N}$ nucleons we effect the same permutation on charge variables and the other variables; if P_{C} represents a given permutation of the charges,

P_0 the same permutation of the other variables, the overall permutation will be represented by the operator

$$P = P_0 P_C.$$

The antisymmetrizing operator for the system of $\mathcal{N}$ nucleons is

$$A = \frac{1}{\mathcal{N}!} \sum_P (-)^p P = \frac{1}{\mathcal{N}!} \sum_P (-)^p P_0 P_C. \qquad \text{(XIV.75)}$$

The states of the system corresponding to a total charge Ze are those vectors Φ of the space $\mathscr{E}_C \otimes \mathscr{E}_0$ that meet the antisymmetrization condition

$$A\Phi = \Phi \qquad \text{(XIV.76)}$$

and satisfy the equation

$$T_3 \Phi = \tfrac{1}{2}(Z-N)\Phi. \qquad \text{(XIV.77)}$$

We shall now show that there is a one-to-one correspondence between the vectors Φ subject to conditions (XIV.76) and (XIV.77), and the vectors φ of $\mathscr{E}_0$ subject to conditions (XIV.70), namely

$$|\Phi\rangle = \sqrt{\frac{\mathcal{N}!}{N!\,Z!}}\, A|\varphi\rangle\, |\zeta\rangle \qquad \text{(XIV.78)}$$

$$|\varphi\rangle = \sqrt{\frac{\mathcal{N}!}{N!\,Z!}}\, \langle\zeta|\Phi\rangle, \qquad \text{(XIV.79)}$$

and that this one-to-one correspondence conserves the scalar product.

Consider a vector $|\varphi\rangle$ obeying conditions (XIV.70). The corresponding $|\Phi\rangle$ obtained from (XIV.78) obviously satisfies (XIV.76), and also (XIV.77) since T_3 commutes with A and $T_3|\zeta\rangle = \frac{1}{2}(Z-N)\,|\zeta\rangle$.

We next show that the partial scalar product (XIV.79) gives back the vector $|\varphi\rangle$. With the aid of (XIV.75) and (XIV.78),

$$\begin{aligned}\sqrt{\frac{\mathcal{N}!}{N!\,Z!}}\, \langle\zeta|\Phi\rangle &= \sqrt{\frac{\mathcal{N}!}{N!\,Z!}}\, \langle\zeta|A|\Phi\rangle \\ &= \frac{1}{N!\,Z!} \sum_P (-)^p P_0|\varphi\rangle\, \langle\zeta|P_C|\zeta\rangle.\end{aligned} \qquad \text{(XIV.80)}$$

Now the $\mathcal{N}!$ permutations can be put into two groups. Those of the first group, F, permute the first Z particles among themselves and/or the last N particles among themselves; the $(N!\,Z!)$ permutations of

F leave the vector $|\zeta\rangle$ unchanged and multiply the vector $|\varphi\rangle$ by $(-)^f$:

$$\langle\zeta|F_C|\zeta\rangle = 1 \qquad F_0|\varphi\rangle = (-)^f|\varphi\rangle.$$

Those of the second group, G, take the vector ζ over into another of the vectors ζ_α; hence

$$\langle\zeta|G_C|\zeta\rangle = 0.$$

Thus the sum on the right-hand side of (XIV.80) has $(N!\,Z!)$ non-zero terms, each of which is equal to $|\varphi\rangle$, giving the desired result (XIV.79).

We easily see that the correspondence (XIV.78) conserves the scalar product, for if $|\Phi\rangle$ and $|X\rangle$ correspond respectively to $|\varphi\rangle$ and $|\chi\rangle$, then since

$$|X\rangle = \sqrt{\frac{\mathcal{N}!}{N!\,Z!}}\,A|\chi\rangle\,|\zeta\rangle$$

and since $|\Phi\rangle$ obeys (XIV.76) and (XIV.78)

$$\langle X|\Phi\rangle = \sqrt{\frac{\mathcal{N}!}{N!\,Z!}}\,\langle\chi|\,\langle\zeta|\Phi\rangle = \langle\chi|\varphi\rangle.$$

It remains to show that the correspondence is of a one-to-one nature. Let $|\Phi\rangle$ be a vector subject to conditions (XIV.76) and (XIV.77) and $|\varphi\rangle$ the vector associated by (XIV.79). In view of (XIV.77), $|\Phi\rangle$ is a linear combination of the vectors $|\zeta_\alpha\rangle$, the coefficients being vectors of $\mathscr{E}_0$:

$$|\Phi\rangle = \sqrt{\frac{\mathcal{N}!}{N!\,Z!}}\sum_\alpha |\varphi_\alpha\rangle\,|\zeta_\alpha\rangle.$$

$|\varphi\rangle$ is the coefficient of ζ in the sum on the right-hand side. A permutation of type F acting on Φ gives

$$F|\Phi\rangle = \sqrt{\frac{\mathcal{N}!}{N!\,Z!}}\sum_\alpha (F_0|\varphi_\alpha\rangle)\,(F_C|\zeta_\alpha\rangle). \qquad \text{(XIV.81)}$$

also

$$F|\Phi\rangle = (-)^f|\Phi\rangle = \sqrt{\frac{\mathcal{N}!}{N!\,Z!}}\sum_\alpha (-)^f\,|\varphi_\alpha\rangle\,|\zeta_\alpha\rangle. \qquad \text{(XIV.82)}$$

Now the action of F_C on one of the $|\zeta_\alpha\rangle$ is to transform it into another of the $|\zeta_\alpha\rangle$ and in particular it leaves $|\zeta\rangle$ invariant. Therefore, the coefficient of $|\zeta\rangle$ in the expansion of $F|\Phi\rangle$ is the coefficient of $F_C|\zeta\rangle$ on the right-hand side of (XIV.81). Equating this to the coefficient of $|\zeta\rangle$ in (XIV.82), we find

$$F_0|\varphi\rangle = (-)^f|\varphi\rangle.$$

which shows that the vector $|\varphi\rangle$ corresponding to $|\Phi\rangle$ does indeed have the antisymmetry properties (XIV.70). Q.E.D.

Any state of Z protons and N neutrons represented by a vector $|\varphi\rangle$ in the ordinary formalism, will be represented in the new formalism by the corresponding vector $|\Phi\rangle$. Since this is a one-to-one correspondence conserving the scalar product, the probability amplitudes calculated with the vectors of the new formalism are equal to the probability amplitudes calculated with those of the old – thus assuring the equivalence of the two formalisms. If a dynamical variable is represented in the ordinary formalism by a certain operator Q, it is represented in the new formalism by an operator $\hat{Q}$ of the space $\mathscr{E}_0 \otimes \mathscr{E}_C$; $\hat{Q}$ is symmetrical with respect to the $\mathscr{N}$ nucleons, it has the same eigenvalue spectrum as Q and its eigenstates can be obtained from those of Q by relation (XIV.78). $\hat{Q}$ is the symmetrical operator whose matrix elements satisfy the equation

$$\langle X|\hat{Q}|\Phi\rangle = \langle\chi|Q|\varphi\rangle. \tag{XIV.83}$$

As an example we construct the operator $\hat{H}$, assuming two-body forces between the nucleons.

The Hamiltonian is

$$H = K + V \tag{XIV.84}$$

where K is the total kinetic energy; if $k_p\,(\xi)$ and $k_n\,(\xi)$ represent the kinetic energy of a proton and neutron respectively, one has

$$K = K_p + K_n,$$

where

$$K_p = \sum_{i\leqslant Z} k_p{}^{(i)} \qquad K_n = \sum_{i<Z} k_n{}^{(i)}.$$

The total potential energy V has $\frac{1}{2}\mathscr{N}(\mathscr{N}-1)$ two-body interaction terms. There are $\frac{1}{2}Z(Z-1)$ proton-proton interaction terms

$$V_{pp} = \sum_{i<j\leqslant Z} v_{pp}^{(ij)},$$

$v_{pp}^{(ij)} \equiv v_{pp}\,(\xi^{(i)}, \xi^{(j)})$ denoting the interaction potential between protons

i and j; likewise there are ZN proton-neutron interaction terms

$$V_{\text{pn}} = \sum_{i \leqslant Z} \sum_{j > Z} v_{\text{pn}}^{(ij)},$$

and $\frac{1}{2}N(N-1)$ neutron-neutron interaction terms

$$V_{\text{nn}} = \sum_{j > i > Z} v_{\text{nn}}^{(ij)}.$$

The total potential energy is therefore

$$V = V_{\text{pp}} + V_{\text{pn}} + V_{\text{nn}}.$$

The operator $\hat{K}$ corresponding to K is

$$\hat{K} = \sum_{i=1}^{\mathscr{N}} (k_{\text{p}}{}^{(i)}\, \Pi_{\varpi}{}^{(i)} + k_{\text{n}}{}^{(i)}\, \Pi_{\nu}{}^{(i)}). \tag{XIV.85}$$

It is indeed symmetrical and commutes notably with A. To show that it satisfies (XIV.83), we return to the definitions of the vectors $|\Phi\rangle$ and $|X\rangle$ and the projectors Π_{ϖ} and Π_{ν}:

$$\begin{aligned} \frac{N!\, Z!}{\mathscr{N}!} \langle X|\hat{K}|\Phi\rangle &= \langle \chi\zeta|A\hat{K}A|\varphi\zeta\rangle \\ &= \langle \chi\zeta|\hat{K}A|\varphi\zeta\rangle \\ &= \langle \chi\zeta|KA|\varphi\zeta\rangle \end{aligned}$$

from which

$$\langle X|\hat{K}|\Phi\rangle = \sqrt{\frac{\mathscr{N}!}{N!\, Z!}} \langle \chi\zeta|K|\Phi\rangle.$$

Since K does not operate on the charge variables, the partial scalar product $\langle\zeta|K|\Phi\rangle$ is equal to the result of K operating on $\langle\zeta|\Phi\rangle$; applying (XIV.79) we find

$$\langle X|\hat{K}|\Phi\rangle = \langle \chi|K|\varphi\rangle.$$

In the same way, the operator corresponding to V is

$$\hat{V} = \hat{V}_{\text{pp}} + \hat{V}_{\text{pn}} + \hat{V}_{\text{nn}}, \tag{XIV.86}$$

where

$$\hat{V}_{\text{pp}} = \sum_{i<j\leqslant \mathscr{N}} v_{\text{pp}}^{(ij)}\, \Pi_{\varpi}{}^{(i)}\, \Pi_{\varpi}{}^{(j)} \tag{XIV.86a}$$

$$\hat{V}_{\text{pn}} = \sum_{i<j\leqslant \mathscr{N}} v_{\text{pn}}^{(ij)}\, [\Pi_{\varpi}{}^{(i)}\, \Pi_{\nu}{}^{(j)} + \Pi_{\nu}{}^{(i)}\, \Pi_{\varpi}{}^{(j)}] \tag{XIV.86b}$$

$$\hat{V}_{\text{nn}} = \sum_{i<j\leqslant \mathscr{N}} v_{\text{nn}}^{(ij)}\, \Pi_{\nu}{}^{(i)}\, \Pi_{\nu}{}^{(j)}. \tag{XIV.86c}$$

This can be verified by the same method as for $\hat{K}$.

The above theory for systems of neutrons and protons also applies to systems containing more than two types of fermions. Consider a system containing r types of similar but distinguishable fermions – n_1 fermions of type 1, n_2 fermions of type 2, ..., n_r fermions of type r. Rather than treat the different types of fermions as different particles, we may think of the r types as r separate states $|1\rangle, |2\rangle, ..., |r\rangle$ of the same fermion, and treat the system as a system of $n_1+n_2+...+n_r$ fermions of this one type of which n_1 are in the state $|1\rangle$, n_2 in the state $|2\rangle$, ..., n_r in the state $|r\rangle$. The equivalence of this "isotopic" formalism to the ordinary one can be demonstrated using the same methods as we have used for nucleon systems. These remarks all apply to boson systems as well if we everywhere replace the operation of antisymmetrization by symmetrization (Problem XIV.9).

15. Utility of Isotopic Spin. Charge Independence

Consider a system of $\mathcal{N}$ nucleons. So long as we are dealing with definite numbers Z and N of protons and neutrons respectively, it is *a priori* simpler to treat the protons and the neutrons as different particles (the ordinary formalism), rather than as nucleons in different charge states (the isotopic-spin formalism).

On the other hand, when dealing with phenomena in which the charge of the nuclear system is not conserved, the isotopic-spin formalism is indispensable. The classic example is β-decay. In the decay of a β^--radioactive nucleus, the number of nucleons remains constant but one of the neutrons is transformed into a proton. In the theory of this phenomenon one treats the nucleus as a system of $\mathcal{N}$ nucleons in interaction with the quantized electron and neutrino fields. The theory of β decay is outside the scope of this book; we mention it only as an example.

This apart, the principal interest of the isotopic spin formalism is due to the fact that nuclear interactions are practically independent of nucleon charge.

The neutron and proton masses are equal to within less than 0.2 %, and therefore the kinetic energy of a nucleon is practically independent of its charge:

$$k_{\mathrm{p}} = k_{\mathrm{n}} = k . \qquad \text{(XIV.87)}$$

In the measure that the purely electromagnetic interactions may be neglected [1]) the nucleon-nucleon potential is also nearly independent of charge.

$$v_{\mathrm{pp}} = v_{\mathrm{pn}} = v_{\mathrm{nn}} = v. \tag{XIV.88}$$

We shall examine the consequences of charge independence under the assumption that only two body forces act between the nucleons [2]).

In the ordinary formalism, the hypothesis of charge independence finds its expression in the following two properties of H:

(i) H does not depend on Z or N, but only on the total number of particles $\mathscr{N}$;

(ii) it is symmetrical with respect to permutations of these $\mathscr{N}$ particles, and not just with respect to permutations of the protons among themselves and/or the neutrons among themselves.

These properties are an immediate consequence of (XIV.87) and (XIV.88) for, if these hold, the Hamiltonian (XIV.84) takes the form

$$H = \sum_{i=1}^{\mathscr{N}} k^{(i)} + \sum_{i<j\leqslant \mathscr{N}} v^{(ij)}, \tag{XIV.89}$$

where $\sum\limits_{i<j\leqslant\mathscr{N}}$ indicates, as in eqs. (XIV.86*a*, *b*, *c*), the summation over all of the $\frac{1}{2}\mathscr{N}(\mathscr{N}-1)$ pairs (ij) of the set of $\mathscr{N}$ particles.

In the isotopic-spin formalism the charge-independence hypothesis is reflected in the Hamiltonian $\hat{H}$ being independent of the charge variables and we have simply

$$\hat{H} = H, \tag{XIV.90}$$

H on the right-hand side being considered as an operator in the space $\mathscr{E}_0 \otimes \mathscr{E}_{\mathrm{C}}$. This can be shown from the definition (XIV.83) of operators

---

[1]) Electromagnetic effects become predominant only for sufficiently large distances between the nucleons ($\gg 10^{-13}$ cm); at large distances v_{pn} and v_{nn} are practically zero, v_{pp} becomes simply the Coulomb repulsion of the two protons. For a discussion of the experimental evidence supporting charge independence, see Blatt and Weisskopf, *loc. cit.*, note 2, p. 576; D. H. Wilkinson, Phil. Mag. 1 (1956) 1031.

[2]) It is not necessary to make this restriction in order to show the equivalence of charge independence to the invariance property (XIV.91). It can be shown in the general case by application of the theorem of § 18, Appendix D.

in the isotopic spin formalism or by directly calculating expressions (XIV.85) and (XIV.86) for $\hat{K}$ and $\hat{V}$, assuming (XIV.87) and (XIV.88); the latter procedure gives for $\hat{V}$

$$\hat{V} = \sum_{i<j\leqslant\mathcal{N}} v^{(ij)} [\Pi_{\varpi}{}^{(i)} \Pi_{\varpi}{}^{(j)} + \Pi_{\varpi}{}^{(i)} \Pi_{\nu}{}^{(j)} + \Pi_{\nu}{}^{(i)} \Pi_{\varpi}{}^{(j)} + \Pi_{\nu}{}^{(i)} \Pi_{\nu}{}^{(j)}],$$

and since

$$\Pi_{\varpi}{}^{(i)} + \Pi_{\nu}{}^{(i)} = 1,$$

$$\hat{V} = \sum_{i<j\leqslant\mathcal{N}} v^{(ij)} = V.$$

Since $\hat{H}$ is independent of the charge variables, it commutes with all three components of the total isotopic spin:

$$[\hat{H}, \boldsymbol{T}] = 0. \tag{XIV.91}$$

We shall now show that the converse is also true, i.e. if $\hat{H}$ satisfies (XIV.91), it can be written in the form of an operator independent of the charge variables.

$\hat{H}$ is a certain function of the ordinary variables ξ and the charge variables τ of each of the particles; in view of our hypothesis regarding the nature of the forces, this function will be of the form

$$\hat{H} = \sum_{i=1}^{\mathcal{N}} \hat{k}^{(i)} + \sum_{i<j\leqslant\mathcal{N}} \hat{v}^{(ij)},$$

where $\hat{k}^{(i)}$ depends only on the variables i, and $\hat{v}^{(ij)}$ only on the variables i and j. However, isotopic spin has the same mathematical properties as ordinary spin, and in particular the components of the vectors $\boldsymbol{\tau}^{(i)}$ have all the properties of the Pauli matrices; it results [cf. eq. (XIII.78–79)] that any function $\hat{H}$ of the components of $\boldsymbol{\tau}^{(1)}, \ldots, \boldsymbol{\tau}^{(\mathcal{N})}$ can always be expressed as a linear function of these operators. Also, since $\hat{H}$ commutes with $\boldsymbol{T}$, it is invariant with respect to rotations in $\mathscr{E}_{\mathrm{C}}$ and is therefore a scalar function of the vectors $\boldsymbol{\tau}^{(1)}, \ldots, \boldsymbol{\tau}^{(\mathcal{N})}$. Thus $\hat{k}^{(i)}$ is a linear, scalar function of $\boldsymbol{\tau}^{(i)}$, hence independent of $\boldsymbol{\tau}^{(i)}$; $\hat{v}^{(ij)}$ is a linear scalar function of $\boldsymbol{\tau}^{(i)}$ and $\boldsymbol{\tau}^{(j)}$, hence necessarily of the form

$$\hat{v}^{(ij)} = a^{(ij)} + (\boldsymbol{\tau}^{(i)} \cdot \boldsymbol{\tau}^{(j)})\, b^{(ij)},$$

where $a^{(ij)}$ and $b^{(ij)}$ are functions of the orbital and spin variables alone. To complete the proof we need only to show that the action of $(\boldsymbol{\tau}^{(i)} \cdot \boldsymbol{\tau}^{(j)})$ on the *antisymmetrical* vectors of the space $\mathscr{E}_0 \otimes \mathscr{E}_{\mathrm{C}}$

is the same as that of an operator acting on the variables of $\mathscr{E}_0$ alone. $(\boldsymbol{\tau}^{(i)} \cdot \boldsymbol{\tau}^{(j)})$ is related to the operator $P_C{}^{(ij)}$ representing the transposition (ij) in charge space by the Dirac identity

$$P_C{}^{(ij)} = \tfrac{1}{2}(1 + \boldsymbol{\tau}^{(i)} \cdot \boldsymbol{\tau}^{(j)}). \qquad \text{(XIV.92)}$$

To establish (XIV.92) we introduce the isotopic spin of the pair (ij)

$$\mathbf{t}_{ij} = \mathbf{t}^{(i)} + \mathbf{t}^{(j)}.$$

Any state in charge space is the sum of a state $|1\rangle$ for which $t_{ij}=1$, and a state $|0\rangle$ for which $t_{ij}=0$. Any triplet state is symmetrical in i and j; any singlet state antisymmetrical in i and j. Thus

$$\begin{aligned} \mathbf{t}_{ij}{}^2 \,|1\rangle &= 2\,|1\rangle & \mathbf{t}_{ij}{}^2 \,|0\rangle &= 0 \\ P_C{}^{(ij)} \,|1\rangle &= \,|1\rangle & P_C{}^{(ij)} \,|0\rangle &= -\,|0\rangle, \end{aligned}$$

and consequently

$$P_C{}^{(ij)} = \mathbf{t}_{ij}{}^2 - 1.$$

From this we deduce (XIV.92) with the aid of the identity

$$\mathbf{t}_{ij}{}^2 = \tfrac{1}{2}(3 + \boldsymbol{\tau}^{(i)} \cdot \boldsymbol{\tau}^{(j)}).$$

It follows that

$$\boldsymbol{\tau}^{(i)} \cdot \boldsymbol{\tau}^{(j)} = 2P_C{}^{(ij)} - 1.$$

But in the space of the antisymmetrical vectors of $\mathscr{E}_0 \otimes \mathscr{E}_C$,

$$P^{(ij)} \equiv P_C{}^{(ij)}\, P_0{}^{(ij)} = -1.$$

Thus

$$P_C{}^{(ij)} = -\,P_0{}^{(ij)}$$

and the operator $\boldsymbol{\tau}^{(i)} \cdot \boldsymbol{\tau}^{(j)}$ may be replaced by

$$-2P_0{}^{(ij)} - 1,$$

which operates on the variables of ordinary space alone. Q.E.D.

The equivalence of charge-independence and rotational invariance in charge space is entirely general [1]). Since all the *mathematical* developments concerning rotations remain valid for the particular case of rotations in charge space (addition of isotopic spins, Wigner–Eckart theorem, selection rules, etc.), this equivalence provides a specially convenient method of taking into account the charge independence of nuclear forces.

---

[1]) Cf. footnote 2, p. 627.

EXERCISES AND PROBLEMS

1. The operator P associated with a permutation p of the N particles of a system of similar particles was defined in § 2 by its action on the basis vectors of a given symmetrical representation $\{Q\}$. Show that this definition does not depend on the representation chosen.

2. We denote by S_n, A_n the symmetrizing and antisymmetrizing operators for the particles 1, 2, ... , n and by S_{n-1}, A_{n-1} the symmetrizing and antisymmetrizing operators for the particles 1, 2, ... , $n-1$. Show that

$$S_n = \frac{1}{n}\,[1 + \sum_{i=1}^{n-1} P_{(in)}]\, S_{n-1} = \frac{1}{n}\, S_{n-1}\,[1 + \sum_{i=1}^{n-1} P_{(in)}]$$

$$A_n = \frac{1}{n}\,[1 - \sum_{i=1}^{n-1} P_{(in)}]\, A_{n-1} = \frac{1}{n}\, A_{n-1}[1 - \sum_{i=1}^{n-1} P_{(in)}].$$

3. Show that among the *symmetrical* observables of a system of N similar particles, there can be a complete set of commuting observables only if $N = 2$.

4. Find the proton-proton scattering cross section (in the center-of-mass system) when the incident proton is completely polarized in a given direction Ou (spin component along Ou equal to $+\frac{1}{2}$), and the target proton: (i) completely polarized in the same direction, (ii) completely polarized in the opposite direction (spin component along Ou equal to $-\frac{1}{2}$), (iii) non-polarized. Compare (XIV.56) with the expressions obtained in these three cases.

5. Expression (XIV.56) gives the scattering cross section for two fermions of spin $\frac{1}{2}$ having a spin-independent interaction. How must it be modified if the two identical particles are: (a) fermions of spin j; (b) bosons of spin j?

6. Calculate the average value $\langle r \rangle$ of the distance from the origin of each electron in the Thomas–Fermi model of the atom and compare with the numerical value of $\langle r \rangle$ for the hydrogen atom (use the integral $\int_0^\infty \chi(x)\mathrm{d}x \simeq 1.8$).

7. An atom of atomic number Z is p times ionized. Calculate the electronic density $\varrho(r)$ using the Thomas–Fermi model. Show that expression (XIV.66) for $\varrho(r)$ is still valid with the same definitions of b and x as in § 13 [eq. (XIV.64–65)] and that the function $\chi(x)$ figuring in that expression is the solution of equation (XIV.67) that vanishes at a certain point x_0 in the interval $(0, \infty)$ and satisfies the conditions

$$\chi(0) = 1 \qquad \chi'(x_0) = -\,p/Zx_0.$$

Examine the general behavior of the curve $\varrho(r)$ and of the electrostatic potential $\Phi(r)$.

8. We consider a system of Z electrons whose Hamiltonian is independent of the spins. Show that the energy spectrum for states having a definite value

M for the component S_z of total spin is the same (same positions and same degeneracy of levels) as that which we obtain if we treat the electrons of spin $\frac{1}{2}$ and those of spin $-\frac{1}{2}$ as different types of fermions and look for the states for which the $(\frac{1}{2}Z + M)$ first electrons have spin $\frac{1}{2}$ and the others spin $-\frac{1}{2}$.

9. Set up the "isotopic" formalism defined in § 14 for a system of $\mathcal{N}$ fermions of r similar but different types, namely n_1 fermions of type 1, n_2 fermions of type 2, ..., n_r fermions of type r $(n_1 + n_2 + \ldots + n_r = \mathcal{N})$. How must this formalism be modified if the $\mathcal{N}$ particles are bosons rather than fermions?

CHAPTER XV *)

INVARIANCE AND CONSERVATION THEOREMS. TIME REVERSAL

1. Introduction

This chapter is devoted to a systematic examination of the invariance properties that the equations of motion of a physical system may have with respect to certain transformations and the consequences of these in terms of the behavior of the system.

Certain mathematical complements are given in section I.

In section II we examine the general properties of transformations and of groups of transformations. With every transformation $\mathcal{T}$ of the variables and dynamical states there is associated a transformation operator T for the ket vectors representing the states. T is of necessity *either unitary linear or unitary antilinear*, and is defined up to an arbitrary phase factor by the law for the transformation of the fundamental observables of the system. In practice, T is always linear except for time reversal. With the various transformations of physics one can form a certain number of groups of transformations and with each such group $\mathcal{G}$ associate a certain group of transformation operators G [1]). After reviewing the most important of these groups we show with some simple examples how one constructs G in the case when $\mathcal{G}$ is a finite group, and in the case when $\mathcal{G}$ is a continuous group whose finite transformations can all be defined as a succession of infinitesimal transformations.

Questions relating specifically to invariance are taken up in section III. The transformations of this section are time-independent and linear, and the results obtained are simple generalizations of those previously obtained for rotations (Ch. XIII). To postulate that the equations of motion of the dynamical states are invariant under the transformations of a certain group $\mathcal{G}$, is equivalent to supposing that the Hamiltonian H commutes with the operators of the group G.

*) The fourth part (Ch. XVI–XIX), apart from a few specifically marked passages which may be omitted in a first reading, is independent of the present chapter and may be taken up first if desired.

1) The few notions regarding groups and their representations used in this chapter are given in sections I and II of Appendix D.

Thus any observable formed with the operators of G is a constant of the motion, and hence to any G-invariance there correspond a certain number of *conservation laws*. By taking into account these symmetries of H, we can simplify its diagonalization and make certain predictions regarding the degeneracies of its eigenvalues.

The invariance under time reversal differs from the rest by its physical significance and by the fact that the corresponding operator is antilinear. It is discussed in section IV.

Throughout this chapter, the striking analogy between Classical Mechanics and Quantum Mechanics will be apparent, especially in the definitions of the transformations, in the connection between the invariance properties of the equations of motion and the symmetries of the Hamiltonian, and in the existence of conservation laws.

I. MATHEMATICAL COMPLEMENTS. ANTILINEAR OPERATORS

2. Three Useful Theorems

THEOREM I. A necessary and sufficient condition that two linear operators A and B be equal, is that

$$\langle u | A | u \rangle = \langle u | B | u \rangle \text{ for any } |u\rangle.$$

THEOREM II. A necessary and sufficient condition that two linear operators A and B be equal to within a phase,

$$A = B\,e^{i\alpha} \tag{XV.1}$$

is that

$$|\langle u | A | v \rangle| = |\langle u | B | v \rangle| \text{ for any } |u\rangle \text{ and } |v\rangle. \tag{XV.2}$$

THEOREM III. If between the vectors of the space $\mathscr{E}$ there exists a one-to-one correspondence $\mathscr{T}$ which is defined up to an arbitrary constant and which conserves the scalar product, then the phases can always be chosen so as to make $\mathscr{T}$ either unitary linear or unitary antilinear.

Theorem I was given in Chapter VII (§ 5). It is included here simply for completeness.

With regard to theorem II, it is obvious that (XV.2) is a consequence of (XV.1). To show that the converse is also true, we choose a particular representation in which we denote the matrix elements of A and B by A_{ij} and B_{ij} respectively. Since the basis vectors of the representation satisfy (XV.2), we have

$$|A_{ij}| = |B_{ij}| \quad \text{for all } i \text{ and } j. \tag{XV.3}$$

Letting $|u\rangle$ be the ith basis vector and $|v\rangle$ a linear combination of the jth and the kth basis vectors, we similarly find

$$|A_{ij}\, x_j + A_{ik}\, x_k| = |B_{ij}\, x_j + B_{ik}\, x_k|$$

for all values of the complex coefficients x_j and x_k. Taking into account (XV.3), this last equation may be written

$$\text{Re}\, [x_j\, x_k^* \,(A_{ij}\, A_{ik}^* - B_{ij}\, B_{ik}^*)] = 0.$$

In order that this be true for any $x_j\, x_k{}^*$, it is necessary that

$$A_{ij}\, A_{ik}^* - B_{ij}\, B_{ik}^* = 0.$$

This, together with (XV.3), gives

$$\frac{A_{ij}}{B_{ij}} = \frac{A_{ik}}{B_{ik}}. \tag{XV.4}$$

For a given i, the same argument may be repeated with different column indices j and k, thus showing that the ratio A_{ij}/B_{ij} is independent of j. Also, we can repeat the demonstration interchanging the role of the rows and the columns, and thereby show that this ratio is also independent of i. Since according to (XV.3) the moduli of the matrix elements of A and B are equal, this ratio must be a number of modulus unity:

$$\frac{A_{ij}}{B_{ij}} = \mathrm{e}^{\mathrm{i}\alpha} \qquad \text{for all } i \text{ and } j.$$

In other words, the operators A and B are equal to within a phase factor $\mathrm{e}^{\mathrm{i}\alpha}$. Q.E.D.

Consider next theorem III. By hypothesis, to each vector $|u\rangle$ of $\mathscr{E}$ there corresponds a vector $|u'\rangle$ given by the law $\mathscr{T}$. This vector is determined up to a phase factor. Let us make a particular choice for the phase of each of the vectors $|u'\rangle$. Then the law $\mathscr{T}$ sets up a one-to-one correspondence between the vectors of $\mathscr{E}$:

$$|u'\rangle = \mathscr{T}\,[|u\rangle] \qquad |u\rangle = \mathscr{T}^{-1}\,[|u'\rangle] \tag{I}$$

and this correspondence conserves the modulus of the scalar product

$$|\langle u'\,|v'\rangle| = |\langle u\,|v\rangle|. \tag{II}$$

Let

$$|1\rangle, |2\rangle, ..., |n\rangle, ... \tag{XV.5}$$

be a complete set of orthonormal vectors in $\mathscr{E}$. The corresponding set

$$|1'\rangle, |2'\rangle, ..., |n'\rangle, ... \tag{XV.5'}$$

is also a complete orthonormal set; it is orthonormal because, by (II), $\mathscr{T}$ conserves the norm and the orthogonality; complete because if there existed a vector $|a'\rangle$ orthogonal to all the vectors of (XV.5′), the vector $|a\rangle \equiv \mathscr{T}^{-1}[|a'\rangle]$ would be orthogonal to all the vectors of (XV.5), which is impossible by hypothesis.

Put

$$u_n \equiv \langle n|u\rangle \qquad u_n' \equiv \langle n'|u'\rangle \tag{XV.6}$$

We want to prove that, with a suitable choice of phases for the "primed" ket vectors, either one or the other of the following relations holds:

$$u_n' = u_n, \quad \text{whatever } |u\rangle \text{ and } n \tag{XV.7a}$$

$$u_n' = u_n^*, \quad \text{whatever } |u\rangle \text{ and } n. \tag{XV.7b}$$

Note that, from condition (II), we obviously have:

$$|u_n'| = |u_n|, \quad \text{whatever } |u\rangle \text{ and } n.$$

Thus, we only have to investigate the phase relationship between u_n' and u_n.

To this effect, we fix the phase of each basis ket $|n'\rangle$ by requiring that $|1'\rangle + |n'\rangle$ correspond to $|1\rangle + |n\rangle$.

We first prove relations (XV.7) in the case when $|u\rangle$ is a "real" ket, i.e. when all the u_n are real. Applying (II) to the scalar product of $|u\rangle$ by $|1\rangle + |n\rangle$ we obtain:

$$|u_1 + u_n| = |u_1' + u_n'|$$

If we choose the phase of $|u'\rangle$ in such a way that $u_1' = u_1$, we obtain the desired result: $u_n' = u_n$. The above argument does not apply when $u_1 = 0$. Its extension to include this case is straightforward, and will not be given here.

Consider now an arbitrary ket $|u\rangle$. Applying (II) to the scalar product of $|u\rangle$ by the "real" ket $|j\rangle + |j+1\rangle + ... + |j+k\rangle$ we obtain:

$$\left|\sum_{s=0}^{k} u_{j+s}\right| = \left|\sum_{s=0}^{k} u'_{j+s}\right| \tag{XV.8}$$

This holds for any j and s. In order to visualize this result, it is convenient to use the following geometrical representations for $|u\rangle$

and $|u'\rangle$. We associate with $|u\rangle$ the polygonal line (Γ) obtained by putting end to end the representative vectors in the complex plane of its successive components $u_1, u_2, \ldots, u_n, \ldots$. Similarly $|u'\rangle$ is represented by the polygonal line (Γ') built up from the representative vectors of $u_1', u_2', \ldots, u_n', \ldots$. (XV.8) means that the distance between any two virtices of (Γ) is equal to the distance between the corresponding virtices of (Γ'). As a consequence either (a) (Γ) can be brought into coincidence with (Γ') by a rotation, or (b) (Γ) can be brought into coincidence with (Γ') by a rotation and a reflection in the real axis.

In case (a), we choose the phase of $|u'\rangle$ by requiring that $u_1' = u_1$. With this choice, (Γ) and (Γ') coincide, i.e.

$$u_n' = u_n, \text{ whatever } n.$$

In case (b), our choice of phase is such that $u_1' = u_1^*$. Then, (Γ') is the mirror image of (Γ) with respect to the real axis, i.e.

$$u_n' = u_n^*, \text{ whatever } n.$$

Finally, we have to show that there are in fact only two possibilities: either all the ket vectors fall into case (a), or they all fall into case (b).

Assume, to be specific, that the particular vector $|j\rangle + e^{i\alpha}|k\rangle$ $(a \neq n\pi)$ falls into case (a). Then, any vector $|u\rangle$ whose components u_j, u_k do not vanish and have a relative phase different from $n\pi$ necessarily also falls into case (a) as is readily seen by applying property (II) to the scalar product of $|u\rangle$ by $|j\rangle + e^{i\alpha}|k\rangle$. The argument is easily extended to include vectors whose components u_j, u_k either vanish or have a relative phase equal to $n\pi$. The same argument applies to case (b).

In conclusion, we have two possibilities:

Case (a). With a suitable choice of phases, relation (XV.7*a*) applies. The correspondence $\mathscr{T}$ is obviously *linear*. More precisely, we have

$$\langle u' | v' \rangle = \langle u | v \rangle \tag{XV.9a}$$

showing that it is a unitary linear correspondence.

Case (b). With a suitable choice of phases, relation (XV.7*b*) applies. The correspondence $\mathscr{T}$ is obviously *antilinear*. More precisely, we have:

$$\langle u' | v' \rangle = \langle u | v \rangle^*. \tag{XV.9b}$$

According to the definition of unitarity for antilinear operators, which is given below, it is a unitary antilinear correspondence. Q.E.D.

3. Antilinear Operators in Hilbert Space

The properties of antilinear operators in Hilbert space are analogous to those of linear operators. We shall briefly list them in the same order as we listed the properties of linear operators in Chapter VII.

DEFINITION. ACTION ON THE KETS

If to each ket $|u\rangle$ of Hilbert space there corresponds a certain ket $|v\rangle$, and if this correspondence is antilinear, then we say that $|v\rangle$ is the result of the action of a certain antilinear operator A on $|u\rangle$, and we write

$$|v\rangle = A\,|u\rangle. \tag{XV.10}$$

The antilinearity property is written

$$A\,(\lambda_1\,|1\rangle + \lambda_2\,|2\rangle) = \lambda_1^*\,(A\,|1\rangle) + \lambda_2^*\,(A\,|2\rangle). \tag{XV.11}$$

An antilinear operator is completely defined by its action on each of the vectors of a complete set of linearly independent vectors of $\mathscr{E}$, and notably by its action on the vectors of a basis in $\mathscr{E}$.

ALGEBRAIC OPERATIONS

Same definition as for linear operators:

(i) *Multiplication by a constant* c. If $c \neq c^*$, note that $c\,A \neq A\,c$;

$$\boxed{c\,A = A\,c^*} \tag{XV.12}$$

(ii) *Sum* of two antilinear operators (mentioned for completeness);

(iii) *Products*: if A_1, A_2 are antilinear operators, the product $A_1\,A_2$ defined by

$$(A_1\,A_2)\,|u\rangle = A_1\,(A_2\,|u\rangle)$$

is a linear operator. If A is antilinear and B linear, the product $A\,B$ is antilinear. More generally, if $A, B, \ldots, L$ contains in all $p+q$ operators of which p are linear and q antilinear, the product $(A\,B\,\ldots\,L)$ is linear or antilinear according as q is even or odd.

These products are all associative, but in general not commutative. The definition of commutators is the same as for linear operators and the corresponding algebraic rules (V.63–66) are still valid.

INVERSE

If the correspondence (XV.10) between $|u\rangle$ and $|v\rangle$ is of a one-to-one character, then it also defines the inverse A^{-1} of A.

$$|u\rangle = A^{-1}\,|v\rangle.$$

The antilinear operators A, B are by definition each the inverse of the other if we simultaneously have

$$A\,B = 1 \qquad B\,A = 1. \tag{XV.13}$$

If each of the operators $A, B, C, \ldots, L$ is either linear or antilinear, and if each of them has an inverse, then the inverse of their product exists and is given by

$$(A\,B\,C \ldots L)^{-1} = L^{-1} \ldots C^{-1}\,B^{-1}\,A^{-1}. \tag{XV.14}$$

ACTION ON THE BRAS

Let A be an antilinear operator and $\langle\chi\,|$ a bra vector; the complex conjugate of the scalar product $\langle\chi\,|(A\,|u\rangle)$, being a linear function of $|u\rangle$, defines a certain bra (cf. § VII.3), which we denote by $\langle\eta\,|$. By definition

$$\langle\eta\,| = \langle\chi\,|A. \tag{XV.15}$$

The correspondence between $\langle\chi\,|$ and $\langle\eta\,|$ is antilinear:

$$(\lambda_1\,\langle 1\,| + \lambda_2\,\langle 2\,|)\,A = \lambda_1^*\,(\langle 1\,|A) + \lambda_2^*\,(\langle 2\,|A). \tag{XV.16}$$

According to this definition, we have the following identity between scalar products

$$\boxed{(\langle\chi\,|A)\,|u\rangle = [\langle\chi\,|\,(A\,|u\rangle)]^*} \tag{XV.17}$$

This is to be compared with the identity (VII.17) for linear operators. In the present case we cannot omit the parentheses.

In order to define the three algebraic operations and the inverse for operators acting on bras, we proceed in the same way as for linear operators. The multiplication by a constant c gives [cf. eq. (XV.12)]:

$$\langle\chi\,|(c\,A) = c^*\,(\langle\chi\,|A) = \langle\chi\,|(A\,c^*). \tag{XV.18}$$

The rest is without change.

IMPORTANT NOTE

Relations (XV.12) and (XV.17) summarize the differences between ordinary manipulations and those involving antilinear operators:

(i) considered as an operator in ket-space or bra-space, a given constant c does not commute with antilinear operators unless it is real;

(ii) in the scalar product one must explicitly show whether A acts on the ket to its right or on the bra to its left.

In practice, parentheses are used as often as is necessary in order to avoid any possible confusion in the meaning of the symbols. Consider, for example, the product $A_1 A_2$ of two antilinear operators; the symbol $\langle u | A_1 A_2 | v \rangle$ is ambiguous, while on the other hand we can write without any possible confusion

$$\langle u |(A_1 A_2) | v\rangle = (\langle u | A_1 A_2) | v\rangle = [(\langle u | A_1)(A_2 | v\rangle)]^* = \langle u |(A_1 A_2 | v\rangle). \tag{XV.19}$$

Similarly, consider the product $(A |u\rangle \langle v|)$ of the linear operator $|u\rangle\langle v|$ by the antilinear operator A; the symbols $A |u\rangle \langle v | w\rangle$ and $\langle w | A | u\rangle \langle v |$ lead to confusion, while we can write without any possible confusion:

$$(A |u\rangle \langle v|) |w\rangle = A (|u\rangle \langle v | w\rangle) = (A |u\rangle) \langle v | w\rangle^* \tag{XV.20}$$

and

$$\langle w |(A |u\rangle \langle v|) = (\langle w | A) |u\rangle \langle v | = [\langle w |(A |u\rangle)]^* \langle v |. \tag{XV.21}$$

4. Antilinear Transformations

ADJOINT (OR HERMITEAN CONJUGATE) ANTILINEAR OPERATORS

$A^\dagger$ is by definition the adjoint of the antilinear operator A if $A^\dagger |u\rangle$ is the ket conjugate to $\langle u | A$ for any $|u\rangle$. It is an antilinear operator.

It follows that for any $|u\rangle$ and $|t\rangle$:

$$\langle t |(A^\dagger |u\rangle) \equiv \langle u |(A |t\rangle). \tag{XV.22}$$

This identity is to be compared with (VII.20). Apart from this, all of the properties set forth in § VII.7 can be taken over without change. In particular:

If each of the operators $A, B, C, \ldots, L$ is either linear or antilinear, then [cf. eq. (XV.14)]

$$(A\,B\,C \ldots L)^{\dagger} = L^{\dagger} \ldots C^{\dagger}\, B^{\dagger}\, A^{\dagger}. \tag{XV.23}$$

ANTIUNITARY OPERATOR

A is antiunitary if it is antilinear and if $A^{-1} = A^{\dagger}$:

$$A\,A^{\dagger} = A^{\dagger}\,A = 1.$$

If $A, B, C, \ldots, L$ contains in all $p+q$ operators of which p are unitary and q antiunitary, the product $A\,B\,C \ldots L$ is unitary or antiunitary according as q is even or odd.

ANTIUNITARY TRANSFORMATION OF LINEAR OPERATORS AND OF VECTORS

An antiunitary operator K defines an antiunitary transformation of the vectors and linear operators of $\mathscr{E}$, in which:

any ket $|u\rangle$ transforms into $|\hat{u}\rangle \equiv K\,|u\rangle$;
any linear operator B into $\hat{B} \equiv K\,B\,K^{\dagger}$;
any bra $\langle v|$ into $\langle \hat{v}| \equiv \langle v|K^{\dagger}$.

In such a transformation:

(i) conjugate relations between bras and kets and Hermitean-conjugate relations between operators are conserved. If B is an observable, $\hat{B}$ is an observable with the same eigenvalue spectrum, the subspace of each eigenvalue of B transforming into the subspace of the same eigenvalue of $\hat{B}$;

(ii) scalar products transform into their complex conjugates

$$\langle \hat{u}|\hat{B}|\hat{v}\rangle = \langle u|B|v\rangle^{*}; \tag{XV.24}$$

(iii) considered as an operator, any constant c transforms into its complex conjugate

$$K\,c\,K^{\dagger} = c^{*}; \tag{XV.25}$$

(iv) any relation between vectors and/or operators is also satisfied by the transforms of these quantities if we replace all coefficients by their complex conjugates. In other words, the transformation K

conserves equations between vectors and/or operators if we agree to treat the coefficients involved as operators. For example the commutation relations

$$[q, p] = \mathrm{i}\,\hbar \qquad [J_x, J_y] = \mathrm{i}\,\hbar\, J_z \tag{XV.26a}$$

transform respectively into

$$[\hat{q}, \hat{p}] = -\mathrm{i}\,\hbar \qquad [\hat{J}_x, \hat{J}_y] = -\mathrm{i}\,\hbar\, \hat{J}_z. \tag{XV.26b}$$

5. Antilinear Operators and Representations

COMPLEX-CONJUGATION OPERATOR K_Q ASSOCIATED WITH A REPRESENTATION $\{Q\}$

By definition, K_Q is the operator that transforms the wave functions of the representation $\{Q\}$ into their complex conjugates. *It depends on the representation in question and notably on the phases of the basis vectors.*

Let $|1\rangle, |2\rangle, \ldots, |n\rangle, \ldots$ denote the basis vectors of $\{Q\}$. K_Q is the antilinear operator which leaves these vectors invariant

$$K_Q\,|n\rangle = |n\rangle. \tag{XV.27}$$

K_Q is thereby unambiguously defined. It is obvious that

$$K_Q{}^{\dagger} = K_Q \qquad K_Q{}^2 = 1 \tag{XV.28}$$

and therefore that K_Q is antiunitary. It clearly has the aforementioned property, namely that:

In the antiunitary transformation K_Q the matrices of the $\{Q\}$ representation are transformed into their complex conjugates, for we have

$$\langle n\,|(K_Q\,|u\rangle) = \langle n\,|u\rangle^* \qquad (\langle v\,|K_Q)\,|n\rangle = \langle v\,|n\rangle^*$$
$$\langle m\,|(K_Q\,B\,K_Q)\,|n\rangle = \langle m\,|B\,|n\rangle^* \quad (B,\ \text{linear operator}).$$

Thus in the $\{Q\}$ representation the action of K_Q merely consists in taking the complex conjugate. The action of any other antilinear operator A may easily be deduced if we note that A is the product of K_Q and a linear operator, i.e. A can be written

$$A = (A\,K_Q)\,K_Q = K_Q\,(K_Q\,A) \tag{XV.29}$$

and $(A\,K_Q)$ and $(K_Q\,A)$ are linear operators, obtained from one another by the transformation K_Q:

$$K_Q\, A = K_Q\, (A\, K_Q)\, K_Q$$

[if A is antiunitary, $(K_Q\, A)$ and $(A\, K_Q)$ are unitary].

CHANGE OF REPRESENTATION

Consider another representation $\{\Xi\}$. We denote by K_Ξ the complex-conjugation operator associated with this representation, and for the rest follow the notation of § VII.21; in particular, the matrix for the transformation of vectors and linear operators is the unitary matrix $S\,(\xi; n) \equiv \langle \xi\, | n \rangle$.

If this matrix is real, the vectors of the new basis are invariant under K_Q; in other words,

$$\text{if } S = S^*, \qquad K_\Xi = K_Q.$$

In this case, the linear operators $A\, K_\Xi$ and $K_\Xi\, A$ associated, in the $\{\Xi\}$ representation, with a given antilinear operator A, are the same as the ones that are associated with A in the $\{Q\}$ representation.

When this is not the case, $A K_\Xi$ differs from $K_\Xi\, A$. It is useful to be able to deduce the matrix $(A\, K_\Xi)_\Xi$ representing $A\, K_\Xi$ in the $\{\Xi\}$ representation from the matrix $(A\, K_Q)_Q$ representing $A\, K_Q$ in the $\{Q\}$ representation. We have

$$\begin{aligned}\langle \xi\, |(A\, K_\Xi)\, |\xi' \rangle &= \langle \xi\, |(A\, K_Q)\, (K_Q\, K_\Xi)\, |\xi' \rangle \\ &= \sum_{mn} \langle \xi\, |m \rangle \, \langle m\, |(A\, K_Q)\, |n \rangle \, \langle n\, |(K_Q\, K_\Xi)\, |\xi' \rangle \\ &= \sum_{mn} \langle \xi\, |m \rangle \, \langle m\, |(A\, K_Q)\, |n \rangle \, \langle n\, |\xi' \rangle^*\end{aligned}$$

i.e.

$$(A\, K_\Xi)_\Xi = S\, (A\, K_Q)_Q\, \tilde{S}. \tag{XV.30}$$

Similarly

$$(K_\Xi\, A)_\Xi = (A\, K_\Xi)_\Xi{}^* = S^*\, (K_Q\, A)_Q\, S^\dagger. \tag{XV.31}$$

II. TRANSFORMATIONS AND GROUPS OF TRANSFORMATIONS

6. Transformations of the Dynamical Variables and Dynamical States of a System

We have already defined what is meant by "rotation of a physical system" and by "permutation of the particles of a physical system".

More generally, to effect a transformation $\mathscr{T}$ of a system, is to replace each of its variables by a new variable and each of its states by a new state, *while conserving the physical properties of the system.*

Thus the transformation $\mathscr{T}$ sets up a one-to-one correspondence between the dynamical variables: a given variable B transforms into another variable

$$B' \equiv \mathscr{T}[B]$$

of the system. By hypothesis, the transform B' has the same spectrum as B, and the eigenstates of each eigenvalue of B' are the transforms of the eigenstates of the same eigenvalue of B; these two conditions express the conservation of physical properties in the transformation of dynamical variables. Although we have been able to formulate this conservation condition without making reference to methods of measurement, the transformation $\mathscr{T}$ is particularly easy to visualize as a transformation applied to the measuring apparatus attached to the variable B: the transform of that apparatus is the apparatus attached to the variable B'. One so defines the displacements of the dynamical variables (rotations, translations), the reflections of the dynamical variables (reflection in a point, in a plane), etc.

From the concept of the transformation of variables we easily pass over to that of the transformation of states. Let $|u\rangle$ be a vector representing a possible dynamical state of the system. It can always be considered as the common eigenvector of a complete set of commuting observables, and is thereby defined up to a phase. Its transform

$$|u'\rangle \equiv \mathscr{T}[|u\rangle]$$

is the common eigenvector of the transformed observables. $\mathscr{T}$ therefore sets up a one-to-one correspondence between state vectors defined up to a phase.

By hypothesis the transformation conserves the physical properties of dynamical states: the system being in the state $|u'\rangle$, the probability that a measurement will give a result corresponding to the state $|v'\rangle$, the transform of $|v\rangle$, is equal to the probability that the same measurement will give a result corresponding to the state $|v\rangle$ when the system is in the state $|u\rangle$. In other words

$$|\langle u' | v' \rangle|^2 = |\langle u | v \rangle|^2 \text{ for all } |u\rangle \text{ and } |v\rangle.$$

The one-to-one correspondence in question therefore conserves the modulus of the scalar product. According to theorem III, the phases of the transformed vectors can always be fixed so as to make the transformation either unitary or antiunitary. We can then write

$$|u'\rangle = T\,|u\rangle, \tag{XV.32}$$

T being a unitary or antiunitary operator according to the transformation; in both cases we have

$$T\,T^\dagger = T^\dagger\,T = 1. \tag{XV.33}$$

From the law (XV.32) for the transformation of vectors, we can easily deduce the law for the transformation of the density operator:

$$\varrho' = T\,\varrho\,T^\dagger. \tag{XV.34}$$

Consider once more the transformation of the observables. Since physical properties are conserved by our transformation, so are average values. Thus for an observable B we have

$$\langle u' | B' | u' \rangle = \langle u | B | u \rangle \text{ for any } |u\rangle$$

or again [1]

$$\langle u | (T^\dagger\,B'\,T) | u \rangle = \langle u | B | u \rangle \text{ for any } |u\rangle.$$

From theorem I and property (XV.33) we therefore have

$$B' = T\,B\,T^\dagger \qquad B = T^\dagger\,B'\,T. \tag{XV.35}$$

From relations (XV.35) we have the important property that any algebraic relation between the observables of the system is conserved in the transformation if T is linear, and is replaced by the complex conjugate relation if T is antilinear.

[1] This result, obvious for T linear, is also true for T antilinear, due to $\langle u \mid B \mid u \rangle$ being real.

This places very restricting conditions on the transformation laws for observables. Any observable B is a certain *real* function $F(\xi)$ of the fundamental observables $\xi_1, \xi_2, \ldots, \xi_n, \ldots,$ of the system. Its transform is necessarily $B' \equiv F(\xi')$. *The transformation* $\mathscr{T}$ *is therefore entirely determined once we know the transformation laws for the fundamental observables*, i.e. once we know the functions $f_1(\xi), \ldots, f_n(\xi), \ldots,$ such that

$$\mathscr{T}[\xi_n] \equiv \xi_n' = f_n(\xi).$$

These will also determine the commutation relations for the ξ'. The latter must satisfy the property of conservation of algebraic relations given above. There are then only two possibilities: *either the transformation conserves the fundamental commutation relations, or it changes the sign* [1]). In the first case, the operator T associated with the transformation is linear; in the second, it is antilinear [cf. eq. (XV.26*a–b*)].

The operator T must satisfy the relations:

$$\xi_n' = T\, \xi_n\, T^\dagger. \qquad \text{(XV.36)}$$

All physical properties of T are contained in these relations. They do not, however, suffice to completely determine T. Let T_1 be another unitary (or antiunitary) operator satisfying the same relations. We have (dropping the index n to simplify the writing)

$$T_1^\dagger\, \xi'\, T_1 = \xi$$

and therefore

$$T_1^\dagger\, T\, \xi\, T^\dagger\, T_1 = \xi$$

or

$$[T_1^\dagger\, T, \xi] = 0 \quad \text{for any } \xi. \qquad \text{(XV.37)}$$

If we make the hypothesis that state space $\mathscr{E}$ is *irreducible* with respect to the observables ξ, i.e., that $\mathscr{E}$ contains no subspace invariant with respect to the ξ, then (XV.37) will be satisfied if, and only if, $T_1^\dagger\, T$ is a constant.

---

1) The transformations of Classical Mechanics are those which preserve the Poisson brackets

$$\{A_{\mathrm{cl}}, B_{\mathrm{cl}}\}$$

of each pair $(A_{\mathrm{cl}}, B_{\mathrm{cl}})$ of dynamical variables of the system (canonical transformations). Similarly the transformations that conserve physical properties in Quantum Mechanics are those which conserve the corresponding expressions:

$$1/i\hbar\, [A, B]$$

This result is contained in Schur's Lemma (§ D.8). It can be directly proven as follows. Let $|u\rangle$ be a simultaneous eigenvector of a *complete* set of commuting observables. Since $C \equiv T_1^{\dagger} T$ commutes with each of these, $|u\rangle$ is necessarily an eigenvector of C: $C\,|u\rangle = c\,|u\rangle$. Since C commutes with any function $F(\xi)$ of the observables of the system, we also have

$$C\ F(\xi)\ |u\rangle = c\ \ F(\xi)\ |u\rangle \quad \text{for any } F(\xi).$$

But the space spanned by the vectors $F(\xi)\ |u\rangle$ is an invariant subspace of $\mathscr{E}$ with respect to the ξ, and since by hypothesis $\mathscr{E}$ is irreducible, this can only be $\mathscr{E}$ itself. Therefore $C = c$.

If we suppose, as we have always done up to the present, that every vector of state space may be considered as an eigenvector of a complete set of commuting observables, then this property of irreducibility is automatically assured (Problem XV.1). Clearly the above discussion is meaningful only if the observables mentioned are physical observables. We shall always suppose $\mathscr{E}$ to be irreducible with respect to physical observables [1]). If such an assumption is made, the constant c is necessarily of modulus 1 since T and T_1 are unitary. Thus we can write

$$T_1 = \mathrm{e}^{i\alpha}\, T.$$

In summary, *with each transformation $\mathscr{T}$ there is associated a unitary or antiunitary operator T, defined up to a phase by the transformation laws for the fundamental variables of the system* [eq. (XV.36)]. *T is unitary if the transformation conserves the commutation relations, antiunitary if it changes their sign.*

The phase of T may be arbitrarily chosen and has no effect on the physical properties of the transformation, not affecting the transformation law for observables, the transformation law for density operators, nor the different algebraic manipulations between operators.

7. Groups of Transformations

With the various transformations at our disposal, we can form a certain number of *groups* of transformations, the word group being taken in its mathematical sense (cf. § D.2).

The *product* $\mathscr{T}_{21} \equiv \mathscr{T}_2 \mathscr{T}_1$ of transformations $\mathscr{T}_1$ and $\mathscr{T}_2$ is the

---

[1]) Cf. reference in note 2, p. 536, in which the irreducibility hypothesis is abandoned.

transformation realized by applying first $\mathscr{T}_1$ and then $\mathscr{T}_2$. The transformation operator T_{21} is to within a phase factor equal to the product $T_2 T_1$. This type of product is therefore *associative*; it is not necessarily commutative.

The *identity* $\mathscr{I}$ is the transformation in which each observable transforms into itself; the corresponding operator is the multiplication by an arbitrary phase factor.

The *inverse* $\mathscr{T}^{-1}$ of a transformation $\mathscr{T}$ is defined by the relations $\mathscr{T}^{-1}\mathscr{T} = \mathscr{T}\mathscr{T}^{-1} = \mathscr{I}$; since $\mathscr{T}$ defines a one-to-one correspondence, the inverse will always exist.

Thus, the transformations defined in § 6 may each be regarded as an element of a certain group $\mathscr{G}$.

Of all the groups, the one whose physical significance is the most immediately apparent is *the group of spatial transformations* (translations, rotations, reflections) *and its various subgroups*. Of the latter we may cite the translation group, the group of rotations (about a point), the group of displacements (translation × rotation), the group of reflections in a point, in a plane, the rotation-reflection group (rotation about a point × reflection in the same point), the groups of symmetries in a crystal.

In the preceding chapter we encountered groups of a different category, the *groups of permutations* of similar particles. We also considered permutations of certain variables to the exclusion of others, and notably the group of permutations in charge space, with which is associated, in the case of nucleon systems, the *group of isotopic rotations* or group of rotations in charge space.

It is convenient to treat separately the transformations that explicitly bring in the time. In the first place there are the Galilean coordinate transformations, mentioned here for completeness (Problem XV.7). These are the non-relativistic equivalents of the pure Lorentz transformations which form with the spatial rotations, the proper Lorentz group, to be discussed in Part 5. There is also the group of time translations, and finally time reversal. Translation and reversal of time are studied in section IV. In the rest of the present section we deal only with transformations not explicitly involving the time.

8. Groups of Transformation Operators

Let $[\mathscr{T}]$ be a set of transformations $\mathscr{T}_1, \mathscr{T}_2, \ldots, \mathscr{T}_i, \ldots$. With each element $\mathscr{T}_i$ of the set we can associate an operator T_i defining the transformation of the vectors and operators of state space. T is defined by its physical properties only to within a phase factor, which we choose arbitrarily for the moment. We thereby obtain a set of transformation operators $[T]$ whose elements are in one-to-one correspondence with those of $[\mathscr{T}]$.

Suppose now that $[\mathscr{T}]$ is a certain group $\mathscr{G}$. It does not necessarily follow that $[T]$ has the group property. In the correspondence between $[\mathscr{T}]$ and $[T]$, products are conserved only to within a phase factor; for each product

$$\mathscr{T}_k = \mathscr{T}_j \mathscr{T}_i$$

we have

$$T_k = \mathrm{e}^{\mathrm{i}\alpha_{ji}^k} T_j T_i,$$

where α_{ji}^k is a certain phase depending on the choice of phase for T_i, T_j and T_k. In order that $[T]$ be a group all of the α_{ji}^k must vanish, and in this case $[T]$ is isomorphic to the group $\mathscr{G}$.

When the phases of the T_i can be chosen in such a way that $[T]$ has the group property, then this is obviously the most convenient choice. This possibility exists for some groups but not for all. It exists for the permutation group (Ch. XIV) but not for the rotation group (§ XIII.15) when the system has an odd number of particles with half-integral spins. In this last case the rotation operators $R(\alpha\,\beta\,\gamma)$ defined by equation (XIII.60) do form a group, but there are two R operators, differing by a sign, for each rotation $\mathscr{R}$; if we take one of them as an element of $[R]$ we thereby establish a one-to-one correspondence between the rotations and the rotation operators, but the product is only conserved up to a sign, and the set $[R]$ does not have the group property.

To obtain a set of transformation operators with the group property, it may be necessary to associate with each $\mathscr{T}_i$ not a single operator T_i but a set (T_i) of operators differing one from another by a phase. If the (T_i) are suitably chosen, the set of transformation operators $\{T\}$ thereby obtained forms a group G and this group is homomorphic to the group $\mathscr{G}$. Let (1) be the set of operators associated with the transformation $\mathscr{I}$; the elements of (1) are the operator 1 and perhaps other elements obtained by multiplying 1 by a phase factor. It is an invariant subgroup of G and the quotient group $G/(1)$ is isomorphic to $\mathscr{G}$ (cf. § D.5).

We can thus form many sets $\{T\}$ having the group property [1]). In practice, we choose one of them once and for all; it is obviously chosen to be as simple as possible. We thereby obtain a group G of transformation operators homomorphic to the group $\mathscr{G}$.

In all the cases encountered up to the present in Quantum Theory, one can always choose G so as to have corresponding to each element of $\mathscr{G}$ *either a single operator of* G (isomorphism) *or, failing this, two operators of* G *of which one is the negative of the other*. The first of these possibilities can always be realized when the system has an even number of half-integral spins. We have already had an example of the second in the rotation of half-integral spins; we shall have another in connection with time reversal; it always appears when the system has an odd number of half-integral spins.

9. Continuous Groups and Infinitesimal Transformations. Translations. Rotations

As an illustration of the theory, we shall construct the group G for some of the groups $\mathscr{G}$. We consider first the continuous groups – those with an infinite number of elements depending on one or several continuous parameters – and more particularly those for which the finite transformations can all be generated by a series of infinitesimal transformations. Such is the case for the rotation group, and for the group of spatial translations. We need then only to know the infinitesimal transformations of the observables to have their transformation under any operation of the group. With each of the infinitesimal transformations of the group can be associated an infinitesimal transformation operator, i.e. a unitary operator differing by an infinitesimal from 1 [2]).

Suppose for simplicity that the group elements depend only on a

---

[1]) One of them, the most complicated of all, is obtained by associating with each $\mathscr{T}_i$ all of the operators obeying (XV.36): in this case, the elements of (T_i) are all obtained by multiplying one of them by an arbitrary phase factor. In practice, it is always possible to impose a reality condition on the T_i that fixes the phase factor up to a sign without violating the group property. The set (T_i) then has just two elements, differing from each other by a sign (cf. note, p. 669).

[2]) It could not be antiunitary. Consider two non-commuting observables: in an infinitesimal transformation they are subject to infinitesimal modifications; their commutator therefore cannot undergo a finite modification and in particular cannot change sign.

continuous parameter α and that the latter be chosen so as to have

$$\mathscr{T}(\alpha) \underset{\alpha\to 0}{\longrightarrow} \mathscr{I}.$$

To the first order in $\delta\alpha$, the infinitesimal transformation operator associated with $\mathscr{T}(\delta\alpha)$ is given by

$$T(\delta\alpha) = 1 - \mathrm{i}\,\Theta\,\delta\alpha$$

where Θ is a Hermitean operator (since T is unitary).

If the observable ξ is transformed into $\xi + \delta\xi$ in the transformation $\mathscr{T}(\delta\alpha)$, we have [eq. (VII.96)]

$$\delta\xi = -\mathrm{i}\,\delta\alpha[\Theta, \xi],$$

i.e.

$$[\Theta, \xi] = \mathrm{i}\frac{\delta\xi}{\delta\alpha}. \tag{XV.38}$$

For a given transformation $\mathscr{T}(\delta\alpha)$, the $\delta\xi/\delta\alpha$ are known and relations (XV.38) define Θ up to a constant [1]).

Consider, for example, the translations of a particle along the axis Ox. Let $\boldsymbol{r} \equiv (x, y, z)$ be the position, $\boldsymbol{p} \equiv (p_x, p_y, p_z)$ the momentum and $\boldsymbol{s} \equiv (s_x, s_y, s_z)$ the spin of the particle. In the translation $\mathscr{T}_x(a)$ of distance a along the axis Ox, the nine fundamental variables are invariant with the exception of x which goes over into $x - a$ [2]):

$$T(a)\,x\,T^{\dagger}(a) = x - a. \tag{XV.39}$$

---

[1]) In Classical Mechanics, the variation $\delta\alpha\,\partial\xi/\partial\alpha$ of each variable ξ in the infinitesimal displacement $\mathscr{T}(\delta\alpha)$ is defined by the Poisson bracket

$$\frac{\partial\xi}{\partial\alpha} = \{\tau, \xi\},$$

where τ is the conjugate momentum associated with the variable α. The observable $\hbar\Theta$ is the quantum analogue of τ. [In an infinitesimal rotation about $\boldsymbol{u}$, τ is the component of the angular momentum along $\boldsymbol{u}$; in a translation along $\boldsymbol{u}$, τ is the component of the momentum along $\boldsymbol{u}$.]

[2]) The transform x' of x is indeed $x - a$ and not $x + a$. Let $|b\rangle$ be an eigenvector of x corresponding to the eigenvalue b. Its transform $|b'\rangle$ is an eigenvector of x corresponding to the eigenvalue $b + a$:

$$x\,|b\rangle = b\,|b\rangle \qquad x\,|b'\rangle = (b+a)\,|b'\rangle.$$

But, from the definition of the transformation of observables

$$x'\,|b'\rangle = b\,|b'\rangle$$

whence

$$x' = x - a.$$

This argument is to be compared with that of § XIII.12.

In particular, in the infinitesimal transformation $\mathscr{T}_x(\delta a)$, $\delta x = -\delta a$ and all of the other variations $\delta y, \ldots, \delta s_z$ vanish. The corresponding Hermitean operator Θ_x therefore obeys the commutation rules

$$[\Theta_x, x] = -\mathrm{i}$$
$$[\Theta_x, y] = \ldots = [\Theta_x, s_z] = 0$$

which gives

$$\Theta_x = \frac{p_x}{\hbar} + k_0,$$

where k_0 is a real arbitrary constant which we put equal to zero. This treatment is easily extended to translations of a set of N particles and gives

$$\boxed{\Theta_x = \frac{P_x}{\hbar}} \tag{XV.40}$$

where $P_x = \sum_{i=1}^{N} p_x^{(i)}$ *is the component along* Ox *of the total momentum* of the N particles.

With the infinitesimal translation $\mathscr{T}_x(\delta a)$ there therefore is associated the infinitesimal unitary operator

$$T_x(\delta a) = 1 - \frac{\mathrm{i}}{\hbar} P_x \, \delta a.$$

The finite-transformation operator $T_x(a)$ can be chosen to be

$$T_x(a) = \exp(-\mathrm{i} P_x \, a/\hbar)$$

as may easily be verified by substituting into relation (XV.39) which defines it. The operators thus defined form a group isomorphic to the group of translations along Ox. We have in particular

$$T_x(a) \; T_x(b) = T_x(b) \; T_x(a) = T_x(a+b).$$

The group of translations along Ox is a subgroup of the translation group proper. A particular translation $\mathscr{T}(\boldsymbol{a})$ is defined by the vector $\boldsymbol{a}$ giving the displacement of the dynamical states of the system. The translation group therefore depends on three continuous parameters – the components of $\boldsymbol{a}$. Its composition law is

$$\mathscr{T}(\boldsymbol{a}) \; \mathscr{T}(\boldsymbol{b}) = \mathscr{T}(\boldsymbol{b}) \; \mathscr{T}(\boldsymbol{a}) = \mathscr{T}(\boldsymbol{a}+\boldsymbol{b}).$$

Generalizing the preceding results to any translation whatever, we associate with the infinitesimal translation $\mathscr{T}(\boldsymbol{\epsilon})$ the operator

$$\boxed{T(\boldsymbol{\epsilon}) \simeq 1 - \frac{\mathrm{i}}{\hbar}(\boldsymbol{P}\cdot\boldsymbol{\epsilon})} \qquad \text{(XV.41)}$$

where $\boldsymbol{P}$ is the total momentum of the N particles of the system. It follows that the operator associated with the translation $\mathscr{T}(\boldsymbol{a})$ is

$$\boxed{T(\boldsymbol{a}) = \mathrm{e}^{-\mathrm{i}\boldsymbol{P}\cdot\boldsymbol{a}/\hbar}} \qquad \text{(XV.42)}$$

The T operators thus defined form a group isomorphic to the translation group since

$$T(\boldsymbol{a})\ T(\boldsymbol{b}) = T(\boldsymbol{b})\ T(\boldsymbol{a}) = T(\boldsymbol{a}+\boldsymbol{b}).$$

The rotation group provides another example of a continuous group with three parameters. The rotation operators have already been defined in Chapter XIII. The defining formula (XIII.55) may be compared with (XV.41) above. The total angular momentum $\boldsymbol{J}$ plays the same role for the rotation group as the total momentum $\boldsymbol{P}$ for the translation group. The component $(\boldsymbol{u}\cdot\boldsymbol{J})$ of the total angular momentum along $\boldsymbol{u}$ is defined up to a constant by the commutation relations (XIII.56) and (XIII.57), which give the infinitesimal rotations about $\boldsymbol{u}$ of scalar and vector observables respectively; the arbitrary constant is fixed by the condition that $\boldsymbol{J}$ itself be a vector operator [1]).

The rotation operators R are defined as products of infinitesimal rotations. This leads to formula (XIII.60) which may be compared with (XV.42) above. The operators in question form a group. This group is isomorphic to the rotation group if the system contains an even number of half-integral spins, but only homomorphic to the latter if the system has an odd number of half-integral spins. This point has already been discussed and will not be taken up again here.

The set of T and R operators defined by (XV.42) and (XIII.60), taken together with all of their products, also forms a group. If the system contains an even number of half-integral spins this group is isomorphic to the displacement group; if not, it is merely homomorphic

[1]) This condition is equivalent to the condition that the $R_{\boldsymbol{u}}(\varepsilon)$ be the infinitesimal operators of a group.

to the displacement group, two operators differing by a sign corresponding to each element of the latter.

10. Finite groups. Reflections

Of all the groups, the group of reflections in a point is without doubt the simplest. It has in all two elements, the identity $\mathscr{I}$ and the reflection $\mathscr{S}_0$: $\mathscr{S}_0^2=\mathscr{I}$. In the transformation $\mathscr{S}_0$ the polar vectors $\boldsymbol{r}$, $\boldsymbol{p}$ change sign and the axial vectors $\boldsymbol{r}\times\boldsymbol{p}$, $\boldsymbol{s}$ are invariant. Since $\boldsymbol{r}$ and $\boldsymbol{p}$ simultaneously change sign, the transformation conserves the commutation relations of the orbital variables; it also conserves those of the components of spin. The operator S_0 defining the reflection of a particle is therefore linear; it is the unitary operator obeying the relations

$$\begin{aligned} S_0\, \boldsymbol{r}\, S_0^\dagger &= -\boldsymbol{r} \\ S_0\, \boldsymbol{p}\, S_0^\dagger &= -\boldsymbol{p} \qquad \text{(XV.43)} \\ S_0\, \boldsymbol{s}\, S_0^\dagger &= \boldsymbol{s}. \end{aligned}$$

It is defined by these up to a phase. In order that in addition the operators S_0 and 1 form a group isomorphic to the reflection group, we must have

$$S_0^2 = 1 \qquad (S_0 = S_0^\dagger) \qquad \text{(XV.44)}$$

which fixes the phase of S_0 to within a sign.

S_0 is completely determined by specifying its action on the basis vectors of a representation, the $\{\boldsymbol{r}, s_z\}$ representation for example. We shall adopt the following definition

$$S_0\, |\boldsymbol{r}\, \mu\rangle = |(-\boldsymbol{r})\, \mu\rangle. \qquad \text{(XV.45)}$$

which is consistent with (XV.43) and (XV.44) (Problem XV.2). According to this definition, the reflection of a wave function is given by the rule

$$S_0\, \psi(\boldsymbol{r}, \mu) = \psi(-\boldsymbol{r}, \mu).$$

The operator S_0 is none other than the *parity* operator introduced in § XIII.23. It is an observable with the two eigenvalues ± 1. These considerations can be extended without difficulty to systems of several particles.

The reflection S_0 commutes with all of the rotations $\mathscr{R}$. The product of the operations of the reflection group with those of the rotation group forms the rotation-reflection group. Note too that S_0 commutes with any rotation operator since the latter are functions of the total angular momentum $\boldsymbol{J}$, and S_0 commutes with $\boldsymbol{J}$, since by (XV.43)

$$S_0 \boldsymbol{J} S_0^{\dagger} = \boldsymbol{J}.$$

Thus the set formed of S_0, the R operators, and their products also forms a group. When the group $[R]$ is isomorphic to the rotation group (integral total spin) this group is isomorphic to the rotation-reflection group; if not (half-integral total spin), it is only homomorphic to the rotation-reflection group; with each element of the rotation-reflection group we have associated two operators, differing by a sign; in particular, the two operators associated with the pure reflection are $+S_0$ and $-S_0$ and the two operators associated with the identity are $+1$ and -1.

We next consider a different type of reflection, reflection in a plane. Let $\mathscr{S}_{\boldsymbol{u}}$ be the reflection in the plane perpendicular to the unit vector $\boldsymbol{u}$. $\mathscr{S}_{\boldsymbol{u}}$ is a particular transformation of the rotation-reflection group, namely the product of $\mathscr{S}_0$ with a rotation through an angle π about $\boldsymbol{u}$ (or $-\boldsymbol{u}$):

$$\mathscr{S}_{\boldsymbol{u}} = \mathscr{S}_0 \mathscr{R}_{\boldsymbol{u}}(\pi). \tag{XV.46}$$

We note that

$$\mathscr{S}_{\boldsymbol{u}}^2 = \mathscr{I}. \tag{XV.47}$$

Consequently $\mathscr{S}_{\boldsymbol{u}}$ and $\mathscr{I}$ form a group, and the study of this group can be patterned after the study of reflections in a point. In addition, with the aid of (XV.43) we can deduce the properties of one of these groups from those of the other.

We shall consider only the case of the single particle. The operator $S_{\boldsymbol{u}}$ is the unitary linear operator obeying the relations

$$\begin{aligned} S_{\boldsymbol{u}} \boldsymbol{r} S_{\boldsymbol{u}}^{\dagger} &= \boldsymbol{r} - 2\boldsymbol{u}(\boldsymbol{u}\cdot\boldsymbol{r}) \\ S_{\boldsymbol{u}} \boldsymbol{p} S_{\boldsymbol{u}}^{\dagger} &= \boldsymbol{p} - 2\boldsymbol{u}(\boldsymbol{u}\cdot\boldsymbol{p}) \\ S_{\boldsymbol{u}} \boldsymbol{s} S_{\boldsymbol{u}}^{\dagger} &= -\boldsymbol{s} + 2\boldsymbol{u}(\boldsymbol{u}\cdot\boldsymbol{s}). \end{aligned} \tag{XV.48}$$

We can take for $S_{\boldsymbol{u}}$ the expression

$$S_{\boldsymbol{u}} = S_0 R_{\boldsymbol{u}}(\pi) = S_0 \, \mathrm{e}^{-\mathrm{i}\pi(\boldsymbol{J}\cdot\boldsymbol{u})} \tag{XV.49}$$

which gives

$$S_{\boldsymbol{u}}^2 = S_0^2 \, \mathrm{e}^{-2\pi\mathrm{i}(\boldsymbol{J}\cdot\boldsymbol{u})} = (-)^{2J}. \tag{XV.50}$$

With this choice of phase we therefore have

$$S_u{}^2 = -1$$

in the case of a half-integral spin. To have a set of transformation operators that form a group, we must associate with $\mathscr{S}_u$ the two operators [1] S_u and $-S_u$.

Another type of finite group is the group of permutations of n similar particles. This group was studied in Chapter XIV. With each permutation we associated a linear, unitary permutation operator; the set of operators thereby obtained forms a group isomorphic to the permutation group [2]. We shall not return to these questions here. We add only the important remark that the permutations commute with the spatial transformations and that, just from the way in which they have been constructed, the permutation operators and the spatial transformation operators have the same property.

III. INVARIANCE OF THE EQUATIONS OF MOTION AND CONSERVATION LAWS

11. Invariant Observables

We shall now consider the question of invariance itself. Let $\mathscr{G}$ be a certain group of transformations. We shall denote by G the group of corresponding transformation operators and by T_i a particular element of G. We suppose that all of the T_i are linear (and unitary). The only transformation leading to the introduction of antilinear operators is time reversal; it will be studied in section IV.

The fact that an observable Q is invariant with respect to the transformations of the group is expressed by the condition $T_i\, Q T_i{}^\dagger = Q$, i.e.,

$$[Q, T_i] = 0 \text{ for any } T_i. \qquad \text{(XV.51)}$$

The consequences of these commutation rules have already been

---

[1] If we consider only the group $\{S_u, \mathscr{I}\}$, it is preferable to put $S_u = \mathrm{i}^{2J} S_0 R_u(\pi)$; this gives $S_u{}^2 = 1$. With this new choice of phase, the multiplication rule (XV.46) is conserved only up to a phase.

[2] The same result could have been obtained by replacing all the operators associated with odd permutations by their negatives. The work of Chapter XIV may all be carried through with this new phase convention, with the sole difference that the formulas are complicated with (−) signs without any of the results being changed.

analysed for the case of the rotation group (§ XIII.17). They can be formulated in a very general way using the group concept and the properties of the linear representations of the group G (cf. Appendix D and in particular § D.9). We shall denote by $|\tau\, j\, \mu\rangle$ the basis vectors of a standard representation suited to the group G. These vectors are labelled with three quantum numbers (or 3 sets of quantum numbers). j indicates the irreducible representation to which $|\tau\, j\, \mu\rangle$ belongs. μ distinguishes between the basis vectors of a given irreducible representation. τ is an additional quantum number permitting, if need be, to distinguish between orthogonal, equivalent, irreducible subspaces. We shall intentionally use the same symbols as in § XIII.6, of which the present discussion constitutes an obvious generalization. The essential property of Q is the generalization of (XIII.120), namely

$$\langle \tau\, j\, \mu\, | Q \,|\tau'\, j'\, \mu'\rangle = \delta_{jj'}\, \delta_{\mu\mu'}\, Q^{(j)}_{\tau\tau'}. \tag{XV.52}$$

A complete proof is given in Appendix D [cf. eq. (D.20)].

In many cases, it is possible to derive this relation without referring explicitly to the general theory of group representation. To this effect, one merely needs to find among the functions of T_i:

(i) a set J of observables invariant under *all* operations of the group and whose eigenvalues can be labelled with the quantum number (or set of quantum numbers) j;

(ii) a set M of observables that commute with each other but not with all of the operations of the group, and whose eigenvalues are labelled by μ.

Q, J, and M clearly form a set of commuting observables and therefore Q has a specially simple representative matrix in any representation in which J and M are diagonal, namely the one given by relation (XV.52).

This method was successfully applied to the rotation group [cf. eq. (XIII.120)]. In this particular case, we found one observable of category (i) namely $\boldsymbol{J}^2$, and one observable of category (ii), namely J_z. It also applies to the rotation-reflection group with $\boldsymbol{J}^2$ and S_0 — that is, the total angular momentum and the parity — for set (i), and the observable J_z for set (ii). Note that there is a certain arbitrary in the choice of the M; in the case of rotations, the usual practice is to take J_z, but J_x or J_y or any other component of $\boldsymbol{J}$ would do as well.

The eigenstates of Q are obtained by separately diagonalizing the matrices $Q^{(j)}_{\tau\tau'}$ which each correspond to a well-defined eigenvalue of J. Thus to each j there corresponds a set $q_s^{(j)}$ of eigenvalues of Q which we distinguish one from another, if need be, by the quantum number (or numbers) s. Let d_j be the number of possible values for μ ($2j+1$ in the case of rotations); to each of these values there corresponds the same matrix $Q^{(j)}_{\tau\tau'}$; thus each non-degenerate eigenvalue of this matrix is a d_j-fold degenerate eigenvalue of Q, each p-fold degenerate eigenvalue of this matrix is a pd_j-fold degenerate eigenvalue of Q. If $d_j \neq 1$, all the eigenvalues of Q corresponding to the quantum number j are degenerate, and the order of their degeneracy is a multiple of d_j. This type of degeneracy is a direct consequence of the invariance of Q with respect to G and will be called a *G-degeneracy*.

12. Symmetry of the Hamiltonian and Conservation Laws

Suppose that the Hamiltonian H is invariant in the transformations of a group $\mathscr{G}$. All that we have said about invariant observables will then apply to it. Starting from the commutation rules

$$[H, T_i] = 0 \text{ for any operator } T_i \text{ of } G, \qquad \text{(XV.53)}$$

we form observables of type J and of type M. These observables form with H a set of observables that can be simultaneously diagonalized. In addition, the spectrum of H has a *G-degeneracy*.

As in Classical Mechanics, the symmetries of the Hamiltonian lead to conservation laws, i.e. since any observable (not explicitly dependent on time) that commutes with H is a constant of the motion, we have the obvious property:

If H is invariant in the transformations of a group, any observable that is a function of the operators of the group is a constant of the motion.

In particular, the observables of the set (J, M) defined above have this property, and since they commute, they can be given precise values simultaneously and keep this set of precise values in the course of time.

Thus with each group is associated a certain number of conservation laws. Whenever the conserved observable has a classical analogue, these laws are identical with the corresponding classical conservation laws.[1]) The most common of these are listed below.

(i) *Translational invariance and conservation of the total momentum.* A necessary and sufficient condition for the Hamiltonian to be invariant under translation is that it be invariant with respect to infinitesimal translations, i.e. that [eq. (XV.41)]

$$[H, \mathbf{P}] = 0, \tag{XV.54}$$

where $\mathbf{P}$ is the total momentum of the system. Thus the three components of total momentum are constants of the motion, and the total momentum is conserved. In addition, since P_x, P_y and P_z commute, they can simultaneously be precisely defined, so that they conserve their respective values in the course of time.

(ii) *Rotational invariance and conservation of the angular momentum* (already studied in Chapter XIII; rotational invariance is expressed by the condition: $[H, \mathbf{J}] = 0$).

(iii) *Reflection invariance and conservation of the parity.* It results from the invariance of the Hamiltonian under reflection in a point,

$$[H, S_0] = 0, \tag{XV.55}$$

that the *parity* S_0 is a constant of the motion.

(iv) *Invariance under permutation and conservation of symmetry.* In a system containing identical particles, the Hamiltonian H is invariant in any permutation P of these particles:

$$[H, P] = 0 \qquad \text{for any } P.$$

It follows that any observable built up from the P is a constant of the motion; this is notably the case with the projectors S and A onto the symmetrical and antisymmetrical states respectively:

$$[H, S] = 0 \qquad [H, A] = 0.$$

S and A are therefore constants of the motion. It was seen in Chapter XIV that this property of the operators S and A is a necessary condition for the internal coherence of the symmetrization postulate.

---

[1]) This is the case with the observables associated with infinitesimal displacements (cf. note on p. 650).

(v) *Charge independence and conservation of isotopic spin.* Let $\mathbf{T}$ be the total isotopic spin of a system of nucleons. If the nucleon-nucleon forces are charge-independent, the Hamiltonian of the system will be invariant with respect to rotations in isotopic-spin space, i.e.

$$[H, \mathbf{T}]=0. \tag{XV.56}$$

Therefore, the components of $\mathbf{T}$ are constants of motion, and so is any observable that is a function of these components. In particular $\mathbf{T}^2$ and T_z are constants of the motion (N.B. The conservation of T_z is simply the conservation of charge).

13. Invariance Properties and the Evolution of Dynamical States

We shall now show that if H is invariant with respect to a group $\mathscr{G}$, then so also is the evolution operator $U(t, t_0)$. The latter is by definition the solution of the integral equation

$$U(t, t_0)=1+\frac{1}{\mathrm{i}\hbar}\int_0^t H\, U(t', t_0)\, \mathrm{d}t'.$$

Multiplying both sides on the left by T_i and on the right by $T_i^\dagger$, and taking into account the unitarity of T_i and property (XV.53), we find

$$T_i\, U(t, t_0)\, T_i^\dagger=1+\frac{1}{\mathrm{i}\hbar}\int_{t_0}^t H\, T_i\, U(t', t_0)\, T_i^\dagger\, \mathrm{d}t'.$$

Since U and $T_i\, U\, T_i^\dagger$ satisfy the same integral equation, they are equal, which gives

$$[U(t, t_0), T_i] = 0 \qquad \text{for any operator } T_i \text{ of } G. \tag{XV.57}$$

Among the physical consequences of the invariance of U in the transformations of the group are the conservation laws of the previous paragraph. Moreover, if $|\psi\,(t)\rangle$ is a solution of the equations of motion, then since U and T_i commute, the transformed vector $T_i\,|\psi\,(t)\rangle$ is also a solution. The dynamical states represented by these two vectors therefore correspond at each instant by the transformation $\mathscr{T}_i$. Consequently the law of motion of the dynamical *states* is invariant with respect to the transformations of the group $\mathscr{G}$:

Two dynamical states initially the transforms one of the other by a certain transformation $\mathscr{T}_i$ of the group $\mathscr{G}$, conserve this property in the course of time.

This invariance property may be equivalently expressed in terms of measuring operations:

Suppose that after having prepared the system in a certain way at time t_0, we perform a specific measuring operation upon it at a later time t. The result of this measurement is not modified if, without changing anything else, we effect a given transformation $\mathscr{T}_i$ of the group both on the initial state (i.e. on the apparatus used to prepare the system) *and on the quantity (quantities) measured* (i.e. on the apparatus used to observe it).

Suppose, for example, that the system is prepared in the pure state represented by the vector $|\varphi\rangle$ and that we measure the probability for it to be found in the pure state represented by $|\chi\rangle$. The transforms of these states are respectively represented by the vectors $T_i\,|\varphi\rangle$ and $T_i\,|\chi\rangle$. From the commutation rule (XV.57), we deduce the equality of the probabilities

$$|\langle\chi\,|T_i^\dagger\,U(t, t_0)\,T_i\,|\varphi\rangle\,|^2 = |\,\langle\chi\,|U(t, t_0)\,|\psi\rangle\,|^2. \tag{XV.58}$$

More generally, let ϱ_0 be the density operator representing the state of the system at the time of preparation t_0, and ϱ that representing it at the time the measurement is made, t. A typical measurement would consist in determining the probability that the value(s) of the quantity (quantities) measured will be found in a certain domain D. If we denote by P_D the projector onto the subspace of the eigenstates corresponding to this domain, that probability is

$$w = \mathrm{Tr}\;\varrho\,P_D = \mathrm{Tr}\;U(t, t_0)\,\varrho_0\,U^\dagger(t, t_0)\,P_D. \tag{XV.59}$$

Suppose now that we start from the initial state $\varrho_0' \equiv T_i\,\varrho_0\,T_i^\dagger$ and that the measurement is made on the transform(s) of the quantity (quantities) considered in the first experiment. The projector corresponding to the eigenvalues of the domain D is $P_D' \equiv T_i\,P_D\,T_i^\dagger$. The result of this new measurement will therefore be

$$w' = \mathrm{Tr}\;U(T_i\,\varrho_0\,T_i^\dagger)\;U^\dagger(T_i\,P_D\,T_i^\dagger). \tag{XV.60}$$

Taking into account the properties of the trace and the unitarity of T_i, relation (XV.57) gives

$$w' = w. \tag{XV.61}$$

In fact, if (XV.58) is valid for any $|\varphi\rangle$ and $|\chi\rangle$, (XV.61) necessarily follows.

What has been done above was to assume that H is invariant with respect to the transformations of a given group $\mathscr{G}$, and to deduce, among other things, that the "law of motion" of the dynamical states is invariant with respect to $\mathscr{G}$. Conversely, we may *postulate that the law of motion is invariant with respect to* $\mathscr{G}$, *and explore the consequences of this postulate.* Such a postulate is equivalent to assuming that for every transformation $\mathscr{T}_i$ of the group, equation (XV.58) is satisfied whatever $|\varphi\rangle$ and $|\chi\rangle$, or (theorem II), that U and $T_i^\dagger\, U\, T_i$ are equal to within a phase:

$$T_i^\dagger\, U(t, t_0)\, T_i = \mathrm{e}^{\mathrm{i}\alpha_i}\, U(t, t_0). \tag{XV.62}$$

The phase factors $\mathrm{e}^{\mathrm{i}\alpha_i}$ are subject to severe limitations. For most of the groups encountered in physics, they are necessarily all equal to 1 [1]).

We shall always suppose this phase condition fulfilled, even when considerations of internal coherence do not require it. The invariance postulate may then be written

$$[T_i, U(t, t_0)] = 0.$$

In the case of the infinitesimal U operator, $U(t+\mathrm{d}t, t) = 1 - (\mathrm{i}/\hbar)\, H\, \mathrm{d}t$, we recover the symmetry of the Hamiltonian:

$$[T_i, H] = 0.$$

Thus any postulate of invariance for the law of motion leads to a symmetry property of the Hamiltonian. For an isolated quantum system (no external field) one usually postulates invariance with respect to the displacement group; this amounts to supposing space

---

[1]) This is due to the fact that the $\mathrm{e}^{\mathrm{i}\alpha_i}$ constitute a one dimensional representation of the group $\mathscr{G}$, and that they are continuous functions of t tending to 1 when $t \to t_0$. If $\mathscr{G}$ is a finite group, or at least if $\mathscr{T}_i$ is an element of a finite group, there exists an integer p such that $\mathscr{T}_i{}^p = \mathscr{I}$; it follows that $\mathrm{e}^{\mathrm{i}\alpha_i}$ is one of the pth roots of unity. The above-mentioned continuity condition requires that $\mathrm{e}^{\mathrm{i}\alpha_i} = 1$. Reflections in a point and reflections in a plane are examples of such transformations. If the only one-dimensional representation of the group $\mathscr{G}$ is the identical representation we obviously have $\mathrm{e}^{\mathrm{i}\alpha_i} = 1$ for every operation of the group; the rotation group and the displacement group fall into this category. On the other hand, if the invariance group of the law of motion is limited to the group of translations, this alone does not necessarily lead to all of the phases α_i being null.

to be homogeneous (translational invariance) and isotropic (rotational invariance). Up to the present this postulate has never come into conflict with experiment.

For a great many years it was also thought that the motion of physical systems was invariant under reflection. This is verified experimentally for all phenomena where the only interactions involved are the electromagnetic interactions and the so-called nuclear interactions, i.e. the interactions responsible for the cohesion of atomic nuclei. However, experiment shows it to be violated by certain interactions, and in particular by those responsible for the β decay of atomic nuclei. These interactions are much weaker than the preceding ones; whenever they can be neglected the motion of a physical system is invariant under reflection and the parity is conserved. This is notably the case in atomic physics where only electromagnetic interactions are involved.

When an external field is present, the invariance properties of the law of motion depend on the symmetries of the field. By way of illustration we shall consider two examples taken from atomic physics – the Stark effect and the Zeeman effect.

14. Symmetries of the Stark and Zeeman Effects

STARK EFFECT

Consider an atomic system in an external electric field $\mathscr{E}$ directed, say, along the z axis. This field is invariant under translation, under rotation about the z axis and under reflection in planes parallel to the z axis; the invariance group involved here is the product of the translation group by the group of reflections in planes containing Oz.

We suppose the motion of the center of mass already separated out, and consider only the possible states of the Hamiltonian H of the relative variables; the latter is invariant with respect to the group of reflections in planes containing Oz. The considerations to follow are based uniquely on this invariance property; they involve neither the detail nor the strength of the coupling of the system with the electric field.

Let $\mathscr{S}_u$ be the reflection in an arbitrarily chosen plane containing Oz, and S_u the corresponding operator. The phase of S_u will be taken so as to have $S_u^2 = 1$. Since the group in question is generated by the reflection $\mathscr{S}_u$ and the infinitesimal rotations about Oz, any transformation operator of the group is a function of S_u and of J_z. Thus we have in all two independent constants of the motion S_u and J_z. Since they do not commute,

$$S_u J_z S_u = -J_z. \tag{XV.63}$$

Certain of the eigenvalues of H are necessarily degenerate.

Continuing, we note that J_z^2 commutes with both J_z and S_u and therefore with all the operators of the group. J_z^2 is the observable of type J of the group (definition of § 11). As the observable of type M we may take either J_z or S_u. In the first case we classify the stationary states according to the eigenvalues of J_z, in the second according to those of the set (J_z^2, S_u).

Suppose that the system contains an even number of half-integral spins. J_z can then take all integral values; we denote a particular one of these by m. If $|\rangle$ is a stationary state corresponding to this value, then $S_u |\rangle$ is a stationary state of the same energy corresponding to the eigenvalue $-m$ of J_z. If $m \neq 0$, these two states are necessarily orthogonal. Thus, if we classify the stationary states according to the eigenvalues of J_z, two opposite eigenvalues m and $-m$ give the same energy spectrum, each level of the spectrum having the same order of degeneracy. In other words, the energy levels depend only on $|m|$ and all the levels corresponding to $|m| \neq 0$ present a degeneracy of even order.

We can equally well obtain this result by classifying the stationary states according to the eigenvalues of the pair (J_z^2, S_u). To denote these eigenvalues we use the symbols m^+ and m^-; m is a non-negative integer whose square is equal to the eigenvalue of J_z^2 and the superscript is positive or negative according as the eigenvalue of S_u is $+1$ or -1. As an example consider a state m^+:

$$J_z^2 |m^+\rangle = m^2 |m^+\rangle \qquad S_u |m^+\rangle = |m^+\rangle.$$

If $m \neq 0$, the vector $J_z |m^+\rangle$ does not vanish and we have, from (XV.63),

$$S_u (J_z |m^+\rangle) = -J_z S_u |m^+\rangle = -(J_z |m^+\rangle).$$

Thus J_z operating on any m^+ state gives a m^- state; if the first is a stationary state, the second is also and corresponds to the same energy level: the energy levels depend only on the positive integer m and all present a degeneracy of even order. The case $m = 0$ is an exception: the energy spectra of the states 0^+ and 0^- may be different.

ZEEMAN EFFECT

Consider now an atomic system in a constant magnetic field $\mathscr{H}$ directed along the z axis. In a reflection in a plane parallel to this axis, $\mathscr{H}$ changes sign. On the other hand, $\mathscr{H}$ is invariant in a reflection $\mathscr{S}_0$ in the origin. The invariance group of the external field is thus the group generated by the translations, the rotations about Oz and the reflection $\mathscr{S}_0$. As in the case of the Stark effect, we examine only the symmetries of the Hamiltonian H of the relative variables. H is invariant in rotation about Oz and in reflection in the origin. Let S_0 be the parity operator and let its phase be fixed so as to have $S_0^2=1$. All of the transformations of the group are expressible as functions of the observables J_z and S_0 and these two observables commute:

$$S_0 J_z S_0 = J_z.$$

Therefore, the invariance of H with respect to the transformations of this group does not lead to any systematic degeneracy [1]).

H, S_0 and J_z can be simultaneously diagonalized and each common eigenvector of these three observables represents a stationary state invariant with respect to the transformations of the group. This result is based uniquely on the symmetry properties of H; it is independent of the detail and of the strength of the coupling of the system with the magnetic field.

IV. TIME REVERSAL AND THE PRINCIPLE OF MICROREVERSIBILITY

15. Time-translation and Conservation of Energy

Of all the transformations involving the time the simplest are the time-translations. In Classical Mechanics, the invariance of the equations of motion under time-translation leads to the well-known conservation of energy law (it requires the Hamiltonian function to be time-independent). We obtain an analogous property in Quantum Mechanics.

Let $|\psi(t)\rangle$ be a possible solution of the equations of motion. To state that the law of motion of the system is invariant under a translation

---

[1]) In other words, the irreducible representations of the group are necessarily all of degree 1.

τ of the time is equivalent to stating that there is another solution $|\psi'(t)\rangle$ which represents at time t the dynamical state that the previous solution represents at time $t+\tau$, i.e.,

$$|\psi'(t)\rangle = \mathrm{e}^{\mathrm{i}\alpha(t,\tau)}\,|\psi(t+\tau)\rangle.$$

In order for every solution of the equations of motion to have this property, it is necessary that the operator U have the property

$$U(t, 0) = \mathrm{e}^{\mathrm{i}\alpha(t,\tau)}\, U(t+\tau, \tau), \qquad \text{(XV.64)}$$

where $\alpha(t, \tau)$ is a phase that may depend on t and τ. For infinitely small t, putting $f(\tau) = \partial\alpha/\partial t|_{t=0}$, we have

$$1 - \frac{\mathrm{i}}{\hbar} H(0)\,\mathrm{d}t = (1 + \mathrm{i}\, f(\tau)\,\mathrm{d}t)\left(1 - \frac{\mathrm{i}}{\hbar} H(\tau)\,\mathrm{d}t\right),$$

i.e.

$$H(\tau) = H(0) + \hbar\, f(\tau). \qquad \text{(XV.65)}$$

If the law of motion is invariant in any time-translation then (XV.64) must hold for all τ. In other words, the Hamiltonian is constant to within the addition of a (real) function of the time. In actual fact, this function can be supposed null without modifying any of the physical properties of the system. To replace the Hamiltonian $H(t)$ by its value at time $t=0$ only has the effect of multiplying $U(t, t_0)$ by the phase factor $[\mathrm{i}\int_0^t f(t')\,\mathrm{d}t']$ (Problem XV.6).

Thus, we may suppose the Hamiltonian to be time-independent if the law of motion is invariant under time-translations. This will always be done in what follows. Eq. (XV.64) then reduces to the invariance of $U(t, t_0)$ in time-translations

$$U(t+\tau, \tau) = U(t, 0). \qquad \text{(XV.66)}$$

16. Time Reversal in Classical Mechanics and in Quantum Mechanics

The systems to be considered in the remainder of this section are all conservative. It often occurs that the laws of motion for such systems are invariant not only with respect to time-translation but also with respect to time reversal. We also encounter this type of invariance in Classical Mechanics.

The Lagrangian function $L_{\text{cl}}(\dot{q}, q)$ of Classical Mechanics is a second-degree polynomial with respect to the velocities. For many systems, terms of the first degree are absent and we have

$$L_{\text{cl}}(\dot{q}, q) = L_{\text{cl}}(-\dot{q}, q).$$

Systems of isolated particles always have this symmetry property. It is not necessarily destroyed by the introduction of a static external field; it is preserved, for example, in a pure electric field. On the other hand a magnetic field introduces a linear coupling with respect to the velocities and therefore destroys it. When it holds, the momenta p are homogeneous linear functions of the velocities and the Hamiltonian function has an analogous symmetry property.

To make the discussion less formal we shall examine the consequences of such a symmetry for the simple particular case of a particle in a static potential. In this case we have

$$H(\boldsymbol{p}, \boldsymbol{r}) \equiv \frac{\boldsymbol{p}^2}{2m} + V(\boldsymbol{r}) = H(-\boldsymbol{p}, \boldsymbol{r}). \tag{XV.67}$$

It follows that all solutions $\boldsymbol{r}(t)$ of the equations of motion are reversible with respect to time: the function $\boldsymbol{r}_{\text{rev}}(t)$ defined by

$$\boldsymbol{r}_{\text{rev}}(t) = \boldsymbol{r}(-t) \tag{XV.68}$$

is also a solution of the equations of motion. The correspondence between these two solutions is represented in Figure XV.1. The

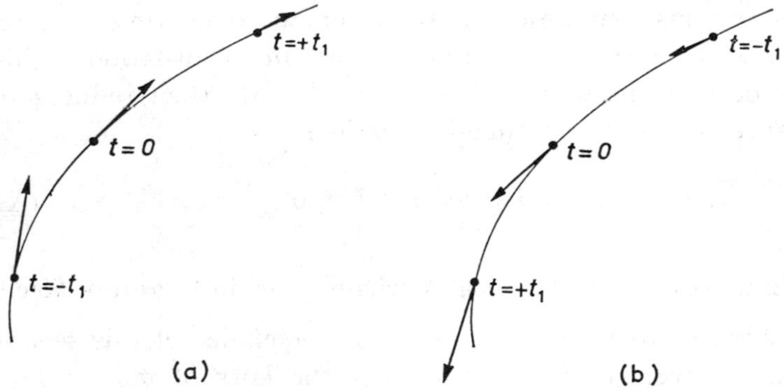

Fig. XV.1. Configuration space representation of two classical trajectories (*a*) and (*b*) that correspond by time reversal:

$$\boldsymbol{r}_a(t) = \boldsymbol{r}_b(-t), \qquad \dot{\boldsymbol{r}}_a(t) = -\dot{\boldsymbol{r}}_b(-t).$$

position of the particle at time t in one of the solutions is equal to its position at time $-t$ in the other; its velocity at time t in one solution is the opposite of its velocity at time $-t$ in the other. The correspondence between momenta is the same as the correspondence between velocities:

$$\boldsymbol{p}_{\text{rev}}(t) = -\boldsymbol{p}(-t). \tag{XV.69}$$

Consider now the analogous quantum system. Its Schrödinger equation is

$$i\hbar \frac{\partial}{\partial t} \psi(\boldsymbol{r}, t) = \left[-\frac{\hbar^2}{2m} \triangle + V(\boldsymbol{r}) \right] \psi(\boldsymbol{r}, t). \tag{XV.70}$$

The Hamiltonian being a real operator, if we change t into $-t$ and take the complex conjugate of both sides we have

$$i\hbar \frac{\partial}{\partial t} \psi^*(\boldsymbol{r}, -t) = \left[-\frac{\hbar^2}{2m} \triangle + V(\boldsymbol{r}) \right] \psi^*(\boldsymbol{r}, -t). \tag{XV.71}$$

In other words, if $\psi(\boldsymbol{r}, t)$ is a solution of the Schrödinger equation, then so is the function

$$\psi_{\text{rev}}(\boldsymbol{r}, t) \equiv \psi^*(\boldsymbol{r}, -t). \tag{XV.72}$$

The correspondence between ψ and ψ_{rev} is strikingly analogous to the correspondence between the two classical solutions discussed above [eqs. (XV.68–69)]; $P(\boldsymbol{r}, t)$ and $\Pi(\boldsymbol{p}, t)$ denoting respectively the probability densities for position and momentum at time t, one can easily show that

$$P_{\text{rev}}(\boldsymbol{r}, t) = P(\boldsymbol{r}, -t) \tag{XV.68$'$}$$

$$\Pi_{\text{rev}}(\boldsymbol{p}, t) = \Pi(-\boldsymbol{p}, -t). \tag{XV.69$'$}$$

17. The Time-reversal Operation. Spinless Particle

As seen in the preceding example, the reversibility of the solutions of the Schrödinger equation with respect to time is due to the invariance of the Hamiltonian $H(\boldsymbol{p}, \boldsymbol{r})$ when $\boldsymbol{p}$ is changed into $-\boldsymbol{p}$. Indeed, this is why it is represented by a real differential operator in Wave Mechanics. We are thus led to define a transformation of the dynamical variables and dynamical states, which we shall call *time reversal*, in which $\boldsymbol{r}$ and $\boldsymbol{p}$ transform respectively into $\boldsymbol{r}$ and $-\boldsymbol{p}$. We denote the operator effecting this transformation by K and the transformation itself by $\mathscr{K}$. By definition

$$K\, \boldsymbol{r}\, K^\dagger = \boldsymbol{r} \qquad K\, \boldsymbol{p}\, K^\dagger = -\boldsymbol{p}. \tag{XV.73}$$

The transformation changes the sign of the commutation relations, and K is therefore an *antiunitary operator* (cf. § 6). It is defined by relations (XV.73) up to a phase factor. Let K_0 be the complex-conjugation operator associated with the representation of Wave Mechanics (this type of antiunitary operator was defined in § 5). Since the matrices representing $\boldsymbol{r}$ and $\boldsymbol{p}$ in this representation are respectively real and pure imaginary, K_0 obviously satisfies relations (XV.73). Therefore we may take K_0 as our time reversal operator:

$$K = K_0.$$

With this choice of phase, the action of K on a wave function gives its complex conjugate:

$$K\Phi(\boldsymbol{r}) = \Phi^*(\boldsymbol{r}).$$

To suppose H invariant in the substitution of $-\boldsymbol{p}$ for $\boldsymbol{p}$ amounts to supposing that

$$[K, H] = 0. \tag{XV.74}$$

The application of the (antiunitary) operator K to both sides of the Schrödinger equation then gives

$$-\mathrm{i}\hbar \frac{\partial}{\partial t} K\,|\psi(t)\rangle = HK\,|\psi(t)\rangle,$$

i.e.

$$\mathrm{i}\hbar \frac{\partial}{\partial t}(K\,|\psi(-t)\rangle) = H(K\,|\psi(-t)\rangle).$$

Thus, if $|\psi(t)\rangle$ satisfies the Schrödinger equation, then so does the vector

$$|\psi(t)\rangle_{\mathrm{rev}} \equiv K\,|\psi(-t)\rangle. \tag{XV.75}$$

The dynamical state represented by the vector $|\psi\rangle_{\mathrm{rev}}$ at a given time t is the time-reversal transform of the state represented by the vector $|\psi\rangle$ at time $-t$. This is just the reversibility property of the solutions of the Schrödinger equation, as found in the preceding paragraph.

From the relations (XV.73) that define it, there results that the transformation $\mathscr{K}$ commutes with all of the spatial transformations (translations, rotations and reflections). We also note that K commutes with the spatial-transformation operators, as defined in section II [1]). In particular K anticommutes with the three components of momentum and therefore commutes with the infinitesimal-translation operators; similarly it anticommutes with the three components of angular momentum,

$$K\,(\boldsymbol{r}\times\boldsymbol{p})\,K^{\dagger} = -(\boldsymbol{r}\times\boldsymbol{p}), \tag{XV.76}$$

and therefore commutes with the infinitesimal-rotation operators.

18. General Definition of Time Reversal

In order to extend the notion of time reversal to the most general systems of particles we must define the time reversal of the spin variables. Since the spin is a particular angular momentum, it must transform like the orbital angular momentum [eq. (XV.76)], i.e.

$$K\,\boldsymbol{s}\,K^{\dagger} = -\boldsymbol{s}. \tag{XV.77}$$

The time-reversal operation inverts the spin. This definition preserves the property of commutation of $\mathscr{K}$ with the spatial transformations and notably with the rotations. Moreover, according to (XV.76) and (XV.77), K anticommutes with the components of the total angular momentum $\boldsymbol{J}$:

$$K\,\boldsymbol{J}\,K^{\dagger} = -\boldsymbol{J} \tag{XV.78}$$

and consequently commutes with the rotation operators (cf. Problem XV.8), i.e. since K is antilinear, (XV.78) leads to:

$$K e^{-i(\boldsymbol{J}\cdot\boldsymbol{u})\varphi/\hbar}\,K^{\dagger} = \exp\left[+\frac{i}{\hbar}\,\varphi(K(\boldsymbol{J}\cdot\boldsymbol{u})K^{\dagger})\right] = e^{-i(\boldsymbol{J}\cdot\boldsymbol{u})\varphi/\hbar}.$$

We next construct the time-reversal operator for a particle of spin s.

---

[1]) If the transformation $\mathscr{K}$ commutes with another transformation $\mathscr{T}$, we necessarily have $KT = e^{i\alpha}\,TK$, the phase factor $e^{i\alpha}$ depending on the choice of the operator T. As may easily be seen, the latter is defined up to a sign if we further require that $KT = TK$.

This permits us to draw certain conclusions as to the possible complexity of the group of operators G associated with a group of transformations $\mathscr{G}$, when the latter commutes with $\mathscr{K}$. We may then take for (T_i) [notation of § 8] the two transformation operators that commute with K. In particular (1) denotes the pair $(+1, -1)$. The set $\{T\}$ formed of these pairs (the one the negative of the other) of operators is obviously a group, and may be chosen as the group G.

This operator is defined by (XV.73) and (XV.77). We denote by K_0 the complex-conjugation operator associated with the $\{\mathbf{r}, s_z\}$ representation, where the relative phases of the basis vectors are fixed by the usual conventions and in particular the basis vectors of spin space are those of the "standard" choice defined in Chapter XIII. We therefore have

$$K_0\, \mathbf{r}\, K_0 = \mathbf{r} \qquad K_0\, \mathbf{p}\, K_0 = -\mathbf{p} \tag{XV.79}$$

$$K_0\, s_x\, K_0 = s_x \qquad K_0\, s_y\, K_0 = -s_y \qquad K_0\, s_z\, K_0 = s_z. \tag{XV.80}$$

Put

$$K = T K_0. \tag{XV.81}$$

Since $T = KK_0$ and $T^\dagger = K_0 K^\dagger$, the (*linear*) unitary transformation T gives:

$$T\, \mathbf{r}\, T^\dagger = \mathbf{r} \qquad T\, \mathbf{p}\, T^\dagger = \mathbf{p} \tag{XV.82}$$

$$T\, s_x\, T^\dagger = -s_x \qquad T\, s_y\, T^\dagger = s_y \qquad T\, s_z\, T^\dagger = -s_z. \tag{XV.83}$$

Eqs. (XV.82) and (XV.83) give the transformation of the variables $\mathbf{r}$, $\mathbf{p}$, $\mathbf{s}$, *in a rotation of the spin alone through an angle* π *about the* y *axis*. Let $Y^{(s)}$ be the operator effecting this rotation

$$Y^{(s)} = \mathrm{e}^{-\mathrm{i}\pi s_y/\hbar}.$$

T and $Y^{(s)}$ differ only by a phase factor, and since this factor has no physical significance we shall put it equal to 1. This gives

$$K = Y^{(s)} K_0 = \mathrm{e}^{-\mathrm{i}\pi s_y/\hbar}\, K_0. \tag{XV.84}$$

For the special case of a particle of spin $\frac{1}{2}$

$$K = -\mathrm{i}\sigma_y K_0. \tag{XV.85}$$

All of this can be extended without difficulty to systems of N particles. The operator K becomes the tensor product of the time-reversal operators for each individual particle. If K_0 is the complex-conjugation operator associated with the standard representation $\{\mathbf{r}^{(1)}\, s_z^{(1)} \ldots \mathbf{r}^{(N)}\, s_z^{(N)}\}$, and $Y^{(S)}$ the operator for the rotation of the intrinsic spins through an angle π about the $0y$ axis, we find, with the choice of phase adopted above,

$$\boxed{K = Y^{(S)} K_0 = \mathrm{e}^{-\mathrm{i}\pi S_y/\hbar}\, K_0} \tag{XV.86}$$

19. Time Reversal and Complex Conjugation

The time-reversal operation $\mathscr{K}$ presents many analogies with complex conjugation. By extension, two linear operators that are time-reversal transforms one of the other will henceforth be called *complex conjugates*. In particular, an operator Q is

(i) *real* if $K\,Q\,K^{\dagger}=Q$

(ii) *pure imaginary* if $K\,Q\,K^{\dagger}=-Q$.

Any real constant is a real operator. The constant i is a pure imaginary operator. The product of i with a real operator is a pure imaginary; the sum and product of two real operators are real operators.

The notion of reality is not to be confused with that of Hermiticity. In this respect we make the following two remarks:

(a) Contrary to what happens in Hermitean conjugation, two complex-conjugate operators are not necessarily represented in a given representation by complex-conjugate matrices.

(b) The above definition of complex conjugation is not the only one possible; any antiunitary transformation whose square is equal to $\mathscr{I}$ can be treated as a complex conjugation.

In *our* definition of complex conjugation, the position observables are all real, the momenta and spins are all imaginary, and the spatial-transformation operators, as defined in section II, are real (Problem XV.8).

The notion of complex conjugation can be extended to include vectors. We define the *complex conjugate of the vector* $|\rangle$ *to be the vector* $K\,|\rangle$. This is not a reciprocal correspondence unless $K^2=1$. It does not necessarily follow from $\mathscr{K}^2=\mathscr{I}$ that $K^2=1$, but only that K^2 commutes with all the dynamical variables, and is therefore a constant. It may easily be shown (Problem XV.9) that the value of this constant is independent of the choice of phase adopted for the definition of K and that the only possible values are ± 1. Moreover this value may be calculated from expression (XV.86) for K; since K_0 commutes with $Y^{(S)}$ and $K_0{}^2=1$, we find

$$K^2=(Y^{(S)})^2=\mathrm{e}^{-2\pi \mathrm{i} S_y/\hbar} \qquad \text{(XV.87)}$$

or, denoting by n the number of particles in the system with half-integral spins,

$$\boxed{K^2=(-)^n} \qquad \text{(XV.88)}$$

If $K^2 = 1$ (n even), the complex conjugation of vectors is a reciprocal correspondence and we can define real vectors. A vector $|r\rangle$ is real if

$$K\,|r\rangle = |r\rangle.$$

By definition a *real representation* is a representation whose basis vectors are all real.

To set up a real basis we may proceed in the following way. We start with an arbitrarily chosen vector $|a\rangle$ and by linear combination of $|a\rangle$ and $K\,|a\rangle$ form the real vector of norm 1

$$|a^r\rangle = c\,|a\rangle + c^*(K\,|a\rangle).$$

The real character of $|a^r\rangle$ is obvious. The constant c is to be adjusted so as to make the norm equal to 1; one easily verifies that it is always possible to do so. We then take a vector $|b\rangle$ orthogonal to $|a^r\rangle$ and form in the same way the real vector $|b^r\rangle$ of norm 1. Since $K\,|a^r\rangle = |a^r\rangle$ and since by hypothesis $\langle a^r\,|b\rangle = 0$, we have

$$\langle a^r\,|(K\,|b\rangle) = (\langle a^r\,|K^\dagger)\,(K\,|b\rangle) = \langle a^r\,|b\rangle^* = 0$$

and consequently $|b^r\rangle$ is orthogonal to $|a^r\rangle$. We then take another vector $|c\rangle$ orthogonal to $|a^r\rangle$ and $|b^r\rangle$ and form the vector $|c^r\rangle$, and so on, until we have formed a complete set.

Real representations have interesting properties. The associated complex-conjugation operator is the operator K itself. Any real operator is represented by a real matrix; two complex-conjugate operators are represented by complex-conjugate matrices. The unitary matrices relating two real representations are real matrices.

If $K^2 = -1$ (n odd), there are no real vectors. However, since $K = -K^\dagger$, we have for any vector $|u\rangle$

$$\langle u\,|(K\,|u\rangle) \equiv \langle u\,|(K^\dagger\,|u\rangle) = -\langle u\,|(K\,|u\rangle) = 0.$$

We therefore have the interesting property that:

Two complex-conjugate vectors $|\rangle$ and $K\,|\rangle$ are orthogonal.

In addition, if a vector $|b\rangle$ is orthogonal to two complex-conjugate vectors $|a\rangle$ and $K\,|a\rangle$, then so is its complex conjugate $K\,|b\rangle$. From this property, easy to verify, we deduce, by an argument patterned on the one for the case $K^2 = 1$, that there exist bases entirely made up of pairs of complex-conjugate vectors.

20. Principle of Microreversibility

Just as we postulate that the law of motion of a given system is invariant under certain spatial transformations (§ 13), we can also postulate that it is reversible with respect to time, i.e. that if $|\psi(t)\rangle = U(t, 0)\,|\psi\rangle$ represents a possible state of motion of the system, then the vector

$$|\psi(t)\rangle_{\text{rev}} = KU(-t, 0)\,|\psi\rangle,$$

also represents a possible state of motion of the system, and is therefore equal, to within a phase factor, to $U(t, 0)\,K\,|\psi\rangle$. This property being assumed to hold for all $|\psi\rangle$, the postulate of reversibility with respect to the time is written

$$U(t, 0)\,K = e^{i\alpha(t)}\,KU(-t, 0).$$

This postulate applies only to conservative systems. If we denote the Hamiltonian by H we have

$$U(t, 0) = e^{-iHt/\hbar} \qquad U(-t, 0) = e^{+iHt/\hbar} = U^\dagger(t, 0)$$

from which

$$U(t, 0) = e^{i\alpha}(KU^\dagger(t, 0)\,K^\dagger). \tag{XV.89}$$

Multiplying both sides on the left by K and on the right by $K^\dagger$, and using the fact that $K^2 = K^{\dagger 2} = (-)^n$ we find that

$$U^\dagger(t, 0) = e^{i\alpha}(KU(t, 0)\,K^\dagger).$$

Comparing this relation with the Hermitean conjugate of (XV.89)

$$U^\dagger(t, 0) = e^{-i\alpha}(KU(t, 0)\,K^\dagger),$$

we see that $e^{i\alpha}$ can take only the values ± 1; but since $e^{i\alpha}$ is a continuous function of t and is equal to 1 when $t = 0$, we necessarily have $e^{i\alpha} = 1$. Applying (XV.89) to the infinitesimal operator

$$U(dt, 0) = 1 - \frac{i}{\hbar} H\,dt$$

gives

$$1 - \frac{i}{\hbar} H\,dt = K\left[1 + \frac{i}{\hbar} H\,dt\right] K^\dagger,$$

i.e.

$$KHK^\dagger = H. \tag{XV.90}$$

Thus, *if the law of motion of a conservative system is reversible with respect to the time, the Hamiltonian is real, and conversely* (the converse was proved in § 17).

The reversibility postulate is usually formulated under the name of the *principle of microreversibility*, in a way that differs somewhat from the above. This other formulation is as follows.

Let w be the probability of finding the system (supposed conservative) at time t in a certain state $|\chi\rangle$ when it was prepared at time t_0 in the state $|\varphi\rangle$; let w_{rev} be the probability of finding it at time t in the state $K\,|\varphi\rangle$ when it was prepared at time t_0 in the state $K\,|\chi\rangle$. The microreversibility principle states that

$$w_{\text{rev}} = w \tag{XV.91}$$

for all $|\varphi\rangle$, $|\chi\rangle$, t_0 and t.

Condition (XV.91) can be written

$$|\,(\langle\varphi\,|K^\dagger)\,(U(t,t_0)\,K\,|\chi\rangle)\,|^2 = |\,\langle\chi\,|U(t,t_0)\,|\varphi\rangle\,|^2.$$

This relation may be compared with relation (XV.58). Since we have

$$(\langle\varphi\,|K^\dagger)\,(UK\,|\chi\rangle) = \langle\varphi\,|(K^\dagger UK)\,|\chi\rangle^* = \langle\chi\,|(K^\dagger U^\dagger K)\,|\varphi\rangle$$

it can be written

$$|\,\langle\chi\,|(K^\dagger U^\dagger K)\,|\varphi\rangle\,| = |\,\langle\chi\,|U\,|\varphi\rangle\,|.$$

Since this relation is satisfied whatever $|\varphi\rangle$ and $|\chi\rangle$, U and $K^\dagger U^\dagger K$ are equal to within a phase factor (Theorem II). The argument used above in connection with $e^{i\alpha}$ can be repeated to show that this phase factor is necessarily equal to 1. The microreversibility principle therefore requires that

$$\boxed{U(t,t_0) = K^\dagger U^\dagger(t,t_0) K} \tag{XV.92}$$

which, in the case of the infinitesimal U operator, is just the condition for the invariance of the Hamiltonian, (XV.90) [1].

It is currently assumed that any quantum system evolving in the absence of external fields satisfies the microreversibility principle. Up

---

[1]) Since $U^\dagger(t_2, t_1) = U(t_1, t_2)$, equation (XV.92) may also be written

$$U(t_2, t_1) = K^\dagger U\,(t_1, t_2) K.$$

to now this hypothesis has not come into conflict with experiment. In the presence of an external field the principle is, or is not, satisfied according to whether the field is, or is not, invariant with respect to time reversal. An electrostatic field has this invariance property. This is easily understood since the sources of such a field are fixed electric charges, and a static charge distribution is not modified by time reversal. The sources of a static magnetic field, on the other hand, are fixed electric currents: time reversal reverses the currents and therefore also the fields. Hence the microreversibility principle cannot be satisfied in the presence of a magnetic field even a time-indepenent magnetic field.

21. Consequence: Kramers Degeneracy

As with any other symmetry, the realness of H is reflected in certain special properties of the corresponding eigenvalue problem.

If $|u\rangle$ is an eigenvector of H,

$$H\,|u\rangle = E\,|u\rangle,$$

its complex conjugate $K\,|u\rangle$ is also an eigenvector of H and corresponds to the same eigenvalue E, i.e. by hypothesis

$$HK = KH$$

and, since E is real,

$$H(K\,|u\rangle) = K(H\,|u\rangle) = (KE\,|u\rangle) = E(K\,|u\rangle).$$

Consequently the subspace $\mathscr{E}_E$ of the eigenvalue E is invariant in the antiunitary transformation K and we may apply the results of § 19. There are two cases to be considered according as $K^2 = \pm 1$.

1st CASE. $K^2 = +1$ (even number of spins $\frac{1}{2}$).

In each subspace $\mathscr{E}_E$ we can choose an orthonormal basis whose vectors are all real. Thus H has (at least) one basis whose vectors are all *real.*

2nd CASE. $K^2 = -1$ (odd number of spins $\frac{1}{2}$).

In each subspace $\mathscr{E}_E$ we can choose an orthonormal basis made up of pairs of complex-conjugate vectors. Thus each subspace $\mathscr{E}_E$ has an even number of dimensions: *each eigenvalue of H is at least twofold degenerate and its degeneracy is necessarily of even order*. This type of degeneracy is called a *Kramers degeneracy.*

Certain systems have no symmetries other than the invariance under time reversal. Such is the case for the atoms in an asymetrical crystal network. Such an atom may be treated as a system in a purely electrostatic external field. Its Hamiltonian is real. If it has an odd number of electrons, all of its levels are doubly degenerate. The degeneracy is removed by the introduction of a magnetic field.

22. Real Rotation-invariant Hamiltonian

If the Hamiltonian H has symmetry properties other than time reversal, the results of the preceding paragraph remain valid but lose much of their interest. Wigner [1]) has systematically studied the properties of H in the case when

(i) H is real: $[K, H]=0$

(ii) H is invariant in the transformations T_i of a group of *linear* transformations: $[T_i, H]=0$

(iii) the transformations T_i commute with time reversal:

$$[K, T_i]=0.$$

We shall discuss here only the case when the invariance group is the rotation group [2]).

Let Y be the operator for rotation through an angle π about the y

---

1) E. P. Wigner, Göttinger Nachrichten, 31 (1932) 546.

2) For a given group G, the fact that H is real has the effect of either doubling the "G degeneracy" or making possible the diagonalization of H in a representation whose basis vectors obey a certain "reality" condition. The detailed result is as follows (cf. Wigner, *loc. cit.*):

Let $\mathsf{G}^{(j)}$ be an irreducible representation of G, $\mathsf{G}^{(j)*}$ the conjugate representation. K acting on a vector of one of these representations gives a vector of the other. Either $\mathsf{G}^{(j)}$ and $\mathsf{G}^{(j)*}$ are equivalent or they are inequivalent; in the first case, the matrix S permitting to pass from the one to the other ($\mathsf{G}^{(j)*}= S\mathsf{G}^{(j)}S^{\dagger}$) has the property $SS^* = \pm 1$. Call G the representation of the group G defined in the subspace of a given eigenvalue of H. Three cases have to be considered:

(*a*) If $\mathsf{G}^{(j)*}$ is inequivalent to $\mathsf{G}^{(j)}$, these two representations appear the same number of times in the decomposition of G in irreducible components (degeneracy doubled);

(*b*) if $\mathsf{G}^{(j)*} \simeq \mathsf{G}^{(j)}$ and $SS^*K^2 = -1$, $\mathsf{G}^{(j)}$ appears an even number of times in the decomposition of G (degeneracy doubled);

(*c*) if $\mathsf{G}^{(j)*} \simeq \mathsf{G}^{(j)}$ and $SS^*K^2 = +1$ the basis vectors of each component $\mathsf{G}^{(j)}$ of G can be chosen to satisfy the "reality" condition: $KS\,|u\rangle = |u\rangle$.

The representations of the rotation group all correspond to case (c).

axis (not to be confused with the operator for the rotation of the spins alone, $Y^{(S)}$, introduced above). Put

$$K_y \equiv Y^\dagger K \equiv e^{i\pi J_y/\hbar} K. \tag{XV.93}$$

$Y^\dagger$ and K commute with $\boldsymbol{J}^2$ and anticommute with J_z. Therefore K_y commutes with $\boldsymbol{J}^2$ and J_z. It also commutes with J_+ and J_-:

$$Y^\dagger K(J_x \pm i J_y) = Y^\dagger(-J_x \pm i J_y)K = (J_x \pm i J_y)Y^\dagger K.$$

Moreover, since $[Y, K]=0$ and $Y^2 = K^2 = (-)^n$ [cf. relation (XV.88)],

$$K_y{}^2 = 1. \tag{XV.94}$$

The antiunitary transformation K_y can be treated as a complex conjugation, as was K in § 19. To distinguish it from the latter, we shall use quotation marks to indicate this new type of conjugation. Thus, a "real" (linear) operator is one that commutes with K_y. The "complex conjugate" of a vector $|\rangle$ is by definition the vector $K_y|\rangle$. Since $K_y{}^2=1$, there exist "real" vectors, "real" representations. The action of a "real" operator on a "real" vector gives a "real" vector; in a "real" representation, the "real" operators are represented by real matrices.

Since $\boldsymbol{J}^2$ and J_z are "real", we can construct a basis in the space of angular momentum $(j\,j)$ whose vectors are all "real". J_+ and J_- also being "real", the vectors of the standard basis that can be constructed from these vectors by the method of § XIII.6, are all "real".

Let $|\tau j\mu\rangle$ be the vectors of a "real" standard basis. If H is invariant under rotation and under time reversal, it will commute with both $\boldsymbol{J}$ and K_y, and will be represented in the $\{\tau j\mu\}$ representation by a real matrix of the form (XV.52), i.e.

$$\langle \tau j\mu | H | \tau' j' \mu' \rangle = \delta_{jj'}\, \delta_{\mu\mu'}\, H^{(j)}_{\tau\tau'}$$

and the $H^{(j)}_{\tau\tau'}$ *are all real.* It follows that *H has a rotational degeneracy and has in addition at least one orthonormal system of eigenvectors forming a "real" standard basis.*

We can set up a "real" basis in $\mathscr{E}$ by taking tensor products of the basis vectors of simpler spaces. Suppose that we have

$$\mathscr{E} = \mathscr{E}_1 \otimes \mathscr{E}_2 \otimes \dots$$

and that we have defined rotation and time-reversal operators in each component space $\mathscr{E}_i$. With each $\mathscr{E}_i$ there is associated a "complex-conjugation" operator $K_y^{(i)} = Y^{(i)\dagger} K^{(i)}$, and the operator K_y for the whole space is the tensor product of these

$$K_y = K_y^{(1)} K_y^{(2)} \dots .$$

The tensor product of "real" vectors is a "real" vector. In particular, we can form a set of "real" basis vectors in $\mathscr{E}$ by taking tensor products of vectors forming a "real" standard basis of angular momentum in each component space. Starting from this basis in $\mathscr{E}$ we can form a standard basis for the total angular momentum in this space by the addition of angular momenta. Since the Clebsch–Gordon coefficients are real, the vectors of the standard basis thus formed are all "real".

We end this chapter with a remark concerning the "reality" of the spherical harmonics.

Let $\omega = (\theta, \varphi)$ be the angular coordinates of the position vector $\boldsymbol{r}$ of a particle, and $Y_l^m(\omega)$ the spherical harmonic representing the state of angular momentum (lm). In this particular case $(\hbar = 1)$,

$$K_y = \mathrm{e}^{-\mathrm{i}\pi l_y} K_0$$

so that [eqs. (B.92) and (C.62)]

$$\begin{aligned} K_y\, Y_l^m(\omega) &= \mathrm{e}^{-\mathrm{i}\pi l_y}\, Y_l^{m*}(\omega) = \mathrm{e}^{-\mathrm{i}\pi l_y}\, (-)^m\, Y_l^{-m}(\omega) \\ &= (-)^l\, Y_l^m\, (\omega). \end{aligned}$$

The spherical harmonic Y_l^m is therefore "real" if l is even, "pure imaginary" if l is odd; on the other hand, the functions

$$\mathscr{Y}_l^m(\omega) \equiv \mathrm{i}^l\, Y_l^m(\omega)$$

form a "real" standard basis for the orbital angular momentum.

Let $\omega_p = (\theta_p, \varphi_p)$ be the angular coordinates of the momentum $\boldsymbol{p}$ of the same particle and $Y_l^m(\omega_p)$ the spherical harmonic representing the state of angular momentum (lm) in the $\{\boldsymbol{p}\}$ representation. One can show (Problem XV.10) that

$$K_0 = S_0 K_p,$$

where S_0 is the parity operator [eq. (XV.45)] and K_p the complex-conjugation operator associated with the $\{\boldsymbol{p}\}$ representation. It follows that

$$K_y Y_l^m(\omega_p) = Y_l^m(\omega_p).$$

The $Y_l^m(\omega_p)$ form a "real" standard basis for the orbital angular momentum. These considerations of "reality" can be extented without difficulty to irreducible tensor operators in general (cf. Problem XV.12).

EXERCISES AND PROBLEMS

1. We suppose that the state vector space $\mathscr{E}$ of a system is the direct sum $\mathscr{E}_1 + \mathscr{E}_2 + \ldots$ of a certain number of subspaces invariant with respect to the ensemble of the *physical* observables of the system. Show that the projectors $P_1, P_2, \ldots$ onto these subspaces commute with each physical observable, and that the vectors of $\mathscr{E}$ do not all have the property of being simultaneous eigenvectors of a complete set of commuting physical observables.

2. Show that the operator S_0 defined by (XV.45) verifies relations (XV.43) and (XV.44) and notably the relation $S_0\, \boldsymbol{p}\, S_0^\dagger = -\boldsymbol{p}$.

3. The operator of reflection in a plane perpendicular to $\boldsymbol{u}$ for a particle of spin $\frac{1}{2}$ is the product of an operator acting on the orbital variables alone with an operator acting on the spin variables alone. Show that for a particular choice of phase factor, the last mentioned operator is equal to $(\boldsymbol{\sigma}\cdot\boldsymbol{u})$. Show that the product $(\boldsymbol{\sigma}\cdot\boldsymbol{v})\,(\boldsymbol{\sigma}\cdot\boldsymbol{u})$ representing two successive reflections in planes perpendicular to the vectors $\boldsymbol{u}$ and $\boldsymbol{v}$ respectively is equal to the operator associated with a rotation of the spin through an angle $2(\boldsymbol{u}, \boldsymbol{v})$ about the axis $(\boldsymbol{u} \times \boldsymbol{v})/|\boldsymbol{u} \times \boldsymbol{v}|$.

4. A beam of particles of spin s is scattered by a spin-dependent potential. Let $\boldsymbol{p}_i$ be the initial momentum. The particles scattered into a certain direction are selected with the aid of a diaphragm. Let $\boldsymbol{p}_f$ be the momentum of these particles and D the scattering plane, i.e. the plane containing $\boldsymbol{p}_i$ and $\boldsymbol{p}_f$. We suppose that the incident particles are non-polarized so that their spin state is represented by the density operator $\varrho_i = 1/(2s+1)$. Show that, if the interaction potential is *invariant under rotation and under reflection in the origin*, then the density operator ϱ_i representing the spin state of the scattered particles is symmetrical with respect to the plane D.

5. Show that the density operator representing the spin state of a particle of spin $\frac{1}{2}$ can be expressed in the form

$$\varrho = \tfrac{1}{2}\,(1 + \boldsymbol{P}\cdot\boldsymbol{\sigma});$$

$\boldsymbol{\sigma} \equiv (\sigma_x, \sigma_y, \sigma_z)$ is twice the spin vector of the particle and $\boldsymbol{P}$ is a vector of length between 0 and 1 that completely defines the state of polarization of the particle.

Returning to Problem XV.4 and supposing $s = \frac{1}{2}$ show that the vector $\mathbf{P}_f$ defining the polarization of the scattered particles is *perpendicular to the scattering plane.*

6. Show that if any real function of time is added to the Hamiltonian of a system the evolution operator $U(t, t_0)$ is simply multiplied by a phase factor.

7. In a Galilean transformation of the coordinate system, the variables $\mathbf{r}$, $\mathbf{p}$, $\mathbf{s}$ of a particle are transformed respectively into $\mathbf{r} - \mathbf{v}t$, $\mathbf{p} - m\mathbf{v}$, $\mathbf{s}$. Show that such a transformation is realized by the operator

$$G(\mathbf{v}, t) = \exp\,[\mathrm{i}\mathbf{v}\cdot(m\mathbf{r} - \mathbf{p}t)/\hbar].$$

The same transformation applied to a system of N particles is realized by the operator $G(\mathbf{v}, t) = \exp\,[\mathrm{i}\mathbf{v}\cdot(M\,\mathbf{R} - \mathbf{P}t)/\hbar]$, where M, $\mathbf{R}$ and $\mathbf{P}$ are respectively the mass, the position and the momentum of the center of mass.

[N.B. For a given value of t, the Galilean transformations form a group; with the phase adopted here, the transformation operators also form a group.] The law of motion is invariant under this transformation if

$$G^{\dagger}(\mathbf{v}, t)\; U(t, t_0)\; G(\mathbf{v}, t_0) = U(t, t_0) \times \text{phase factor}.$$

Show that this condition is equivalent to the "condition of Galilean invariance of the Schrödinger equation":

$$G^{\dagger}(\mathbf{v}, t)\left[\mathrm{i}\hbar\frac{\partial}{\partial t} - H\right]G(\mathbf{v}, t) = \left[\mathrm{i}\hbar\frac{\partial t}{\partial} - H\right] + f,$$

where f is an arbitrary real function of the time, and that this condition is indeed fulfilled by the Schrödinger Hamiltonian (one finds: $f = 0$).

8. Show that the translation and rotation operators and the reflection operator S_0 [definition (XV.45)] commute with the time-reversal operator K and that this property does not depend on the choice of the arbitrary phase involved in the definition of K.

9. Show that if the square of an antiunitary operator is equal to a constant, that constant is either $+1$ or -1.

10. Let K_p be the complex-conjugation operator associated with the $\{\mathbf{p}\}$ representation, K_0 the complex-conjugation operator associated with the $\{\mathbf{r}\}$ representation, S_0 the reflection operator [definition (XV.45)]. Show that $K_0 = S_0 K_p$. Deduce that in time-reversal the wave function $\Phi(\mathbf{p})$ transforms into

$$K\Phi(\mathbf{p}) = \Phi^*(-\mathbf{p}).$$

11. Suppose that we have a system that is invariant under time-reversal. Let B be a pure imaginary (cf. § 19) observable of this system (momentum, spin, orbital angular momentum, etc.). Show that

(i) if a stationary state is non-degenerate, the average value of B in that state is null;

(ii) the trace of the projection of B onto the subspace of any energy eigenvalue is null.

12. Denote by $T_q^{(k)}$ $(q = -k, -k+1, \ldots, +k)$ the standard components of an irreducible tensor operator $\mathbf{T}^{(k)}$. By definition the complex conjugate of $\mathbf{T}^{(k)}$ is the tensor operator whose $q = 0$ component is the time-reversal transform of $T_0^{(k)}$ (with this definition the Cartesian components of real vector operators are invariant under time reversal, and those of imaginary vector operators change sign). Show that the standard components of the complex conjugate of $\mathbf{T}^{(k)}$ are the operators that are the "complex conjugates" (*in the sense of* § 22) of the corresponding components of $(-)^k\, \mathbf{T}^{(k)}$; and that in particular in a "real" standard representation the matrix element $\langle \tau j \mu \mid \mathbf{T}_q^{(k)} \mid \tau' j' \mu' \rangle$ is real if $\mathrm{i}^k\, \mathbf{T}^{(k)}$ is real, and pure imaginary if $\mathrm{i}^k\, \mathbf{T}^{(k)}$ is pure imaginary.

[N.B. This property has a direct application in angular correlation problems, for it gives, to within a sign, the relative phases of the contributions from the different multipoles.]

« Si les plats que je vous offre sont mal préparés, c'est moins la faute de mon cuisinier que celle de la chimie, qui est encore dans l'enfance. »
(*La Rôtisserie de la reine Pédauque*).

Anatole France

PART FOUR

METHODS OF APPROXIMATION

CHAPTER XVI

STATIONARY PERTURBATIONS

1. General Introduction to Part Four

The few problems in Quantum Mechanics that can be exactly solved relate to very special and very simple systems. In practice no physical system can be studied without approximation; the physicist's art consists precisely in determining the relative importance of the different effects and adopting in each case the appropriate approximation method. There are, properly speaking, as many methods of approximation as there are problems and there is no question of treating them all here. In this book we give only those methods sufficiently general to merit a systematic development. Some have already been treated, notably the classical approximation and the WKB method of Chapter VI, and the phase shift method for scattering problems of Chapter X. The others will be the subject of this fourth part.

Mathematically, the study of a quantum system consists in determining its evolution operator $U(t, t_0)$, or at least determining certain characteristic properties of $U(t, t_0)$. When the Hamiltonian H is independent of time, this reduces to solving the eigenvalue problem for H, for in this case,

$$U(t, t_0) = \mathrm{e}^{-\mathrm{i}H(t-t_0)/\hbar},$$

and the properties of U are thus directly related to those of H. We have a more complicated situation when H depends on the time; clearly, however, the eigenvalues and eigenfunctions of H (which are then time-dependent) will be of importance for determining the properties of U.

On the whole, collision problems, which bring in the continuous spectrum of eigenvalues, are more difficult than problems relating to bound states. Collision problems are considered in the last chapter of this part (Chapter XIX). The three other chapters (Ch. XVI–XVIII) are concerned essentially with the study of bound states, although the methods set forth can eventually be extended to the study of non-bound states. The bound state problems can themselves be separated into two categories. We have, on the one hand, the determination of stationary states, or more precisely the solutions of the eigenvalue problem for H; on the other, the problem of transitions from one state to another. Three types of methods are commonly employed for the approximate solution of the eigenvalue problem for H. The first, the WKB method (Ch. VI), is based on the classical approximation: the large quantum number and small wave-length approximation. The second, the stationary perturbation method, starts from the exact solution of the eigenvalue problem for an operator H_0 differing little from H, and the eigenfunctions and eigenvalues of H are then expressed as power series in the difference $H-H_0$. The third, the variational method, can be used, failing the other two, when one has an intuitive idea of the general form of the sought-for eigenfunctions. Stationary perturbations are treated in the present chapter and the variational method in Chapter XVIII. Chapter XVII is devoted to the calculation of transitions and, more generally, to the principle methods of investigating the evolution of bound states when the Hamiltonian is modified in the course of time.

I. PERTURBATION OF A NON-DEGENERATE LEVEL

2. Expansion in Powers of the Perturbation

It is assumed that the Hamiltonian H can be written as the sum of an "unperturbed Hamiltonian" H_0 and a perturbation term which it is convenient to write in the form λV, where λ is a real parameter and V, like H_0, a time-independent Hermitean operator:

$$H = H_0 + \lambda V. \tag{XVI.1}$$

We suppose the eigenvalue problem for H_0 solved. Thus we know its eigenvalues

$$E_1^0,\ E_2^0,\ \ldots,\ E_i^0,\ \ldots$$

and the corresponding set of eigenvectors $|E_i^0\,\alpha\rangle$; the quantum number α distinguishes between the eigenvectors belonging to a degenerate eigenvalue:

$$H_0|E_i^0\,\alpha\rangle = E_i^0|E_i^0\,\alpha\rangle. \tag{XVI.2}$$

The spectrum of H varies continuously with λ, coinciding with the spectrum of H_0 when $\lambda=0$. Consider a given eigenvalue E_a^0 of

H_0. We wish to calculate the eigenvalue (or eigenvalues) of H that tend to $E_a{}^0$ when $\lambda \to 0$, and to determine the corresponding eigenstates of H. To simplify the writing, we suppose that the spectrum of H_0 is entirely discrete; all what follows remains valid if a part of the spectrum of H_0 is continuous so long as $E_a{}^0$ belongs to the discrete spectrum.

The method is particularly simple *when the eigenvalue $E_a{}^0$ is non-degenerate*. Throughout the present section we shall assume this to be so.

Let E be the eigenvalue of H that tends to $E_a{}^0$ when $\lambda \to 0$. It will also be a non-degenerate eigenvalue. The corresponding eigenvector, $|\psi\rangle$, is defined to within a constant which may be arbitrarily fixed. We shall adopt the following definition for $|\psi\rangle$:

$$H|\psi\rangle = E|\psi\rangle \tag{XVI.3}$$
$$\langle 0|\psi\rangle = \langle 0|0\rangle = 1 \tag{XVI.4}$$

where we have put: $|E_a{}^0\rangle = |0\rangle$. With this definition, $|\psi\rangle$ tends to $|0\rangle$ when $\lambda \to 0$.

If the perturbation λV is sufficiently small it is reasonable to assume that E and $|\psi\rangle$ can be expanded into rapidly converging power series in λ i.e. we may write:

$$E = E_a{}^0 + \lambda\varepsilon_1 + \lambda^2\varepsilon_2 + \ldots + \lambda^n\varepsilon_n + \ldots \tag{XVI.5}$$
$$|\psi\rangle = |0\rangle + \lambda|1\rangle + \lambda^2|2\rangle + \ldots + \lambda^n|n\rangle + \ldots. \tag{XVI.6}$$

By retaining only the first terms in these series one obtains approximate expressions for E and $|\psi\rangle$.

The perturbation method consists in determining the successive expansion coefficients in (XVI.5) and (XVI.6). To this end, we substitute expression (XVI.1), (XVI.5) and (XVI.6) into both sides of (XVI.3), which then becomes an equality between two power series in λ. In order that this equality be satisfied, the coefficients of each power of λ must separately be equal, giving, successively:

$$(H_0 - E_a{}^0)|0\rangle = 0 \tag{XVI.7^0}$$
$$(H_0 - E_a{}^0)|1\rangle + (V - \varepsilon_1)|0\rangle = 0 \tag{XVI.7^1}$$
$$(H_0 - E_a{}^0)|2\rangle + (V - \varepsilon_1)|1\rangle - \varepsilon_2|0\rangle = 0 \tag{XVI.7^2}$$
$$\cdots\cdots \qquad \cdots\cdots$$
$$(H_0 - E_a{}^0)|n\rangle + (V - \varepsilon_1)|n-1\rangle \ldots - \varepsilon_n|0\rangle = 0. \tag{XVI.7^n}$$
$$\cdots\cdots \qquad \cdots\cdots$$

Condition (XVI.4) becomes

$$\langle 0|1\rangle = \langle 0|2\rangle = \ldots = \langle 0|n\rangle = \ldots = 0. \qquad \text{(XVI.8)}$$

Equation (XVI.7^0) determines the eigenvalue and the eigenvector to the zeroth order. With conditions (XVI.8), equation (XVI.7^1) determines the first-order corrections to these two quantities, equation (XVI.7^2) the second-order corrections, ..., equation (XVI.7^n) the nth-order corrections.

Let us show that equation (XVI.7^n) effectively determines ε_n and $|n\rangle$ in terms of the lower order corrections. To do this we project onto the basis vectors of H_0. Projecting onto $|0\rangle$ we obtain, with the aid of (XVI.8)

$$\varepsilon_n = \langle 0|V|n-1\rangle. \qquad \text{(XVI.9)}$$

Projecting onto the other basis vectors of H_0 we obtain the corresponding components of $|n\rangle$ along each of them:

$$\langle E^0\alpha|n\rangle = \frac{1}{E_a{}^0 - E^0}\,[\langle E^0\alpha|(V-\varepsilon_1)|n-1\rangle - \varepsilon_2\,\langle E^0\alpha|n-2\rangle - \ldots$$
$$\ldots - \varepsilon_{n-1}\,\langle E^0\alpha|1\rangle]$$
$$(E_a{}^0 \neq E^0).$$

Since $\langle 0|n\rangle = 0$, $|n\rangle$ is thereby completely determined. It is convenient to put

$$Q_0 \equiv 1 - |0\rangle\,\langle 0| = \sum_{E^0 \neq E_a{}^0} \Sigma_\alpha\, |E^0\alpha\rangle\,\langle E^0\alpha|$$

and

$$\frac{Q_0}{a} \equiv Q_0\,\frac{1}{E_a{}^0 - H^0}\,Q_0 = \sum_{E^0 \neq E_a{}^0} \frac{\Sigma_\alpha |E^0\alpha\rangle\,\langle E^0\alpha|}{E_a{}^0 - E_0}. \qquad \text{(XVI.10)}$$

With these notations one may write

$$|n\rangle = \frac{Q_0}{a}\,[(V-\varepsilon_1)\,|n-1\rangle - \varepsilon_2|n-2\rangle - \ldots - \varepsilon_{n-1}|1\rangle]. \qquad \text{(XVI.11)}$$

Equations (XVI.9) and (XVI.11) are equivalent to (XVI.7^n), which completes the demonstration.

3. First-order Perturbations

The first-order corrections, from equation (XVI.7^1), are obtained by writing equations (XVI.9) and (XVI.11) for the case $n = 1$.

Equation (XVI.9) gives the first-order correction to the energy level

$$\boxed{\varepsilon_1 = \langle 0|V|0\rangle} \qquad \text{(XVI.12)}$$

whence the expression for E to the first order:

$$E = \langle 0|H|0\rangle + O(\lambda^2). \qquad \text{(XVI.13)}$$

This is just the average value of the Hamiltonian H calculated with the eigenvector of the unperturbed Hamiltonian H_0.

Equation (XVI.11) gives the first-order correction to the eigenvector:

$$|1\rangle = \frac{Q_0}{a}(V - \varepsilon_1)|0\rangle$$

but since $Q_0|0\rangle = 0$ this expression reduces to

$$|1\rangle = \frac{Q_0}{a} V|0\rangle. \qquad \text{(XVI.14)}$$

The vector $|\psi\rangle$ is therefore given to the first order by the expression

$$|\psi\rangle = \left(1 + \lambda \frac{Q_0}{a} V\right)|0\rangle + O(\lambda^2) \qquad \text{(XVI.15)}$$

and its norm by

$$\begin{aligned} \langle\psi|\psi\rangle &= \langle 0|0\rangle + \langle\psi|Q_0|\psi\rangle \\ &\simeq \langle 0|0\rangle + \lambda^2 \langle 1|1\rangle = 1 + \lambda^2 \langle 1|V \frac{Q_0}{a^2} V|0\rangle \\ &= 1 + O(\lambda^2). \end{aligned}$$

According to (XVI.14), the components of the first-order correction to $|0\rangle$ along the other basis vectors of H_0 are given by the equation:

$$\lambda \langle E^0\alpha|1\rangle = \frac{\langle E^0\alpha|(\lambda V)|0\rangle}{E_a{}^0 - E^0}. \quad (E^0 \neq E_a{}^0) \quad \text{(XVI.16)}$$

The component along $|E^0\alpha\rangle$ is therefore equal to the perturbation matrix element linking $|0\rangle$ to $|E^0\alpha\rangle$ divided by the *energy difference* between these two unperturbed eigenstates. The smallness of this quantity is a measure of how rapidly the perturbation series converges.

4. Ground State of the Helium Atom

As a first example [1]) we use the perturbation method to evaluate the ground-state energy of the helium atom and, more generally, the ground-state energy of any $(Z-2)$ times ionized atom. Such an atom is made up of a nucleus of charge Ze and two electrons. The nucleus is supposed infinitely heavy so that the Hamiltonian H is the Hamiltonian of two electrons in the potential

$$-\frac{Ze^2}{r_1}-\frac{Ze^2}{r_2}+\frac{e^2}{r_{12}}$$

where $\mathbf{r}_1$, and $\mathbf{r}_2$ are the position vectors of the first and second electrons respectively and $r_{12}=|\mathbf{r}_1-\mathbf{r}_2|$ their mutual distance.

If one neglects the mutual repulsion term e^2/r_{12}, the Hamiltonian reduces to that of two independent particles in the Coulomb field $-Ze^2/r$, and the corresponding eigenvalue problem can be solved exactly. We shall take this as our "unperturbed Hamiltonian" and treat the e^2/r_{12} as a perturbation. The ground-state of H_0 corresponds to both electrons in the 1s state.

Let E_{H} be the binding energy of the ground-state of the hydrogen atom. The energy of the ground-state of H_0, being the sum of the energies of the two electrons, will then be

$$E_a{}^0 = -\,2Z^2E_{\mathrm{H}}.$$

The corresponding eigenfunction is the product of the eigenfunctions for each particle, namely (cf. § B3)

$$\Phi_a(\mathbf{r}_1,\,\mathbf{r}_2) = \mathrm{e}^{-(r_1+r_2)/a}/\pi a^3,$$

where

$$a=a_0/Z=\hbar^2/Zme^2(\simeq Z^{-1}\times 0.53\times 10^{-8}\ \mathrm{cm}).$$

The effect of the perturbation $V=e^2/r_{12}$ is given, in the first order, by formula (XVI.12) $(\lambda=1)$:

$$\begin{aligned}\varepsilon_1 &= \int \Phi_a\, V\, \Phi_a\, \mathrm{d}\mathbf{r}_1\, \mathrm{d}\mathbf{r}_2\\ &= \frac{e^2}{\pi^2a^6}\int \frac{\mathrm{e}^{-2(r_1+r_2)/a}}{|\mathbf{r}_1-\mathbf{r}_2|}\,\mathrm{d}\mathbf{r}_1\,\mathrm{d}\mathbf{r}_2.\end{aligned} \qquad \text{(XVI.17)}$$

---

[1]) This example is taken from L. Pauling and E. B. Wilson, *loc. cit.*, note, p. 614/615.

This is the electrostatic energy of two spherical distributions of electricity with densities $-e\varrho_1(r_1)$ and $-e\varrho_2(r_2)$ respectively, where

$$\varrho_1(r) = \varrho_2(r) = \mathrm{e}^{-2r/a}/\pi a^3. \tag{XVI.18}$$

To calculate the integral

$$I = \int \mathrm{d}\boldsymbol{r}_1 \int \mathrm{d}\boldsymbol{r}_2 \, \frac{\varrho_1(r_1)\, \varrho_2(r_2)}{|\boldsymbol{r}_1 - \boldsymbol{r}_2|}$$

we employ the expansion (B.99). After integration over the angles we obtain

$$\begin{aligned} I &= 16\pi^2 \int_0^\infty \mathrm{d}r_1 \int_0^\infty \mathrm{d}r_2\, \varrho_1(r_1)\, \varrho_2(r_2)\, r_1^2\, r_2^2/r_> \\ &= 16\pi^2 \int_0^\infty \varrho_1(r_1)\, r_1\, \mathrm{d}r_1 \left\{ \int_0^{r_1} \varrho_2(r_2)\, r_2^2\, \mathrm{d}r_2 + r_1 \int_{r_1}^\infty \varrho_2(r_2)\, r_2\, \mathrm{d}r_2 \right\}. \end{aligned} \tag{XVI.19}$$

After calculating I, with the aid of (XVI.18), we find that $\varepsilon_1 = e^2 I$ is equal to

$$\varepsilon_1 = \tfrac{5}{4} Z E_{\mathrm{H}}. \tag{XVI.20}$$

One expects the error of this approximation to be smaller when the energy of mutual repulsion of the electrons is smaller compared with the energy of attraction of the nucleus, and thus for higher Z. This is seen to be the case in table XVI.1, where the observed binding

TABLE XVI.1

Binding energies for He, Li^+, Be^{++} *in the ground state*

The energies are all given in electronvolts. Columns 2, 3, 4 give respectively the unperturbed energy, the first-order perturbation and the sum of the two i.e., the ground state energy to the first order in perturbation theory. Column 5 gives the result of the variational calculation of § XVIII.6, Column 6 the experimental value for the energy of the ground state (from L. Pauling and E. B. Wilson, *loc. cit.*).

	1	2	3	4	5	6
	Z	$E_a{}^0$	ε_1	$E_{\text{pert}} = E_a{}^0 + \varepsilon_1$	E_{var}	E_{exp}
He . .	2	−108	34	− 74	− 76.6	− 78.6
Li^+ . .	3	−243.5	50.5	−193	−195.6	−197.1
Be^{++} . .	4	−433	67.5	−365.5	−368.1	−370.0

energies of the ground states of He, Li^+ and Be^{++} are compared with those given by the perturbation theory. The perturbation expansion converges more rapidly than *a priori* considerations might lead one to think and the calculation of the binding energy to the first order gives a value in reasonable accord with observation, even in the case of helium ($Z=2$).

5. Coulomb Energy of Atomic Nuclei

In an atomic nucleus the distance between nucleons is of the order of 10^{-13} cm. At such distances the so-called nuclear forces are much stronger than the Coulomb repulsion of the protons and the latter may therefore be treated as a perturbation. H_0 will then be the sum of the kinetic energy of the nucleons and the potential energy of specifically nuclear origin; V will be made up of the coulomb repulsion terms

$$V = \sum_{i<j\leqslant Z} \frac{e^2}{r_{ij}} \tag{XVI.21}$$

($r_{ij}=|\mathbf{r}_i-\mathbf{r}_j| =$ distance between protons i and j).

We wish to apply perturbation theory to calculate the shift E_c due to these Coulomb terms.

Let j denote the spin of the unperturbed state. This state has a degeneracy of order $(2j+1)$, i.e. there exist $(2j+1)$ orthonormal unperturbed states $\Phi_\mu{}^j$, corresponding each to a different value μ of the J_z component of the total angular momentum.

In spite of this degeneracy, we can apply the results of the perturbation theory developed above. This is because the perturbing potential V being, like H_0, invariant under rotation, we can treat the eigenvalue problem in the subspace $\mathscr{E}(j\mu)$ of the states of given angular momentum $(j\mu)$; in this subspace the ground state is not degenerate and the first-order correction to its energy is correctly given by formula (XVI.12):

$$E_c \simeq \langle \Phi_\mu{}^j | V | \Phi_\mu{}^j \rangle. \tag{XVI.22}$$

This correction is seen to be independent of μ: the Coulomb perturbation does not remove the degeneracy. This is true, in fact, in all orders: since H, like H_0, is invariant under rotation, it necessarily presents, like H_0, a rotational degeneracy.

The function $\Phi_\mu{}^j$ depends on the coordinates and intrinsic spins of the Z protons and $N=\mathcal{N}-Z$ neutrons. Since it is antisymmetrical with respect to the protons, the $\frac{1}{2}Z(Z-1)$ terms of V make equal contributions; we therefore have $E_c=\frac{1}{2}Z(Z-1)\,\varepsilon$, where

$$\varepsilon = \langle \Phi_\mu^j | (e^2/r_{12}) | \Phi_\mu^j \rangle$$
$$= \sum_{\text{spins}} \int |\Phi_\mu^j|^2 \, (e^2/r_{12}) \, d\boldsymbol{r}_1 \, d\boldsymbol{r}_2 \ldots d\boldsymbol{r}_Z \, d\boldsymbol{r}_{Z+1} \ldots d\boldsymbol{r}_{\mathcal{N}}$$

$\sum_{\text{spins}}$ extends over all the spin variables of the nucleons. Let us put

$$\varrho(\boldsymbol{r}_1, \boldsymbol{r}_2) = \sum_{\text{spins}} \int |\Phi_\mu^j|^2 \, d\boldsymbol{r}_3 \ldots d\boldsymbol{r}_{\mathcal{N}}.$$

$\varrho(\boldsymbol{r}_1, \boldsymbol{r}_2)$ is the probability density for simultaneously finding proton 1 at point $\boldsymbol{r}_1$, and proton 2 at point $\boldsymbol{r}_2$. We then have

$$\varepsilon = \int (e^2/r_{12}) \, \varrho(\boldsymbol{r}_1, \boldsymbol{r}_2) \, d\boldsymbol{r}_1 \, d\boldsymbol{r}_2 .$$

To evaluate E_c we employ the very crude model where correlations between the two protons are neglected [1]),

$$\varrho(\boldsymbol{r}_1, \boldsymbol{r}_2) \simeq \varrho(\boldsymbol{r}_1) \, \varrho(\boldsymbol{r}_2) \tag{XVI.23}$$

and where the density $\varrho(\boldsymbol{r})$ is taken to be that of a uniform distribution of charge in a sphere of radius R:

$$\varrho(\boldsymbol{r}) = \begin{cases} \dfrac{3}{4\pi R^3} & \text{if} \quad r < R \\ 0 & \text{if} \quad r > R \end{cases} \tag{XVI.24}$$

The calculation is analogous to the one of § 4. Substituting the above densities into the integral I, as given by (XVI.19), we finally obtain

$$E_c \simeq \frac{3}{5} Z(Z-1) \frac{e^2}{R}. \tag{XVI.25}$$

Although formula (XVI.25) constitutes a relatively rough evaluation of E_c, it can be used to verify the charge-independence of nuclear forces (cf. § XIV.15). The isotopic spin formalism lends itself well to this purpose. According to the independence hypothesis, the unperturbed Hamiltonian is invariant under rotations in charge space, and states of the same isotopic spin multiplet have the same binding energy. The observed differences between the binding energies

---

[1]) Thus we certainly over-estimate E_c for, all things being equal, the Pauli principle requires $\varrho(\boldsymbol{r}_1, \boldsymbol{r}_2)$ to be smaller when $\boldsymbol{r}_1 = \boldsymbol{r}_2$.

of two members of a given isotopic-spin multiplet will then be equal to the difference of their Coulomb energies. If we take

$$R = 1.45 \times \mathcal{N}^{\frac{1}{3}} \times 10^{-13} \text{ cm},$$

it is possible with formula (XVI.25) to reasonably account for the difference in the ground state energies of mirror nuclei.

6. Higher-order Corrections

The second-order corrections, from equation (XVI.7[2]), are obtained by writing equations (XVI.9) and (XVI.11) for the special case $n=2$ and using the first-order corrections (XVI.12) and (XVI.14). This gives

$$\varepsilon_2 = \langle 0|V|1\rangle = \langle 0|V \frac{Q_0}{a} V|0\rangle \tag{XVI.26}$$

$$|2\rangle = \frac{Q_0}{a}(V-\varepsilon_1)|1\rangle = \left[\frac{Q_0}{a} V \frac{Q_0}{a} - \frac{Q_0}{a^2} V|0\rangle\langle 0|\right] V|0\rangle. \tag{XVI.27}$$

Corrections of higher order are similarly obtained. The formulas are lengthy to write out but simplify in the important special case when all the lower-order corrections to the unperturbed energy vanish. Thus, if

$$\varepsilon_1 = \varepsilon_2 = \ldots = \varepsilon_{n-1} = 0, \tag{XVI.28}$$

the recurrence formulas (XVI.9) and (XVI.11) give

$$\varepsilon_n = \langle 0|V\left(\frac{Q_0}{a} V\right)^{n-1}|0\rangle \tag{XVI.29}$$

$$|n\rangle = \frac{Q_0}{a} V|n-1\rangle = \left(\frac{Q_0}{a} V\right)^2 |n-2\rangle = \ldots = \left(\frac{Q_0}{a} V\right)^n |0\rangle. \tag{XVI.30}$$

and condition (XVI.28) reads

$$\langle 0|V|0\rangle = \langle 0|V \frac{Q_0}{a} V|0\rangle = \ldots = \langle 0|V\left(\frac{Q_0}{a} V\right)^{n-2}|0\rangle = 0. \tag{XVI.28$'$}$$

It rarely happens that the calculations are continued to the nth-order when this condition is not fulfilled. The perturbation method is useful only if convergence is sufficiently rapid for the lowest-order corrections to suffice. The complexity of the calculations increases rapidly with order and soon becomes prohibitive.

Nonetheless, the general behavior of the higher-order corrections is of interest for investigating the convergence of the perturbation expansion. Writing (XVI.26) in terms of the matrix elements of V in the $\{|E^0\alpha\rangle\}$ representation we find for ε_2 the expression

$$\varepsilon_2 = \sum_{E^0 \neq E_a{}^0} \frac{\sum_\alpha |\langle 0|V|E^0\alpha\rangle|^2}{E_a{}^0 - E^0}. \tag{XVI.31}$$

The magnitude of the effect caused by the perturbation varies as the ratio of the matrix elements $\lambda\langle 0|V|E^0\alpha\rangle$ to the energy difference $|E_a{}^0 - E^0|$. More generally, one may say, roughly speaking, that the convergence of the perturbation series depends on the smallness of the ratio of the matrix elements $\lambda\langle E^0\alpha|V|E^{0\prime}\alpha'\rangle$ linking two eigenstates of H_0 of energy E^0 and $E^{0\prime}$ to the differences $|E_a{}^0 - E^0|$ and $|E_a{}^0 - E^{0\prime}|$ between these energies and the unperturbed energy $E_a{}^0$.

One can obtain an upper limit for ε_2 by over-estimating in absolute value each term on the right-hand side of (XVI.31). Replacing each denominator by the separation $\delta E_{\min}$ of $E_a{}^0$ from its nearest neighbor, we get

$$|\varepsilon_2| \leqslant \frac{1}{\delta E_{\min}} \sum_{E^0 \neq E_a{}^0} \sum_\alpha \langle 0|V|E^0\alpha\rangle \langle E^0\alpha|V|0\rangle$$

or

$$|\varepsilon_2| \leqslant \frac{1}{\delta E_{\min}} \langle 0|V\, Q_0\, V|0\rangle.$$

Replacing Q_0 by its definition we have

$$\langle 0|VQ_0V|0\rangle = \langle 0|V(1-|0\rangle\langle 0|)V|0\rangle = \langle 0|V^2|0\rangle - \langle 0|V|0\rangle^2 = (\Delta V)^2$$

where $(\Delta V)^2$ is the root-mean-square deviation of the perturbing potential in the state $|0\rangle$. Thus we can write

$$|\varepsilon_2| \leqslant \frac{(\Delta V)^2}{\delta E_{\min}}. \tag{XVI.32}$$

7. Stark Effect for a Rigid Rotator

In general, the calculation of ε_2, which involves the infinite series of matrix elements in (XVI.31), is much more difficult than the calculation of ε_1, which involves a single matrix element of V. However, it sometimes happens that most of the matrix elements of (XVI.31) vanish, so that the sum on the right-hand side contains only a limited number of terms.

As an example we consider the Stark level-shift for a rigid rotator. This type of problem occurs in the study of the polarizability of diatomic molecules in an electric field. The rigid rotator represents the motion of the nuclei in a diatomic molecule in the limit when the vibrational quanta are treated as infinitely large. The only degrees of freedom of the rotator are the angular variables (θ, φ) fixing its spatial orientation. Let $\mathbf{L}$ denote the rotator's angular momentum and $I = mr_0^2$ its moment of inertia ($m \equiv$ reduced mass, $r_0 \equiv$ mutual distance of the nuclei); its Hamiltonian is:

$$H_0 = \frac{\mathbf{L}^2}{2I}$$

and its eigenfunctions are the spherical harmonics $Y_l^m(\theta, \varphi)$. We denote the vector represented by Y_l^m by $|lm\rangle$. The corresponding energy eigenvalue depends only on l:

$$H_0|lm\rangle = E_l^0|lm\rangle \qquad E_l^0 = \frac{\hbar^2}{2I}\, l(l+1).$$

In the presence of a uniform electric field $\mathscr{E}$, directed along the z axis, the Hamiltonian contains the additional term

$$V = -\, d\mathscr{E} \cos \theta,$$

where d is the electric dipole moment of the rotator. We shall calculate the effect of this term using the perturbation theory.

In the $\{|lm\rangle\}$ representation, nearly all of the matrix elements of V vanish [1]). In order to have

$$\langle l_1 m_1|V|l_2 m_2\rangle \neq 0$$

it is necessary [cf. (C.16) and (C.17)] that

$$m_1 = m_2 \quad \text{and} \quad l_1 = l_2 \pm 1.$$

[1]) These noteworthy properties are due to the fact that V is the $q = 0$ component of an irreducible tensor operator of order 1 and that its parity is (-1).

When these conditions are fulfilled, we can deduce the matrix element from the following formula [cf. (B.90)]:

$$\langle lm|\cos\theta\,|l-1\;m\rangle = \langle l-1\;m|\cos\theta\,|lm\rangle = \left(\frac{l^2-m^2}{4l^2-1}\right)^{\frac{1}{2}}. \qquad \text{(XVI.33)}$$

Except for the level $l=0$, all of the unperturbed levels are degenerate. However, H_0 and $H \equiv H_0+V$ both commute with L_z and therefore one can separately solve the eigenvalue problem for H in each of the subspaces $\mathscr{E}_m$ of a given eigenvalue m of L_z. In each of these subspaces the spectrum of H_0 is non-degenerate and the perturbation method described above is applicable.

Thus we consider the unperturbed state $|lm\rangle$ in $\mathscr{E}_m$. By the selection rules given above,

$$\langle lm|V|lm\rangle = 0.$$

Thus the first-order correction to the energy level vanishes. By these same selection rules the second-order correction, given by (XVI.31), reduces to the two terms corresponding to $l \pm 1$:

$$\begin{aligned}\varepsilon_2{}^{lm} &= \frac{2I(d\mathscr{E})^2}{\hbar^2}\sum_{l'\neq l}\frac{|\langle lm|\cos\theta\,|l'm\rangle|^2}{l(l+1)-l'(l'+1)}\\ &= \frac{2I(d\mathscr{E})^2}{\hbar^2}\left[\frac{|\langle lm|\cos\theta\,|l+1\;m\rangle|^2}{l(l+1)-(l+1)\,(l+2)}+\frac{|\langle lm|\cos\theta\,|l-1\;m\rangle|^2}{l(l+1)-l(l-1)}\right].\end{aligned}$$

The bracket on the right-hand side is easily calculated with the aid of (XVI.33) and gives

$$\varepsilon_2{}^{lm} = \frac{(d\mathscr{E})^2}{E_l{}^0}\,\frac{l(l+1)-3m^2}{2(2l-1)\,(2l+3)}.$$

Thus, the energy spectrum is given to the second order by the formula

$$E_{lm} \simeq E_l{}^0\left[1+\left(\frac{d\mathscr{E}}{E_l{}^0}\right)^2\frac{l(l+1)-3m^2}{2(2l-1)\,(2l+3)}\right]. \qquad \text{(XVI.34)}$$

The degeneracy is only partly removed since the energy E_{lm} depends only on l and m^2. States with m differing by a sign will still coincide. This residual degeneracy remains in all orders; it results from H being invariant with respect to the symmetries of the Stark effect, that is, invariant with respect to the group of reflections in planes containing Oz. We shall return to this question in § 13.

II. PERTURBATION OF A DEGENERATE LEVEL

8. Elementary Theory

Let us suppose that the eigenvalue E_a^0 of the unperturbed Hamiltonian is g_a-fold degenerate. We retain the notations of § 2 and denote by $\mathscr{E}_a^0$ the subspace corresponding to E_a^0 and by P_0 the projector onto $\mathscr{E}_a^0$.

We can now have more than one eigenvalue of H tending to E_a^0 when $\lambda \to 0$. We shall denote these eigenvalues by $E_1, E_2, \ldots, E_n$, their orders of degeneracy by $g_1, g_2, \ldots, g_n$ and their respective subspaces by $\mathscr{E}_1, \mathscr{E}_2, \ldots, \mathscr{E}_n$. We have

$$g_1 + g_2 + \ldots + g_n = g_a$$

and the space $\mathscr{E}_1 \boldsymbol{+} \mathscr{E}_2 \boldsymbol{+} \ldots \boldsymbol{+} \mathscr{E}_n$ tends toward $\mathscr{E}_a^0$ when $\lambda \to 0$. If P is the projector onto $\mathscr{E}_1 \boldsymbol{+} \mathscr{E}_2 \boldsymbol{+} \ldots \boldsymbol{+} \mathscr{E}_n$, it is a continuous function of λ and

$$P \xrightarrow[\lambda \to 0]{} P_0.$$

The perturbation theory determination of the eigenvalues and eigenfunctions of H is more complicated than when the unperturbed eigenvalue is non-degenerate. In section III we shall give a rigorous solution to the problem allowing its resolution to any order. Here we leave rigour aside and limiting ourselves to the lowest orders investigate what the method of § 2 gives when applied to the present problem.

Let E be one of the eigenvalues $E_1, E_2, \ldots, E_n$ and $|\psi\rangle$ one of the eigenvectors corresponding to E. In the limit when $\lambda \to 0$, $|\psi\rangle$ tends toward a certain vector $|0\rangle$, which for the moment can only be specified to the extent of saying it belongs to the space $\mathscr{E}_a^0$. We assume that E and $|\psi\rangle$ can be represented by expansions (XVI.5) and (XVI.6) with the normalization condition (XVI.4). The coefficients are related to each other by equations (XVI.7) and (XVI.8) and can be determined by recurrence.

Equation (XVI.7^0) requires that $|0\rangle$ belong to $\mathscr{E}_a^0$:

$$P_0 |0\rangle = |0\rangle. \tag{XVI.35}$$

Projection of (XVI.7^1) onto $\mathscr{E}_a^0$ gives

$$P_0(V - \varepsilon_1)|0\rangle = 0 \tag{XVI.36}$$

and projection onto the complementary space gives

$$Q_0|1\rangle = \frac{Q_0}{a} V|0\rangle, \tag{XVI.37}$$

where we have put

$$Q_0 = 1 - P_0 \tag{XVI.38}$$

and defined Q_0/a in accordance with (XVI.10).

Equation (XVI.36) is an eigenvalue equation in the subspace $\mathscr{E}_a{}^0$: ε_1 is the eigenvalue of the operator $P_0 V P_0$ in $\mathscr{E}_a{}^0$ and $|0\rangle$ the corresponding eigenvector. In the $|E^0\alpha\rangle$ representation it becomes

$$\sum_{\alpha'} \langle E_a{}^0\alpha|V|E_a{}^0\alpha'\rangle \langle E_a{}^0\alpha'|0\rangle = \varepsilon_1 \langle E_a{}^0\alpha|0\rangle.$$

Thus the first-order correction ε_1 is obtained by diagonalizing the $g_a \times g_a$ matrix whose elements are given by

$$V_{\alpha\alpha'} \equiv \langle E_a{}^0\alpha|V|E_a{}^0\alpha'\rangle.$$

The possible values for ε_1 *are the eigenvalues of this matrix.* If there are g_a different eigenvalues they are all non-degenerate and the perturbation has completely removed the degeneracy. If there are less than g_a different eigenvalues, some of them will be degenerate and the degeneracy will only have been partly removed.

If the first-order correction ε_1 is a non-degenerate eigenvalue, the corresponding eigenstate $|0\rangle$ is completely determined to the zeroth order; it is defined to within a constant by (XVI.7⁰) and (XVI.7¹). The projection $Q_0|1\rangle$ of the first-order correction to $|\psi\rangle$ onto the complement of $\mathscr{E}_a{}^0$ is given by (XVI.37). Its projection onto $\mathscr{E}_a{}^0$ remains undetermined except for condition (XVI.4). If $\mathscr{E}_1$ is g_1-fold degenerate, equations (XVI.7⁰) and (XVI.7¹) show only that $|0\rangle$ belongs to the corresponding g_1-dimensional subspace; for a more precise determination of $|0\rangle$ one must proceed to higher orders.

Having chosen one of the values ε_1, we obtain the second-order correction ε_2 by projecting (XVI.7²) onto the subspace of ε_1. This subspace, which we denote $\mathscr{E}_a{}^{(1)}$, is contained in $\mathscr{E}_a{}^0$; we denote the corresponding projector by $P^{(1)}$ and the projector onto its complement in $\mathscr{E}_a{}^0$ by P':

$$P_0 = P^{(1)} + P' \qquad P^{(1)} + P' + Q_0 = 1.$$

We then have

$$P^{(1)}H_0 = P^{(1)}P_0H_0$$
$$= E_a{}^0 P^{(1)}$$
$$P^{(1)}V = P^{(1)}V(P^{(1)} + P' + Q_0)$$
$$= \varepsilon_1 P^{(1)} + P^{(1)}VQ_0.$$

The projection of equation (XVI.7²), gives

$$P^{(1)}VQ_0|1\rangle - \varepsilon_2 P^{(1)}|0\rangle = 0$$

whence, with the aid of (XVI.37),

$$P^{(1)}\left[\left(V\frac{Q_0}{a}V\right) - \varepsilon_2\right]|0\rangle = 0. \qquad \text{(XVI.39)}$$

Equation (XVI.39) is for the second-order corrections the analogue of (XVI.36) for the first. In the same way as ε_1 was the eigenvalue of P_0VP_0 in $\mathscr{E}_a{}^0$, ε_2 is the eigenvalue of $P^{(1)}V(Q_0/a)P^{(1)}$ in $\mathscr{E}_a{}^{(1)}$. The corresponding eigenvector is $|0\rangle$.

If ε_1 is a non-degenerate eigenvalue ($g_1 = 1$), then $|0\rangle$ is determined by the equations of lower order and we have

$$\varepsilon_2 = \langle 0|V\frac{Q_0}{a}V|0\rangle$$

as in the non-degenerate case. If on the contrary $g_1 > 1$, the calculation of ε_2 involves finding the eigenvalues of a $g_1 \times g_1$ matrix. If these are found to be all different, the degeneracy is completely removed in the second order; if not, we must, if need be, proceed to higher orders.

It sometimes happens that a degeneracy remains in all orders. We have already had examples in the Coulomb energy of nuclei (§ 5) and in the Stark effect for a rigid rotator (§ 7). Examination of the symmetries of H_0 and H usually enables one to predict to what extent the degeneracy of an unperturbed level is likely to be removed by the perturbation λV. A systematic discussion of this point is given in § 13; we first illustrate the method with some examples of first-order calculations taken from atomic physics.

9. Atomic Levels in the Absence of Spin-Orbit Forces

In Chapter XIV, we studied the energy levels of a Z-electron atom in the central field approximation (§ XIV.12). In this approximation the Hamiltonian H is replaced by

$$H_{\mathrm{C}} = \sum_{i=1}^{Z} \left[\frac{\boldsymbol{p}_i^{\,2}}{2m} + V_{\mathrm{C}}(r_i)\right].$$

This takes into account only the average value of the electrostatic repulsion of the electrons. Let us denote by V_1 the difference between the exact Coulomb interaction and the potential of H_{C}

$$V_1 = \sum_{i<j} \frac{e^2}{|\boldsymbol{r}_i - \boldsymbol{r}_j|} - \sum_i \left[V_{\mathrm{C}}(r_i) + \frac{Ze^2}{r_i}\right]. \qquad \text{(XVI.40)}$$

If we neglect the terms in H depending on electron spin, we can write

$$H \simeq H_{\mathrm{C}} + V_1 \qquad \text{(XVI.41)}$$

and the spectrum of H can be deduced from that of H_{C} by treating V_1 as a perturbation. The modifications required by the inclusion of spin-dependent force will be considered in § 10.

As a general rule, the eigenvalues of H_{C} are all strongly degenerate. The perturbation V_1 at least partly removes this degeneracy. The levels of H in the neighbourhood of a given eigenvalue of H_{C} are obtained by diagonalizing V_1 in the subspace of that eigenvalue. In particular, the ground and first excited states of H are obtained by diagonalizing V_1 in the subspace $\mathscr{E}_0$ of the lowest eigenvalue E_0 of H_{C}.

The symmetries of H considerably simplify the problem of diagonalization. Since H (like H_{C}) is independent of the spins, it is invariant not only under overall rotations, but also under rotations of the orbital variables alone and the spin variables alone; H commutes not only with the total angular momentum $\boldsymbol{J}$ but also with the total orbital angular momentum $\boldsymbol{L}$ and the total spin $\boldsymbol{S}$ [1]). Since H_{C} has the same symmetries as H, the operator $P_0 V_1 P_0$ will also commute with $\boldsymbol{L}$ and $\boldsymbol{S}$; its eigenstates in $\mathscr{E}_0$ can be labelled by the eigenvalues of $\boldsymbol{L}^2$, $\boldsymbol{S}^2$, L_z and S_z and its eigenvalues depend only on L and S and each have a degeneracy of order $(2L+1)$ $(2S+1)$.

Denote the vectors of a standard basis $\{\boldsymbol{L}^2\, L_z, \boldsymbol{S}^2\, S_z\}$ in $\mathscr{E}_0$ by $|\gamma LSM_LM_S\rangle$; the quantum number γ distinguishes between vectors having the same orbital angular momentum and spin. In the corre-

[1]) Moreover, H is invariant under permutation of the orbital variables alone, but by the theorem of § D.18 this is equivalent, because of the Pauli principle, to the rotational invariance of the spins.

sponding representation, the matrix of $P_0 V_1 P_0$ takes the very simple form:

$$\langle \gamma L S M_L M_S | V_1 | \gamma' L' S' M_L' M_S' \rangle = \delta_{LL'}\, \delta_{SS'}\, \delta_{M_L M_L'}\, \delta_{M_S M_S'}\, \mathscr{V}^{(LS)}_{\gamma\gamma'}.$$

To effect the diagonalization we need only to diagonalize the matrices $\mathscr{V}^{(LS)}$ corresponding to each pair of quantum numbers (LS).

As an example we consider the carbon atom. Its ground state configuration is 1s² 2s² 2p², i.e., two complete shells, 1s and 2s, and an incomplete 2p shell with 2 electrons. It is $\binom{6}{2} = 15$ fold degenerate. For the purpose of finding the possible values for the pair (LS) and their degeneracy, i.e., the number of corresponding series of $(2L+1)$ $(2S+1)$ vectors, one may ignore the closed shells and consider only the two 2p electrons (Problem XVI.3).

With neglect of the Pauli principle, the different spectral terms that can be formed with two 2p electrons are

$$^3\mathrm{S} \quad ^3\mathrm{P} \quad ^3\mathrm{D} \quad ^1\mathrm{S} \quad ^1\mathrm{P} \quad ^1\mathrm{D}.$$

As the triplet and singlet spin states are respectively symmetrical and antisymmetrical in the exchange of the spins, and as the states S and D on the one hand, and P on the other, are respectively symmetrical and antisymmetrical in the interchange of the orbital variables, the terms of this list that satisfy the Pauli principle are

$$^3\mathrm{P} \quad ^1\mathrm{S} \quad ^1\mathrm{D},$$

in all $9+1+5=15$ linearly independent antisymmetrical states, as predicted. In the $\{LSM_LM_S\}$ basis (in this particular case the quantum number γ is superfluous), the perturbation V_1 is necessarily diagonal. It has, in all, three different eigenvalues, $\mathscr{V}(^3\mathrm{P})$, $\mathscr{V}(^1\mathrm{S})$ and $\mathscr{V}(^1\mathrm{D})$, respectively 9-, 1- and 5-fold degenerate; these are not difficult to calculate numerically when the individual-state wave functions are known. The calculation shows that the level ^{3}P is distinctly lower than the other two (Fig. XVI.1) [1]).

---

[1]) In general, the levels of a given configuration are in order of decreasing total spin (*Hund's rule*). This is because the second term in (XVI.40) gives the same contribution to all levels so that the order of succession of the levels depends only on the magnitude of the repulsive term $\sum e^2/|\mathbf{r}_i - \mathbf{r}_j|$. This term decreases with the mutual distance of the electrons and therefore as the orbital part of the wave function becomes more antisymmetrical. The spin part of

10. Spin-Orbit Forces. *LS* and *jj* Coupling

H is only approximately given by (XVI.41). It also contains spin-dependent terms which we shall denote by V_2:

$$H = H_C + V_1 + V_2. \tag{XVI.42}$$

In a first approximation, each electron moves independently of the others in the potential $V_C(r)$ and its spin $\boldsymbol{s}$ is coupled to its orbital angular momentum in accordance with (XIII.95); thus to a very good approximation

$$V_2 \simeq \sum_{i=1}^{Z} (\boldsymbol{l}_i \cdot \boldsymbol{s}_i)\, g(r_i) \tag{XVI.43}$$

where

$$g(r) = \frac{1}{2m^2 c^2} \frac{1}{r} \frac{dV_C}{dr}. \tag{XVI.44}$$

To correctly take this effect into account we must replace V in the treatment of § 9 by $V_1 + V_2$. However, $V_1 + V_2$ is less symmetrical than V_1: $V_1 + V_2$ commutes with $\boldsymbol{J}$, but neither with $\boldsymbol{L}$ nor with $\boldsymbol{S}$. The problem of diagonalizing the perturbation in the subspace of the unperturbed eigenvalue is therefore greatly complicated by adding the spin-orbit term. It becomes relatively simple only when one of V_1 or V_2 is much smaller than the other.

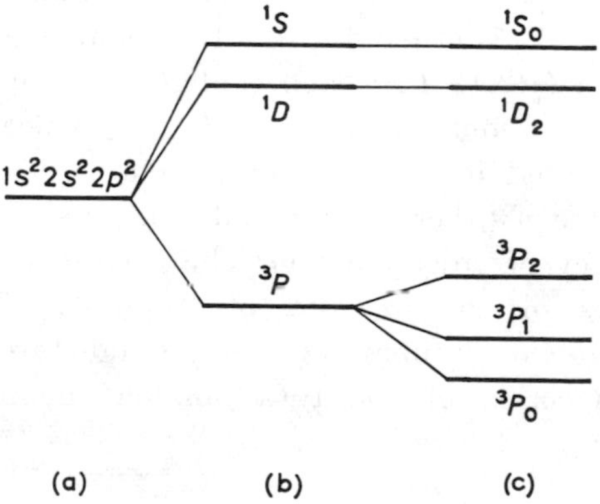

Fig. XVI.1. The levels of the ground state of the carbon atom; (a) in the central field approximation ($V_1 = V_2 = 0$); (b) neglecting spin-orbit coupling ($V_2 = 0$); (c) including spin-orbit coupling.

---

the wave function is more symmetrical for larger S (§ D.18) and therefore the orbital part is more antisymmetrical for larger S.

If $V_1 \gg V_2$, one may neglect V_2 in a first approximation. Each configuration will then give a series of levels each corresponding to a well-defined pair (LS) and each having (cf. § 9) a degeneracy of order $(2L+1)(2S+)1$; the corresponding eigenvectors are particular linear combinations of Slater determinants formed of the individual-states of the configuration. They are eigenvectors of $\mathbf{L}^2$, $\mathbf{S}^2$, L_z and S_z. V_2 is then treated as a small perturbation in the subspace corresponding to each of these levels. To each possible value of $J (J = L+S, L+S-1, \ldots, |L-S|)$ there corresponds an eigenvalue of V_2 with a degeneracy of order $(2J+1)$. The corresponding eigenvectors $|\gamma LSJM\rangle$ are eigenvectors of $\mathbf{L}^2$, $\mathbf{S}^2$, $\mathbf{J}^2$ and J_z. This method of coupling the Slater determinants of the configuration to form the eigenvectors of the total angular momentum is called *Russel–Saunders coupling* or *LS coupling.*

If $V_2 \gg V_1$, one may neglect V_1 in a first approximation. The Hamiltonian then becomes $H_C + V_2$ which is the Hamiltonian for independent particles moving in the potential $V_C + (\boldsymbol{l}\cdot\mathbf{s})\, g(r)$. Let the total angular momentum of each individual particle be $\mathbf{j} = \boldsymbol{l} + \mathbf{s}$. The spin-orbit coupling term $(\boldsymbol{l}\cdot\mathbf{s})\, g(r)$ partly removes the degeneracy of the individual states of non-zero orbital angular momentum by splitting each of them into the two levels $j = l \pm \frac{1}{2}$. The corresponding eigenvectors are specified by the quantum numbers $(nljm)$. The treatment of $H_C + V_2$ is otherwise in all ways analogous to the treatment of H_C itself (§ XIV.12); each configuration of H_C gives rise to a certain number of configurations of $H_C + V_2$. Once these are determined, V_1 is treated in each of them as a perturbation. To each possible eigenvalue of J there corresponds one (or several) eigenvalue(s) with a degeneracy of order $(2J+1)$. The corresponding eigenvectors are eigenvectors of the $\mathbf{j}_i^2$, and of $\mathbf{J}^2$ and J_z. This method of coupling the Slater determinants of the ground-state configuration to form the eigenvectors of the total angular momentum is called *jj coupling.*

The following table summarizes these two methods.

	LS Coupling			*jj* Coupling
(V_1)	$\mathbf{L} = \sum_i \boldsymbol{l}_i$	$\mathbf{S} = \sum_i \mathbf{s}_i$	(V_2)	$\mathbf{j}_i = \boldsymbol{l}_i + \mathbf{s}_i$
(V_2)	$\mathbf{J} = \mathbf{L} + \mathbf{S}$		(V_1)	$\mathbf{J} = \sum_i \mathbf{j}_i$

The relative importance of V_2 increases rapidly with Z [1]). In the light and medium atoms $V_1 \gg V_2$ and LS coupling is an excellent approximation; in heavier atoms (starting from Pb say), V_1 and V_2 are of the same order of magnitude and the level structure of the ground state configuration is intermediate between those given by LS and jj coupling.

11. The Atom in LS Coupling. Splitting Due to Spin-Orbital Coupling

Let us consider the effect of the spin-orbit coupling in the LS coupling case ($V_1 \gg V_2$). We treat V_2 as a perturbation of the levels of $H_C + V_1$.

The spectrum of the unperturbed Hamiltonian has been described in § 9. Each level corresponds to a specified value of L and S and has a degeneracy of order $(2L+1)(2S+1)$; the subspace of the corresponding eigenvectors is spanned by a set of vectors of well-defined orbital angular momentum and spin which we shall denote by $|\alpha LSM_LM_S\rangle$. The quantum number α indicates the configuration of H_C to which the level belongs, and also distinguishes between levels of the same configuration which have the same values for L and S.

The perturbation energy is obtained by diagonalizing V_2 in the subspace $\mathscr{E}(\alpha LS)$ of each of the unperturbed levels. It will now be shown that the matrix elements of V_2 in each subspace $\mathscr{E}(\alpha LS)$ are the same as those of the operator $A(\mathbf{L}\cdot\mathbf{S})$, where A is a constant characteristic of the unperturbed level (αLS):

$$\langle \alpha LSM_LM_S|V_2|\alpha LSM_L'M_S'\rangle = A\,\langle \alpha LSM_LM_S|(\mathbf{L}\cdot\mathbf{S})|\alpha LSM_L'M_S'\rangle. \tag{XVI.45}$$

Proof: As the basis vectors are antisymmetrical, the contributions to the matrix element from the Z terms of V_2 [eq. (XVI.43)] are equal. Hence we need only to treat one of them, that of the term $(\boldsymbol{l}_1\cdot\mathbf{s}_1)\,g(r_1)$ say, (no confusion being possible, we drop the index 1 in what follows). From an arbitrary component l_m of $\boldsymbol{l}$ and an arbi-

---

[1]) V_1 is a fluctuation term whose effect on the energy of each electron increases roughly as $\sqrt{Z}$. The spin-orbit coupling energy of each electron increases roughly as Z^2. It can be evaluated using the Thomas–Fermi model; the coupling is proportional to the average value of $(1/r)(\mathrm{d}V_C/\mathrm{d}r)$ which with the notation of § XIV.13 is approximately given by

$$\frac{1}{r}\frac{\mathrm{d}V_C}{\mathrm{d}r} \simeq \frac{Z^2e^2}{b^3}\frac{\mathrm{d}}{\mathrm{d}x}\left(\frac{\chi}{x}\right).$$

trary component s_μ of $\mathbf{s}$, one can form the operator $g(r)l_m s_\mu$ which is simultaneously component of a vector operator irreducible with respect to rotations of the orbital variables alone, and component of a vector operator irreducible with respect to rotations of the spin variables alone. The operator $L_m S_\mu$ has the same property. Applying the Wigner–Eckart theorem, we easily deduce (cf. Problem XIII.1)

$$\langle \alpha LSM_LM_S | gl_m s_\mu | \alpha LSM_L' M_S' \rangle = a \langle \alpha LSM_LM_S | L_m S_\mu | \alpha LSM_L' M_S \rangle,$$

where a is a constant independent of the magnetic quantum numbers M_L, M_L', M_S, M_S', m, μ. It follows that

$$\langle \alpha LSM_LM_S | g(r)\,(\boldsymbol{l}\cdot\mathbf{s})\,| \alpha LSM_L' M_S' \rangle = a \langle \alpha LSM_LM_S | (\mathbf{L}\cdot\mathbf{S}) | \alpha LSM_L' M_S' \rangle.$$

One obtains (XVI.45) by multiplying each term by Z and putting $A = Za$.

In the subspace $\mathscr{E}(\alpha LS)$, V_2 is not diagonal in the $\{\alpha LSM_LM_S\}$ representation but being invariant under rotation it is obviously diagonal in the $\{\alpha LSJM\}$ representation whose basis vectors are the eigenvectors of $\mathbf{J}^2$ and J_z in $\mathscr{E}(\alpha LS)$. Since

$$\mathbf{J}^2 = \mathbf{L}^2 + \mathbf{S}^2 + 2\mathbf{L}\cdot\mathbf{S}$$

one has, with the aid of (XVI.45)

$$\langle \alpha LSJM | V_2 | \alpha LSJM \rangle = \tfrac{1}{2} A \langle \alpha LSJM | (\mathbf{J}^2 - \mathbf{L}^2 - \mathbf{S}^2) | \alpha LSJM \rangle$$
$$= \tfrac{1}{2} A\hbar^2 [J(J+1) - L(L+1) - S(S+1)]. \quad \text{(XVI.46)}$$

Thus the unperturbed level (αLS) splits into as many levels as there are possible values for J ($J = L+S, \ldots, |L-S|$). The degeneracy of each of these levels is of order $(2J+1)$ and the perturbation energy is given by formula (XVI.46).

In Figure XVI.1, we have given the level-scheme for the ground-state configuration of carbon in LS coupling. Only the ^{3}P state is affected by the spin-orbit energy term; it gets split into three levels: $^3P_0$, $^3P_1$ and $^3P_2$. Since in this particular case $A > 0$, these levels occur in order of increasing J and the lowest of them is a $^3P_0$ state.

12. The Zeeman and Paschen–Back Effects

In the last three paragraphs we have examined the structure of atomic levels in the absence of an external field. Let us now consider an atom placed in a constant magnetic field $\mathscr{H}$. The Hamiltonian is obtained from the Hamiltonian of the atom without external field, H_0, by adding the term [cf. eq. (XIII.96)]

$$W = -\frac{e}{2mc}[\mathscr{H}\cdot(\mathbf{L}+2\mathbf{S})] \tag{XVI.47}$$

(as well as a "diamagnetic" term in $\mathscr{H}^2$ which we neglect).

Zeeman Effect

For sufficiently small $\mathscr{H}$, W may be treated as a perturbation. Since H_0 is invariant under rotation, each level of H_0 corresponds to a definite value J of the total angular momentum. We shall suppose $J \neq 0$ [1]), in which case the level has a degeneracy of order $(2J+1)$. This degeneracy is removed by the perturbation W.

Let E_0 be one of the unperturbed levels, J its angular momentum and $|E_0JM\rangle$ the eigenvectors of $\mathbf{J}^2$ and J_z that span the subspace of the eigenvalue E_0. The level-shifts caused by the magnetic field are the eigenvalues of the matrix

$$\langle E_0JM|W|E_0JM'\rangle.$$

This matrix is automatically diagonalized if we take the z axis parallel to $\mathscr{H}$ since W then commutes with J_z.

Also, according to the Wigner–Eckart theorem, the matrix elements of the vector operators $\mathbf{L}+2\mathbf{S}$ and $\mathbf{J}$ in the subspace of E_0 are proportional:

$$\langle E_0JM|(\mathbf{L}+2\mathbf{S})|E_0JM'\rangle = g\,\langle E_0JM|\mathbf{J}|E_0JM'\rangle. \tag{XVI.48}$$

The proportionality factor, g, the so-called Landé factor, is equal to the ratio of the reduced matrix elements of these operators; it is a magnitude characteristic of the level E_0 considered. In particular,

$$\langle E_0JM|(L_z+2S_z)|E_0JM'\rangle = gM\hbar\delta_{MM'}.$$

With the above-mentioned choice of axes,

$$W = -\frac{e\mathscr{H}}{2mc}(L_z+2S_z)$$

---

[1]) If $J = 0$ (diamagnetic atom) the level shift vanishes to the first order in $\mathscr{H}$. In the calculation of this shift to the second order in $\mathscr{H}$ the contribution of the "diamagnetic term" cannot be neglected.

whence, if we denote the Bohr magneton by μ_B [eq. (XIII.74)]

$$\langle E_0 JM | W | E_0 JM' \rangle = -\, M g \mu_B \mathscr{H} \delta_{MM'}.$$

Thus the perturbation completely removes the degeneracy and the $(2J+1)$ levels obtained are given by the Zeeman formula

$$E = E_0 - M g \mu_B \mathscr{H} \qquad (M = -J, -J+1, \ldots, +J) \qquad \text{(XVI.49)}$$

Calculation of the Landé factor in LS coupling

The Landé factor g is defined by equation (XVI.48). We suppose that the LS coupling scheme is valid for the atom considered and therefore, following the notation of § 11, the atomic levels in the absence of the external field will be characterized by the quantum numbers αLSJ.

To determine g we calculate in two different ways the average value

$$\langle \mathbf{J}\cdot(\mathbf{L}+2\mathbf{S})\rangle \equiv \langle \alpha LSJM | (\mathbf{J}\cdot(\mathbf{L}+2\mathbf{S})) | \alpha LSJM \rangle.$$

(*a*) With the aid of the identity

$$\mathbf{J}\cdot(\mathbf{L}+2\mathbf{S}) = \mathbf{J}^2 + \mathbf{S}^2 + \tfrac{1}{2}(\mathbf{J}^2 - \mathbf{L}^2 - \mathbf{S}^2)$$

we have

$$\langle \mathbf{J}\cdot(\mathbf{L}+2\mathbf{S})\rangle = \tfrac{1}{2}[3J(J+1) + S(S+1) - L(L+1)]\,\hbar^2.$$

(*b*) Directly multiplying the matrices in the $\{\alpha LSJM\}$ representation, and applying (XVI.48), we find (cf. Problem XIII.19)

$$\begin{aligned}\langle \mathbf{J}\cdot(\mathbf{L}+2\mathbf{S})\rangle &= \sum_{i=xyz} \sum_{M'} \langle \alpha LSJM | J_i | \alpha LSJM' \rangle \\ &\qquad \times \langle \alpha LSJM' | (L_i + 2S_i) | \alpha LSJM \rangle \\ &= g \,\langle \alpha LSJM | \mathbf{J}^2 | \alpha LSJM \rangle \\ &= g\, J(J+1)\,\hbar^2.\end{aligned}$$

Equating these two results gives

$$g = 1 + \frac{J(J+1) + S(S+1) - L(L+1)}{2J(J+1)}. \qquad \text{(XVI.50)}$$

Paschen–Back Effect

The above theory of the Zeeman Effect is justified only if the splitting of the levels by the perturbation W is small compared with the distance between the unperturbed levels. When LS coupling is valid this supposes W to be small compared with the spin-orbit coupling V_2, or more precisely [cf. eq. (XVI.46) and (XVI.49)], that

$$|g|\mu_B \mathscr{H} \ll A\hbar^2.$$

Let us suppose that, on the contrary, the magnetic field is so strong that we have

$$A\hbar^2 \ll \mu_B \mathscr{H}.$$

In this case the spin-orbit coupling has a negligible effect as compared with that of the magnetic coupling. The latter can therefore be treated as a perturbation of the levels of the Hamiltonian

$$H_C + V_1.$$

Following the notations of § 11, each of these unperturbed levels is labelled by the quantum numbers (αLS) and has a degeneracy of order $(2S+1)$ $(2L+1)$. The perturbation partly removes this degeneracy. The effect is known as the Paschen–Back effect. One obtains the displacements relative to an unperturbed level $E_{\alpha LS}$ by diagonalizing W in the corresponding subspace. Since W commutes with L_z and S_z, the perturbation matrix is diagonal in the $\{\alpha LSM_LM_S\}$ representation:

$$\langle \alpha LSM_LM_S|W|\alpha LSM_L'M_S'\rangle = -\mu_B \mathscr{H}(M_L + 2M_S)\delta_{M_LM_L'}\,\delta_{M_SM_S'}.$$

Hence the level shifts are given by the formula

$$E = E_{\alpha LS} - \mu_B \mathscr{H}(M_L + 2M_S)$$
$$(M_L = -L, \ldots, +L; \qquad M_S = -S, \ldots, +S).$$

If $L \neq 0$ and $S \neq 0$ certain of the levels obtained are still degenerate. The introduction of the small spin-orbit coupling term at least partially removes these residual degeneracies.

13. Symmetry of H and Removal of Degeneracy [1]

The preceding examples (§ 5, 7, 9, 10, 11, 12) show the importance of symmetry considerations in perturbation calculations of degenerate levels. The existence of degenerate eigenvalues can almost always be associated with the symmetries of the Hamiltonian; knowledge of

[1] This paragraph, the only one of this chapter calling upon the results of Chapter XV and the few notions of group theory used there, may be omitted in a first reading.

the invariance groups of H_0 and H allows one to predict within what limits the degeneracy of a level $E_a{}^0$ can be removed by the perturbation, and considerably facilitates the calculation of the perturbation energies.

In all the examples previously studied, the unperturbed Hamiltonian H_0 was invariant with respect to a certain group G_0, and the perturbation λV invariant with respect to a certain subgroup G of G_0. Thus, for the case of the Stark effect for a rigid rotator (§ 7), G_0 was the rotation reflection group and G the group of reflections with respect to planes containing the z axis (cf. Ch. XV, § 14).

We return to the notation of § (XV. 11). With the operators of G we can form the observables J and M with eigenvalues labelled by the quantum numbers j and μ respectively. To each value of j there corresponds a definite irreducible representation of the group. Denote the degree of this representation by d_j; for a given j there are d_j possible values for μ distinguishing between the d_j basis vectors of the representation. To each pair of eigenvalues $(j\mu)$ there corresponds a certain subspace $\mathscr{E}(j\mu)$ of the state-vector space $\mathscr{E}$. Since H and H_0 are invariant with respect to G, and consequently commute with J and M, one can separately solve the corresponding eigenvalue problems in each of the subspaces $\mathscr{E}(j\mu)$. We obtain the same spectra with the same degeneracies in the d_j subspaces corresponding to a given value of j.

Suppose that $E_a{}^0$ is an eigenvalue of H_0 in $\mathscr{E}(j\mu)$ with a degeneracy of order p_j. According to the above,

$$g_a = \textstyle\sum_j p_j\, d_j. \tag{XVI.51}$$

In the subspace $\mathscr{E}(j\mu)$, the introduction of the perturbation may more or less completely remove the degeneracy in the unperturbed energy (supposing $p_j > 1$); if H has no symmetries other than those of the group G, the degeneracy in question is in general completely removed and one obtains p_j distinct levels. *Hence, in the total space* $\mathscr{E}$, *the introduction of the perturbation splits the unperturbed level into at most* $\sum_j p_j$ *distinct levels; each of these levels corresponds to a specified value of* j *and has a degeneracy of order* d_j *when the degeneracy is completely removed in* $\mathscr{E}(j\mu)$, *and otherwise has a degeneracy which is a multiple of* d_j.

These results are based only on the fact that H has the symmetry

G and is a continuous function of λ tending to H_0 when $\lambda \to 0$. *They are exact in all orders of the perturbation calculation.*

If the subspace $\mathscr{E}_a{}^0$ is irreducible with respect to the group G, the sum (XVI.51) will contain just one term [1]), and the degeneracy of the level $E_a{}^0$ cannot be removed in any order. This is what generally occurs when H_0 has no symmetries other than those of H ($G_0 = G$). We have already had an example of this in the calculation of the Coulomb energy of the nucleus (§ 5).

In the case of § 7 on the other hand, G is definitely a subgroup of G_0. The subspace $\mathscr{E}_l{}^0$ of the eigenvalue $E_l{}^0$ is $(2l+1)$-fold degenerate. It is irreducible with respect to G_0 but reducible (if $l \neq 0$) with respect to G. In this particular case (cf. § XV.14), J is the operator $l_z{}^2$ with eigenvalues m^2 which we can label with the quantum number $|m|$ ($|m| = 0, 1, 2, \ldots$); the number of dimensions of the corresponding irreducible subspace is

$$d_{|m|} = \begin{cases} 2 & \text{if} \quad |m| \neq 0 \\ 1 & \text{if} \quad |m| = 0. \end{cases}$$

For this case (XVI.51) becomes:

$$g_l \equiv 2l + 1 = \sum_{|m|=0}^{l} d_{|m|}.$$

Thus the perturbation splits the level $E_l{}^0$ into at most $l+1$ distinct levels, one of which, $|m| = 0$, is non-degenerate, while all the rest are doubly degenerate. This is just what was found in § 7. It should be stressed that these symmetry considerations give only an upper limit for the removal of the degeneracy; this limit will be attained if the perturbation calculation is continued to sufficiently high orders. In the case of § 7 it was attained in the second order.

14. Quasi-Degeneracy

When two levels $E_a{}^0$, $E_b{}^0$ are so close together that corrections introduced by the perturbation V are large with respect to $|E_a{}^0 - E_b{}^0|$, the preceding methods lose their validity. One can nonetheless apply perturbation methods to this "quasi-degenerate" case if one appropriately modifies the definition of the unperturbed Hamiltonian and the perturbation.

---

[1]) $\mathscr{E}_a{}^0$ is an invariant subspace with respect to G and defines a certain representation of degree g_a of this group, which we denote $\mathbf{G}_a$. From (XVI.51), its decomposition in irreducible parts is: $\mathbf{G}_a \simeq \sum_j p_j \mathbf{G}^{(j)}$.

Let P_i^0 denote the projector onto the subspace of the eigenvalue E_i^0 of H_0. One has

$$H_0 = \sum_i E_i^0 P_i^0.$$

The modification mentioned above consists essentially in replacing the terms $E_a^0 P_a^0$ and $E_b^0 P_b^0$ in this expression by $E_\alpha^0(P_a^0 + P_b^0)$, where E_α^0 is a quantity intermediate between E_a^0 and E_b^0. One thereby obtains a new unperturbed Hamiltonian whose eigenvalue E_α^0 has a degeneracy of order $g_a + g_b$. The correction to E_α^0 due the perturbation

$$V + (E_a^0 - E_\alpha^0)P_a^0 + (E_b^0 - E_\alpha^0)P_b^0$$

can then be calculated.

In treating the Paschen–Back effect (§ 12) the method applied was essentially the one described here. There the field $\mathscr{H}$ was relatively strong so that the level shifts of a given LS term were no longer small as compared with their mutual separation. We then took $H_C + V_1$ as the unperturbed Hamiltonian rather than $H_C + V_1 + V_2$, which amounts to replacing the group of neighboring levels $E_{\alpha LSJ}$ $(J = |L-S|, \ldots, L+S)$ by the single level $E_{\alpha LS}$. Normally one would then make a perturbation calculation of the corrections to $E_{\alpha LS}$ due to the perturbation $V_2 + W$. In the pure Paschen–Back effect, $\mathscr{H}$ is so strong that in a first approximation one may neglect V_2 in this calculation ($V_2 \ll W$), which is what was done in § 12. When V_2 and W are of the same order of magnitude this approximation is no longer valid and the perturbation calculation is considerably complicated (Problems XVI.7 and XVI.8).

III. EXPLICIT FORMS FOR THE PERTURBATION EXPANSION IN ALL ORDERS [1]

15. The Hamiltonian H and its Resolvent $G(z)$ [2]

In this section we briefly set forth a method for explicitly giving the perturbation expansion in all orders; the method, due to Kato [3],

---

[1] This section may be omitted in a first reading.

[2] Some authors use the term Green's function instead of resolvent.

[3] T. Kato, *Prog. Theor. Phys.* 4, 154 (1949). Kato is mainly interested in the conditions of convergence of the perturbation method, and his method lends itself particularly well to a discussion of this question. In most cases encountered, the perturbation expansion is an asymptotic expansion. In this section we leave aside these mathematical aspects of Kato's work.

consists in using the expansion of the resolvent $G(z)$ of the Hamiltonian H into a power series in the perturbation. In this paragraph we define $G(z)$ and describe some of its properties.

By definition, if H is an observable, its *resolvent* is the function

$$G(z) \equiv \frac{1}{z-H} \tag{XVI.52}$$

of the complex variable z [1]).

Figure XVI.2 shows the complex z-plane with the spectrum of H marked on the real axis; it has in general a discrete part and a continuous part, the latter being to the right of the discrete part and extending to infinity. $G(z)$ is an analytic function whose singularities constitute the spectrum of H.

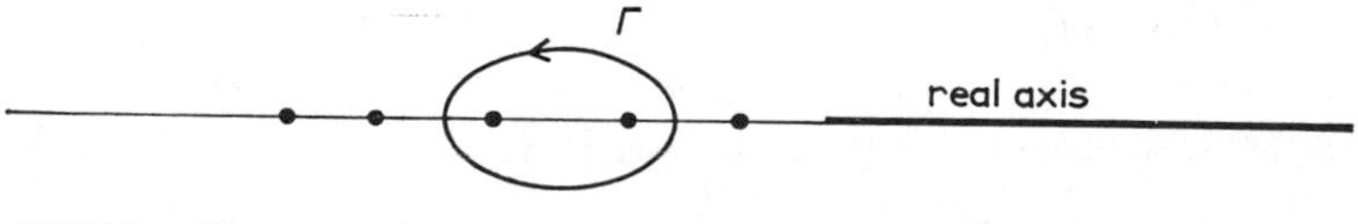

Fig. XVI.2. The complex z plane and the definition of the contour Γ. The spectrum of H is indicated in heavy print on the real axis.

For simplicity we shall suppose the spectrum of H to be entirely discrete. We denote the eigenvalues by $E_0, E_1, \ldots, E_i, \ldots$ and the projector onto the subspace of E_i by P_i

$$HP_i = E_i P_i. \tag{XVI.53}$$

[1]) By definition, an operator Q of Hilbert space is bounded if there exists a constant M such that

$$\frac{\langle u|Q^\dagger Q|u\rangle}{\langle u|u\rangle} \leqslant M$$

for any $|u\rangle$; the lowest value of M is by definition the upper bound or norm of the said operator and is denoted $\|Q\|$. In all rigor, the different operations of algebra and analysis, and in particular the notions of convergence of series, of differentiation, etc. can be extended without restriction only to the bounded operators of Hilbert space (cf. M. H. Stone, *Linear transformations in Hilbert space* (Amer. Math. Soc., New York, 1932).

From the mathematical point of view, the great interest of $G(z)$ is that it is *bounded* in the whole of the complex plane except for the eigenvalues of H: it is an analytic function of z whose singular points constitute the spectrum of H. If $\Delta(z)$ is the square of the distance from z to the closest eigenvalue of H, we have

$$\|G(z)\| = 1/\Delta(z).$$

One then has the orthogonality and closure relations:

$$P_i P_j = \delta_{ij} P_i \tag{XVI.54}$$

$$\sum_i P_i = 1. \tag{XVI.55}$$

From definition (XVI.52)

$$G(z)\, P_i = \frac{P_i}{z - E_i}$$

and therefore

$$G(z) = \sum_i \frac{P_i}{z - E_i}. \tag{XVI.56}$$

Each discrete eigenvalue E_i of H is a simple pole of $G(z)$ whose residue is the projector P_i, i.e.

$$P_i = \frac{1}{2\pi \mathrm{i}} \oint_{\Gamma_i} G(z)\, \mathrm{d}z, \tag{XVI.57}$$

where Γ_i is a closed contour in the complex plane enclosing E_i and excluding all other singularities of $G(z)$. More generally, if Γ is a closed contour in the complex plane not going through any of the eigenvalues of H (Fig. XVI.2) and if P_Γ is the sum of the projectors P_i relating to eigenvalues inside this contour, then

$$P_\Gamma = \frac{1}{2\pi \mathrm{i}} \oint_{\Gamma} G(z)\, \mathrm{d}z. \tag{XVI.58}$$

Multiplying (XVI.58) by H and taking into account the identity

$$(z - H) G \equiv G (z - H) \equiv 1$$

we obtain the important formula

$$H P_\Gamma = \frac{1}{2\pi \mathrm{i}} \oint_{\Gamma} z G(z)\, \mathrm{d}z. \tag{XVI.59}$$

16. Expansion of $G(z)$, P and HP into Power Series in λV

We now consider the perturbation problem itself.

The resolvents of H and of H_0 are respectively:

$$G \equiv \frac{1}{z - H_0 - \lambda V} \qquad G_0 \equiv \frac{1}{z - H_0}. \tag{XVI.60}$$

We note that

$$\frac{1}{z-H_0-\lambda V} = \frac{1}{z-H_0}\,[(z-H_0-\lambda V)+\lambda V]\,\frac{1}{z-H_0-\lambda V}$$

$$= \frac{1}{z-H_0} + \frac{1}{z-H_0}\,\lambda V\,\frac{1}{z-H_0-\lambda V}.$$

G is therefore the solution of the integral equation:

$$G = G_0(1+\lambda VG). \qquad \text{(XVI.61)}$$

Iteration of this equation gives G as an expansion in powers of the perturbation[1]):

$$G = \sum_{n=0}^{\infty} \lambda^n G_0(VG_0)^n. \qquad \text{(XVI.62)}$$

Adopting the notation of § 8, we now look for the expansion of P as a power series in the perturbation. For sufficiently small λ, there certainly exists a contour in the complex z plane simultaneously enclosing the unperturbed eigenvalue $E_a{}^0$ and the eigenvalues of H that tend to $E_a{}^0$ in the limit when $\lambda \to 0$, and excluding all other eigenvalues of H and of H_0. Let such a contour be denoted by Γ_a. From (XVI.58),

$$P = \frac{1}{2\pi \mathrm{i}} \oint_{\Gamma_a} G(z)\, \mathrm{d}z.$$

Substituting for G the expression in equation (XVI.62) and interchanging the order of summation and integration, we obtain the expansion of P as a power series in λ

$$P = P_0 + \sum_{n=1}^{\infty} \lambda^n A^{(n)}, \qquad \text{(XVI.63)}$$

where

$$A^{(n)} = \frac{1}{2\pi \mathrm{i}} \oint_{\Gamma_a} G_0(VG_0)^n\, \mathrm{d}z. \qquad \text{(XVI.64)}$$

The only singularity of the function $G_0\,(VG_0)^n$ inside the contour Γ_a is a pole of order $n+1$ in $E_a{}^0$. As seen from (XVI.64), $A^{(n)}$ is just the residue of that pole.

---

[1]) The radius of convergence for this expansion is $\|\lambda VG_0\|$. It is therefore absolutely convergent if $\|\lambda V\| < \Delta_0(z)$, where $\Delta_0(z)$ is the square of the distance from z to the nearest eigenvalue of H_0.

In order to calculate this residue we use the expansion of G_0 in a Laurent series about $E_a{}^0$. The coefficients are easily calculated using (XVI.56), and one finds

$$G_0 = \frac{P_0}{z - E_a{}^0} + \sum_{k=1}^{\infty} (-)^{k-1} (z - E_a{}^0)^{k-1} \frac{Q_0}{a^k}.$$

Following Kato we introduce the quantity S^k ($k \geqslant 0$) defined by

$$S^k = \begin{cases} -P_0 & \text{if } k = 0 \\ \dfrac{Q_0}{a^k} & \text{if } k \geqslant 1 \end{cases} \tag{XVI.65}$$

so that our expansion becomes

$$G_0 = \sum_{k=0}^{\infty} (-)^{k-1} (z - E_a{}^0)^{k-1} S^k. \tag{XVI.66}$$

$A^{(n)}$ is the coefficient of $(z - E_a{}^0)^{-1}$ in the Laurent expansion of $G_0(VG_0)^n$. Taking (XVI.66) into account one easily finds

$$A^{(n)} = - \sum_{(n)} S^{k_1} V S^{k_2} V \dots V S^{k_{n+1}}, \tag{XVI.67}$$

where $\sum_{(p)}$ extends over *all* sets of the non-negative integers

$$k_1, k_2, \dots, k_{n+1}$$

such that:

$$k_1 + k_2 + \dots + k_{n+1} = p. \tag{XVI.68}$$

As an illustration we give the first few terms in the expansion of P:

$$\begin{aligned} P = P_0 &+ \lambda \left(P_0 V \frac{Q_0}{a} + \frac{Q_0}{a} V P_0 \right) \\ &+ \lambda^2 \left(P_0 V \frac{Q_0}{a} V \frac{Q_0}{a} + \frac{Q_0}{a} V P_0 V \frac{Q_0}{a} + \frac{Q_0}{a} V \frac{Q_0}{a} V P_0 \right. \\ &\quad \left. - P_0 V P_0 V \frac{Q_0}{a^2} - P_0 V \frac{Q_0}{a^2} V P_0 - \frac{Q_0}{a^2} V P_0 V P_0 \right) + \dots \end{aligned} \tag{XVI.69}$$

Starting from (XVI.59), one obtains the expansion of HP in the same way. One finds:

$$(H - E_a{}^0) P = \sum_{n=1}^{\infty} \lambda^n B^{(n)}, \tag{XVI.70}$$

where

$$B^{(n)} = \sum_{(n-1)} S^{k_1} V S^{k_2} V \ldots V S^{k_{n+1}}. \tag{XVI.71}$$

Thus

$$(H - E_a{}^0)P = \lambda P_0 V P_0 + \lambda^2 \left(P_0 V P_0 V \frac{Q_0}{a} + P_0 V \frac{Q_0}{a} V P_0 + \frac{Q_0}{a} V P_0 V P_0 \right) + \ldots \tag{XVI.72}$$

17. Calculation of Eigenvalues and Eigenstates

The desired eigenvalues and eigenvectors of H are the eigenvalues and eigenvectors of the operator HP of the space $\mathscr{E}$ of which P is the projector. Since we know how to form P and HP, we have reduced the problem to that of diagonalizing a matrix in a g_a-dimensional space.

Non-degenerate case: $g_a = 1$

In this case the eigenvalue of H is $P|0\rangle$. The expansion of its norm, $\langle 0|P|0\rangle$, is easily obtained from that of the operator P. $P|0\rangle$ is a multiple of the eigenvector $|\psi\rangle$ formed in section I; the norm of the latter is easily shown to be $1/\langle 0|P|0\rangle$.

The eigenenergy E_a is given by the equation $HP = E_a P$. Since $\mathrm{Tr}\, P = \mathrm{Tr}\, P_0 = 1$, we have [eq. (XVI.70)]

$$E_a = \mathrm{Tr}\, HP = E_a{}^0 + \sum_{n=1}^{\infty} \lambda^n (\mathrm{Tr}\, B^{(n)}),$$

i.e.

$$\varepsilon_n = \mathrm{Tr}\, B^{(n)}. \tag{XVI.73}$$

Since each of the terms of $B^{(n)}$ contains P_0 at least once, and since, by the well-known property of the trace, one has the identity

$$\mathrm{Tr}\, M P_0 N = \mathrm{Tr}\, P_0 N M = \langle 0|NM|0\rangle,$$

it is easy to cast ε_n into the form of the average value of a certain operator in the unperturbed state $|0\rangle$. The first few terms of the expansion of E_a are given by

$$E_a = E_a{}^0 + \lambda \langle 0|V|0\rangle + \lambda^2 \langle 0|V \frac{Q_0}{a} V|0\rangle + \lambda^3 \left(\langle 0|V \frac{Q_0}{a} V \frac{Q_0}{a} V|0\rangle - \langle 0|V \frac{Q_0}{a^2} V|0\rangle \langle 0|V|0\rangle \right) + \ldots \tag{XVI.74}$$

in agreement with the results of section I [eq. (XVI.12) and (XVI.26)].

Degenerate case: $g_a \neq 1$

Rather than directly solve the eigenvalue problem for HP in $\mathscr{E}_a$, one can substitute a similar diagonalization problem in $\mathscr{E}_a{}^0$.

Let us suppose that any vector of $\mathscr{E}_a$ may be considered as the projection in $\mathscr{E}_a$ of a certain well-defined vector of $\mathscr{E}_a{}^0$ (this assumption was implicitly made in the non-degenerate case). Since $\mathscr{E}_a$ and $\mathscr{E}_a{}^0$ have the same number of dimensions, it follows that the projector P establishes a one-to-one correspondence between the vectors of $\mathscr{E}_a$ and the vectors of $\mathscr{E}_a{}^0$, and one can deduce that such a correspondence is also established by P_0. This property of "non-orthogonality" of the two subspaces is obviously realized for λ sufficiently small.

Thus any eigenvector of H in $\mathscr{E}_a$ can be put into the form $P|E_a{}^0\alpha\rangle$ and satisfies the equation:

$$HP|E_a{}^0\alpha\rangle = E_\alpha P|E_a{}^0\alpha\rangle.$$

A necessary and sufficient condition for this equality between vectors of $\mathscr{E}_a$ to be satisfied is that their projections on $\mathscr{E}_a{}^0$ be equal:

$$P_0HP|E_a{}^0\alpha\rangle = E_\alpha P_0P|E_a{}^0\alpha\rangle.$$

If we put

$$H_a = P_0HPP_0, \qquad K_a = P_0PP_0. \tag{XVI.75}$$

the preceding equation becomes

$$H_a|E_a{}^0\alpha\rangle = E_\alpha K_a|E_a{}^0\alpha\rangle. \tag{XVI.76}$$

K_a and H_a may be treated as operators in the space $\mathscr{E}_a{}^0$. K_a is a positive-definite Hermitian operator, H_a a Hermitian operator of this space. Equation (XVI.76) is a generalized eigenvalue equation. The eigenvalues E_α are the solutions of the secular equation (cf. § VII.17)

$$\det (H_a - xK_a) = 0.$$

They are the desired eigenenergies. The projections of the corresponding eigenvectors $|E_a{}^0\alpha\rangle$ in $\mathscr{E}_a$ are the eigenvectors of H.

The expansions of H_a and K_a are easily deduced from those of HP and P respectively [eq. (XVI.69) and (XVI.72)]:

$$K_a = P_0 - \lambda^2 P_0 V \frac{Q_0}{a^2} VP_0 + \ldots \tag{XVI.77}$$

$$H_a = E_a{}^0 K_a + \lambda P_0 V P_0 + \lambda^2 P_0 V \frac{Q_0}{a} VP_0 + \ldots \tag{XVI.78}$$

To a given order of approximation the eigenvalues E_α are obtained by stopping the expansions of H_a and K_a at that order. The results thereby obtained may differ from those of the elementary theory by quantities of higher order.

To the first order the results of the two methods are exactly the same. In making the comparison one must be careful to distinguish between $|E_a{}^0\alpha\rangle$ and the vector $|0\rangle$ of the elementary theory. $|0\rangle$ is the limit of $|E_a{}^0\alpha\rangle$ when $\lambda \to 0$.

A method very similar to that of Kato but leading to simpler expansions has been given by Bloch [1]). It is based on the fact that the operator $\mathscr{U}$ defined by

$$PP_0 \equiv \mathscr{U}K_a, \qquad \mathscr{U}P_0 \equiv \mathscr{U} \tag{XVI.79}$$

has a particularly simple expansion:

$$\mathscr{U} = \sum_{n=0}^{\infty} \lambda^n\, \mathscr{U}^{(n)} \tag{XVI.80}$$

$$\mathscr{U}^{(n)} = \sum_{(n)}{}' S^{k_1}VS^{k_2}V \ldots VS^{k_n}VP_0 \tag{XVI.81}$$

$\sum'_{(n)}$ being extended over all sets of non-negative integers $k_1, k_2, \ldots, k_n$ satisfying the conditions

$$\begin{aligned} &k_1+k_2+\ldots+k_p \geqslant p \quad (p=1, 2, \ldots, n-1) \\ &k_1+k_2+\ldots+k_n = n. \end{aligned} \tag{XVI.82}$$

Observe that $P_0\,\mathscr{U} = P_0$ and that $P\mathscr{U} = \mathscr{U}$. The action of $\mathscr{U}$ on a vector of $\mathscr{E}_a{}^0$ gives the vector of $\mathscr{E}_a$ of which it is the projection in $\mathscr{E}_a{}^0$.

According to the definition of $\mathscr{U}$, equation (XVI.76) is equivalent to

$$(P_0H\mathscr{U} - E_\alpha)\, K_a|E_a{}^0\alpha\rangle = 0. \tag{XVI.83}$$

This equation corresponds, in the method of Bloch, to equation (XVI.76) in the method of Kato. It is an ordinary eigenvalue equation for the *non-Hermitean* operator [2]) $P_0H\mathscr{U} \equiv H_aK_a{}^{-1}$ of $\mathscr{E}_a{}^0$. The eigenvalues are the desired eigenenergies; the corresponding eigenvectors, $K_a|E_a{}^0\alpha\rangle$ are the projections of the eigenvectors of H onto

---

1) C. Bloch, Nuclear Physics, **6**, (1958) 329.

2) Considered as an operator of the space $\mathscr{E}_a{}^0$, K_a has an inverse, as an operator of the entire Hilbert space it obviously has not.

$\mathscr{E}_a{}^0$; the eigenvectors themselves are obtained by application of the operator $\mathscr{U}$. The expansion of $P_0H\mathscr{U}$ is easily deduced from that of $\mathscr{U}$ if we recall that

$$P_0H\mathscr{U} = E_a{}^0P_0 + \lambda P_0V\mathscr{U}.$$

The first few terms are:

$$P_0H\mathscr{U} = E_a{}^0P_0 + \lambda P_0VP_0 + \lambda^2 P_0V\frac{Q_0}{a}VP_0 + \ldots$$

These are seen to be simpler than those of H_a and K_a [eq. (XVI.77) and (XVI.78)].

In the non-degenerate case the energy is simply

$$E_a = \langle 0|H\mathscr{U}|0\rangle$$

from which we immediately extract the successive coefficients in its expansion:

$$\varepsilon_n = \sum\nolimits'_{(n-1)} \langle 0|VS^{k_1}VS^{k_2}V \ldots VS^{k_n}V|0\rangle.$$

EXERCISES AND PROBLEMS

1. The interaction $V(q)$ is added to the Hamiltonian $(p^2 + m^2\omega^2q^2)/2m$. Calculate with the perturbation theory the first- and second-order energy-level shifts for the following two cases:

(a) $$V = \tfrac{1}{2}m\alpha^2q^2$$

(b) $$V = bq.$$

In both cases the shifts can be exactly calculated. Compare the exact result with that of the perturbation theory.

2. Consider a hydrogen atom in the Schrödinger theory (Chapter XI). To what extent can the degeneracy of each level be removed by a constant electric field $\mathscr{E}$ (interaction $-e\mathscr{E}\cdot\mathbf{r}$)? Show that in the first order the level $n = 2$ splits into three equidistant levels (level distance $3\mathscr{E}\hbar^2/me$) and give the order of degeneracy of each.

3. Show that in the central field approximation the total angular momentum, the total orbital angular momentum and the total spin of the electrons of a complete shell are null. From this result deduce that the number of linearly independent vectors (LSM_LM_S) for a given configuration is the same as that obtained on taking into account only the electrons of incomplete shells.

4. What are the spectral terms of the ground state configuration of the carbon atom in jj coupling? Show that one obtains the same values for the total angular momentum J, with the same multiplicity, in jj and LS coupling (§ 11). Explain why.

5. The ground state configuration of the nitrogen atom ($Z = 7$) is $1s^2 2s^2 2p^3$. What are the different spectral terms in LS coupling?

6. Apply the considerations of § 13 to the study of the complex atoms of § 9, 10, 11. List the symmetries of H_C, V_1 and V_2 and show how and within what limits the successive introduction of the perturbations $V_i (i = 1, 2)$ removes the degeneracy of the levels of H_C: (a) in LS coupling (b) in jj coupling.

7. The ground-state configuration of a sodium atom ($Z = 11$) is $1s^2 2s^2 2p^6 3s^1$ and its first excited configuration is $1s^2 2s^2 2p^6 3p^1$. Therefore the ground-state of sodium is ${}^2S_{1/2}$ and its first two excited states are ${}^2P_{1/2}$ and ${}^2P_{3/2}$. Investigate the effect of a constant magnetic field $\mathscr{H}$ on these levels. Calculate the respective Landé factors. The intensity of $\mathscr{H}$ is gradually increased from the Zeeman region to the Paschen-Back. Give an expression for the ${}^2P$ levels as a function of the parameter $\varrho = \mu_B \mathscr{H}/A\hbar^2$ where μ_B is the Bohr magneton and A the spin-orbit coupling constant introduced in § 11 ($A > 0$); draw the corresponding curves.

8. Same question as in the preceding problem for the ground-state (${}^3P$) of the carbon atom. [The levels are given as roots of secular equations, one of which is of the third degree; the main features of the curves can be obtained without solving these secular equations.]

9. The different levels $E_1, E_2, \ldots, E_n$ obtained from a g_a-fold degenerate level upon introduction of the perturbation V can be characterized by their center of gravity $\langle E \rangle$ and their root-mean-square deviation ΔE, defined respectively (with the notations of § 8) by

$$\langle E \rangle = \frac{1}{g_a} \sum_{i=1}^{n} g_i E_i \qquad (\Delta E)^2 = \frac{1}{g_a} \sum_{i=1}^{n} g_i (E_i - \langle E \rangle)^2.$$

Show that to the first order in V one has

$$\varepsilon \equiv \langle E \rangle - E_a^0 \simeq \frac{1}{g_a} \operatorname{Tr} P_0 V, \qquad (\Delta E)^2 \simeq \frac{1}{g_a} \operatorname{Tr} P_0 (V - \varepsilon) P_0 (V - \varepsilon).$$

Apply these formulas to the perturbation

$$V = A(\mathbf{L} \cdot \mathbf{S}) + \frac{e\hbar}{2mc} \mathscr{H} \cdot (\mathbf{L} + 2\mathbf{S})$$

of the two preceding problems. Show that in these cases $\varepsilon = 0$; give the expression for ΔE and examine its variation as a function of the parameter ϱ defined in Problem XVI.7.

CHAPTER XVII

APPROXIMATE SOLUTIONS OF THE TIME-DEPENDENT SCHRÖDINGER EQUATION

1. Change of "Representation" and Perturbation Treatment of a Part of the Hamiltonian

This chapter, with its two sections, is devoted to methods of obtaining approximate solutions to the time-dependent Schrödinger equation. Knowing that our quantum system is in a certain dynamical state at time t_0, we wish to determine its state at a later time t. The problem, therefore, is to determine as exactly as possible the operator $U(t, t_0)$ describing the evolution in time of the dynamical states of the system in the Schrödinger "representation".

Let us briefly recall the main properties of $U(t, t_0)$. This operator is completely determined once the Hamiltonian $H(t)$ of the system is given. It is defined by the integral equation

$$U(t, t_0) = 1 - \mathrm{i}\hbar^{-1} \int_{t_0}^{t} H(\tau)\, U(\tau, t_0)\, \mathrm{d}\tau \qquad \text{(XVII.1)}$$

or, equivalently, by the Schrödinger equation

$$\mathrm{i}\hbar \frac{\partial}{\partial t} U(t, t_0) = H(t)\, U(t, t_0) \qquad \text{(XVII.2)}$$

and the initial condition

$$U(t_0, t_0) = 1. \qquad \text{(XVII.3)}$$

Since $H(t)$ is Hermitean, U is unitary:

$$U(t, t')\, U^{\dagger}(t, t') = U^{\dagger}(t, t')\, U(t, t') = 1. \qquad \text{(XVII.4)}$$

In addition, we have the composition law [1])

$$U(t, t') = U(t, t'')\, U(t'', t') \qquad \text{(XVII.5)}$$

---

[1]) To demonstrate this formula, the physical sense of which is obvious, we note that if V is unitary and time-independent, then $U(t, t'')V$ is a solution of the Schrödinger equation (XVII.2). For it to be equal to $U(t, t')$ for any value of t, it is sufficient that it be equal for a particular value of t, say $t = t''$; this gives $V = U(t'', t')$.

whence

$$U^{\dagger}(t, t') = U(t', t). \qquad \text{(XVII.6)}$$

An equivalent definition of U may be obtained by replacing (XVII.1) by its Hermitean conjugate. Taking (XVII.6) into account, we then obtain

$$U(t, t_0) = 1 - i\hbar^{-1} \int_{t_0}^{t} U(t, \tau)\, H(\tau)\, d\tau. \qquad \text{(XVII.7)}$$

The methods described in this chapter are based on the following formal development. We suppose that the Hamiltonian H can be put in the form

$$H(t) \equiv H^{(0)}(t) + V(t), \qquad \text{(XVII.8)}$$

where $H^{(0)}(t)$ is the Hamiltonian of a Schrödinger equation whose solution is known. Let $U^{(0)}(t, t_0)$ be the evolution operator corresponding to $H^{(0)}$:

$$i\hbar \frac{\partial}{\partial t} U^{(0)}(t, t_0) = H^{(0)}(t)\, U^{(0)}(t, t_0) \qquad U^{(0)}(t_0, t_0) = 1. \qquad \text{(XVII.9)}$$

Since $U^{(0)}(t, t_0)$ is known, U will be determined if we can form the unitary operator

$$U_{\mathrm{I}}(t, t_0) \equiv U^{(0)\dagger}(t, t_0)\, U(t, t_0). \qquad \text{(XVII.10)}$$

The physical significance of U_{I} has been given in § VIII.14: U_{I} is the evolution operator for the states in the intermediate "representation" derived from the Schrödinger representation by the unitary transformation $U^{(0)\dagger}(t, t_0)$. A simple calculation, the details of which were given in § VIII.14, shows that the time dependence of U_{I} is determined by the Hamiltonian

$$V_{\mathrm{I}}(t) \equiv U^{(0)\dagger}(t, t_0)\, V(t)\, U^{(0)}(t, t_0). \qquad \text{(XVII.11)}$$

In other words, $U_{\mathrm{I}}(t, t_0)$ is defined by

$$i\hbar \frac{\partial}{\partial t} U_{\mathrm{I}}(t, t_0) = V_{\mathrm{I}}(t)\, U_{\mathrm{I}}(t, t_0) \qquad U_{\mathrm{I}}(t_0, t_0) = 1 \qquad \text{(XVII.12)}$$

or equivalently, by

$$U_{\mathrm{I}}(t, t_0) = 1 - i\hbar^{-1} \int_{t_0}^{t} V_{\mathrm{I}}(\tau)\, U_{\mathrm{I}}(\tau, t_0)\, d\tau. \qquad \text{(XVII.13)}$$

$U_{\mathrm{I}}(t, t_0)$ has all the properties of an evolution operator, and in particular satisfies equations (XVII.1–7) with $H(t)$ everywhere replaced by $V_{\mathrm{I}}(t)$.

The solution of integral equations (XVII.1), (XVII.7) and (XVII.13) can at least formally be obtained by iteration. Thus, substituting for $U_{\mathrm{I}}(\tau, t_0)$ in the right-hand side of (XVII.13) the expression

$$1 - \mathrm{i}\hbar^{-1} \int_{t_0}^{\tau} V_{\mathrm{I}}(\tau')\, U_{\mathrm{I}}(\tau', t_0)\, \mathrm{d}\tau'$$

we get

$$U_{\mathrm{I}}(t, t_0) = 1 - \mathrm{i}\hbar^{-1} \int_{t_0}^{t} V_{\mathrm{I}}(\tau)\, \mathrm{d}\tau + (\mathrm{i}\hbar)^{-2} \int_{t_0}^{t} \mathrm{d}\tau \int_{t_0}^{\tau} \mathrm{d}\tau'\, V_{\mathrm{I}}(\tau)\, V_{\mathrm{I}}(\tau')\, U(\tau', t_0). \quad \text{(XVII.14)}$$

Successive iterations give the expansion

$$U_{\mathrm{I}}(t, t_0) = 1 + \sum_{n=1}^{\infty} U_{\mathrm{I}}^{(n)}(t, t_0), \quad \text{(XVII.15)}$$

where $U_{\mathrm{I}}^{(n)}$ is the integral

$$U_{\mathrm{I}}^{(n)} \equiv (\mathrm{i}\hbar)^{-n} \int_{t>\tau_n>\tau_{n-1}>\ldots>\tau_1>t_0} \mathrm{d}\tau_n\, d\tau_{n-1} \ldots \mathrm{d}\tau_1\, V_{\mathrm{I}}(\tau_n)\, V_{\mathrm{I}}(\tau_{n-1}) \ldots V_{\mathrm{I}}(\tau_1). \quad \text{(XVII.16)}$$

From this result, with the aid of definitions (XVII.10) and (XVII.11), we get the following expansion for U:

$$U(t, t_0) = U^{(0)}(t, t_0) + \sum_{n=1}^{\infty} U^{(n)}(t, t_0) \quad \text{(XVII.17)}$$

$$U^{(n)}(t,t_0) = (\mathrm{i}\hbar)^{-n} \int_{t>\tau_n>\tau_{n-1}>\ldots>\tau_1>t_0} \mathrm{d}\tau_n\, \mathrm{d}\tau_{n-1} \ldots \mathrm{d}\tau_1\, U^{(0)}(t,\tau_n)\, V(\tau_n)\, U^{(0)}(\tau_n,\tau_{n-1})\, V(\tau_{n-1}) \ldots \times \ldots U^{(0)}(\tau_2, \tau_1)\, V(\tau_1)\, U^{(0)}(\tau_1, t_0). \quad \text{(XVII.1}$$

Expansions (XVII.15) and (XVII.17) are power series in V which converge the more rapidly the closer $U^{(0)}(t, t_0)$ to $U(t, t_0)$. They are the basis of the methods set forth in this chapter. $U^{(0)}$ represents the zero order approximation, $U^{(1)}$, $U^{(2)}$, ..., $U^{(n)}$, ... respectively the corrections of order 1, 2, ..., n, ... to that approximation. In practice the calculation of these corrections becomes increasingly complicated with higher orders and one usually takes only those of the lowest order.

I. TIME DEPENDENT PERTURBATION THEORY

2. Definition and Perturbation Calculation of Transition Probabilities

The above method applies in particular when $H^{(0)}$ is *time-independ-*

ent. In this case the evolution operator $U^{(0)}(t, t')$ becomes simply

$$U^{(0)}(t, t') = \exp\,[-\mathrm{i}H^{(0)}(t-t')/\hbar]. \tag{XVII.19}$$

We suppose the eigenvalue problem for $H^{(0)}$ to be solved. Unless otherwise specified, the spectrum will be assumed entirely discrete in order to simplify the writing. Let $|a\rangle, |b\rangle, \ldots, |k\rangle \ldots$ be a complete set of eigenvectors of $H^{(0)}$ and $E_a{}^0, E_b{}^0, \ldots, E_k{}^0, \ldots$ the corresponding eigenvalues. We shall use the notation

$$\omega_{kl} = (E_k{}^0 - E_l{}^0)/\hbar \tag{XVII.20}$$

$$V_{kl}(t) = \langle k|V(t)|l\rangle. \tag{XVII.21}$$

ω_{kl} is the "Bohr frequency" relative to the transition $l \to k$, $V_{kl}(t)$ the corresponding matrix element of $V(t)$.

We suppose that at the initial time t_0 the system is in an eigenstate of $H^{(0)}$, the state a say. We wish to calculate the probability that if a measurement is made at a later time t, the system will be found to be in a different eigenstate of $H^{(0)}$, the state b say. This quantity, by definition *the probability of transition from a to b*, will be denoted by $W_{a\to b}$. Clearly

$$W_{a\to b} = |\langle b|U(t, t_0)|a\rangle|^2. \tag{XVII.22}$$

If V were null, the vector representing the state of the system at time t would differ from the vector $|a\rangle$ representing the initial state only by a factor $\exp\,[-\mathrm{i}E_a{}^0(t-t_0)/\hbar]$, and $W_{a\to b}$ would vanish. The expansion of the probability amplitude $\langle b|U(t, t_0)|a\rangle$ into a power series in V is obtained by substituting expansion (XVII.17) for $U(t, t_0)$:

$$\langle b|U(t, t_0)|a\rangle = \sum_{n=1}^{\infty} \langle b|U^{(n)}|a\rangle. \tag{XVII.23}$$

$U^{(n)}$ is given by (XVII.18).

In the $\{H^{(0)}\}$ representation defined above, the contributions of successive order to the amplitude are:

$$\langle b|U^{(1)}|a\rangle = -\mathrm{i}\hbar^{-1}\int_{t_0}^{t} \mathrm{d}\tau\,[\mathrm{e}^{-\mathrm{i}E_b^0(t-\tau)/\hbar}\,V_{ba}(\tau)\,\mathrm{e}^{-\mathrm{i}E_a^0(\tau-t_0)/\hbar}] \tag{XVII.24^1}$$

$$\begin{aligned}\langle b|U^{(2)}|a\rangle = (\mathrm{i}\hbar)^{-2}\sum_k \int_{t_0}^{t}\mathrm{d}\tau\int_{t_0}^{\tau}\mathrm{d}\tau'\,[\mathrm{e}^{-\mathrm{i}E_b^0(t-\tau)/\hbar}\,V_{bk}(\tau)\,\mathrm{e}^{-\mathrm{i}E_k^0(\tau-\tau')/\hbar}\\ \times V_{ka}(\tau')\,\mathrm{e}^{-\mathrm{i}E_a^0(\tau'-t_0)/\hbar}]\end{aligned} \tag{XVII.24^2}$$

$$\langle b|U^{(3)}|a\rangle = (\mathrm{i}\hbar)^{-3} \sum_k \sum_l \int_{t_0}^{t} \mathrm{d}\tau \int_{t_0}^{\tau} \mathrm{d}\tau' \int_{t_0}^{\tau'} \mathrm{d}\tau'' \, [\mathrm{e}^{-\mathrm{i}E_b^0(t-\tau)/\hbar} V_{bk}(\tau) \times \mathrm{e}^{-\mathrm{i}E_k^0(\tau-\tau')/\hbar} V_{kl}(\tau') \, \mathrm{e}^{-\mathrm{i}E_l^0(\tau'-\tau'')/\hbar} V_{la}(\tau'') \, \mathrm{e}^{-\mathrm{i}E_a^0(\tau''-t_0)/\hbar}]. \quad \text{(XVII.24}^3\text{)}$$

In all of these expressions, the summations are extended over all of the basis vectors of $\{H^{(0)}\}$.

These contributions of successive order may be schematically represented by the diagrams of Figure XVII.1.

Diagram (*i*) represents the first-order contribution, or more exactly, it represents the product in brackets on the right-hand side of (XVII.24¹). The full line describes the evolution of the system in the course of time. From t_0 to τ, this is determined by the unperturbed Hamiltonian $H^{(0)}$, and the system therefore remains in the state a, its state vector simply being multiplied by the factor

$$\exp\,[-\mathrm{i}E_a{}^0(\tau - t_0)/\hbar].$$

At time τ the system, under the influence of the perturbation, passes from a to b giving the transition matrix element $V_{ba}(\tau)$. From τ to t it evolves again according to $H^{(0)}$, and therefore remains in state b, giving the factor $\exp\,[-\mathrm{i}E_b(t-\tau)/\hbar]$. Thus, following the diagram from bottom to top, one obtains the three factors in the bracket in their order from right to left. The first-order contribution is obtained by integrating these products over τ.

Likewise, diagram (*ii*) represents the second-order correction. The system evolves according to $H^{(0)}$ from t_0 to τ', then under the influence

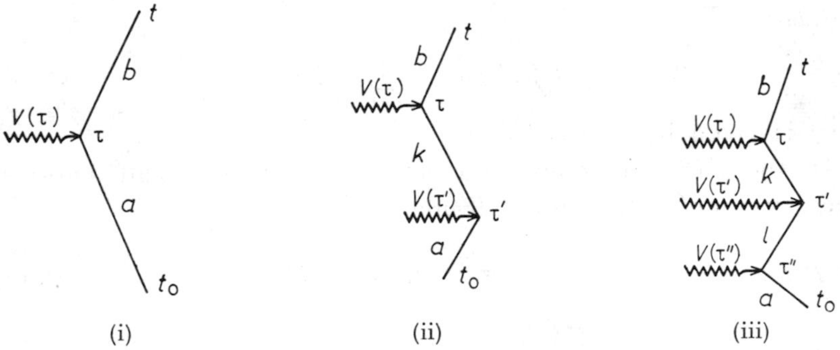

Fig. XVII.1. Diagrams representing the contributions of successive order to the transition probability amplitude from a to b: (*i*) first order, (*ii*) second order, (*iii*) third order.

of $V(\tau')$, passes from the initial state a to the intermediate state k, then evolves according to $H^{(0)}$ from τ' to τ, then under the influence of $V(\tau)$ passes from state k to the final state b, and finally evolves according to $H^{(0)}$ from τ to t. We thereby obtain in their order of succession from right to left the five factors in the bracket of the right-hand side of (XVII.24²). The second-order contribution is obtained by integrating over τ' and $\tau (t_0 < \tau' < \tau < t)$ and summing over all of the intermediate states. Referring to this manner of representing the development of the second-order transitions in time, one often calls the state k a *virtual state*, as opposed to the real states a and b, and says that the second-order transition is effected through a virtual state.

In the same way, the third-order transitions, represented by diagram (*iii*), are effected through the two virtual states k and l. The perturbing potential comes into play three times in all, successively at times τ'', τ' and τ, taking the system from a into l, from l into k and from k into b. Similarily, the nth order transitions are made through $(n-1)$ virtual states.

The quantity obtained in taking the first n terms of expansion (XVII.23) is the sought for probability amplitude with a precision of order n. The square of its modulus gives, by definition, the transition probability to order n [1]), namely

$$W_{a\to b} \simeq |\langle b|U^{(1)}|a\rangle + \langle b|U^{(2)}|a\rangle + \ldots + \langle b|U^{(n)}|a\rangle|^2.$$

In particular, the *first-order transition probability* is given by

$$W_{a\to b} \simeq |\langle b|U^{(1)}|a\rangle|^2 = \hbar^{-2} \left|\int_{t_0}^{t} e^{i\omega_{ba}\tau}\, V_{ba}(\tau)\, d\tau\right|^2. \quad \text{(XVII.25)}$$

Observe that in this approximation

$$W_{b\to a} \simeq W_{a\to b}.$$

This relation ceases, in general, to be verified in approximations of higher order. It is not to be confused with the property of microreversibility, $W_{Kb\to Ka} = W_{a\to b}$, which is satisfied only if the Hamiltonian is

---

1) The expression obtained correctly represents the expansion of $W_{a\to b}$ in powers of V up to at least the order $n+1$. The precision obtained is of a higher order than $n+1$ if $\langle b|U^{(1)}|a\rangle = 0$.

invariant under time-reversal, in which case it is exactly true in all orders. (§ XV.20).

3. Semi-classical Theory of Coulomb Excitation of Nuclei

As an application of the theory we shall consider the Coulomb excitation of a nucleus by a charged particle, for example a proton [1]).

We suppose that a beam of mono-ergic protons collides with a nuclear target. In the course of the collision nuclei make transitions from their ground state into excited states. We propose to calculate the cross section for the transition to a given excited state β.

Denote by Ze the charge of the nucleus, by R its radius and by J_α and J_β, E_α and E_β, the spins and energies of states α and β respectively. There are $(2J_\alpha+1)$ linearly independent states α which may be distinguished one from another by the component M_α of the spin along a given quantization axis. They are represented by the vectors $|\alpha\, J_\alpha\, M_\alpha\rangle$. If H_N is the Hamiltonian for the nucleus, then

$$H_N|\alpha\, J_\alpha\, M_\alpha\rangle = E_\alpha|\alpha_\alpha\, J_\alpha\, M_\alpha\rangle \qquad (M_\alpha = -J_\alpha, \ldots, J_\alpha),$$

and similarly

$$H_N|\beta\, J_\beta\, M_\beta\rangle = E_\beta|\beta\, J_\beta\, M_\beta\rangle \qquad (M_\beta = -J_\beta, \ldots, J_\beta).$$

Denote by $E=\frac{1}{2}Mv^2$ the incident energy in the proton-nucleus center-of-mass system, by $\varDelta E = E_\beta - E_\alpha$ the excitation energy of the nucleus, by $\varOmega_\alpha$ the direction of the incident proton, by $\varOmega_\beta$ the direction of the inelastically scattered proton and by θ the angle between these two directions. The quantity to be calculated is the cross section

$$\mathrm{d}\sigma(\varOmega_\alpha\, M_\alpha \rightarrow \varOmega_\beta\, M_\beta)/\mathrm{d}\varOmega$$

for the process where the proton is inelastically scattered into the direction $\varOmega_\beta$, the nucleus passing from the state $(\alpha\, J_\alpha\, M_\alpha)$ to the state $(\beta\, J_\beta\, M_\beta)$.

We now examine the proton-nucleus interaction. For a large distance r from the incident proton to the center of mass of the nucleus

---

[1]) On Coulomb exitation and its applications in the study of nuclear structure, see Alder *et al.*, Rev. Mod. Phys. 22 (1956) 432; the semi-classical treatment given here is due to K. A. Ter–Martyrosian, J. Exptl. Theoret. Phys. URSS 28 (1952) 284.

($r \gg R$) it reduces to the pure Coulomb interaction Ze^2/r. As r becomes smaller it increasingly deviates from this simple form. So long as $r > R$ the deviation is of purely electromagnetic origin and reduces essentially to the difference between the exact Coulomb interaction and the term Ze^2/r, namely

$$V = e^2 \sum_{i=1}^{Z} \left(\frac{1}{|\mathbf{r} - \mathbf{r}_i|} - \frac{1}{r} \right) \qquad \text{(XVII.26)}$$

($\mathbf{r}_i$, position vector of the ith proton in the nucleus).

Once the proton has "penetrated" into the nucleus ($r < R$) the nuclear interactions proper enter into play and prevail largely over the electromagnetic interactions.

If the energy E is sufficiently low, the Coulomb repulsion Ze^2/r prevents the proton from approaching the nucleus and therefore remains the dominant interaction throughout the collision. The proton-nucleus motion is then governed in a first approximation by the Hamiltonian

$$H^{(0)} \equiv H_N + \left(\frac{\mathbf{p}^2}{2M} + \frac{Ze^2}{r} \right),$$

where $\mathbf{p}^2/2M$ is the kinetic energy of the proton. The motion of the proton separates completely from that of the nucleus. The latter remains in its ground state while the proton undergoes an elastic scattering process with a differential cross section given by the Rutherford formula (VI.29)

$$\mathrm{d}\sigma_{\mathrm{R}}/\mathrm{d}\Omega = \tfrac{1}{4}\, a^2 \sin^{-4} \tfrac{1}{2}\, \theta$$

a is half the distance of closest approach in the classical motion:

$$a = \tfrac{1}{2} \frac{Ze^2}{E}. \qquad \text{(XVII.27)}$$

The above approximation is justified so long as

$$a \gg R. \qquad \text{(XVII.28)}$$

In addition, we shall suppose that

$$\frac{\Delta E}{E} \ll 1 \qquad \text{(XVII.29)}$$

$$\gamma \gg 1, \qquad \text{(XVII.30)}$$

where

$$\gamma \equiv \frac{a}{\lambda\!\!\!^{-}} = \frac{Ze^2}{\hbar v}. \qquad \text{(XVII.31)}$$

Due to the deviation of the proton-nucleus interaction from Ze^2/r, inelastic collisions may occur. Since by condition (XVII.28) the proton "penetrates" very little into the nucleus, these deviations reduce essentially to the term V. Because of condition (XVII.30), the Coulomb scattering may be treated classically (§ VI.5). The motion of the proton is that of a wave-packet of negligible dimensions whose center $\mathbf{r}(t)$ obeys the corresponding classical equations of motion. In a given inelastic collision $(\Omega_\alpha M_\alpha \to \Omega_\beta M_\beta)$ we can also treat the motion of the proton classically. The solution to the classical equations of motion is known if V is neglected. This implies that the energy ΔE transferred from the proton to the nucleus during the collision is also neglected. This approximation is legitimate if condition (XIII.29) is met. The trajectory of the proton $\mathbf{r}(t)$ being thus determined, V *is a time-dependent perturbation* acting on the dynamical variables of the nucleus:

$$V(t) = e^2 \sum_{i=1}^{Z} \left[\frac{1}{|\mathbf{r}(t) - \mathbf{r}_i|} - \frac{1}{r(t)}\right]$$

and can induce the transition $(\alpha J_\alpha M_\alpha) \to (\beta J_\beta M_\beta)$. The transition probability $W_{\alpha\to\beta}$ being small (one can verify *a posteriori* that $W_{\alpha\to\beta} \ll 1$), we take only the first-order approximation. From (XVII.25),

$$W_{\alpha\to\beta} = \hbar^{-2} \left| \int_{-\infty}^{+\infty} \mathrm{e}^{\mathrm{i}(\Delta E)t/\hbar} \langle \beta J_\beta M_\beta | V(t) | \alpha J_\alpha M_\alpha \rangle \, \mathrm{d}t \right|^2. \qquad \text{(XVII.32)}$$

The cross section in question is the product of this probability and the Rutherford cross section

$$\mathrm{d}\sigma(\Omega_\alpha M_\alpha \to \Omega_\beta M_\beta) = (\tfrac{1}{4}a^2 \sin^{-4} \tfrac{1}{2}\theta)\, W_{\alpha\to\beta}\, \mathrm{d}\Omega. \qquad \text{(XVII.33)}$$

It remains to calculate $W_{\alpha\to\beta}$. We shall give only the outline of this calculation, omitting details. The polar coordinates of $\mathbf{r}_i$ and $\mathbf{r}(t)$ are denoted by (r_i, Ω_i) and (r, Ω) respectively. The latter are functions of t. If $|\mathbf{r}(t) - \mathbf{r}_i|^{-1}$ is expanded into spherical harmonics [eq. (B.99)], one finds

$$V(t) = \sum_{l=1}^{\infty} \sum_{m=-l}^{+l} (-)^m\, Q_l^m\, T_l^{-m}, \qquad \text{(XVII.34)}$$

where

$$Q_l^m = \sum_{i=1}^{Z} e r_i^l Y_l^m(\Omega_i) \qquad \text{(XVII.35)}$$

$$T_l^m(t) = \frac{4\pi e}{2l+1} \frac{Y_l^m(\Omega)}{r^{l+1}}. \qquad \text{(XVII.36)}$$

This expansion is valid only if $r_i < r$, condition always fulfilled since the proton does not "penetrate" into the nucleus. Substituting into formula (XVII.32), we obtain

$$W_{\alpha\to\beta} = |\sum_{lm} (-)^m S_l^{-m} \langle \beta J_\beta M_\beta | Q_l^m | \alpha J_\alpha M_\alpha \rangle|^2 \qquad \text{(XVII.37)}$$

$$S_l^m = \int_{-\infty}^{+\infty} e^{i(\Delta E)t/\hbar} T_l^m(t)\, dt/\hbar. \qquad \text{(XVII.38)}$$

The coefficients S_l^m depend on the classical trajectory of the proton alone, and can be determined by numerical integration.

The $(2l+1)$ operators $Q_l^m(m = -l, \ldots, +l)$ are the standard components of the *electric* 2^l-*pole* moment $\mathbf{Q}^{(l)}$ (cf. § XIII.33). Therefore the only non-zero matrix elements figuring in formula (XVII.37) are those satisfying the angular momentum and parity selection rules:

$$\begin{aligned} &|J_\alpha - J_\beta| \leqslant l \leqslant J_\alpha + J_\beta \qquad m = M_\beta - M_\alpha \\ &\Pi_\alpha \Pi_\beta = (-)^l \end{aligned} \qquad \text{(XVII.39)}$$

(Π_α, Π_β parities of states α and β respectively). Also, by the Wigner–Eckart theorem,

$$\langle \beta J_\beta M_\beta | Q_l^m | \alpha J_\alpha M_\alpha \rangle = (2J_\beta + 1)^{-\frac{1}{2}} \langle J_\alpha l M_\alpha m | J_\beta M_\beta \rangle \langle \beta \| \mathbf{Q}^{(l)} \| \alpha \rangle.$$

Owing to the selection rules (XVII.39), the sum in (XVII.37) is limited to a finite number of values of l of well-defined parity, and to a single value of m. A rough calculation shows that, all things being equal, the "$l+2$" contribution is about $(R/a)^2$ times the "l" contribution. We are justified, therefore, in keeping only the term corresponding to the smallest value of l allowed by the selection rules, either $|J_\alpha - J_\beta|$ or $|J_\alpha - J_\beta| + 1$ as the case may be. Calling this value l_0 we have

$$W_{\alpha\to\beta} \simeq \frac{\langle J_\alpha l_0 M_\alpha m | J_\beta M_\beta \rangle^2}{(2J_\beta + 1)} |S_{l_0}^{-m}|^2 |\langle \beta \| \mathbf{Q}^{(l_0)} \| \alpha \rangle|^2 \qquad (m = M_\beta - M_\alpha).$$

Substituting this expression in (XVII.33) we obtain a theoretical expression for the cross section which may be compared with experiment.

In an experiment where the target nuclei are not oriented, and where the polarization of the excited nuclei is not observed, the measured cross section is that obtained by averaging the cross section defined above over the $2J_\alpha+1$ possible values of M_α, and summing it over the $2J_\beta+1$ possible values of M_β. Taking into account the orthogonality relations for the Clebsch–Gordon coefficients, this gives

$$\frac{\mathrm{d}\sigma_{\alpha\to\beta}}{\mathrm{d}\Omega} = \frac{a^2}{4(2J_\alpha+1)\,(2l_0+1)}\,|\langle\beta\|\mathbf{Q}^{(l_0)}\|\alpha\rangle|^2\left[\sin^{-4}\tfrac{1}{2}\theta\,\textstyle\sum_m|S_{l_0}^m|^2\right]$$

The angular dependence of this cross section is given by the expression in brackets and must be calculated numerically. Observe that the initial and final states of the nucleus enter into this formula only through their spin, their parity and the square of the modulus of the electric 2^{l_0}-pole transition moment, $\langle\beta\|\mathbf{Q}^{(l_0)}\|\alpha\rangle$, and that this last mentioned quantity appears only as a simple proportionality constant. The comparison of this formula with experiment is therefore a very direct way to determine these characteristic quantities of nuclear structure.

4. Case when V is Independent of Time. Conservation of Unperturbed Energy

When V does not depend explicitly on the time, the integrals over the time in formulas (XVII.24) are easily effected and certain simple properties appear. Let us limit the discussion to the *first-order transitions.*

We take $t_0=0$. Then, from (XVII.25)

$$W_{a\to b} \simeq |V_{ba}|^2\, f(t,\,\omega_{ba})/\hbar^2, \tag{XVII.40}$$

where

$$f(t,\,\omega) \equiv \Big|\int_0^t \mathrm{e}^{\mathrm{i}\omega\tau}\,\mathrm{d}\tau\Big|^2 = 2\,(1-\cos\omega t)/\omega^2. \tag{XVII.41}$$

$f(t,\,\omega)$ as a function of ω is shown in Fig. XVII.2. Note the very sharp peak about the value $\omega=0$; its width is equal to $2\pi/t$. Note in passing that

$$\int_{-\infty}^{+\infty} f(t,\,\omega)\,\mathrm{d}\omega = 2\pi t \tag{XVII.42}$$

as may easily be shown using the method of residues, and that, from (A.15*b*),

$$f(t, \omega) \underset{t\to\infty}{\sim} 2\pi t\delta(\omega). \qquad \text{(XVII.43)}$$

For a given value of t, $W_{a\to b}$ depends in a simple way on the final state b. To within a constant it is the squared modulus of the perturbation matrix element $\langle b|V|a\rangle$ *weighted* by the factor $f(t, \omega_{ba})$ which depends on the Bohr frequency for the transition $a \to b$. Since this weight factor has a very pronounced peak of width $2\pi/t$ at the point $\omega_{ba}=0$, the transition will be made preferentially towards states whose energy is situated in a band of width

$$\delta E_0 \simeq 2\pi\hbar/t$$

about the energy of the initial state. In other words, *the transitions conserve the unperturbed energy to within* $2\pi\hbar/t$.

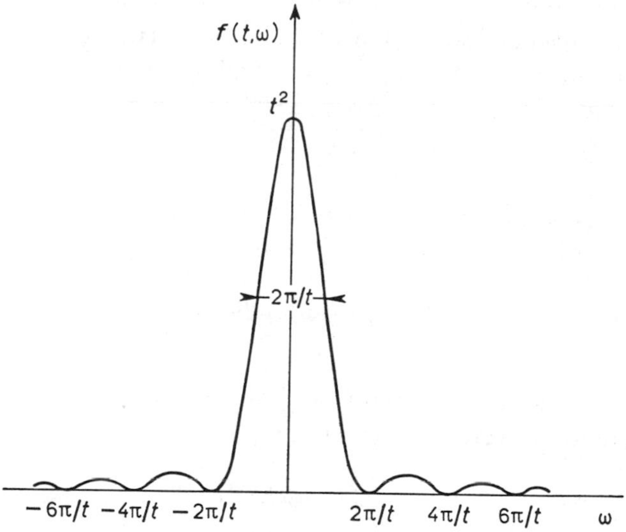

Fig. XVII.2. The function $f(t, \omega) = 2(1 - \cos \omega)/\omega^2$.

This result is in some ways analogous to the time-energy uncertainty relation (§ IV.10 and VIII.13). However, one must take note that here the energy in question is $H^{(0)}$ and not the total energy of the system, including the perturbation, and the time t is the time after which the measurement of $H^{(0)}$ is made and not the time characterizing the evolution of the system.

For a given state b, the variation of $W_{a\to b}$ with t is also given by the factor $f(t, \omega_{ba})$. If the transition exactly conserves the unperturbed energy ($\omega_{ba}=0$) it simply increases as t^2. If not, it is a function that oscillates between 0 and $4/\omega_{ba}^2$ with period $2\pi/\omega_{ba}$. $W_{a\to b}$ oscillates with the same period about the average value $2|V_{ba}|^2/(E_b-E_a)^2$ and has the t^2 behavior only for values of t small compared with that period.

Rather than consider transitions to a particular state, we may consider *transitions to a group of states of neighboring energies*. This is what is always done for transitions to states of the continuous spectrum. One may then, under certain limiting conditions to be presently specified, define a *probability of transition per unit time.*

Let us therefore consider a particular sequence of eigenvectors of $H^{(0)}$ belonging to the continuous spectrum. $|b\rangle$ will denote a particular one of these, and $E(b)$ the corresponding eigenvalue of $H^{(0)}$.

In the definition of transition probabilities, attention must be paid to the normalization of the $|b\rangle$. We shall suppose them normalized such that

$$\langle b|b'\rangle = \delta(b-b')/n(b),$$

where $n(b)$ is some real positive function. The projector onto the states of a certain domain B of the variable b is (cf. § VIII.13):

$$P_{\mathrm{B}} = \int_{\mathrm{B}} |b\rangle\, n(b)\, \mathrm{d}b\, \langle b|.$$

If we take $E(b)$ as a new variable and denote by $\mathrm{B}(E)$ the corresponding domain of integration, we find

$$P_{\mathrm{B}} = \int_{\mathrm{B}(E)} |b\rangle\, \varrho_b(E)\, \mathrm{d}E\, \langle b| \qquad \text{(XVII.44)}$$

where

$$\varrho_b(E) = n(b)\, \mathrm{d}b/\mathrm{d}E. \qquad \text{(XVII.45)}$$

$\varrho_b(E)$ is known as the *density of the levels b at energy E*. According to (XVII.44), it is indeed the number of vectors $|b\rangle$ per unit interval of energy; it will be observed that $\varrho_b(E)$ depends on the normalization of the $|b\rangle$.

The transition probability $W_{a\to B}$ into one of the states of the domain B is then

$$W_{a\to B} \equiv \langle a|U^{\dagger}(t, 0)\, P_B\, U(t, 0)|a\rangle = \int_{B(E)} W_{a\to b}\, \varrho_b(E)\, dE. \qquad (XVII.46)$$

Formula (XVII.46) is obtained by replacing P_B by expression (XVII.44) and putting

$$W_{a\to b} = |\langle b|U(t, 0)|a\rangle|^2. \qquad (XVII.47)$$

Here $W_{a\to b}$ formally represents the probability for the transition $a \to b$ defined by equation (XVII.22). The various steps in the calculation of that quantity are all valid here. In particular, by substituting (XVII.40) into the right-hand side of (XVII.44), one obtains the transition probability $W_{a\to B}$ to the first order in the perturbation:

$$W_{a\to B} \simeq \int |V_{ba}|^2\, \varrho_b\, f(t, \omega_{ba})\, dE/\hbar^2 \qquad (XVII.48)$$

here $V_{ba} \equiv \langle b|V|a\rangle$ depends on E through the parameter b.

As a definite example consider the transitions to the levels b inside the interval $(E_1 - \frac{1}{2}\varepsilon, E_1 + \frac{1}{2}\varepsilon)$, and suppose the width ε sufficiently small that V_{ba} and ϱ_b are practically constant over the interval so that they can be taken outside the integral sign. We also suppose t sufficiently large for ε to be much greater than the period of oscillation of the function f:

$$\varepsilon \gg 2\pi\hbar/t. \qquad (XVII.49)$$

The integral on the right-hand side of (XVII.49) is then easily evaluated. Two cases are to be considered:

(*i*) The central peak of f is outside the domain of integration (transitions not conserving the energy). One may then replace f by its value averaged over several oscillations, which leads to the time-independent expression

$$W_{a\to B} \simeq 2\varepsilon\, \varrho_b(E_1)|V_{ba}|^2/(E_1 - E_a)^2.$$

(*ii*) The central peak of f is in the domain of integration (energy-conserving transitions); the main contribution comes from this peak, and only a small error is involved in extending the limits of the integral to infinity, whence [eq. (XVII.42)]:

$$W_{a\to B} \simeq 2\pi\hbar^{-1}|V_{ba}(E_a)|^2\, \varrho_b(E_a)\, t.$$

Owing to inequality (XVII.49), this probability is greater than the sum of all the others.

We now introduce the probability of transition per unit time:

$$w_{a\to\mathrm{B}} \equiv \mathrm{d}W_{a\to\mathrm{B}}/\mathrm{d}t.$$

From the preceding results we can conclude that this quantity vanishes for transitions not conserving the energy, and that for those transitions which do conserve the energy it is given by the important formula

$$\boxed{w_{a\to\mathrm{B}} \simeq \frac{2\pi}{\hbar}\,|V_{ba}|^2\,\varrho_b} \tag{XVII.50}$$

in which the matrix element $V_{ba} \equiv \langle b|V|a\rangle$ and the level density ϱ_b relate to states b whose energy is equal to that of the initial state.

For formula (XVII.50) to be valid, t must be sufficiently large for conditions (XVII.49) to be met, and at the same time be sufficiently small for the first-order approximation to be justified ($w_{a\to\mathrm{B}}\,t \ll 1$).

The above demonstration has the advantage of bringing out the significance and the conditions of validity of formula (XVII.50). The latter can be more simply obtained by replacing f by its asymptotic expression (XVII.43) in the right-hand side of (XVII.40), which gives

$$W_{a\to b} \underset{t\to\infty}{\sim} 2\pi\hbar^{-1}\,|V_{ba}|^2\,\delta(E_b - E_a)\,t, \tag{XVII.51}$$

and then substituting this into the definition of $W_{a\to\mathrm{B}}$ [eq. (XVII.46)].

5. Application to the Calculation of Cross-sections in the Born Approximation

From formula (XVII.50) one may deduce an expression for the collision cross sections in the so-called *Born approximation*, that is, to the first order in the interaction potential between the particle and the target. Here we shall give a simple derivation, of this formula somewhat at the expense of rigor. A rigorous derivation of the same formula will be given in Chapter XIX.

We consider the simplest possible case, the scattering of a particle by a potential $V(\mathbf{r})$. The latter is treated as a perturbation. The unperturbed Hamiltonian is that of a free particle:

$$H = H^{(0)} + V(\mathbf{r}) \qquad H^{(0)} = \mathbf{p}^2/2m.$$

The eigenstates of $H^{(0)}$ are the plane waves $e^{i\mathbf{k}\cdot\mathbf{r}}$. Such a wave represents a state of momentum $\mathbf{p}=\hbar\mathbf{k}$ *normalized to unit density*. We shall denote the corresponding ket vectors by $|\mathbf{k}\rangle$: they obey the orthogonality and closure relations

$$\langle\mathbf{k}|\mathbf{k}'\rangle = (2\pi)^3\,\delta(\mathbf{k}-\mathbf{k}') \qquad \int |\mathbf{k}\rangle\,\frac{\mathrm{d}\mathbf{k}}{(2\pi)^3}\,\langle\mathbf{k}| = 1.$$

In the space of the $\mathbf{k}$ vectors, the density of the states thus normalized is therefore constant and equal to $(2\pi)^{-3}$: the number of states in the interval $(\mathbf{k}, \mathbf{k}+\mathrm{d}\mathbf{k})$ is $\mathrm{d}\mathbf{k}/(2\pi)^3$. We are interested in the states of momentum in a particular direction Ω, and denote their density, as defined in the previous paragraph, by $\varrho(E)$ [eq. (XVII.45)] [*a priori* this function could depend on Ω; we shall see that in fact it does not]: $\varrho(E)\,\mathrm{d}\Omega\,\mathrm{d}E$ is the number of states whose momentum is in the solid angle $(\Omega, \Omega+\mathrm{d}\Omega)$ and whose energy $E=p^2/2m$ is in the band $(E, E+\mathrm{d}E)$. We have, therefore

$$\varrho(E)\,\mathrm{d}\Omega\,\mathrm{d}E = \mathrm{d}\mathbf{k}/(2\pi)^3 = \mathrm{d}\mathbf{p}/(2\pi\hbar)^3$$

and since $\mathrm{d}\mathbf{p}=p^2\,\mathrm{d}\Omega\,\mathrm{d}p$, this gives

$$\varrho(E)\,\mathrm{d}E = p^2\,\mathrm{d}p/(2\pi\hbar)^3,$$

and therefore

$$\varrho(E) = \frac{p^2}{(2\pi\hbar)^3}\frac{\mathrm{d}p}{\mathrm{d}E} = \frac{mp}{(2\pi\hbar)^3}. \tag{XVII.52}$$

Let us now proceed to calculate the scattering cross section from a mono-ergic incident beam of energy $E=\frac{1}{2}mv_a^2$ into a given direction Ω_b. Let $\hbar\,\mathbf{k}_a$ be the momentum of the incident particles and $\hbar\,\mathbf{k}_b$ the momentum corresponding to the same energy E but with direction Ω_b. Starting from the initial state $|\mathbf{k}_a\rangle$, we know that the probability per unit time $w_{a\to\mathrm{B}}\,\mathrm{d}\Omega$ that the system make a transition into one of the states b with momentum in the solid angle $(\Omega_b, \Omega_b+\mathrm{d}\Omega)$ and energy close to E is given to the first order by formula (XVII.50):

$$w_{a\to\mathrm{B}}\,\mathrm{d}\Omega \simeq 2\pi\hbar^{-1}\,|\langle\mathbf{k}_b|V|\mathbf{k}_a\rangle|^2\,\varrho(E)\,\mathrm{d}\Omega. \tag{XVII.53}$$

Let $\mathrm{d}\sigma_{a\to b}/\mathrm{d}\Omega$ be the differential scattering cross section. $\mathrm{d}\sigma_{a\to b}$ is the number of particles scattered into the solid angle $(\Omega_b, \Omega_b+\mathrm{d}\Omega)$ per unit time and per unit incident flux. Since $|\mathbf{k}_a\rangle$ represents a wave of flux v_a, we have

$$\mathrm{d}\sigma_{a\to b} = w_{a\to\mathrm{B}}/v_a.$$

Substituting for $w_{a\to B}$ from the approximate expression (XVII.53) we have

$$\frac{\mathrm{d}\sigma_{a\to b}}{\mathrm{d}\Omega} \simeq \frac{2\pi}{\hbar v_a} |\langle \mathbf{k}_b|V|\mathbf{k}_a\rangle|^2 \varrho_b(E), \qquad \text{(XVII.54)}$$

where $\varrho_b(E)$ is the density of final states [eq. (XVII.52)], and

$$\langle \mathbf{k}_b|V|\mathbf{k}_a) \equiv \int \mathrm{e}^{\mathrm{i}(\mathbf{k}_a-\mathbf{k}_b)\mathbf{r}}\, V(\mathbf{r})\, \mathrm{d}\mathbf{r}$$

is the matrix element of the potential responsible for the transition.

6. Periodic Perturbation. Resonances

To the first order [formula (XVII.25)], the probability of transition $W_{a\to b}$ is proportional to the squared modulus of the amplitude of the frequency ω_{ba} in the harmonic analysis of the function $V_{ba}(t)$, where by convention we have put $V_{ba}=0$ outside the interval (t_0, t). This harmonic analysis is particularly simple for V independent of time and gives rise, as we have seen, to the "conservation of the unperturbed energy". It is also very simple in the more general case where V is a periodic function of the time, and here we have a phenomenon of great practical importance — the phenomenon of *resonance*.

Suppose that V is a sinusoidal function of time with frequency ω. Since it is a Hermitian operator it can be put in the form

$$V = A\,\mathrm{e}^{\mathrm{i}\omega t} + A^\dagger\,\mathrm{e}^{-\mathrm{i}\omega t},$$

where A is a certain time-independent operator. To the first order, the probability of transition $W_{a\to b}$ is given by (taking $t_0=0$):

$$W_{a\to b} \simeq \hbar^{-2}\, |\langle b|A|a\rangle \int_0^t \mathrm{e}^{\mathrm{i}(\omega_{ba}+\omega)\tau}\,\mathrm{d}\tau + \langle b|A^\dagger|a\rangle \int_0^t \mathrm{e}^{\mathrm{i}(\omega_{ba}-\omega)\tau}\,\mathrm{d}\tau|^2$$

which may be compared with expression (XVII.40).

The amplitude of transition is here made up of two terms. For t sufficiently large the first term is small unless $\omega_{ba}+\omega$ is close to 0, that is, unless E_b is to be found in a band (of width $2\pi\hbar/t$) about the point

$$E_b = E_a - \hbar\,\omega, \qquad \text{(XVII.55)}$$

while the second term is small except in a band (of the same width) about the point

$$E_b = E_a + \hbar\,\omega. \qquad \text{(XVII.55')}$$

In practice, t is sufficiently large ($t \gg 2\pi/\omega$) for these regions not to overlap. $W_{a\to b}$ is then small except for transitions in which *the unperturbed system emits or absorbs the quantity of energy* $\hbar\omega$, as indicated by equations (XVII.55) and (XVII.55′) respectively.

In the first case only the first term is involved in the transition amplitude and the transition probability reduces to the expression

$$W_{a\to b} \simeq |A_{ba}|^2 \, f(t, \omega_{ba} + \omega)/\hbar^2.$$

The essential difference between this result and (XVII.40) is that here ω_{ba} is replaced by $\omega_{ba}+\omega$. In complete analogy with the work of § 4 we can now consider transitions to a group of levels in an energy band ΔE ($\gg 2\pi\hbar/t$) about the point $E_a - \hbar\omega$ and define, under suitable conditions, a probability of transition per unit time; this is again given by formula (XVII.50) with the sole difference that V_{ba} and ϱ_b now relate to states b with energy $\hbar\omega$ less than the initial state. The same considerations apply to transitions in which the system absorbs a quantity of energy $\hbar\omega$ (cf. Problem XVII.2).

Consider now the more general case when V is any periodic function of the time, of frequency ω. Here we merely state the results; the demonstrations are left to the reader. One then has the Fourier expansion

$$V = \sum_{s=1}^{\infty} (A_s \, \mathrm{e}^{\mathrm{i}s\omega t} + A_s^\dagger \, \mathrm{e}^{-\mathrm{i}s\omega t}).$$

If $t \gg 2\pi/\omega$ the contributions to the first-order transition probability from different terms of this series do not interfere since each causes transitions corresponding to a different energy transfer. In the "A_s transitions" the system loses, to within $2\pi\hbar/t$, the energy $s\hbar\omega$; in the "$A_s^\dagger$ transitions" it gains, to within $2\pi\hbar/t$, the energy $s\hbar\omega$.

II. SUDDEN OR ADIABATIC CHANGE OF THE HAMILTONIAN

7. The Problem and the Results

A frequently occurring problem is that of finding the modification in the state of the system when we change the external field. The classic example is that of an atomic system put into a magnetic field. As a general rule, the results obtained depend critically on the time T during which the modification of the Hamiltonian takes place.

In this section we examine the limiting cases when T is very small (sudden change) and very large (adiabatic change).

We suppose the Hamiltonian to change-over in a continuous way from a certain initial value H_0 at time t_0 to a certain final value H_1, at time t_1. We put

$$T = t_1 - t_0 \qquad s = (t - t_0)/T$$

and denote by $H(s)$ the value taken by the Hamiltonian at time $t = t_0 + sT$. $H(s)$ is a continuous function of s and we have:

$$H(0) = H_0 \qquad H(1) = H_1.$$

The evolution of the system from t_0 to t_1 now depends only on the parameter T measuring the speed of the passage from H_0 to H_1. It is convenient to put

$$U(t, t_0) = U_T(s).$$

Our problem is essentially to determine $U(t_1, t_0)$, that is, $U_T(1)$, and to examine its dependence on T.

The results are remarkably simple for the two limiting cases mentioned above.

In the limit when $T \to 0$, i.e. in the case of an infinitely rapid passage, the dynamical state of the system remains unchanged:

$$\lim_{T\to 0} U_T(1) = 1. \qquad \text{(XVII.56)}$$

In the limit when $T \to \infty$, i.e. in the case of an infinitely slow, or adiabatic passage, if the system is initially in an eigenstate of H_0 it will, at time t_1, under certain conditions to be specified later, *have passed into the eigenstate of H_1, that derives from it by continuity*. This important result is known as the *Adiabatic Theorem* [1]).

8. Rapid Passage and the Sudden Approximation

The first of the above results follows immediately from equation (XVII.1) for the operator describing the evolution of the system.

---

[1]) It is also called Ehrenfest's theorem. The work of Ehrenfest on the subject relates to Classical Mechanics and the Old Quantum Theory. The extension of the theorem to Quantum Mechanics is due essentially to M. Born and V. Fock, Zeit. f. Phys. **51** (1928) 165. See also T. Kato, Journ. Phys. Soc. Jap. **5** (1950) 435; K. O. Friedrichs, *On the Adiabatic Theorem in Quantum Theory*, Report IMM.NYU–218, (New York, 1955).

With the notations of § 7 it reads

$$U_T(s) = 1 - i\hbar^{-1}\, T \int_0^s H(s)\, U_T(s)\, \mathrm{d}s.$$

In the limit when $T \to 0$ the second term on the right-hand side goes to zero and we obtain the desired result (XVII.56).

For T sufficiently small we may, in a first approximation, suppose that $U_T(1) \simeq 1$. This is called the *sudden approximation.*

Let $|0\rangle$ denote the state vector of the system at time t_0 and Q_0 the projector onto the space of the vectors orthogonal to $|0\rangle$. Supposing $|0\rangle$ to be of norm 1, we have

$$Q_0 = 1 - |0\rangle\,\langle 0|.$$

The sudden approximation consists in writing

$$U(t_1, t_0)|0\rangle \simeq |0\rangle.$$

A measure of the error involved in this approximation is given by the probability ϖ of finding the system in a state other than the initial state:

$$\begin{aligned} \varpi &= \langle 0|U^\dagger(t_1, t_0)\, Q_0\, U(t_1, t_0)|0\rangle \\ &= \langle 0|U_T{}^\dagger(1)\, Q_0\, U_T(1)|0\rangle. \end{aligned} \qquad \text{(XVII.57)}$$

The corrections to this approximation can be calculated by the perturbation method set forth in § 1. In the present case

$$(H^{(0)} = 0,\ V = H),$$

the zero order approximation is simply the operator 1 and expansion (XVII.17) gives

$$U_T(1) = 1 - i\hbar^{-1} T \int_0^1 H(s)\, \mathrm{d}s + (i\hbar)^{-2}\, T^2 \int_0^1 \mathrm{d}s_1 \int_0^{s_1} \mathrm{d}s_2\, H(s_1)\, H(s_2) + \dots. \qquad \text{(XVII.58)}$$

In particular, substituting this expansion into the right-hand side of (XVII.57), one obtains the expansion of ϖ in powers of T. As $Q_0|0\rangle = 0$, the lowest-order term is in T^2, and is obtained by substituting in the first two terms of (XVII.58). Put

$$\bar{H} = \int_0^1 H(s)\, \mathrm{d}s = \frac{1}{T} \int_{t_0}^{t_1} H\, \mathrm{d}t. \qquad \text{(XVII.59)}$$

We then have

$$\varpi = \frac{T^2}{\hbar^2} \langle 0|\bar{H}\, Q_0\, \bar{H}|0\rangle + O(T^3).$$

And since

$$\langle 0|\bar{H} Q_0 \bar{H}|0\rangle = \langle 0|\bar{H}^2|0\rangle - \langle 0|\bar{H}|0\rangle^2 = (\Delta\bar{H})^2$$

where $\Delta\bar{H}$ is the root mean square deviation of the observable $\bar{H}$ in the state $|0\rangle$, one has

$$\varpi = \frac{T^2(\Delta\bar{H})^2}{\hbar^2} + O(T^3). \qquad \text{(XVII.60)}$$

Thus the condition for the validity of the sudden approximation, $\varpi \ll 1$, requires that [1])

$$\boxed{T \ll \hbar/\Delta\bar{H}} \qquad \text{(XVII.61)}$$

Condition (XVII.61) is nothing else but a particular form of the time-energy uncertainty relation. Following definition (XVII.59), $\bar{H}$ is the Hamiltonian of the system averaged over the interval (t_0, t_1). The evolution of the system is therefore roughly governed by the Hamiltonian $\bar{H}$ during that time interval. According to the time-energy uncertainty relation, the state of a system obeying such an equation of motion cannot appreciably be modified before a time $\hbar/\Delta\bar{H}$ has elapsed. Condition (XVII.61), therefore, is indeed the condition that the modification of the state after a time T will be negligible.

9. Sudden Reversal of a Magnetic Field

As an application we consider what happens to an atom in a constant magnetic field when the direction of the field is suddenly reversed. We suppose the atom to be one for which the LS coupling scheme holds, and the field to be sufficiently strong to completely decouple the total angular momentum $\boldsymbol{L}$ from the total spin $\boldsymbol{S}$ (Paschen–Back effect). For simplicity we shall also suppose the magnetic field to be

---

[1]) The condition $\varpi \ll 1$ does not necessarily imply that $U_1(t_1, t_0)\,|0\rangle \simeq |0\rangle$ but only that these two vectors differ essentially only by a phase factor. However, formula (XVII.60) supposes a rapid convergence of the expansion (XVII.58), and in general (XVII.61) is a sufficient condition for this to be so.

always parallel to the z axis, and to pass from the value $-\mathscr{H}_0$ to the value $\mathscr{H}_0$ according to the linear law

$$\mathscr{H}(t) = \mathscr{H}_0[2s-1] = \mathscr{H}_0[2(t-t_0)/T-1]. \qquad \text{(XVII.62)}$$

According to the study of Chapter XVI (§ 9–12), the Hamiltonian of the system is of the form

$$H = H^{(0)} + A(\mathbf{L}\cdot\mathbf{S}) - \frac{e}{2mc}(L_z + 2S_z)\,\mathscr{H}(t) \qquad \text{(XVII.63)}$$

$H^{(0)}$ is the unperturbed Hamiltonian in the LS coupling scheme. Since according to law (XVII.62) the time average of the magnetic field is zero, the time average of H is equal to the Hamiltonian of the atom without external field:

$$\overline{H} = H^{(0)} + A(\mathbf{L}\cdot\mathbf{S}).$$

We shall now suppose that initially the system is in an eigenstate of H. Since at that time we have the conditions of the Paschen–Back effect, the state vector will be very nearly equal to one of the vectors $|\alpha LSM_LM_S\rangle$ defined in § XVI.11. We therefore put: $|0\rangle = |\alpha LSM_LM_S\rangle$. The calculation of $\Delta\overline{H}$ is straightforward. Since $|\alpha LSM_LM_S\rangle$ is an eigenvector of $H^{(0)}+AL_zS_z$ the only contribution comes from the difference $\frac{1}{2}A(L_+S_-+L_-S_+)$. The calculation gives

$$\Delta\overline{H} = \tfrac{1}{2}A\hbar^2[2(L(L+1)-M_L^2)\,(S(S+1)-M_S^2)-2M_LM_S]^{\frac{1}{2}}.$$

The bracket is a numerical factor of the order of 1 (it vanishes in the two extreme cases $M_L = \pm L$, $M_S = \pm S$). The deviation $\Delta\overline{H}$ is therefore of the order of magnitude of $A\hbar^2$, i.e. of the order of magnitude of the splitting of the LS levels by spin-orbit coupling.

In consequence, if

$$T \ll \frac{1}{A\hbar} \qquad \text{(XVII.64)}$$

the rapid passage condition (XVII.61) is met: the state vector remains practically constant when we reverse the field. For the dynamical state of the atom to remain constant it is sufficient that the state vector be modified only by a phase factor; inequality (XVII.64) is therefore a sufficient but not a necessary condition for the atom to remain in the same state when the field is reversed. We shall return to this point at the end of § 14.

10. Adiabatic Passage. Generalities. Trivial Case

In the rest of this section we shall examine the other extreme case, that of a very slow modification of the Hamiltonian. We follow the notations of § 7.

We first wish to establish the Adiabatic Theorem, which is a property of the states of the discrete spectrum of $H(s)$. Although it is in no way an essential assumption, for the sake of simplicity we shall suppose the spectrum of H to be entirely discrete [1]).

Denote the eigenvalues of H by $\varepsilon_1, \varepsilon_2, ..., \varepsilon_j ...$, and the projectors onto their respective subspaces by $P_1, P_2, ..., P_j, ...$. These quantities are all supposed to be *continuous functions of s*. In addition we suppose that:

(*i*) *the eigenvalues remain distinct* throughout the whole transition period $0 \leqslant s \leqslant 1$:

$$\varepsilon_j(s) \neq \varepsilon_k(s), \qquad \text{whatever } j \text{ and } k \tag{XVII.65}$$

(*ii*) *the derivatives* $\mathrm{d}P_j/\mathrm{d}s$, $\mathrm{d}^2P_j/\mathrm{d}s^2$ are well-defined and piece-wise continuous in the whole interval.

The evolution operator $U_T(s)$ satisfies the Schrödinger equation

$$\mathrm{i}\hbar \frac{\mathrm{d}}{\mathrm{d}s} U_T(s) = TH(s)\, U_T(s), \tag{XVII.66}$$

the Hamiltonian $H(s)$ being given by the expression

$$H(s) = \textstyle\sum_j \varepsilon_j(s)\, P_j(s). \tag{XVII.67}$$

The Adiabatic Theorem states that $U_T(s)$ has the asymptotic property [2]):

$$\lim_{T\to\infty} U_T(s)\, P_j(0) = P_j(s) \lim_{T\to\infty} U_T(s) \qquad (j = 1, 2, ...). \tag{XVII.68}$$

---

[1]) It is sufficient that the discrete eigenvalues and their respective subspaces satisfy the continuity, "non-crossing" and differentiability conditions indicated below. See T. Kato, *loc. cit.*, note, p. 740.

[2]) This property is equivalent to the one given in § 7, for if $|j\rangle$ is an eigenvector of $H(0)$ belonging to the eigenvalue $\varepsilon_j(0)$, then $P_j(0)\,|j\rangle = |j\rangle$ and (XVII.68) gives

$$\lim_{T\to\infty} U_T(s)\,|j\rangle = P_j(s) \lim_{T\to\infty} U_T(s)\,|j\rangle.$$

Thus the vector $U_T(s)\,|j\rangle$ tends toward a vector of the subspace of $\varepsilon_j(s)$ when $T \to \infty$ as stated in § 7.

Let us first suppose that the subspace of each eigenvalue of $H(s)$ remains unchanged

$$P_j(s) = P_j(0) \equiv P_j \qquad (j = 1, 2, \dots).$$

In this case $H(s)$ takes the simple form

$$H(s) = \sum_j \varepsilon_j(s)\, P_j$$

and commutes with each projector P_j whatever s; each P_j is therefore a constant of the motion:

$$U_T(s)\, P_j\, U_T^{\dagger}(s) = P_j. \tag{XVII.69}$$

Relation (XVII.69) is verified for any T and *a fortiori* for $T \to \infty$.

In addition, equation (XVII.66) is exactly integrable in this particular case and gives

$$\begin{aligned} U_T(s) &= \exp\left(-\mathrm{i}T \int_0^s H(\sigma)\, \mathrm{d}\sigma/\hbar\right) \\ &= \sum_j \mathrm{e}^{-\mathrm{i}T\varphi_j(s)/\hbar}\, P_j. \end{aligned} \tag{XVII.70}$$

where we use the notation

$$\varphi_j(s) = \int_0^s \varepsilon_j(\sigma)\, \mathrm{d}\sigma. \tag{XVII.71}$$

We therefore have the result that if at time t_0 the state vector of the system is an eigenvector of H_0 belonging to the eigenvalue $\varepsilon_j(0)$, at time t_1 it differs from this only by the phase factor $\mathrm{e}^{-\mathrm{i}T\varphi_j(1)/\hbar}$.

11. "Rotating Axis Representation"

In the general case, the exact integration of the Schrödinger equation is no longer possible as the eigenvectors of the Hamiltonian $H(s)$ are effecting a certain rotational motion in Hilbert space. The first step in treating the general case will be to eliminate this rotational motion as far as possible through an appropriate change of "representation".

To this effect, we introduce a unitary operator $A(s)$ having the property

$$P_j(s) = A(s)\, P_j(0)\, A^{\dagger}(s) \qquad (j = 1, 2, \dots). \tag{XVII.72}$$

The unitary transformation $A(s)$ takes any set of basis vectors of $H(0)$ over into a set of basis vectors of $H(s)$, each eigenvector of $H(0)$

being carried over into one of the eigenvectors of $H(s)$ that derive from it by continuity.

$A(s)$ is unambiguously defined by the initial condition

$$A(0) = 1 \tag{XVII.73}$$

and the differential equation

$$\mathrm{i}\hbar \, \mathrm{d}A/\mathrm{d}s = K(s)\, A(s) \tag{XVII.74}$$

where $K(s)$ is an appropriate Hermitian operator. For (XVII.72) to be satisfied it is necessary and sufficient that $K(s)$ obey the commutation relations

$$[K(s), P_j(s)] = \mathrm{i}\hbar \, \mathrm{d}P_j/\mathrm{d}s \qquad (j = 1, 2, \dots). \tag{XVII.75}$$

These are necessary since they are immediately obtained upon differentiating both sides of (XVII.72) with respect to s. They are sufficient since, $A(s)$ and $P_j(s)$ satisfying equations (XVII.74) and (XVII.75) respectively, the expression

$$A^{\dagger}(s)\, P_j(s)\, A(s)$$

has a vanishing derivative with respect to s, and is therefore equal to its initial value $P_j(0)$.

$K(s)$ is not completely defined by relations (XVII.75) which are still satisfied if we add to $K(s)$ the operator $\sum_k P_k(s) f_k(s) P_k(s)$, where the $f_k(s)$ are arbitrary operators depending on s. In other words the projections $P_j(s)K(s)P_j(s)$ ($j = 1, 2, \dots$) may be arbitrarily fixed. For reasons that will presently become clear, we remove the arbitrary by imposing the additional condition

$$P_j(s)\, K(s)\, P_j(s) = 0 \qquad (j = 1, 2, \dots). \tag{XVII.76}$$

This gives (Problem XVII.5)

$$K(s) = \mathrm{i}\hbar \textstyle\sum_j (\mathrm{d}P_j/\mathrm{d}s)\, P_j(s).$$

The unitary transformation $A^{\dagger}(s)$ carries the vectors and operators of the Schrödinger "representation" over into the vectors and operators of a new "representation", the "rotating axis representation". The observable $H(s)$ transforms into

$$H^{(A)}(s) = A^{\dagger}(s)\, H(s)\, A(s)$$

giving, with the aid of (XVII.67) and (XVII.72),

$$H^{(A)}(s) = \sum_j \varepsilon_j(s)\, P_j(0). \tag{XVII.77}$$

Similarly $K(s)$ becomes

$$K^{(A)}(s) = A^\dagger(s)\, K(s)\, A(s). \tag{XVII.78}$$

The evolution operator in this new "representation" is

$$U^{(A)}(s) \equiv A^\dagger(s)\, U_T(s). \tag{XVII.79}$$

It is defined [cf. § 1, eq. (XVII.12), where one must take $V = TH - K$] by

$$i\hbar\, \mathrm{d}U^{(A)}/\mathrm{d}s = [TH^{(A)}(s) - K^{(A)}(s)]\, U^{(A)}(s), \tag{XVII.80}$$

$$U^{(A)}(0) = 1. \tag{XVII.81}$$

12. Proof of the Adiabatic Theorem

Equation (XVII.80) would be easily integrable if one could neglect $K^{(A)}$ as compared with $TH^{(A)}$. We would then have the trivial case studied in § 10. Let us denote by $\Phi_T(s)$ the solution of the resulting Schrödinger equation:

$$i\hbar\, \mathrm{d}\Phi_T/\mathrm{d}s = TH^{(A)}(s)\, \Phi_T(s) \tag{XVII.82}$$

$$\Phi_T(0) = 1. \tag{XVII.83}$$

We find [eq. (XVII.70)]

$$\Phi_T(s) = \sum_j \mathrm{e}^{-\mathrm{i}T\varphi_j(s)/\hbar}\, P_j(0) \tag{XVII.84}$$

the φ_j being still defined by (XVII.71).

However, referring to (XVII.77) and (XVII.78) we see that $H^{(A)}(s)$ and $K^{(A)}(s)$ are independent of T. We may therefore expect that in the limit $T \to \infty$ the effect of $K^{(A)}$ on the right-hand side of (XVII.80) will be completely masked by that of $TH^{(A)}$, and that $U^{(A)}(s)$ will tend towards $\Phi_T(s)$. As we shall see, this is indeed the case, and therefore [eq. (XVII.79)]

$$U_T(s) \underset{T\to\infty}{\sim} A(s)\, \Phi_T(s). \tag{XVII.85}$$

To prove this result we begin by effecting a new unitary transformation and putting

$$W \equiv \Phi_T{}^\dagger\, U^{(A)} = \Phi_T{}^\dagger\, A^\dagger\, U_T. \tag{XVII.86}$$

We easily deduce the equation satisfied by this new unitary operator from (XVII.80) and (XVII.82). In its integral form it reads

$$W(s) = 1 + \frac{\mathrm{i}}{\hbar} \int_0^s \bar{K}(\sigma)\, W(\sigma)\, \mathrm{d}\sigma, \qquad \text{(XVII.87)}$$

where

$$\bar{K}(s) \equiv \Phi_T^{\dagger}(s)\, K^{(A)}(s)\, \Phi_T(s) \qquad \text{(XVII.88)}$$

$$= \Phi_T^{\dagger} A^{\dagger} K A \Phi_T. \qquad \text{(XVII.89)}$$

We are going to show that the kernel $\bar{K}(s)$ is a sum of oscillating functions whose frequencies increase indefinitely with T, and that in consequence the integral on the right-hand side of the Volterra equation (XVII.87) tends to zero when $T \to \infty$.

Any operator Q can be decomposed as follows [1]):

$$Q = \textstyle\sum_j \sum_k P_j(0)\, Q\, P_k(0).$$

We shall henceforth employ the notation

$$Q_{jk} \equiv P_j(0)\, Q\, P_k(0).$$

From (XVII.72), (XVII.84) and (XVII.89)

$$\left.\begin{aligned} \bar{K}_{jk} &= \mathrm{e}^{\mathrm{i}T(\varphi_j - \varphi_k)/\hbar}\, K^{(A)}_{jk} \\ K^{(A)}_{jk} &= A^{\dagger}(s)\, P_j(s)\, K(s)\, P_k(s)\, A(s). \end{aligned}\right. \qquad \text{(XVII.90)}$$

According to condition (XVII.76), the $K^{(A)}_{jj}$ $(j = 1, 2, \ldots)$ all vanish, and therefore the diagonal parts $\bar{K}_{jj}$ of the decomposition of $\bar{K}$ are all exactly null:

$$\bar{K}_{jj} = 0 \qquad (j = 1, 2, \ldots). \qquad \text{(XVII.91)}$$

The non-diagonal parts $\bar{K}_{jk}$ $(j \neq k)$ contain the oscillating factor

$$\mathrm{e}^{\mathrm{i}T(\varphi_j - \varphi_k)/\hbar} \equiv \exp\, [\mathrm{i}\hbar^{-1}\, T \int_0^s (\varepsilon_j(\sigma) - \varepsilon_k(\sigma))\, \mathrm{d}\sigma].$$

The circular frequency of the oscillations is obtained by differentiating the phase of the exponential with respect to s, which gives

$$T\, |\varepsilon_j(s) - \varepsilon_k(s)|/\hbar.$$

---

1) The procedure employed here amounts to using a representation in which $H(0)$ is diagonal and at the same time avoiding the various complications arising from the possible degeneracy of the levels of $H(0)$ and the arbitrariness in the phase of the basis vectors.

According to the hypothesis (XVII.65) the difference $\varepsilon_j - \varepsilon_k$ never vanishes, and therefore the frequency increases as T when $T \to \infty$.

Consider now the operator

$$F(s) \equiv \int_0^s \bar{K}(\sigma)\, \mathrm{d}\sigma. \qquad \text{(XVII.92)}$$

According to (XVII.91) its diagonal elements are all null:

$$F_{jj} = 0.$$

The non-diagonal elements are given by the expression

$$F_{jk} = \int_0^s \mathrm{e}^{\mathrm{i}T(\varphi_j - \varphi_k)/\hbar}\, K_{jk}^{(A)}\, \mathrm{d}\sigma \qquad (j \neq k). \qquad \text{(XVII.93)}$$

$K_{jk}^{(A)}$ is a continuous function of s independent of T. The phase of the exponential, however, does depend on T and F_{jk} is therefore of the form $\int_0^s \mathrm{e}^{\mathrm{i}T\alpha(\sigma)}\, f(\sigma)\, \mathrm{d}\sigma$, where $f(\sigma)$ is a continuous function and $\alpha(\sigma)$ is a continuous monotonic function. Such an integral is known to go to zero when $T \to \infty$. Indeed, integrating by parts, it becomes

$$F_{jk}(s) = \frac{\hbar}{\mathrm{i}T}\left[\mathrm{e}^{\mathrm{i}T(\varphi_j - \varphi_k)/\hbar}\, \frac{K_{jk}^{(A)}}{\varepsilon_j - \varepsilon_k}\Bigg|_0^s - \int_0^s \mathrm{e}^{\mathrm{i}T(\varphi_j - \varphi_k)/\hbar}\left[\frac{\mathrm{d}}{\mathrm{d}\sigma}\left(\frac{K_{jk}^{(A)}}{\varepsilon_j - \varepsilon_k}\right)\right]\mathrm{d}\sigma\right]. \qquad \text{(XVII.94)}$$

Clearly the expression in brackets remains finite if $K_{jk}^{(A)}$ and the derivatives of $K_{jk}^{(A)}$, ε_j and ε_k with respect to s remain finite. F_{jk} therefore tends asymptotically to zero as $1/T$. In conclusion, when $T \to \infty$ we have

$$F(s) = \mathrm{O}\left(\frac{1}{T}\right).$$

Now the integral on the right-hand side of (XVII.87) can be written, after integration by parts,

$$F(s)\, W(s) - \int_0^s F(\sigma)\, \frac{\mathrm{d}W}{\mathrm{d}\sigma}\, \mathrm{d}\sigma,$$

or again,

$$F(s)\, W(s) - \mathrm{i}\hbar^{-1} \int_0^s F(\sigma)\, \bar{K} W(\sigma)\, \mathrm{d}\sigma \qquad \text{(XVII.95)}$$

where we have taken into account the equation $\mathrm{d}W/\mathrm{d}s = \mathrm{i}\bar{K} W/\hbar$. Both terms in (XVII.95) contain the factor F, and hence tend to zero as $1/T$ when $T \to \infty$. In consequence [1])

$$W = 1 + O\left(\frac{1}{T}\right). \qquad \text{(XVII.96)}$$

Substituting (XVII.96) into the definition (XVII.86) of W, one finds

$$U_T(s) \underset{T\to\infty}{\sim} A(s)\, \Phi_T(s) \left[1 + O\left(\frac{1}{T}\right)\right] \qquad \text{(XVII.97)}$$

which completes the proof of (XVII.85).

Since $\Phi_T(s)$ commutes with the projectors $P_j(0)$ [cf. eq. (XVII.84)] and since the unitary operator $A(s)$ has the property (XVII.72), one has

$$A(s)\, \Phi_T(s)\, P_j(0) = P_j(s)\, A(s)\, \Phi_T(s).$$

Therefore the asymptotic expression (XVII.97) does indeed verify relations (XVII.68). Q.E.D.

13. Adiabatic Approximation

If T is sufficiently large or, better, *if the basis vectors of $H(t)$ rotate sufficiently slowly*, we can, in a first approximation, replace $U_T(1)$ by its asymptotic form:

$$U(t_1, t_0) \equiv U_T(1) \simeq A(1)\, \Phi_T(1). \qquad \text{(XVII.98)}$$

This is called *the adiabatic approximation.*

Let $|0\rangle$ be the vector of norm 1 representing the system at time t_0 and let Q_0 be the projector onto the complementary space. The adiabatic approximation consists in writing

$$U(t, t_0)|0\rangle \simeq A(1)\, \Phi_T(1)|0\rangle.$$

---

[1]) In all rigor, the above argument is only valid if the operator $K(s)$ is bounded over the whole interval (0, 1) (cf. note, p. 713). It can then be shown that $\|F(s)\|$ tends uniformly to zero with respect to s as $1/T$. Denote by $\varkappa$ and ε the upper limits of $\|K(s)\|$ and of $\|F(s)\|$ respectively. Since W, Φ and A are unitary, the norms of K, $K^{(A)}$, $\bar{K}$ and KW are equal; similarly the norms of F and FW are equal. It follows that

$$\|FW\| \leqslant \varepsilon, \quad \left\|\int_0^s F\bar{K}W\, d\sigma\right\| < \varepsilon\varkappa s.$$

And since $W-1$ is given by (XVII.95),

$$\|W - 1\| \leqslant \varepsilon(1 + \varkappa s).$$

A measure of the error involved in this approximation is given by the probability η of finding the system at time t_1 in a state different to $A(1)\Phi_T(1)|0\rangle$. The projector onto the space orthogonal to this vector is

$$Q_1 \equiv A(1)\,\Phi_T(1)\,Q_0\,\Phi_T{}^{\dagger}(1)\,A^{\dagger}(1),$$

so that

$$\begin{aligned}\eta &\equiv \langle 0|U^{\dagger}(t_1, t_0)\,Q_1\,U(t_1, t_0)|0\rangle \\ &= \langle 0|W^{\dagger}(1)\,Q_0\,W(1)|0\rangle.\end{aligned}$$

Corrections to the adiabatic approximation may be calculated by the perturbation method of § 1. Here $A(1)\Phi_T(1)$ plays the role of $U^{(0)}$ and $W(1)$ that of U_{I}. The method consists in retaining only the initial terms in the expansion of W obtained by iteration of equation (XVII.87). If we go only to first order we find

$$W(1) \simeq 1 + (\mathrm{i}F/\hbar), \tag{XVII.99}$$

where F is the operator $F(1)$ defined by (XVII.92).

This expansion may also be used to evaluate η. A treatment analogous to the calculation of ϖ in the case of the sudden approximation gives

$$\eta \simeq \hbar^{-2}\,\langle 0|F\,Q_0\,F|0\rangle = (\Delta F/\hbar)^2, \tag{XVII.100}$$

where ΔF is the root-mean-square-deviation of the observable F in the state $|0\rangle$. The condition $\eta \ll 1$, condition for the validity of the adiabatic approximation [1]), becomes

$$\Delta F \ll \hbar.$$

In the general form given here this result is much less useful than the corresponding result for the sudden approximation [relation (XVII.61)]. The observable F involved here is much more difficult to construct than the observable $\bar{H}$ of the sudden approximation. $\bar{H}$ is the result of a simple integration of $H(t)$; to calculate F one must solve the eigenvalue problem for $H(t)$ at each point of the interval (t_0, t_1) and construct the operator $A(s)$ for each of these points.

Let us examine the validity conditions for the adiabatic approxi-

---

[1]) The same remarks can be made in this connection as were made in the note, p. 742 in connection with the criterion for the validity of the sudden approximation.

mation in the case when the system is initially in an eigenstate of $H(0)$. This is, in fact, the only case of practical interest.

Henceforth we shall use the variable t itself rather than the substitute s. We thus denote the eigenvalues of the Hamiltonian at time t by $\varepsilon_j(t)$, the corresponding projectors by $P_j(t)$, the operator giving our "rotating axes" by $A(t)$ and the operator $\Phi_T(s)$ by $\Phi(t)$. Definitions (XVII.67) and (XVII.84) are therefore superceded by the definitions:

$$H(t) = \sum_j \varepsilon_j(t)\, P_j(t) \tag{XVII.101}$$

$$\Phi(t) = \sum_j \exp\,[-\mathrm{i} \int_{t_0}^{t} \varepsilon_j(\tau)\, \mathrm{d}\tau/\hbar]\, P_j(0). \tag{XVII.102}$$

Equations (XVII.73) and (XVII.74) defining A become

$$\mathrm{i}\hbar\, \mathrm{d}A/\mathrm{d}t = K'(t)\, A(t) \qquad A(0) = 1 \tag{XVII.103}$$

with

$$K'(t) \equiv K(s)/T = \mathrm{i}\hbar \sum_j (\mathrm{d}P_j/\mathrm{d}t)\, P_j(t). \tag{XVII.104}$$

From its definition, (XVII.92), we get

$$F \equiv F(t_1) = \int_{t_0}^{t_1} \Phi^\dagger(t)\, A^\dagger(t)\, K'(t)\, A(t)\, \Phi(t)\, \mathrm{d}t. \tag{XVII.105}$$

It is further assumed, for simplicity, that the spectrum of $H(t)$ is completely non-degenerate. We choose a set of basis vectors $|1\rangle_0, |2\rangle_0, \ldots, |j\rangle_0, \ldots$ of the Hamiltonian H_0 and denote the set of basis vectors of $H(t)$ obtained from these by application of the transformation $A(t)$ by $|1\rangle_t, |2\rangle_t, \ldots |j\rangle_t, \ldots$. For any t,

$$\left.\begin{aligned} |j\rangle_t &= A(t)\, |j\rangle_0 \\ H(t)\, |j\rangle_t &= \varepsilon_j(t)\, |j\rangle_t \\ P_j(t) &= |j\rangle_t\, {}_t\langle j| \end{aligned}\right\} \quad (j = 1, 2, \ldots). \tag{XVII.106}$$

Let $|i\rangle_0$ be the state vector of the system at time t_0. In the adiabatic approximation, its state vector at time t_1 will be equal to within a phase factor to $|i\rangle_1 \equiv A(t_1)|i\rangle_0$:

$$U(t_1, t_0)|i\rangle_0 \simeq \exp\,[-\mathrm{i} \int_{t_0}^{t_1} \varepsilon_i(\tau)\, \mathrm{d}\tau/\hbar]\, |i\rangle_1. \tag{XVII.107}$$

The probability $p_{i\to j}$ $(j \neq i)$ of finding the system in another eigenstate of $H(t)_1$, say $|j\rangle_1$, is by definition

$$p_{i\to j} = |{}_1\langle j|U(t_1, t_0)|i\rangle_0|^2.$$

The perturbation calculation described above gives

$$p_{i\to j} \simeq |{}_0\langle j|F|i\rangle_0|^2/\hbar^2. \tag{XVII.108}$$

In agreement with the result (XVII.100), we have

$$\eta_i = \sum_{j\neq i} p_{i\to j} \simeq \hbar^{-2} \sum_{j\neq i} {}_0\langle i|F|j\rangle_0\, {}_0\langle j|F|i\rangle_0$$

With the aid of equations (XVII.102), (XVII.104) and (XVII.105), and the properties of $|j\rangle_t$ as given by (XVII.106), we find

$${}_0\langle j|F|i\rangle_0 = \mathrm{i}\hbar \int_{t_0}^{t_1} \alpha_{ji}(t) \exp\,[\mathrm{i} \int_{t_0}^{t} \omega_{ji}(\tau)\,\mathrm{d}\tau]\,\mathrm{d}t,$$

where

$$\begin{aligned}\alpha_{ji} &\equiv {}_0\langle j|A^\dagger(t)\,(\mathrm{d}P_i/\mathrm{d}t)\,A(t)|i\rangle_0 \\ &= {}_t\langle j|(\mathrm{d}|i\rangle_t/\mathrm{d}t)\end{aligned} \tag{XVII.109}$$

$$\omega_{ji}(t) = [\varepsilon_j(t) - \varepsilon_i(t)]/\hbar. \tag{XVII.110}$$

Therefore, from (XVII.108)

$$p_{i\to j} \simeq |\int_{t_0}^{t_1} \alpha_{ji}(t) \exp\,[\mathrm{i} \int_{t_0}^{t} \omega_{ji}(\tau)\,\mathrm{d}\tau]\,\mathrm{d}t|^2. \tag{XVII.111}$$

The physical interpretation of the quantities α_{ji} and ω_{ji} can be read directly from definitions (XVII.109) and (XVII.110). $\alpha_{ji}(t)$ is a measure of the speed of rotation of the eigenvectors of $H(t)$. It is the component along $|j\rangle_t$ of the velocity of the axis $|i\rangle_t$. $\omega_{ji}(t)$ is the "Bohr frequency" of the transition $i \to j$.

The integrand on the right-hand side of (XVII.111) is the product of the function $\alpha_{ji}(t)$ by an oscillating exponential of frequency $\omega_{ji}(t)$. If α_{ji} and ω_{ji} are time-independent it is easily integrated to give

$$p_{i\to j} \simeq \left|\frac{\alpha_{ji}}{\omega_{ji}}\right|^2 2(1 - \cos \omega_{ji}\, T).$$

$p_{i\to j}$ is therefore a quantity of the order of $|\alpha_{ji}/\omega_{ji}|^2$. If α_{ji} and ω_{ji}, instead of being just constant, exhibit a sufficiently smooth variation in time, then $p_{i\to j}$ will at most be of the order of magnitude of the maximum value attained by the ratio $|\alpha_{ji}/\omega_{ji}|^2$ in the interval (t_0, t_1):

$$p_{i\to j} \lesssim \max \left|\frac{\alpha_{ji}(t)}{\omega_{ji}(t)}\right|^2. \tag{XVII.112}$$

Similarly η_i is at most of the order of magnitude of the quantity obtained on summing the right-hand side of (XVII.112) over all states j different to i. This sum will generally be smaller than the expression $|\alpha_i^{\max}/\omega_i^{\min}|^2$ in which $\omega_i^{\min}$ is the minimum value of the Bohr frequency for the transition from i to its nearest neighbor and $\alpha_i^{\max}$ is the maximum value of the positive quantity $\alpha_i(t)$ defined by

$$\alpha_i^2(t) = \sum_{j \neq i} |\alpha_{ji}(t)|^2.$$

Returning to the definition (XVII.109) of α_{ji} and noting that [1])

$${}_t\langle i| \left(\frac{\mathrm{d}}{\mathrm{d}t} |i\rangle_t\right) = 0 \qquad \text{(XVII.113)}$$

we see that α_i is the length of the vector $\mathrm{d}|i\rangle_t/\mathrm{d}t$, that is, the "angular velocity" of the eigenvector $|i\rangle_t$. The condition $\eta_i \ll 1$ is therefore, in most cases, certainly satisfied if

$$\boxed{\left|\frac{\alpha_i^{\max}}{\omega_i^{\min}}\right|^2 \equiv \left|\frac{\text{maximum angular velocity of } |i\rangle_t}{\text{minimum Bohr frequency of } |i\rangle_t}\right|^2 \ll 1} \qquad \text{(XVII.114)}$$

Condition (XVII.114) may be taken as a criterion for the validity of the adiabatic approximation. It is in fact too restrictive, but has the advantage of being relatively easy to handle. It is to be particularly noted that it is not necessary to determine $A(t)$ in order to calculate either $\alpha_i(t)$ or the quantity $|\alpha_{ji}(t)|$ figuring in the right-hand side of (XVII.112); we need only to solve the eigenvalue problem for $H(t)$ and to determine to within a phase factor the vectors $|i\rangle_t$, $|j\rangle_t$.

---

[1]) From (XVII.104) and (XVII.106) we have

$$\frac{\mathrm{d}}{\mathrm{d}t} |j\rangle_t = \frac{\mathrm{d}}{\mathrm{d}t} A(t)\, |j\rangle_0 = \frac{\mathrm{d}P_j}{\mathrm{d}t} |j\rangle_t \qquad (j = 1, 2, \ldots).$$

Confronting this result and the one we obtain from term by term differentiation of the identity $P_j(t)\, |j\rangle_t = |j\rangle_t$ we find $P_j(\mathrm{d}|j\rangle_t/\mathrm{d}t) = 0$; therefore

$${}_t\langle j| \left(\frac{\mathrm{d}}{\mathrm{d}t} |j\rangle_t\right) = 0 \qquad (j = 1, 2, \ldots). \qquad \text{(XVII.113')}$$

The vectors $|j\rangle_t$ are defined to within a phase factor by the condition that they are eigenvectors of $H(t)$. This phase factor is fixed by condition (XVII.113').

Furthermore, we can show that

$$\alpha_{ji}(t) = -\, {}_t\langle j|\, \frac{\mathrm{d}H}{\mathrm{d}t}\, |i\rangle_t/\hbar\omega_{ji}(t)$$

(cf. Problem (XVII.6).

14. Adiabatic Reversal of a Magnetic Field

Let us now return to the problem of § 9, following the same notation. We start from the same initial conditions, but now suppose condition (XVII.64) no longer to be satisfied.

The Hamiltonian being given by (XVII.63), we see that α, L, S and $M_J \equiv M_L + M_S$ are good quantum numbers ($H(t)$ commutes with $J_z \equiv L_z + S_z$, whatever t). Therefore, if $|\alpha L S M_L M_S\rangle$ is the initial state-vector, its subsequent evolution will be in the space of vectors having the same values of α, L, S and $M_L + M_S$.

We shall examine in detail the case when the system is initially in a ^{2}P state. There are in all 6 different ^{2}P states, linear combinations of the 6 basis vectors $|\alpha 1 \tfrac{1}{2} M_L M_S\rangle$ ($M_L = 1, 0, -1$; $M_S = \tfrac{1}{2}, -\tfrac{1}{2}$) which will henceforth be denoted $|M_L M_S\rangle$. Since they are all eigenstates of $H^{(0)}$, we can take the corresponding eigenvalue as the zero of the energy. The levels corresponding to the energy H are easily determined (Problem XVI.7). They are functions of the parameter $\varrho = \mu_{\mathrm{B}}\mathscr{H}/A\hbar^2$ ($\mu_{\mathrm{B}} \equiv \mathrm{e}\hbar/2mc$ = Bohr magneton) and are plotted in Figure XVII.3. Each level corresponds to a well-defined value of $M_J = M_L + M_S$, and the corresponding eigenvector tends toward a particular $|M_L M_S\rangle$ in each of the limits $\varrho \to \pm\infty$, as indicated in the figure. We shall successively examine the cases $M_J = \tfrac{3}{2}$ and $M_J = \tfrac{1}{2}$.

We first consider the case when $M_J = \tfrac{3}{2}$. There is just one state for this value of J_z, and the corresponding vector is $|1\ \tfrac{1}{2}\rangle$. It is necessarily an eigenvector of H for any t. A simple calculation gives

$$H|1\ \tfrac{1}{2}\rangle = A\hbar^2(\tfrac{1}{2} - 2\varrho(t))|1\ \tfrac{1}{2}\rangle.$$

If the atom is initially in the state $|1\ \tfrac{1}{2}\rangle$, we will have a case of the trivial integration of the Schrödinger equation described in § 10. In the course of time the atom remains in the same state, its state vector simply being multiplied by the phase factor

$$\exp\left[-\mathrm{i}A\hbar \int_{t_0}^{t} (\tfrac{1}{2} - 2\varrho(\tau))\, \mathrm{d}\tau\right].$$

In the case of a linear variation of the magnetic field [law (XVII.62)], the state vector at the end of a time T is equal to

$$\exp(-\mathrm{i}A\hbar T)|1\ \tfrac{1}{2}\rangle.$$

This is true whatever T. In particular, in the limit when $A\hbar T \ll 1$, we get the result given by the sudden approximation, i.e. the vector $|1\ \frac{1}{2}\rangle$ itself.

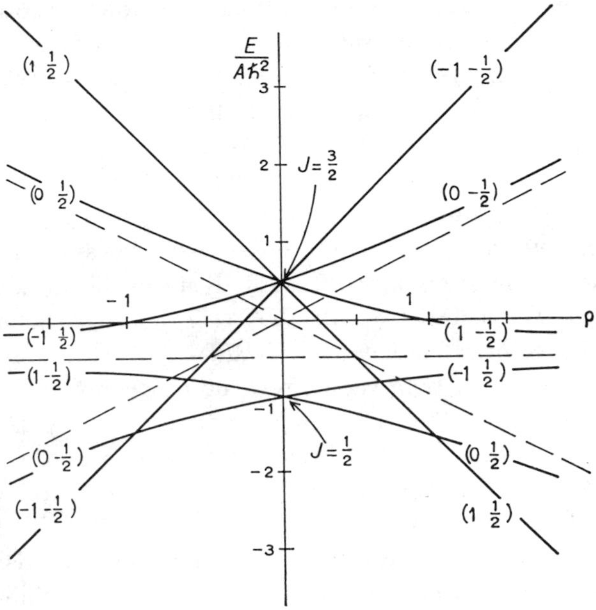

Fig. XVII.3. Position of the ^{2}P levels as a function of the intensity of the magnetic field $\mathscr{H}$ ($\varrho = \mu_B \mathscr{H}/A\hbar^2$). The numbers in parenthesis at the end of each curve are the quantum numbers ($M_L M_S$) of the eigenstates in the two limits $\varrho \to \pm\infty$.

We next consider the case when $M_J = \frac{1}{2}$. To this value of J_z there correspond two eigenstates of H, each a linear combination of the vectors $|0\ \frac{1}{2}\rangle$ and $|1\ -\frac{1}{2}\rangle$. In order to solve the eigenvalue problem for $H(t)$ in the subspace spanned by these two vectors we take the two of them as basis vectors, in which case $H(t)$ is represented by the matrix

$$A\hbar^2 \begin{pmatrix} -\varrho & \frac{1}{2}\sqrt{2} \\ \frac{1}{2}\sqrt{2} & -\frac{1}{2} \end{pmatrix}.$$

If we introduce the Pauli matrices $\boldsymbol{\sigma} \equiv (\sigma_x, \sigma_y, \sigma_z)$ this matrix can be written in the particularly convenient form:

$$H(t) = \tfrac{1}{4}A\hbar^2 [(-2\varrho - 1) + \boldsymbol{b}\cdot\boldsymbol{\sigma}] \qquad \text{(XVII.115)}$$

the vector $\boldsymbol{b}$ having the components

$$b_x = 2\sqrt{2}, \qquad b_y = 0, \qquad b_z = 1 - 2\varrho.$$

We also introduce $\boldsymbol{u}$, the unit vector along $\boldsymbol{b}$:

$$\boldsymbol{b} = b\boldsymbol{u} \qquad b = \sqrt{8 + (1-2\varrho)^2}$$

$$\boldsymbol{u} \equiv \left(\frac{2\sqrt{2}}{b}, 0, \frac{1-2\varrho}{b}\right). \qquad \text{(XVII.116)}$$

Note that the vector $\boldsymbol{b}$ and the vector operator $\boldsymbol{\sigma}$ belong to a three-dimensional space having nothing whatever to do with ordinary three-dimensional space; we have merely employed a simple mathematical artifice that permits certain properties to be deduced by geometrical arguments analogous to those made in ordinary space.

From (XVII.115) and (XVII.116),

$$H(t) = \tfrac{1}{4}A\hbar^2 [(-1 - 2\varrho) + b(\boldsymbol{\sigma}\cdot\boldsymbol{u})] \qquad \text{(XVII.117)}$$

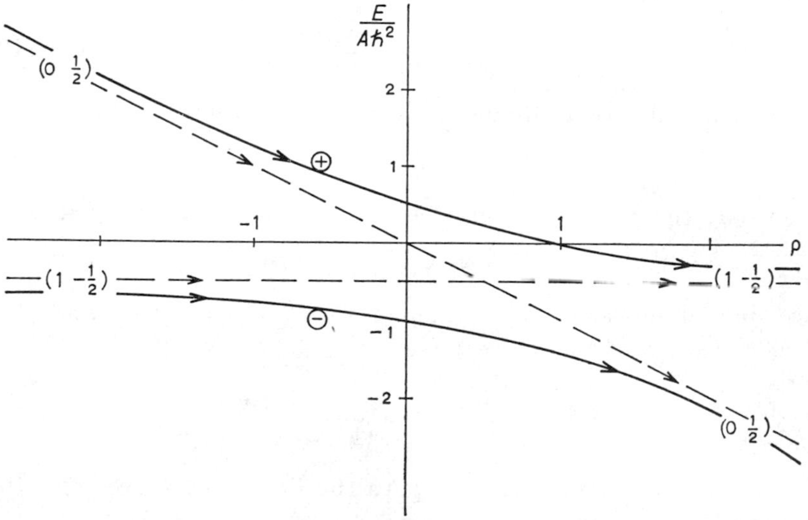

Fig. XVII.4. Evolution of the two ^{2}P levels with $M_J = \frac{1}{2}$ when the magnetic field is reversed (same notations as Figure XVII.3). The full line represents adiabatic reversal, the broken line rapid reversal.

$H(t)$ is therefore a function of the operator $(\boldsymbol{\sigma}\cdot\boldsymbol{u})$. It results that the corresponding eigenvalue problem is easily solved — we obtain the eigenvalues $\frac{1}{4}A\hbar^2(-1-2\varrho \pm b)$ and the projectors $P_\pm = \frac{1}{2}(1 \pm \boldsymbol{\sigma}\cdot\boldsymbol{u})$. We shall denote the corresponding eigenvectors by $|+\rangle$ and $|-\rangle$. They are defined to within a phase that may be fixed by the first of conditions (XVII.106), but since that phase does not come into what follows we need not be concerned with it here. It is easy to follow the continuous evolution of these two levels and their projectors as functions of the parameter $\varrho(t)$ (Figs. XVII.3 and XVII.4). When ϱ goes from $-\infty$ to ∞, the eigenvector $|+\rangle$ goes (except for a phase factor) from $|0\ \frac{1}{2}\rangle$ to $|1\ -\frac{1}{2}\rangle$, and the corresponding energy level follows the upper branch of the hyperbola in Figure 4; at the same time the eigenvector $|-\rangle$ goes from $|1\ -\frac{1}{2}\rangle$ into $|0\ \frac{1}{2}\rangle$, and the corresponding level follows the lower branch of the hyperbola.

Suppose, for example, that initially the system is in the state $|0\ \frac{1}{2}\rangle$. If the field is reversed slowly enough, the state vector of the system will always be equal to the vector $|+\rangle$ (to within a phase factor) and the system will effectively be in the state $|1\ -\frac{1}{2}\rangle$ once the field is reversed. The criterion for the validity of this adiabatic passage can be determined by applying the considerations of the preceding paragraph. Using the same notation we find, [relation (XVII.112)],

$$\eta_+ = p_{+\to-} \lesssim \max\left|\frac{\alpha(t)}{\omega(t)}\right|^2 \ll 1, \qquad \text{(XVII.118)}$$

where $\omega(t)$ is the Bohr frequency for the transition $+\to-$,

$$\omega(t) = \tfrac{1}{2}A\hbar b = \tfrac{1}{2}A\hbar\sqrt{8+(1-2\varrho)^2},$$

and $\alpha(t)$ is the projection onto $|-\rangle$ of the speed of $|+\rangle$, whence

$$|\alpha(t)| = |\langle -|(\mathrm{d}P_+/\mathrm{d}t)|+\rangle| = \tfrac{1}{2}|\langle -|(\boldsymbol{\sigma}\cdot\mathrm{d}\boldsymbol{u}/\mathrm{d}t|+\rangle|.$$

Since $\mathrm{d}\boldsymbol{u}/\mathrm{d}t$ is a vector perpendicular to $\boldsymbol{u}$ and since $|+\rangle$ and $|-\rangle$ are eigenvectors of $(\boldsymbol{\sigma}\cdot\boldsymbol{u})$, we have

$$|\alpha(t)| = \tfrac{1}{2}\left|\frac{\mathrm{d}\boldsymbol{u}}{\mathrm{d}t}\right| = \frac{\sqrt{8}}{8+(1-2\varrho)^2}\left|\frac{\mathrm{d}\varrho}{\mathrm{d}t}\right|.$$

If the field is reversed according to the linear law (XVII.62), the maximum of $|\alpha/\omega|$ is attained when $\varrho = +\frac{1}{2}$, i.e.

$$\max\left|\frac{\alpha}{\omega}\right| = \tfrac{1}{2}\frac{\mu_{\mathrm{B}}\mathscr{H}_0}{A\hbar^2}\times\frac{1}{A\hbar T}.$$

Condition (XVII.118) is thus realized if

$$T' = \frac{2A\hbar^2}{\mu_B \mathscr{H}_0} T \gg (1/A\hbar). \qquad \text{(XVII.119)}$$

T' is the time necessary for the magnetic coupling energy $\mu_B \mathscr{H}$ to go from $-2A\hbar^2$ to $2A\hbar^2$. It is essentially during this period that $|+\rangle$ makes its rotation from the position $|0\ \tfrac{1}{2}\rangle$ to the position $|1\ -\tfrac{1}{2}\rangle$. Eq. (XVII.119) expresses that this period must be long as compared with $1/A\hbar$, period characteristic of the transition $+ \to -$.

It is interesting to compare this condition of adiabatic passage with the rapid-passage condition (XVII.64). The latter, in fact, is too restrictive. It is a necessary condition for the state-vector to remain practically unchanged during the whole time T that the field is being reversed, but, with the exception of the interval T' defined above, the eigenvectors of the Hamiltonian remain practically fixed during this time, and the state-vector of the system is simply multiplied by a phase factor. For the dynamical state itself to remain unchanged, that is, for the state vector to remain unchanged except for a *phase factor* during the reversal of the field, it is sufficient that the rapid passage condition be realized for the time T' during which the rotation of the eigenvectors of H takes place, i.e.

$$T' \ll \frac{1}{A\hbar} \qquad \text{(XVII.120)}$$

(cf. Problem XVII.8).

EXERCISES AND PROBLEMS

1. Let u_1 and u_2 be two orthogonal eigenstates corresponding to a doubly degenerate level of the Hamiltonian H_0 of a system. The introduction of a constant perturbation V removes the degeneracy and splits the level into two levels a distance ε apart. Suppose that the system is initially in the state u_1 and that the perturbation V is introduced during a time T. If $W_{1\to 2}$ is the probability of finding the system in the state u_2 after the perturbation has been "turned off", show that $W_{1\to 2}$ is a periodic function of T with angular frequency $\varepsilon/\hbar$ and verify that in the limit when $\varepsilon T \ll \hbar$ we obtain the result given by the first-order perturbation theory. What is necessary in order that $W_{1\to 2}$ vanish whatever T?

2. A hydrogen atom is subject to an oscillating electric field $\mathscr{E} = \mathscr{E}_0 \cos \omega t$ whose circular frequency ω is greater than its ionization frequency $me^4/2\hbar^3$. If the atom is initially in its ground state, what is the probability per unit time of a transition to an ionized state (suppose that we may use plane waves to

represent ionized states)? What is the angular distribution of the electron emitted in this exitation process? [N.B. The process described here is that of the photoelectric effect for which one thus obtains a semi-classical treatment in which the electromagnetic field is not quantized. The results are the same as those given by the correct treatment with the quantized electromagnetic field (cf. Problem XXI.12).]

3. In β decay an atomic nucleus emits an electron with a velocity that is usually close to c, and its charge goes from Ze to $(Z+1)e$. Show that the effect of this transition on the other electrons may be treated in the sudden approximation. Verify that the method applies to the disintegration of triton H^3 ($\equiv$ 1 proton + 2 neutrons) into He^3 ($\equiv$ 1 neutron + 2 protons), where the average kinetic energy of the disintegration electron is only 16 keV (mc^2 = 500 keV). The triton atom is initially in its ground state; what is the probability of finding, after the decay, an He^+ ion in the 1s state? In the 2s state? In a state $l \neq 0$?

4. Let $H(t)$ be the Hamiltonian of a non-conservative system. We suppose that there exists a time-independent vector $|u\rangle$ satisfying the equation $H(t)\,|u\rangle = \varepsilon(t)\,|u\rangle$. Show that the vector

$$\exp\left(-\mathrm{i}\int_{t_0}^{t} \varepsilon(\tau)\,\mathrm{d}\tau/\hbar\right)|u\rangle$$

satisfies the Schrödinger equation for the system.

5. Let $P_1, P_2, \ldots, P_j, \ldots$ be a complete set of orthogonal projectors. We suppose each of them to be a continuous, differentiable function of a parameter s, and that the variations with respect to s conserve the orthogonality and closure relations:

$$P_j P_k = \delta_{jk} P_k \qquad \textstyle\sum_j P_j = 1.$$

Show that the operator

$$K(s) \equiv \mathrm{i}\hbar \textstyle\sum_j (\mathrm{d}P_j/\mathrm{d}s)\, P_j \equiv -\mathrm{i}\hbar \sum_j P_j(\mathrm{d}P_j/\mathrm{d}s)$$

is Hermitean and that it obeys the commutation relations (XVII.75). Show also that it obeys the identities:

$$P_j K P_j = 0 \qquad (j = 1, 2, \ldots)$$
$$P_j K P_k = \mathrm{i}\hbar P_j(\mathrm{d}P_k/\mathrm{d}s)\, P_k = -\mathrm{i}\hbar P_j(\mathrm{d}P_j/\mathrm{d}s)\, P_k.$$

6. The $P_j(s)$ ($j = 1, 2 \ldots$) being defined as in the preceding problem, show that the derivative of the operator

$$H(s) = \textstyle\sum_j \varepsilon_j(s)\, P_j(s),$$

where the $\varepsilon_j(s)$ are differentiable functions of s, obeys the equation

$$P_j(\mathrm{d}H/\mathrm{d}s)\, P_k = (\varepsilon_k - \varepsilon_j)\, P_j(\mathrm{d}P_k/\mathrm{d}s)\, P_k + \delta_{jk}(\mathrm{d}\varepsilon_k/\mathrm{d}s)\, P_k.$$

Deduce from this that the "angular velocity" $\alpha_{ji}(t)$ defined by equation (XVII.109) is also given by the relation:

$$\alpha_{ji}(t) = \frac{-1}{\hbar\omega_{ji}(t)} {}_t\langle j|\ \frac{\mathrm{d}H}{\mathrm{d}t}\ |i\rangle_t \qquad (j \neq i).$$

7. A uniform magnetic field $\mathscr{H}$ of fixed magnitude rotates with a constant angular velocity α about an axis making a given angle θ with it. Into this field is put an infinitely heavy particle of spin $\boldsymbol{J}$. We take $\hbar = 1$, we denote a unit vector parallel to the magnetic field by $\boldsymbol{u}(t)$ and we put $\gamma = \mu\mathscr{H}$, where μ is the gyromagnetic ratio of the particle. The motion of the spin $\boldsymbol{J}$ is therefore governed by the Hamiltonian $H(t) = -\gamma(\boldsymbol{J}\cdot\boldsymbol{u})$. Let $t = 0$ be the initial time, J_0 the component of $\boldsymbol{J}$ along $\boldsymbol{u}(0)$, J_z its component along the axis of rotation of the field.

Construct the unitary operator giving the "rotating axes", then show that the evolution operator in the Schrödinger representation is exactly given by the formula:

$$U(t) = \exp\left(-\mathrm{i}\alpha J_z t\right) \exp\left[\mathrm{i}(\gamma J_0 + \alpha J_z)\, t\right].$$

Verify the adiabatic theorem for this example; show by direct calculation and by the method of § 13 that the criterion for the validity of the adiabatic approximation is that $(\alpha \sin\theta/\gamma)^2 \ll 1$.

8. We consider the Schrödinger equation of the system defined in § 14 in the case when $M_j = \frac{1}{2}$. Let $\begin{pmatrix} u \\ v \end{pmatrix}$ be the components of its solution in the representation defined in that paragraph. We take $t_0 = -\frac{1}{2}T$ and put

$$T' = 2A\hbar^2 T/\mu_{\mathrm{B}}\mathscr{H}_0 \ (\ll T) \qquad \varkappa = 4/A\hbar T'.$$

Show that:

$$u = y \exp\left(-\mathrm{i}\varkappa\, \xi^2\right) \qquad v = \mathrm{i}(\mathrm{d}y/\mathrm{d}\xi) \exp\left(-\mathrm{i}\varkappa\, \xi^2\right),$$

where y, considered as a function of the variable $\xi = A\hbar t/\sqrt{2}$, obeys the equation

$$y'' - \tfrac{1}{2}\mathrm{i}(\sqrt{2} + 4\varkappa\xi)\, y' + y = 0.$$

If we put $x = \xi + (\sqrt{2}/4\varkappa)$, the general solution to this equation can be written in the form

$$y = A_0 F\left(\frac{\mathrm{i}}{4\varkappa}\middle|\frac{1}{2}\middle|\mathrm{i}\varkappa\, x^2\right) + A_1 x F\left(\frac{1}{2} + \frac{\mathrm{i}}{4\varkappa}\middle|\frac{3}{2}\middle|\mathrm{i}\varkappa\, x^2\right).$$

The initial state being $|0\ \tfrac{1}{2}\rangle$, show, using the asymptotic form of the hypergeometric functions, that the probability ϖ for it to be in the same state at the end of a time T, is given by the formula [valid if $T \gg (T'/A\hbar)^{\frac{1}{2}}$]

$$\varpi = \left(\frac{1-\gamma}{1+\gamma}\right)^2, \qquad \gamma = \tanh\frac{\pi}{4\varkappa}.$$

Verify that conditions (XVII.119) and (XVII.120) do in fact correspond to adiabatic and rapid passage respectively.

CHAPTER XVIII

THE VARIATIONAL METHOD AND ASSOCIATED PROBLEMS

1. The Ritz Variational Method

Apart from the WKB method, which can only be applied in a very narrow domain, there are two principal methods for the approximate determination of the energy levels and wave functions of the discrete spectrum: the perturbation method (Chapter XVI) and the variational method. The present chapter is devoted to the second of these methods.

The variational method is a very general one that can be used whenever the equations can be put into variational form. The principle involved is the following. The desired solutions belong to a certain function space $\mathscr{F}$. Let Ψ be an arbitrary function of that space. Let us suppose that the solutions of the equation being studied are the functions of $\mathscr{F}$ for which a certain functional $Q[\Psi]$ is stationary. That equation is therefore equivalent to the variational equation

$$\delta Q = 0. \qquad \text{(XVIII.1)}$$

The Ritz variational method consists in seeking the solutions of equation (XVIII.1) among the functions of a space $\mathscr{F}'$ more restricted than $\mathscr{F}$.

Suppose, for example, that $\mathscr{F}$ is the set of all wave functions of a given quantum system. For $\mathscr{F}'$ we may take a subset of particular wave functions $\Phi(a, b, c)$ labelled with a certain number of continuous parameters $a, b, \ldots$, and spanning only a part of $\mathscr{F}$. Considered as a functional of the Φ, the quantity Q reduces to a simple function of the variational parameters $a, b, \ldots$,

$$q(a, b, \ldots) \equiv Q[\Phi(a, b, \ldots)].$$

Each set of values $a_0, b_0, \ldots$, for which this function is stationary, defines an approximate solution $\Phi_0(a_0, b_0, c_0,)$ of equation (XVIII.1).

The success of the method depends essentially on the choice of the trial-function space $\mathscr{F}'$. The trial function must be simple enough to lend itself easily to the calculation, but must vary in a sufficiently large or well-chosen domain for the solutions obtained to be close to the exact ones.

In practice the stationary values of Q have a definite physical significance. One of the chief virtues of the variational method is to automatically furnish a precise evaluation of these quantities. Clearly the difference between $Q[\Phi_0]$ and $Q[\Psi_0]$ is smaller the closer the approximate solution Φ_0 to the exact solution Ψ_0; but in addition, since $Q[\Psi]$ is stationary at the point $\Psi = \Psi_0$ this difference is an infinitesimal of higher order than the difference between Φ_0 and Ψ_0. Thus the variational method is especially useful for evaluating quantities that can be put in the form of stationary functionals. This is notably the case for the energy levels of bound states. We shall see in Chapter XIX that it can also be applied to the calculation of collision amplitudes.

The calculation of the levels of the discrete spectrum by the variational method is described in section 1 of this chapter. In the remaining two sections we treat two important problems by methods more or less directly related to the variational method: the determination of the wave functions of complex atoms in the central field approximation by the methods of Hartree and of Fock–Dirac (Section II) and the treatment of molecules in the Born–Oppenheimer adiabatic approximation (Section III).

I. VARIATIONAL METHOD FOR BOUND STATES

2. Variational Form of the Eigenvalue Problem

The stationary functional involved in the determination of bound states by the variational method is the average value of the energy. We shall prove the following theorem [1]):

THEOREM. *Let H denote the Hamiltonian of a quantum system and $E[\Psi]$ the average value of its energy*

$$E[\Psi] \equiv \frac{\langle\Psi|H|\Psi\rangle}{\langle\Psi|\Psi\rangle}. \tag{XVIII.2}$$

Any state-vector for which this average value, considered as a functional of the vectors of state-vector space, is stationary, is an eigenvector of the

---

[1]) This theorem is a general result relative to the discrete spectra of Hermitean operators in Hilbert space. Only the Hermitean character of H is involved in the following demonstration.

discrete spectrum of H, and conversely. The corresponding eigenvalue is the stationary value of the functional $E[\Psi]$.

It is to be noted that the vectors $|\Psi\rangle$ introduced here have a *finite norm*: the function space $\mathscr{F}$ (definition of § 1) is the *Hilbert space* of the dynamical states of the system. The theorem therefore states that the eigenfunctions of H in this Hilbert space are the solutions of the variational equation

$$\delta E = 0. \tag{XVIII.3}$$

We also note that the functional $E[\Psi]$ is independent both of the norm and of the phase of $|\Psi\rangle$. Therefore, any supplementary condition that may be imposed on these quantities will not effect the validity of the theorem. In particular, it is sometimes convenient to limit the domain of variation of $|\Psi\rangle$ to vectors of norm 1, as is done in some of the examples of this chapter.

Proof of the theorem

Calculating the variation of $E[\Psi]$, we get

$$\begin{aligned}\langle\Psi|\Psi\rangle\,\delta E &= \delta(\langle\Psi|H|\Psi\rangle) - E\delta(\langle\Psi|\Psi\rangle)\\ &= \langle\delta\Psi|(H-E)|\Psi\rangle + \langle\Psi|(H-E)|\delta\Psi\rangle.\end{aligned}$$

So long as $\langle\Psi|\Psi\rangle$ remains finite and non-null, equation (XVIII.3) is therefore equivalent to

$$\langle\delta\Psi|(H-E)|\Psi\rangle + \langle\Psi|(H-E)|\delta\Psi\rangle = 0. \tag{XVIII.4}$$

The ket $|\delta\Psi\rangle$ is the variation of $|\Psi\rangle$, the bra $\langle\delta\Psi|$ the variation of the bra conjugate to $|\Psi\rangle$. The variations $|\delta\Psi\rangle$ and $\langle\delta\Psi|$ are therefore not independent. They may, however, be treated as such, for, equation (XVIII.4) being satisfied by any infinitesimal ket $|\delta\Psi\rangle$, we may replace $|\delta\Psi\rangle$ by $\mathrm{i}|\delta\Psi\rangle$, thus obtaining a second equation

$$-\mathrm{i}\,\langle\delta\Psi|(H-E)|\Psi\rangle + \mathrm{i}\,\langle\Psi|(H-E)|\delta\Psi\rangle = 0, \tag{XVIII.4'}$$

and by taking linear combinations of (XVIII.4) and (XVIII.4′) we can deduce the two equivalent equations:

$$\langle\delta\Psi|(H-E)|\Psi\rangle = 0, \qquad \langle\Psi|(H-E)|\delta\Psi\rangle = 0.$$

These are equivalent to the single equation (XVIII.4) if we agree to consider the variations $|\delta\Psi\rangle$ and $\langle\delta\Psi|$ as arbitrary and independent [1]).

We then have the two relations:

$$(H-E)|\Psi\rangle = 0, \qquad \langle\Psi|(H-E) = 0,$$

i.e.

$$(H-E[\Psi])|\Psi\rangle = 0 \tag{XVIII.5a}$$

$$(H^\dagger - E^*[\Psi])|\Psi\rangle = 0. \tag{XVIII.5b}$$

Now H is Hermitean ($H=H^\dagger$), so that relations (XVIII.5a) and (XVIII.5b) are identical. Equation (XVIII.3) is therefore equivalent to equation (XVIII.5a): any ket $|\Psi_1\rangle$ for which E is stationary is an eigenket of H belonging to the eigenvalue $E[\Psi_1]$.

Conversely, let $|\Psi_1\rangle$ be an eigenket of finite norm and E_1 the corresponding eigenvalue:

$$H|\Psi_1\rangle = E_1|\Psi_1\rangle.$$

Scalar multiplication on the left by $\langle\Psi_1|$ gives

$$E_1 = E[\Psi_1].$$

Therefore $|\Psi_1\rangle$ satisfies equation (XVIII.5a), and also equation (XVIII.5b) since H is Hermitean and E_1 real. Consequently, $E[\Psi]$ is indeed stationary for $\Psi=\Psi_1$. Q.E.D.

The fundamental theorem is complemented by the following lemma:

LEMMA. *Whatever may be the dynamical state of the system, the average value of its energy is equal to or greater than the energy of the ground state*:

$$E[\Psi] \geqslant E_0. \tag{XVIII.6}$$

To prove this inequality it suffices to calculate the difference between the right- and left-hand sides in a representation where H is diagonal. To simplify the writing we suppose that the spectrum of H is entirely discrete. Let $E_0, E_1, \ldots, E_n, \ldots,$ be the energy levels in increasing order and $P_0, P_1, \ldots, P_n, \ldots$ the projectors onto their respective subspaces. Using the decomposition of unity, we find

$$E[\Psi]-E_0 \equiv \frac{\langle\Psi|(H-E_0)|\Psi\rangle}{\langle\Psi|\Psi\rangle} = \sum_{n=1}^{\infty} (E_n-E_0)\frac{\langle\Psi|P_n|\Psi\rangle}{\langle\Psi|\Psi\rangle}.$$

[1]) This is a general rule. It is due to the fact that (XVIII.4) is a linear relation between $|\delta\Psi\rangle$ and $\langle\delta\Psi|$ while the correspondence between bras and kets is antilinear.

Since each term in this sum is either positive or null, so is the sum itself, proving (XVIII.6).

3. Variational Calculation of Discrete Levels

It was seen in the general discussion of § 1 that one can obtain approximate solutions to the variational equation (XVIII.3) by restricting the domain of variation of the vectors $|\Psi\rangle$ to only a part of state-vector space. If this more restricted domain $\mathscr{F}'$ is well chosen, we thereby obtain certain eigenvectors of H to a good approximation, and the corresponding energy eigenvalues to a still better approximation.

The method takes a particularly simple form *when the trial function depends linearly on the variational parameters*, i.e. when $\mathscr{F}'$ is also a vector space. $\mathscr{F}'$ is then a subspace of $\mathscr{F}$, the term subspace having its usual meaning (§ VII.2).

We denote by P the projector onto $\mathscr{F}'$, by Φ an arbitrary vector of $\mathscr{F}'$ and by H_P the projection of the Hamiltonian onto $\mathscr{F}'$:

$$H_P \equiv PHP. \qquad \text{(XVIII.7)}$$

$E[\Phi]$ [definition (XVIII.2)] is equal to the average value of H_P. However, H_P is Hermitean and transforms the vectors of $\mathscr{F}'$ linearly into vectors of $\mathscr{F}'$; thus it can be treated as a Hermitean operator of $\mathscr{F}'$ to which the fundamental theorem of § 2 is applicable. The variational equation

$$\delta E[\Phi] = 0 \qquad \text{(XVIII.8)}$$

is therefore equivalent to the eigenvalue equation

$$H_P \Phi = E\Phi. \qquad \text{(XVIII.9)}$$

Thus the variational approximation here consists in replacing the eigenvalue problem for H by a problem of the same type but *a priori* easier to solve since defined in a more restricted space.

Note the analogy with the perturbation method (§ XVI.8). In particular, if $\mathscr{F}'$ is the subspace of a given eigenvalue of the unperturbed Hamiltonian, the levels given by the variational method are identical with those given by a first-order perturbation calculation.

4. A Simple Example: The Hydrogen Atom

In order to gain some familiarity with the method it will now be applied to the calculation of the ground state of the hydrogen atom and the results compared with the exact ones of Chapter XI.

We put:

$$a_0 = \hbar^2/me^2 \qquad E_{\mathrm{H}} = \tfrac{1}{2}(e^2/\hbar c)^2\, mc^2 \qquad \varrho = r/a_0.$$

Since we are looking for eigenstates of well-defined angular momentum (lm), we take trial functions of the form

$$\Phi = a_0^{-3/2}\, \frac{u(\varrho)}{\varrho}\, Y_l^m(\theta, \varphi).$$

A simple calculation gives

$$E[\Phi] = -E_{\mathrm{H}} \frac{\int_0^\infty u^* \left(\dfrac{\mathrm{d}^2}{\mathrm{d}\varrho^2} - \dfrac{l(l+1)}{\varrho^2} + \dfrac{2}{\varrho}\right) u \,\mathrm{d}\varrho}{\int_0^\infty |u|^2 \,\mathrm{d}\varrho}.$$

We limit ourselves to s-states $(l=m=0)$ and calculate the stationary values of the energy for the three different trial functions;

$$u_1 = \varrho \mathrm{e}^{-b\varrho}, \qquad u_2 = \frac{\varrho}{b^2+\varrho^2}, \qquad u_3 = \varrho^2\, \mathrm{e}^{-b\varrho}.$$

Each of these trial functions depends on only the one parameter b. In each case, therefore, $E[\Phi]$ reduces to a function of b and the variational calculation consists in finding the minimum of that function. The calculations are not difficult and the results are given in table XVIII.1. First are listed, as functions of b, the analytical expressions for the norm of the trial function $N^2 = \langle\Phi|\Phi\rangle$, and for the average value of the energy, then the position $b_{\min}$ of the minimum and its value E_{var}. It is interesting to compare E_{var} with the ground state energy $E_0 = -E_{\mathrm{H}}$, and also the approximate solution Ψ_{var} with the ground state eigenfunction Ψ_0. For this purpose the normalized radial parts $(u/N)_{\mathrm{var}}$ are given in table XVIII.1 and the corresponding curves shown in Figure XVIII.1; they are to be compared with the exact radial function $2\varrho \mathrm{e}^{-\varrho}$. The table also gives the average value $\langle r\rangle_{\mathrm{var}}$ corresponding to each of the three approximate solutions Ψ_{var}, as well as the quantity $\varepsilon \equiv 1 - |\langle\Psi_0|\Psi_{\mathrm{var}}\rangle|^2$ (Ψ_0 and Ψ_{var} being supposed normalized to unity); ε is a good measure of the difference between Ψ_{var} and the ground state (it is the *square* of the modulus of the amplitude of the component of Ψ_{var} orthogonal to Ψ_0).

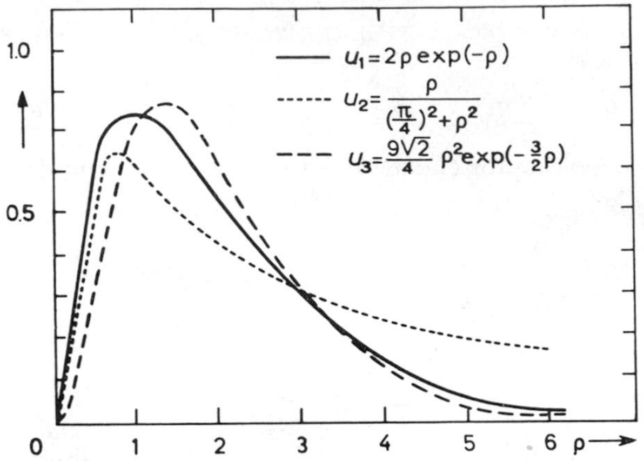

Fig. XVIII.1. Radial functions (normalized to unity) given by the variational calculation of § 4 for the ground state of the hydrogen atom.

All three trial functions have in common with the ground state wave function that they have no radial nodes. Therefore, they are expected to resemble more this function than those of the excited states, and the values E_{var} are expected to be closer to the ground state energy $-E_{\text{H}}$ than to any of the other levels (first excited level: $E_1 = -\frac{1}{4}E_{\text{H}}$). To show that these predictions are indeed verified we have given under each value of E_{var} in Table XVIII.1 the corresponding value of the ratio $(E_{\text{var}} - E_0)/(E_1 - E_0)$ which is a good measure of the error involved in the variational calculation of the ground state energy. The best result is given by the trial function u_1, which gives the exact ground-state wave function and the exact eigenvalue: note that u_1 has the same behavior at the origin ($\propto \varrho$) and the same exponentially-decreasing asymptotic behavior as the *s*-state eigenfunctions (with an attractive potential other than the Coulomb potential we would not obtain the exact wave function but the result would still be excellent). The function u_2 has the proper behavior at the origin but an asymptotic behavior totally different from that of the exact solution; the value that it gives, $E_{\text{var}} = -0.81 E_{\text{H}}$ is still very satisfactory. The function u_3, which on the contrary has a very inexact behavior at the origin, ($\propto \varrho^2$), but a correct exponential falling-

TABLE XVIII.1

Variational calculation of the ground state of the hydrogen atom

		1	2	3
$u(b, \varrho)$	=	$\varrho\,e^{-b\varrho}$	$\dfrac{\varrho}{b^2+\varrho^2}$	$\varrho^2\,e^{-b\varrho}$
N^2	=	$1/4b^3$	$\pi/4b$	$3/4b^5$
$E(b)/E_H$	=	$b^2 - 2b$	$(\pi - 8b)/2\pi b^2$	$\frac{1}{3}b^2 - b$
b_{min}	=	1	$\frac{1}{4}\pi$	$\frac{3}{2}$
E_{var}	=	$-E_H$	$-0.81\,E_H$	$-0.75\,E_H$
$\dfrac{E_{var} - E_0}{E_1 - E_0}$	=	0	0.25	0.33
$(u/N)_{var}$	=	$2\varrho\,e^{-\varrho}$	$\varrho[(\frac{1}{4}\pi)^2 + \varrho^2]^{-1}$	$\frac{1}{4}\times 9\sqrt{2}\,\varrho^2\,e^{-3/2\varrho}$
$\langle r\rangle_{var}$	=	$1.5\,a_0$	∞	$1.66\,a_0$
$\varepsilon = 1 - \|\langle\Psi_0\|\Psi_{var}\rangle\|^2$	=	0	0.21	0.05

off at infinity, gives a poorer result. Consideration of the quantities $\langle r\rangle_{var}$ and ε shows that u_3, on the whole, resembles more the exact solution than does u_2; the fact that it gives a poorer result underlines the importance of behavior at the origin for the calculation of the energy, importance essentially due to the attractive character of the potential.

5. Discussion. Application to the Calculation of Excited Levels

The variational method is a very powerful one, but it is difficult to assess the significance of the results.

There is no infallible method for knowing to what level it is giving an approximate value, nor, *a fortiori*, for estimating the error. However, it is often possible to give a reply to the first of these questions by comparing the general form of the Ψ_{var} obtained (number of nodes, behavior at the origin and at infinity) with that of the exact solution, or at least with our *a priori* knowledge of the exact solution. In practice, one chooses trial functions with a simple analytical form and a very limited number of oscillations (or nodes). They have therefore every chance to be close to the ground state.

The above considerations show that *the variational method is especially suitable for the calculation of the ground-state level*, for which it gives an upper limit [Lemma (XVIII.6)]. Unfortunately, there is no sure method for evaluating the order of magnitude of the error (cf. Problem XVIII.1). Everything depends on the choice and on the flexibility of the trial function, that is, on the choice and on the extension of the function space $\mathscr{F}'$.

The necessity for more complex trial functions, the difficulty in interpreting the results and particularly in knowing the size and sign of the error, make the application of the variational method to the calculation of excited levels more hazardous. There are, however, two situations in which it can be of use in such calculations.

In the first place, when the ground state wave function Ψ_0 is known, the trial function Φ can be chosen from among wave functions that are orthogonal to Ψ_0. In this case, the functional $E[\Phi]$ is at least equal to the energy E_1 of the first excited state

$$E[\Phi] \geqslant E_1 \qquad \text{(XVIII.10)}$$

and the variational method gives an upper limit for E_1 (cf. Problem XVIII.2). When the exact ground state solution is unknown, it may happen that we have an approximate one, Φ_0 (determined, for example, by a variational calculation). In this case, we may apply the variational method to the calculation of E_1 starting from trial functions orthogonal to Φ_0 providing that the difference between Φ_0 and Ψ_0 is sufficiently small, i.e. if

$$\varepsilon_0 = 1 - |\langle\Psi_0|\Phi_0\rangle|^2 \ll 1$$

(Ψ_0 and Φ_0 being of norm 1). The stationary solution Φ_1 (which we suppose of norm 1) is no longer orthogonal to Ψ_0 and inequality (XVIII.10) may be violated, but necessarily (Problem XVIII.3)

$$|\langle\Phi_1|\Psi_0\rangle|^2 < \varepsilon_0 \qquad \text{(XVIII.11)}$$

from which it follows that

$$E[\Phi_1] \geqslant E_1 - \varepsilon_0(E_1 - E_0). \qquad \text{(XVIII.12)}$$

The second favorable situation occurs when H has certain symmetry properties. Suppose, for example, that H is invariant under rotation. The eigenfunctions and eigenvalue can then be classified according to the quantum numbers j, m. Let the functions of angular momentum (jm) span a space $\mathscr{E}\,(jm)$. Choosing a trial function in $\mathscr{E}$ we can make a variational calculation of the levels (jm) and notably of the lowest of them, for which the variational method automatically gives an upper limit (Problem XVIII.4).

6. Ground State of the Helium Atom

In this paragraph we shall apply the variational method to the calculation of the ground state energy of the He atom and, more generally, of $(Z-2)$-times ionized atoms like Li^+, Be^{++}, etc. The same problem has already been treated by the perturbation method in § XVI.4; unless otherwise specified we shall follow the same notation.

As trial function we take the function given by the zero order perturbation theory:

$$\Phi_a(\mathbf{r}_1, \mathbf{r}_2) = \frac{1}{\pi a^3}\, e^{-(r_1+r_2)/a}$$

except that here a will be treated as a variational parameter rather than being given the value a_0/Z.

The trial function being of norm 1, the average value of the energy is given by

$$E(a) = \langle \varphi_a | H | \varphi_a \rangle = \iint \varphi_a{}^*(H\varphi_a)\, \mathrm{d}\mathbf{r}_1\, \mathrm{d}\mathbf{r}_2.$$

The Hamiltonian of the system can be put in the form

$$H = k_1 + k_2 + v_1 + v_2 + V_{12},$$

where $k_i (i=1, 2)$ denotes the kinetic energy of the ith electron, $v_i = Ze^2/r_i$ its interaction with the nucleus, and V_{12} the interaction of the two electrons. $E(a)$ is therefore the sum of the average values of these five operators. The calculation of these quantities is greatly simplified by the observation that the wave function φ_a can be put in the form $\varphi_a = f_a(\mathbf{r}_1) f_a(\mathbf{r}_2)$, where $f_a(\mathbf{r})$ is the eigenfunction for the ground state of an electron in a Coulomb field of charge $Z'e$ with

$$Z' = a_0/a.$$

It follows that the total energy of such an electron is $-Z'^2 E_H$, the average value of its kinetic energy $+Z'^2\, E_H$ and the average value of its potential energy $-2Z'^2 E_{\rm H}$ (Problem XI.1). Consequently

$$\langle \varphi_a | k_i | \varphi_a \rangle = Z'^2 E_{\rm H}$$
$$\langle \varphi_a | v_i | \varphi_a \rangle = -2Z'^2 E_{\rm H}(Z/Z') = -2ZZ' E_{\rm H}.$$

The calculation of § XVI.4 (eq. XVI.17–20) is still valid and gives

$$\langle \varphi_a | V_{12} | \varphi_a \rangle = \tfrac{5}{4} Z' E_{\rm H},$$

whence

$$E(a) = 2E_{\rm H}(Z'^2 - 2(Z - \tfrac{5}{16})Z').$$

This expression, considered as a function of a, or, equivalently, as a function of Z', has a minimum for

$$Z' = Z - \tfrac{5}{16}. \qquad \text{(XVIII.13)}$$

The value at this minimum is

$$E_{\rm var} = -2(Z - \tfrac{5}{16})^2 E_{\rm H}. \qquad \text{(XVIII.14)}$$

The numerical values of $E_{\rm var}$ corresponding to the atoms He, Li^+ and Be^{++} are given in table 1 of § XVI.4 (column 5). It is interesting to compare these values with the value given by the first-order perturbation calculation. Note that

$$\begin{aligned} E_{\rm var} &= -2Z^2 E_{\rm H} + \tfrac{5}{4} Z E_{\rm H} - \tfrac{25}{128} E_{\rm H} \\ &= E_{\rm pert} - \tfrac{25}{128} E_{\rm H}, \end{aligned}$$

and therefore that the value found is smaller than the value given by the perturbation calculation by the Z-independent quantity:

$$\tfrac{25}{128} E_{\rm H} = 2.64 \text{ eV}.$$

It is, therefore, a better approximation, as one might have expected. $E_{\rm var}$ is nonetheless greater than the experimental value $E_{\rm exp}$, in agreement with inequality (XVIII.6).

The eigenfunction given by this variational calculation has a simple physical interpretation. It represents two independent particles moving in a Coulomb field whose charge $Z'e$ is given by equation (XVIII.13); this charge is smaller than the charge of the nucleus by $\frac{5}{16}e$; the difference represents, in this approximation, the screening effect felt by each electron in its motion in the Coulomb field of the nucleus due to the presence of the other electron.

By increasing the flexibility of the trial function one obtains a value $E_{\rm var}$ still closer to the exact eigenvalue. In particular, rather than having the trial function φ_a depending on just the one variational parameter a, we can take the product of φ_a by a polynomial of given degree in r_1, r_2, and r_{12} whose coefficients are also treated as variational parameters. The value found for E_{var} progressively decreases and approaches the exact value as the complexity of the polynomial is increased. Preceding in this way, Hylleraas has obtained a theoretical value in excellent agreement with experiment [1]).

II. THE HARTREE AND FOCK–DIRAC ATOMS

7. The Self-consistent Field Method

We have already given the broad outline of the quantum mechanical treatment of complex atoms. One starts from the independent particle approximation in which each electron moves independently of the others in a potential representing the attraction of the nucleus and the average repulsive effect of the other electrons. In this approximation one represents the atomic wave function by a certain Slater determinant which should be chosen as near as possible to the exact solution of the Schrödinger equation of the atom. The best choice is the function obtained by the variational method using an arbitrary Slater determinent Φ as trial function. This very important particular case of the variational method is called the self-consistent field method. Here we shall describe the main steps without going into the details of calculation [2]).

The application of this method is not limited to atoms. It can also be applied to the electrons in a molecule or in a solid and, more generally, to systems of identical particles in any external field whatever. Although atoms are specifically quoted throughout this section, the following treatment is readily applicable to these more general cases.

---

1) Hylleraas, Zeit. f. Phys. **65** (1930) 209: the details of Hylleraas' treatment are given in Condon and Shortly, *Theory of Atomic Spectra* (Cambridge, 4th ed., 1957), p. 345. Hylleraas' method converges very rapidly. With eight variational parameters the calculated value is slightly below the experimental one, in apparent contradiction with the inequality (XVIII.6). In fact E_{exp} is slightly above the eigenvalue E_0 of the ground state of H due to relativistic effects which can be estimated. The Hylleraas method is a (very precise) method for calculating E_0, and not E_{exp}.

2) For a detailed treatment of the method and its practical applications, cf. D. R. Hartree, *The Calculation of Atomic Structures* (Wiley, 1957). Cf. also Condon and Shortly, *loc. cit.*, note 1, this page.

8. Calculation of $E[\Phi]$

The Hamiltonian of the system of Z electrons is written

$$H = H_1 + H_2 \tag{XVIII.13}$$

$$H_1 = \sum_{i=1}^{Z} h^{(i)}, \qquad h^{(i)} = \frac{\mathbf{p}^{(i)2}}{2m} + V(\mathbf{r}^{(i)}) \tag{XVIII.14}$$

$$H_2 = \sum_{i<j} w^{(ij)}. \tag{XVIII.15}$$

The first term, H_1, includes the kinetic energy and the potential energy due to the external field (the electric field of the nucleus); it is the sum of Z identical, individual Hamiltonians. The second term, H_2, is the interaction energy of the electrons, i.e. a sum of $\frac{1}{2}Z(Z-1)$ identical terms representing respectively the interaction of each pair of electrons; $w^{(ij)}$ is the potential between electron i and electron j. If we neglect the spin dependent forces, $w^{(ij)}$ is simply the repulsive electrostatic potential

$$w^{(ij)} = e^2/r_{ij} \qquad (r_{ij} \equiv |\mathbf{r}_i - \mathbf{r}_j|). \tag{XVIII.16}$$

The following treatment does not depend on this particular form for $w^{(ij)}$; it supposes simply that $w^{(ij)}$ is a function of the dynamical variables of the ith and jth electrons alone, and that this function is symmetrical in the permutation (ij).

As $E[\Phi]$ is independent of the normalization of the trial function Φ, the latter may always be normalized to unity. With the notation of Chapter XIV, we write it in the form

$$|\Phi\rangle \equiv (Z!)^{\frac{1}{2}}\, A|\hat{\Phi}\rangle, \tag{XVIII.17}$$

where A is the antisymmetrizer defined by equation (XIV.26):

$$A \equiv \frac{1}{Z!} \sum_P (-)^p\, P, \tag{XVIII.18}$$

and where $|\hat{\Phi}\rangle$ is the tensor product of Z arbitrary, orthonormal, individual kets:

$$|\hat{\Phi}\rangle \equiv |\alpha\rangle^{(1)}|\beta\rangle^{(2)} \ldots |\zeta\rangle^{(Z)} \equiv |\alpha^{(1)}\beta^{(2)} \ldots \zeta^{(Z)}\rangle \tag{XVIII.19}$$

$$\langle\lambda|\mu\rangle \equiv \delta_{\lambda\mu} \qquad (\lambda, \mu = \alpha, \beta, \ldots, \zeta). \tag{XVIII.20}$$

The normalization condition is then automatically satisfied:

$$\langle\Phi|\Phi\rangle = 1. \tag{XVIII.21}$$

$E[\Phi]$ is the sum of the average values of H_1 and H_2. Their calculation is made easier by the fact that H_1 and H_2, being invariant under permutation, commute with A, and that A is a projector ($A^2 = A$).

The average value of H_1 becomes successively:

$$\begin{aligned}\langle H_1 \rangle \equiv \langle \Phi | H_1 | \Phi \rangle &= Z! \, \langle \hat{\Phi} | H_1 A | \hat{\Phi} \rangle \\ &= \sum_{i=1}^{Z} \sum_P (-)^p \, \langle \hat{\Phi} | h^{(i)} P | \hat{\Phi} \rangle \\ &= \sum_{i=1}^{Z} \langle \hat{\Phi} | h^{(i)} | \hat{\Phi} \rangle .\end{aligned}$$

Replacing $|\hat{\Phi}\rangle$ by its definition, (XVIII.19), the last line becomes:

$$\langle H_1 \rangle = \textstyle\sum_\lambda \langle \lambda | h | \lambda \rangle \qquad (\lambda = \alpha, \beta, \ldots, \zeta). \qquad \text{(XVIII.22)}$$

Thus $\langle H_1 \rangle$ is just the sum of the average values of the individual Hamiltonian h relative to the Z individual quantum states occupied by the electrons.

Similarly, $\langle H_2 \rangle$ can be put into the form of a sum of matrix elements of the operator w between two-electron states. We have, successively:

$$\begin{aligned}\langle H_2 \rangle \equiv \langle \Phi | H_2 | \Phi \rangle &= Z! \, \langle \hat{\Phi} | H_2 A | \hat{\Phi} \rangle \\ &= \sum_{i<j} \sum_P (-)^p \, \langle \hat{\Phi} | w^{(ij)} P | \hat{\Phi} \rangle \\ &= \sum_{i<j} \langle \hat{\Phi} | w^{(ij)} \, (1 - P_{(ij)}) | \hat{\Phi} \rangle \end{aligned}$$

i.e.

$$\langle H_2 \rangle = \textstyle\sum' (\langle \lambda^{(1)} \mu^{(2)} | w^{(12)} | \lambda^{(1)} \mu^{(2)} \rangle - \langle \lambda^{(1)} \mu^{(2)} | w^{(12)} | \mu^{(1)} \lambda^{(2)} \rangle) \quad \text{(XVIII.23)}$$

the sum $\sum'$ being extended over the $\frac{1}{2}Z(Z-1)$ pairs of individual states λ, μ that can be formed from the Z individual states $\alpha, \beta, \ldots, \zeta$. The first term in the brackets is the average value of the interaction energy relative to the ket $|\lambda^{(1)} \, \mu^{(2)}\rangle$ for which electron 1 is in the state λ and electron 2 in the state μ; the second term is the *exchange term*, that is, the matrix element of w between the states $|\lambda^{(1)} \, \mu^{(2)}\rangle$ and $|\mu^{(1)} \, \lambda^{(2)}\rangle$ [Note that the exchange term is real and that we have: $\langle \lambda^{(1)} \mu^{(2)} | w^{(12)} | \mu^{(1)} \lambda^{(2)} \rangle = \langle \mu^{(1)} \lambda^{(2)} | w^{(12)} | \lambda^{(1)} \mu^{(2)} \rangle$. This property is due to $w^{(12)}$ being Hermitean and invariant in the permutation (1 2)]. $\langle H_2 \rangle$ can also be written

$$\langle H_2 \rangle = \tfrac{1}{2} \textstyle\sum_\lambda \sum_\mu (\langle \lambda^{(1)} \mu^{(2)} | w^{(12)} | \lambda^{(1)} \mu^{(2)} \rangle - \langle \lambda^{(1)} \mu^{(2)} | w^{(12)} | \mu^{(1)} \lambda^{(2)} \rangle) \quad \text{(XVIII.24)}$$
$$(\lambda, \mu = \alpha, \beta, \ldots, \zeta).$$

And finally

$$E[\Phi] = \langle H_1 \rangle + \langle H_2 \rangle, \qquad \text{(XVIII.25)}$$

where $\langle H_1 \rangle$ and $\langle H_2 \rangle$ are given by equations (XVIII.22) and (XVIII.24).

9. The Fock–Dirac equations

The variational solution of the Schrödinger equation in the self-consistent field approximation is the solution that makes $E[\Phi]$ stationary with respect to the Z orthonormal vectors $|\lambda\rangle$ ($\lambda = \alpha, \beta, \ldots, \zeta$). To say that E is stationary with respect to variations of Z vectors obeying the Z^2 conditions (XVIII.20) is equivalent to saying (method of Lagrange multipliers) that there exist Z^2 constants $\varepsilon_{\lambda\mu}$ ($\lambda, \mu = \alpha, \beta, \ldots, \zeta$) such that the variational equation

$$\delta E - \sum_{\lambda} \sum_{\mu} \varepsilon_{\lambda\mu}\, \delta\langle \mu | \lambda \rangle = 0 \qquad \text{(XVIII.26)}$$

is satisfied.

The Z^2 constants $\varepsilon_{\lambda\mu}$ can be regarded as the elements of a certain $Z \times Z$ matrix, ε. ε is a Hermitean matrix, for, E being real, δE is real too, and we can subtract equation (XVIII.26) from its complex conjugate to get

$$\textstyle\sum_{\lambda} \sum_{\mu} (\varepsilon_{\lambda\mu} - \varepsilon^*_{\mu\lambda})\, \delta\langle \mu | \lambda \rangle = 0,$$

which requires that

$$\varepsilon_{\lambda\mu} = \varepsilon^*_{\mu\lambda}.$$

The Z vectors $|\alpha\rangle, |\beta\rangle, \ldots, |\zeta\rangle$ constitute an orthonormal basis in a certain subspace $\mathscr{E}_{\Phi}$ of the space of the individual states. A change of basis in this subspace results in $|\Phi\rangle$ being multiplied by a phase factor. To see this, denote by S the $Z \times Z$ unitary matrix defining the change of basis and by $|\alpha'\rangle, |\beta'\rangle, \ldots, |S'\rangle$ the new basis vectors:

$$|\lambda'\rangle = \textstyle\sum_{\lambda} |\lambda\rangle\, S_{\lambda\lambda'}.$$

According to a well-known property of the products of determinants, the Slater determinant of these Z new vectors is equal to the product of that of the Z old ones by det S. Consequently,

$$|\Phi'\rangle = (\det S)\, |\Phi\rangle.$$

Since S is unitary $|\det S| = 1$. It follows that the functional $E[\Phi]$ is invariant under a change of basis and the variational equation (XVIII.26) defines the sequence $|\alpha\rangle, |\beta\rangle, \ldots, |\zeta\rangle$ to within such a change of basis.

It is easy to show from (XVIII.26) that the analogous equation

$$\delta E - \sum_\lambda \sum_\mu \varepsilon'_{\lambda\mu}\, \delta \langle \mu' | \lambda' \rangle = 0$$

is also true, where the matrix ε' is the transform of ε in the transformation $S^\dagger$:

$$\varepsilon'_{\lambda\mu} = (S^\dagger\, \varepsilon\, S)_{\lambda\mu}.$$

In particular, S can be chosen to make ε' diagonal. Since the variational problem is not modified by limiting the choice of basis, we shall henceforth require that ε be diagonal. The variational equation (XVIII.26) then becomes

$$\delta E - \sum_\lambda e_\lambda\, \delta \langle \lambda | \lambda \rangle = 0. \qquad \text{(XVIII.26')}$$

Returning to equations (XVIII.22), (XVIII.24) and (XVIII.25) we easily calculate δE, and the left-hand side of (XVIII.26) then takes the form of a homogeneous linear combination of the $2Z$ variations $\langle \delta\lambda |$ and $| \delta\lambda \rangle$ ($\lambda = \alpha, \beta, \ldots, \zeta$). Writing that it vanishes whatever these variations, considered as being independent [cf. note, p. 765] and making use of the fact that H is Hermitean, one obtains – the details will not be given here – a set of Z equations for the Z orthogonal vectors

$$|\alpha\rangle, |\beta\rangle, \ldots, |\zeta\rangle,$$

namely the equations

$$h^{(1)}|\lambda\rangle^{(1)} + \textstyle\sum_\mu {}^{(2)}\langle \mu | w^{(12)} | \mu \rangle^{(2)} | \lambda \rangle^{(1)} - \sum_\mu {}^{(2)}\langle \mu | w^{(12)} | \lambda \rangle^{(2)} | \mu \rangle^{(1)} = e_\lambda | \lambda \rangle^{(1)} \qquad \text{(I)}$$
$$(\lambda = \alpha, \beta, \ldots, \zeta).$$

Note the absence of factors $\frac{1}{2}$ in the last two terms on the left-hand side. Scalar multiplication of both sides by ${}^{(1)}\langle \lambda |$ and summation over λ gives

$$\textstyle\sum_\lambda e_\lambda = \langle H_1 \rangle + 2 \langle H_2 \rangle = E[\Phi] + \langle H_2 \rangle. \qquad \text{(XVIII.27)}$$

This relation will be discussed further on.

In practice, one represents the individual kets by their wave functions

$$u_\lambda(q) \equiv \langle q|\lambda\rangle,$$

where $q \equiv (\mathbf{r}, m_s)$ denotes the space and spin coordinates.

It is convenient to introduce the "electron density":

$$\varrho(q, q') \equiv \langle q|\varrho|q'\rangle = \sum_\mu u_\mu(q)\, u_\mu^*(q'). \qquad \text{(XVIII.28)}$$

It is the matrix representative of the projector onto the space $\mathscr{E}_\Phi$ defined above:

$$\varrho = \sum_\mu |\mu\rangle\, \langle\mu|.$$

The diagonal element

$$\varrho(q) \equiv \varrho(q, q) = \sum_\mu |u_\mu(q)|^2 \qquad \text{(XVIII.29)}$$

is the probability density for finding an electron at the point q.

The interaction $w^{(ij)}$ is a certain real, symmetrical function of the variables $q^{(i)}, q^{(j)}$ which will henceforth be denoted $w(q^{(i)}, q^{(j)})$. Put:

$$W_{\text{exc}}(q, q') = \varrho(q, q')\, w(q, q') \qquad \text{(XVIII.30)}$$

$$W(q) = \int \varrho(q')\, w(q, q')\, \mathrm{d}q' \qquad \text{(XVIII.31)}$$

$\int \mathrm{d}q'$ denoting, by convention, integration over the spatial coordinates and summation over the spin coordinate. With these notations, (I) becomes the set of integrodifferential equations:

$$\left[-\frac{\hbar^2}{2m}\Delta + V(q)\right] u_\lambda(q) + W(q)\, u_\lambda(q) - \int W_{\text{exc}}(q, q')\, u_\lambda(q')\, \mathrm{d}q' = e_\lambda\, u_\lambda(q) \qquad \text{(II)}$$

$$(\lambda = \alpha, \beta, \ldots, \zeta).$$

These are called *the Fock–Dirac integrodifferential equations.*

This set of equations can be solved by iteration. Starting from an approximate value ϱ_0 for the density, one obtains, by substitution in (XVIII.30) and (XVIII.31), approximate values for W and W_{exc}. Substituting these in (II) one obtains an eigenvalue equation whose first Z solutions $u_\alpha^{(1)}, \ldots, u_\zeta^{(1)}$ lead to a new value ϱ_1 for the density. Starting from ϱ_1 and repeating these operations we get a new value ϱ_2, and so on. If it converges, the sequence $\varrho_0, \varrho_1, \varrho_2, \ldots$ tends to the exact solution ϱ. The criteria for convergence and the rate of convergence will not be discussed here. They obviously depend on the choice of ϱ_0.

10. Discussion

Each of equations (II) resembles a Schrödinger equation determining one of the Z individual states occupied by the Z electrons of the atom. These are not, however, true eigenvalue equations, since operators W and W_{exc} depend on the electron density and consequently the eigensolutions $u_\alpha, u_\beta, \dots, u_\zeta$ enter into the definition of the Hamiltonian. Nevertheless, it is interesting to examine this individual Hamiltonian, and to try to give a physical significance to its various terms.

For this purpose, denote the density of electrons in the $(Z-1)$ occupied states other than the state λ by $\varrho^{(\lambda)}$:

$$\varrho^{(\lambda)} \equiv \sum_{\mu \neq \lambda} |\mu\rangle \langle\mu| \equiv \varrho - |\lambda\rangle \langle\lambda|, \qquad \varrho^{(\lambda)}(q, q') \equiv \varrho(q, q') - u_\lambda(q)\, u_\lambda{}^*(q')$$

and the expressions obtained by replacing ϱ by $\varrho^{(\lambda)}$ in definitions (XVIII.30) and (XVIII.31) by $W_{\text{exc}}^{(\lambda)}$ and $W^{(\lambda)}$ respectively. We also introduce the average potential $X^{(\lambda)}$ created by the electron in the state $|\lambda\rangle$:

$$X^{(\lambda)}(q) = \int |u_\lambda(q')|^2\, w(q, q')\, \mathrm{d}q'. \tag{XVIII.32}$$

$W^{(\lambda)}$ is the average potential created by the electrons situated in the $(Z-1)$ other occupied states, while W is the average potential created by all of the electrons:

$$W(q) = W^{(\lambda)}(q) + X^{(\lambda)}(q).$$

The equation of system (II) relating to the state λ can now be put in the form

$$\left[-\frac{\hbar^2}{2m}\Delta + V(q)\right] u_\lambda(q) + W^{(\lambda)}(q)\, u_\lambda(q) - \int W_{\text{exc}}^{(\lambda)}(q, q')\, u_\lambda(q')\, \mathrm{d}q' = e_\lambda\, u_\lambda(q) \tag{III}$$
$$(\lambda = \alpha, \beta, \dots, \zeta)$$

since $W^{(\lambda)}(q)\, u_\lambda(q)$ differs from $W(q)\, u_\lambda(q)$ by the "self-energy term" $X^{(\lambda)}(q)\, u_\lambda(q)$, and further,

$$\int W_{\text{exc}}^{(\lambda)}(q, q')\, u_\lambda(q')\, \mathrm{d}q' = \int W_{\text{exc}}(q, q')\, u_\lambda(q')\, \mathrm{d}q' - X^{(\lambda)}(q)\, u_\lambda(q).$$

In the form (III), the "Schrödinger equation" for the electron in the state λ is easily interpreted. The Hamiltonian represents the energy of the electron in the field consisting of the field of the nucleus and the average field of the other electrons. It is made up of four terms, the kinetic energy $-\hbar^2\Delta/2m$, the nuclear potential $V(q)$, the average potential $W^{(\lambda)}(q)$ from the presence of the $(Z-1)$ other electrons, and a fourth term, also due to the other electrons, representing the *exchange effect* between the state λ and the $(Z-1)$ other occupied states. We see that the exchange effect leads to a non-local potential defined by the kernel $W^{(\lambda)}_{\text{exc}}(q, q')$.

This interpretation suggests that the eigenvalue e_λ represents the energy of the electron in the state λ. The Z quantities $e_\alpha, e_\beta, \ldots, e_\zeta$ given by the Fock–Dirac equations do in fact represent to a good approximation the *ionization energy* of the Z electrons of the atom. It is to be observed, however, that the sum of these individual energies does not represent the total energy of the system of Z electrons. In summing the individual energies, we count once their kinetic energy, once their energy of interaction with the nucleus, but twice their energy of mutual interaction; to obtain the total energy, we must therefore subtract the average value of the mutual-interaction energy, that is, the quantity $\langle H_2 \rangle$. This result has already been obtained above [eq. (XVIII.27)].

11. The Hartree Equations

If one neglects the exchange terms in system (III), one obtains a much simpler set of equations:

$$\left[-\frac{\hbar^2}{2m}\Delta + V(q) + W^{(\lambda)}(q)\right] u_\lambda(q) = e_\lambda u_\lambda(q) \qquad \text{(IV)}$$
$$(\lambda = \alpha, \beta, \ldots, \zeta).$$

These equations, proposed by Hartree in virtue of intuitive arguments alone, can also be obtained by the variational method if we take a simple product of individual kets like the $|\hat{\Phi}\rangle$ of equation (XVIII.19) as the trial function, rather than the antisymmetrized product $|\Phi\rangle$ of equation (XVIII.17) [1].

The Hartree system, like the Fock–Dirac, can be solved by iteration. Owing to the absence of exchange terms, the calculations are considerably shorter. However, this system is less symmetrical than the

---

[1]) This does not constitute a valid justification of these equations, since unlike the kets $|\Phi\rangle$, the $|\hat{\Phi}\rangle$ do not belong to the space of the ket vectors of the system.

Fock–Dirac since the Hartree Hamiltonian, $h + W^{(\lambda)}$, is not the same for all of the individual states. This results in the eigensolutions of the Z Hartree equations not being mutually orthogonal, and leads to some difficulties in the application of the method. These difficulties will not be discussed here.

III. THE STRUCTURE OF MOLECULES

12. Generalities. Separation of the Electronic and Nuclear Motions

A molecule is a bound state of several atoms, and therefore consists of a certain number of atomic nuclei with electrons circulating about them. To find the stationary states of such a complex system is a very difficult problem. It has, however, a simplifying feature: *the mass of the electrons is much smaller than the mass of the nuclei* while the forces to which they are subjected are of comparable magnitude. As a consequence, the motion of the nuclei is very much slower than that of the electrons, and, to a very good approximation, these two motions, electronic and nuclear, can be treated separately. Indeed, in a first approximation the electrons "see" the nuclei as fixed force centers and their dynamical state is that of a system of electrons circulating about fixed nuclei. Since the latter move slowly, the dynamical state of the electrons adiabatically follows this gradual evolution in the potential to which they are subject (cf. Chapter XVII, section II). Conversely, since the electrons describe many revolutions during any appreciable displacement of the nuclei, the latter are essentially subject to only the average effect. The motion of nuclei is obtained to a very good approximation by replacing their interaction with electrons by its average value over several electron revolutions. Application of this procedure leads to a Schrödinger equation in which the electron variables have completely disappeared. The approximation upon which this method of separation of variables is based is called the *adiabatic approximation*.

The object of this section is to give an outline of the method and to discuss the conditions for its validity. We first complete the foregoing discussion with a semi-classical analysis of the nuclear motion, and by a rough evaluation of the different effects.

The potential in the Schrödinger equation for the nuclei depends only on the mutual distances of the latter. Since the molecule exists, this potential must have a minimum for certain well-defined, finite values of the internuclear distances: this minimum corresponds to the point of stable equilibrium of the system about which the nuclei can make small oscillations. To these internal *vibrations* of the nuclei are superposed motions of *translation* and *rotation* of the system as a whole. The translational motion can be completely separated from the others by the introduction of the center of mass, which moves like a free particle whose mass equals the total mass of the system. In what follows we shall suppose this separation made, and consider only the vibrational and rotational motion of the nuclei.

Denote by m the mass of the electron, by M a mass of the order of magnitude of the nuclear masses, and by a the average mutual distance of the nuclei in the molecule. One has, roughly [1]):

$$a \simeq 10^{-8}\text{ cm} \qquad m/M \simeq 10^{-3}\text{–}10^{-5}. \tag{XVIII.33}$$

The linear dimensions of the molecule being of the order of a, this quantity gives the order of magnitude of the amplitude of the electronic motion. According to the uncertainty relations, the momentum of the electrons is of the order of $\hbar/a$, which corresponds to a kinetic energy of about $\hbar^2/ma^2$. This last mentioned quantity gives an order of magnitude for the binding energy of the ground state of the electrons and also an order of magnitude for the separation of the electronic levels:

$$\varepsilon_{\text{el}} \simeq \hbar^2/ma^2 \tag{XVIII.34}$$

(compare this evaluation with that of § XI.3).

As for the motion of the nuclei, we first consider their rotations. The moment of inertia of the system is of the order of Ma^2. Since the square of the angular momentum varies by quanta of the order of $\hbar^2$, the rotational energy will vary by quanta of the order of

$$\varepsilon_{\text{rot}} \simeq \hbar^2/Ma^2. \tag{XVIII.35}$$

In a first approximation, the vibrations can be considered as harmonic vibrations of quanta $\varepsilon_{\text{vib}} = \hbar\omega$. We take the zero of potential energy at the position of stable equilibrium of the nuclei. If one of the nuclei is removed a distance a, the system acquires a potential energy $\frac{1}{2}M\omega^2 a^2$; but, since this amounts to completely separating one

---

[1]) The mass ratio is the least favourable for the hydrogen molecule. In that case:

$$(m/M)_{\text{H}_2} \simeq 0.5 \times 10^{-3}.$$

of the atoms from the rest, and therefore to an increase in the energy of the order of ε_{el}, we have

$$M\omega^2 a^2 \simeq \hbar^2/ma^2$$

and therefore,

$$\varepsilon_{\text{vib}} \simeq \hbar^2/(mM)^{\frac{1}{2}}\, a^2. \qquad \text{(XVIII.36)}$$

Comparison of (XVIII.34–36) leads to:

$$\varepsilon_{\text{rot}} \ll \varepsilon_{\text{vib}} \ll \varepsilon_{\text{el}}.$$

In a more precise way, if we follow Born and Oppenheimer [1]) and introduce the parameter

$$\varkappa = (m/M)^{\frac{1}{4}}, \qquad \text{(XVIII.37)}$$

we find

$$\varepsilon_{\text{rot}} \simeq \varkappa^2\, \varepsilon_{\text{vib}} \simeq \varkappa^4\, \varepsilon_{\text{el}}. \qquad \text{(XVIII.38)}$$

Now a level separation ε is associated with a classical frequency $\varepsilon/\hbar$. We can therefore conclude that the motion of the electrons is more rapid than the vibrational motion of the nuclei, itself more rapid than the rotational motion of the ensemble, in agreement with the remarks at the beginning of this paragraph. The ratio of the frequencies of these different motions is of the order of $\varkappa^2$, i.e. about 0.01: during a complete revolution of the whole molecule the nuclei make about 100 oscillations about their equilibrium positions and the electrons effect about 10 000 revolutions.

13. Motion of the Electrons in the Presence of Fixed Nuclei

Keeping in mind the semi-classical discussion of the preceding paragraph, we now consider the problem of finding the stationary states of the molecule. Since our purpose is to give more an outline than a detailed account, we shall not hesitate to make simplifying assumptions when they do not affect the principle of the method. In particular we shall treat the electrons and the nuclei as spinless particles.

We label the degrees of freedom of the electrons and of the nuclei with the indices i and j respectively. We denote by x_i and X_j the coordinates of the electrons and of the nuclei respectively and by

[1]) M. Born and J. R. Oppenheimer, Ann. der Phys. 84 (1927) 457; with regard to the original theory of Born and Oppenheimer, see § 16.

M_j the mass of the nucleus of coordinate X_j. We denote by T_e the kinetic energy of the electrons, by T_N that of the nuclei, and by V the interaction potential between the various particles in the molecule. The molecular Hamiltonian H is the sum of these three terms:

$$H = T_\mathrm{N} + T_\mathrm{e} + V. \qquad \text{(XVIII.39)}$$

We have:

$$T_\mathrm{N} = -\sum_j \frac{\hbar^2}{2M_j} \frac{\partial^2}{\partial X_j{}^2}, \qquad T_\mathrm{e} = -\sum_i \frac{\hbar^2}{2m} \frac{\partial^2}{\partial x_i{}^2} \qquad \text{(XVIII.39')}$$

$V \equiv V(x, X)$ is a certain function of the electron and nuclear coordinates – it is the sum of the Coulomb interactions of each pair of particles in the system.

Consider the simpler Hamiltonian

$$H^{(0)} = T_\mathrm{e} + V \qquad \text{(XVIII.40)}$$

obtained by neglecting the kinetic energy of the nuclei in (XVIII.39). $H^{(0)}$ is the Hamiltonian of the system in the limit when $M_j \to \infty$, and its stationary states are those of a system of electrons in the presence of fixed nuclei. Indeed, since $H^{(0)}$ contains no derivatives with respect to the X_j,

$$[X_j, H^{(0)}] = 0,$$

and therefore $H^{(0)}$ and the X_j can simultaneously be diagonalized. In other words, to solve the eigenvalue problem for $H^{(0)}$, we can assign definite values X_j' to the nuclear position coordinates, and look for the eigenvectors of $H^{(0)}$ among the eigenvectors corresponding to these particular values of the X_j. Denote a given set of the X_j' by the symbol X'. To each set X' there corresponds a set of eigenvalues $W_n(X')$ of $H^{(0)}$ labelled by the quantum number n. For a given n and X' there will be one or several linear independent eigenvectors, which in the latter case we may distinguish one from another by an additional index, s say. Thus the Schrödinger equation for $H^{(0)}$ takes the form

$$H^{(0)}|nsX'\rangle = W_n(X')|nsX'\rangle. \qquad \text{(XVIII.41)}$$

In the $\{xX\}$ representation, the eigenvector $|nsX'\rangle$ is represented by the wave function

$$\varphi_{ns}(x, X')\, \delta(X - X') \qquad \text{(XVIII.42)}$$

and the function φ is the solution of the Schrödinger equation

$$[T_e + V(x, X')]\, \varphi_{ns}(x, X') = W_n(X')\, \varphi_{ns}(x, X'). \quad \text{(XVIII.43)}$$

In (XVIII.43), X' plays the role of a simple parameter, and we have the Schrödinger equation for the electrons of the molecule when the positions of the nuclei are fixed at X'. To each solution of this equation there corresponds an eigenfunction of $H^{(0)}$ of the form (XVIII.42), and all the solutions of (XVIII.43) for all possible values of X' constitute a complete set of eigenfunctions of $H^{(0)}$. Normalization being important in what follows, we shall always take orthonormal eigenfunctions, which will automatically be the case if $\varphi_{ns}(x, X')$, considered as a function of the x alone, has a norm equal to 1.

The eigenvalue problem (XVIII.43) is analogous to the problem of finding the stationary states of an atom and can be solved by analogous methods, that of self-consistent fields for example. In the present case however there are several centers of force, and the symmetry of atomic problems is thereby largely, if not totally, destroyed.

Let us briefly discuss this question of symmetry [1]). The potential $V(x, X)$ is invariant under translation, rotation and reflection of the whole system, and also under time reversal and permutation of the identical particles. Suppose that the positions of the nuclei are now fixed at X'. The symmetries of $V(x, X')$ considered as a function of the x alone will be those of the ones given above that leave the nuclear configuration X' unchanged. Thus in a diatomic molecule like ClH, $V(x, X')$ is invariant under rotation about the axis joining the hydrogen and chlorine nuclei, and under reflection in planes passing through that axis. With the invariance under time reversal these are the only remaining symmetries. In sufficiently complex molecules, only the invariance under time reversal remains. The symmetries of $H^{(0)}$, considered as a function of the x alone, are obviously the same as those of $V(x, X')$. The degeneracy of the level $W_n(X')$ is associated with these symmetry properties (cf. Chapter XV).

To avoid complications due to degeneracy, we shall assume that $V(x, X')$ has only the time-reversal invariance. Then, since we are

---

[1]) For a general treatment of the symmetry properties of electronic wave functions in molecules cf. L. D. Landau and E. M. Lifshitz, *Quantum Mechanics* (Pergamon Press, London, 1958).

dealing with a molecule (and not with a free radical) the number of electrons is even, and are in the first case discussed in § XV.21. Assuming further that there is no accidental degeneracy, we conclude that $W_n(X')$ is non-degenerate and we choose the phase so as to have $\varphi_n(x, X')$ real.

We conclude this paragraph with the following two remarks.

Considered as an operator acting on the variables x alone, $H^{(0)}$ is a continuous function of the parameters X', as are its eigenvalues, and also its eigenfunctions once their phases have been fixed, i.e. for a given n, $W_n(X')$ and $\varphi_n(x, X')$ are continuous functions of X'.

Considered as an operator acting on all of the variables [cf. eq. (XVIII.41)], $H^{(0)}$ is invariant with respect to the various transformations enumerated above in connection with $V(x, X)$. Therefore, any vector obtained from $|nX'\rangle$ by one of these transformations, is an eigenvector of $H^{(0)}$ belonging to the same eigenvalue $W_n(X')$. In other words, $W_n(X')$ is unchanged by the application of these transformations to the X'. In particular, $W_n(X')$ depends only on the mutual distances of the nuclei, i.e. on the geometrical figure that they form, and does not change when that figure is displaced (translation and rotation) or replaced by its image (reflection).

14. The Adiabatic Approximation

In the preceding paragraph we have considered the stationary states of the electrons when the nuclei are fixed. Suppose now that the nuclei are slowly moving according to a certain law $X'(t)$. If this motion is sufficiently slow, the dynamical state of the electrons will adiabatically follow the resulting modification of the potential in which they move: if at time t_0 they are in the state $(n, X'(t_0))$ corresponding to the level $W_n(X'(t_0))$ – i.e. the state represented by the wave function $\varphi_n(x, X'(t_0))$ – then at time t they will be in the state $(n, X'(t))$ obtained from $(n, X'(t_0))$ by continuity, n remaining fixed.

The conditions for the validity of this approximation were discussed in § XVII.13 [cf. criterion (XVII.114)]. The probability η_n of finding the electrons in a state different to (n, X') is given by

$$\eta_n \simeq \left|\frac{\alpha_n}{\omega_n}\right|^2, \qquad \text{(XVIII.44)}$$

where α_n is the "angular velocity" of the vector $\varphi_n(x, X')$ and ω_n

the minimum Bohr frequency associated with the level $W_n(X')$.

To evaluate this quantity we make use of the semi-classical analysis of § 12. The separation of the electronic levels being given by (XVIII.34), we have

$$\omega_n \simeq \varepsilon_{\text{el}}/\hbar \simeq \hbar/ma^2. \tag{XVIII.45}$$

To evaluate α_n, we first make an estimate of the norm of $\partial\varphi_n/\partial X_j'$, φ_n being by hypothesis a real function of norm 1. We know that to separate an atom from the rest of the molecule its nucleus must be removed to a distance of the order of a from its position of equilibrium; i.e. an increment of the order of $\Delta X_j' \simeq a$ is necessary to transform the function $\varphi_n(x, X')$ into a function that is orthogonal to it. It follows that $\partial\varphi_n/\partial X_j$ is roughly equal to this last-mentioned function divided by a, and its norm is of the order of $1/a^2$:

$$\int \left(\frac{\partial\varphi_n}{\partial X_j}\right)^2 \mathrm{d}x \simeq \frac{1}{a^2}. \tag{XVIII.46}$$

Now α_n^2 is by definition the norm of the (real) function $\mathrm{d}\varphi_n/\mathrm{d}t$. If $v_j = \mathrm{d}X_j'/\mathrm{d}t$ is the velocity of X_j', α_n^2 is the norm of the function $\sum_j v_j\,(\partial\varphi_n/\partial X_j)$, giving roughly

$$\alpha_n^2 \simeq \frac{1}{a^2}\sum_j v_j^2.$$

If we denote the kinetic energy of the nuclei by t_{N}, we have

$$\alpha_n^2 \simeq \frac{t_{\mathrm{N}}}{Ma^2}. \tag{XVIII.47}$$

Substituting (XVIII.45) and (XVIII.47) into (XVIII.44) we find

$$\eta_n \simeq \varkappa^4\,\frac{t_{\mathrm{N}}}{\varepsilon_{\text{el}}}. \tag{XVIII.48}$$

This semi-classical analysis can be used as a guide for finding the stationary states of the molecule. Consider then the eigenvalue problem for the Hamiltonian H. From (XVIII.39) and (XVIII.40),

$$H = H^{(0)} + T_{\mathrm{N}}. \tag{XVIII.49}$$

If the term for the kinetic energy of the nuclei, T_{N}, could be neglected, the molecular Hamiltonian would reduce to $H^{(0)}$, and each stationary state $|nX'\rangle$ would correspond to a definite electronic quantum number n, and a definite arrangement of the nuclei X'. The nuclei would remain fixed at X' and the motion of the electrons would be represented by the function $\varphi_n(x, X')$. T_{N} couples the eigenvectors of $H^{(0)}$ corresponding to neighbouring X'.

In the adiabatic approximation, one neglects the coupling between vectors with different electronic quantum numbers, and one assumes n to be a good quantum number:

$$n \simeq Cst. \tag{XVIII.50}$$

The eigenvectors of H are then linear combinations of $|nX'\rangle$ corresponding to a definite value of n, hence of the form

$$\int |nX'\rangle\, \psi(X')\, \mathrm{d}X', \tag{XVIII.51}$$

where $\psi(X')$ is an arbitrary function of the X'. In the $\{x, X\}$ representation, such vectors are represented by wave functions of the form

$$\Phi_n(x, X) \equiv \varphi_n(x, X)\, \psi(X). \tag{XVIII.52}$$

We can obtain the eigenfunctions of H in this approximation by *application of the variational method with $\Phi_n(x, X)$ as the trial function.* We have here a case where the trial function varies in a subspace of state-vector space, namely the space $\mathscr{E}_n$ of vectors of the form (XVIII.51). We know (§ 3) that the method then leads to an eigenvalue equation in this subspace [eq. (XVIII.9)]. In the present case, one obtains a Schrödinger equation for the unknown function $\psi(X)$. The Hamiltonian of this equation, which we denote by H_n, is the projection of H onto $\mathscr{E}_n$; it acts only on the dynamical variables of the nuclei. The eigenvalues of H_n are the molecular energy levels relative to the electronic quantum number n.

The error being made can be evaluated on the basis of the discussion of the beginning of this paragraph. Let Φ_n be a particular one of our approximate solutions, and Ψ_n the corresponding exact solution. They are both supposed normalized to unity. The difference

$$\delta\Psi \equiv \Psi_n - \Phi_n$$

represents the deviation of the exact solution from the adiabatic limit. It is a vector essentially outside the subspace $\mathscr{E}_n$, whose norm is equal to the quantity η_n defined above. Thus, with the aid of (XVIII.48),

$$\iint |\delta\Psi|^2 \, \mathrm{d}x \, \mathrm{d}X \simeq \varkappa^4 \left\langle \frac{T_\mathrm{N}}{\varepsilon_\mathrm{el}} \right\rangle \simeq \varkappa^4 \frac{\varepsilon_\mathrm{vib}}{\varepsilon_\mathrm{el}} \simeq \varkappa^6.$$

In other words, we have roughly

$$\delta\Psi \simeq \varkappa^3 \, \Phi', \tag{XVIII.53}$$

where Φ' is a function orthogonal to the space $\mathscr{E}_n$ and of norm 1. Since the functional

$$E[\Psi] \equiv \frac{\langle\Psi|H|\Psi\rangle}{\langle\Psi|\Psi\rangle}$$

is stationary about the solution Ψ_n, the calculation of the energy with the function Φ_n involves an error of the second order with respect to the variation $\delta\Psi$, i.e.,

$$\begin{aligned}\delta E &\simeq \langle\delta\Psi|H|\delta\Psi\rangle = \varkappa^6 \, \langle\Phi'|H|\Phi'\rangle \\ &\simeq \varkappa^6 \, \varepsilon_\mathrm{el}.\end{aligned}$$

Comparing with (XVIII.38),

$$\delta E/\varepsilon_\mathrm{rot} \simeq \varkappa^2 \qquad (\simeq 10^{-2} \ll 1). \tag{XVIII.54}$$

Thus, the adiabatic approximation introduces an error of order $\varkappa^3$ in the determination of the molecular wave function [eq. (XVIII.53)] and an error in the determination of the energy that is $\varkappa^2$ times smaller than the separation of the rotational levels [eq. (XVIII.54)].

15. Hamiltonian for the Nuclei in the Adiabatic Approximation

By applying the variational method, we shall now determine the "Schrödinger equation" for the function $\psi(X)$.

We recall that $\varphi_n(x, X)$ is the real solution of equation (XVIII.43) whose norm with respect to integration over the x is equal to 1:

$$\varphi_n{}^*(x, X) = \varphi_n(x, X) \tag{XVIII.55}$$

$$\int \varphi_n{}^2(x, X) \, \mathrm{d}x = 1. \tag{XVIII.56}$$

φ_n, being a continuous function of the X, is thus defined up to a sign, which may be arbitrarily fixed. The following equations, obtained by differentiating (XVIII.56), will be of use in what follows:

$$\int \varphi_n \frac{\partial \varphi_n}{\partial X_j} \,\mathrm{d}x = 0. \qquad \text{(XVIII.56')}$$

$$\int \varphi_n \frac{\partial^2 \varphi_n}{\partial X_j^2} \,\mathrm{d}x = - \int \left(\frac{\partial \varphi_n}{\partial X_j}\right)^2 \mathrm{d}x. \qquad \text{(XVIII.56'')}$$

The function $\psi(X)$ is an arbitrary, square-integrable function of the coordinates X.

The domain of variation of the trial function being thus specified, we now propose to put the functional $E[\Phi_n]$ in the form of a functional of $\psi(X)$. From the properties of φ_n one easily obtains:

$$\langle \Phi_n | \Phi_n \rangle \equiv \iint |\Phi_n|^2 \,\mathrm{d}x \,\mathrm{d}X = \int |\psi|^2 \,\mathrm{d}X. \qquad \text{(XVIII.57)}$$

One may also write

$$\langle \Phi_n | H | \Phi_n \rangle \equiv \iint \Phi_n^* (H \Phi_n) \,\mathrm{d}x \,\mathrm{d}X = \int \psi^* (H_n \psi) \,\mathrm{d}X \qquad \text{(XVIII.58)}$$

if one agrees to put

$$H_n \psi \equiv \int \varphi_n(x, X) \,[H \varphi_n(x, X)\, \psi(X)] \,\mathrm{d}x. \qquad \text{(XVIII.59)}$$

Consequently,

$$E[\Phi_n] = \frac{\int \psi^* (H_n \psi) \,\mathrm{d}X}{\int |\psi|^2 \,\mathrm{d}X}. \qquad \text{(XVIII.60)}$$

Identity (XVIII.59) is the defining relation for a certain operator H_n of $\psi(X)$ space. It is clearly a linear operator and also can be shown to be Hermitean (as will be verified below). In the adiabatic approximation, the eigenfunctions of the molecular Schrödinger equation are those for which $E[\Phi_n]$ is stationary with respect to variations of $\psi(X)$. According to (XVIII.60), these are the solutions of the eigenvalue equation

$$H_n \psi = E \psi. \qquad \text{(XVIII.61)}$$

This is the required "Schrödinger equation".

The molecular energy levels corresponding to the electronic quantum number n are the eigenvalues of H_n. The corresponding eigenfunctions are the Φ_n obtained by substituting for $\psi(X)$ in (XVIII.52) the corresponding solution (or solutions) of the Schrödinger equation (XVIII.61).

Making use of the properties of the φ_n we can carry out many of the integrations in (XVIII.59) and obtain a more workable expression for H_n.

From (XVIII.43)

$$H^{(0)}\,\varphi_n(x, X)\,\psi(X) = W_n(X)\,\varphi_n(x, X)\,\psi(X);$$

from which, with the aid of (XVIII.56),

$$\int \varphi_n[H^{(0)}\,\varphi_n\,\psi]\,\mathrm{d}x = W_n(X)\,\psi(X). \qquad \text{(XVIII.62)}$$

From expression (XVIII.39′) for the kinetic energy of the nuclei one has

$$T_{\mathrm{N}}\,\varphi_n\,\psi = \textstyle\sum_j \left(\dfrac{-\hbar^2}{2M_j}\right)\left[\varphi_n\,\dfrac{\partial^2\psi}{\partial X_j^2} + 2\,\dfrac{\partial\varphi_n}{\partial X_j}\,\dfrac{\partial\psi}{\partial X_j} + \dfrac{\partial^2\varphi_n}{\partial X_j^2}\,\psi\right],$$

from which one may calculate

$$\int \varphi_n(T_{\mathrm{N}}\,\varphi_n\,\psi)\,\mathrm{d}x$$

by multiplying both sides by $\varphi_n(x, X)$ and integrating over x. We separately consider the contributions from the three terms in the bracket on the right-hand side. Using (XVIII.56) we immediately have that the contribution of the first term is simply.

$$T_{\mathrm{N}}\,\psi \equiv \textstyle\sum_j \left(\dfrac{-\hbar^2}{2M_j}\right)\dfrac{\partial^2\psi}{\partial X_j^2}. \qquad \text{(XVIII.63)}$$

The contribution of the second term vanishes because of (XVIII.56′). That of the third term is the product of ψ by a certain function $W_n'(X)$ that with the aid of (XVIII.56″) can be written in the form

$$W_n'(X) = \textstyle\sum_j \dfrac{\hbar^2}{2M_j}\displaystyle\int \left(\frac{\partial\varphi_n}{\partial X_j}\right)^2 \mathrm{d}x. \qquad \text{(XVIII.64)}$$

Thus, finally

$$\int \varphi_n(T_{\mathrm{N}}\,\varphi_n\,\psi)\,\mathrm{d}x = (T_{\mathrm{N}} + W_n')\,\psi. \qquad \text{(XVIII.65)}$$

From the definition (XVIII.59) and equations (XVIII.49), (XVIII.62) and (XVIII.65) we have

$$H_n = T_{\mathrm{N}} + W_n' + W_n. \qquad \text{(XVIII.66)}$$

The three terms in formula (XVIII.66) are easily interpreted.

The potential energy $W_n(X)$ is the average of $H^{(0)}$, that is, it is the sum of the mutual interaction energy of the nuclei and the average value of the energy of the electrons in the quantum state n corresponding to a determined position X of the nuclei. According to the discussion of § 12, $W_n(X)$ has an absolute minimum for a certain point X_0, the point of stable equilibrium for the figure formed by the nuclei.

The other two terms come from the kinetic energy of the nucleons averaged over the dynamical state of the electrons, which gives, in addition to the kinetic energy proper, T_N, a potential energy term $W_n'(X)$. The latter [1]) constitutes a small correction to the potential W_n; substituting the estimate (XVIII.46) into expression (XVIII.64), we find

$$W_n'(X_0) \simeq \frac{\hbar^2}{Ma^2}.$$

W_n' is therefore a positive quantity of the order of magnitude of the rotational quanta.

16. The Born–Oppenheimer Method

The original treatment of molecules, due to Born and Oppenheimer [2]) differs somewhat from the variational method described above. It consists in expanding the Hamiltonian H into a power series in $\varkappa$ and solving the corresponding eigenvalue problem by the usual methods of perturbation theory.

In the preceding paragraph we denoted the position of the minimum of $W_n(X)$ by X_0. This point of equilibrium is, in fact, defined only up to a rotation since W_n is invariant in an overall rotation of the nuclei (note in passing that in general W_n' is not). More precisely, let us put $X = (\omega, \xi)$, where ω denotes the three angular variables (two for diatomic molecules) fixing the overall orientation of the nuclei and ξ the set of radial variables fixing the positions of the nuclei relative to one another; W_n depends only on the ξ, and the equilibrium position corresponds to a certain set of values for the radial variables.

Following Born and Oppenheimer, one introduces the new radial variables u defined by

$$\xi = \xi_0 + \varkappa u.$$

The u represent, in convenient units, the distance of the nuclei from their equilibrium positions. Since $\varkappa$ is roughly equal to the

---

[1]) The appearance of this term is analogous to that of the centrifugal energy term in the equations of motion of a classical system when one adopts a rotating system of reference.

[2]) *Loc. cit.*, note, p. 783.

ratio of the amplitude of vibration of the nuclei to the amplitude of the motion of the electrons, the domain of variation of the u is of the same order of magnitude as that of the x, i.e. of the order of a.

Having made this change of variable, one obtains the expansion of H in powers of $\varkappa$ by expanding the potential in H in powers of u. The term T_{N} is of order $\varkappa^2$. The expansion must be pushed to the order of $\varkappa^4$ to accurately obtain the rotational levels. If it is stopped at order $\varkappa^5$ one obtains, to within infinitesimals of higher order, the results given by the adiabatic approximation. Differences appear only when we proceed to order $\varkappa^6$ and beyond, in agreement with the order-of-magnitude analysis of § 12.

17. Notions on Diatomic Molecules

We shall not proceed any further with the general study of molecules in the adiabatic approximation. In particular, we shall not discuss the separation of vibrations and rotations; in order to perform this separation, it is convenient to somewhat modify the application of the variational method by introducing three sets of variables in place of two, namely, the angular variables fixing the orientation of the whole, the variables fixing the positions of the nuclei with respect to one another and the variables fixing the positions of the electrons with respect to the nuclei. In concluding we shall limit ourselves to a few summary indications concerning diatomic molecules.

Once the separation of the center of mass has been effected, the dynamical variables of the two nuclei describe the relative motion of the one with respect to the other. Thus in this case the set of coordinates X reduces to the coordinates of the vector $\boldsymbol{R} = \boldsymbol{R}_1 - \boldsymbol{R}_2$ giving the position of the first nucleus with respect to the second. The coordinates of the electrons with respect to the center of mass of the nuclei will still be collectively denoted by x. Neglecting, for simplicity, the spins [1]), we denote the (orbital) angular momentum of the electrons by $\boldsymbol{L}$, that of the nuclei by $\boldsymbol{G}(\boldsymbol{G} = \boldsymbol{R} \times \boldsymbol{P})$ and the total angular momentum of the system by $\boldsymbol{K}$

$$\boldsymbol{K} = \boldsymbol{G} + \boldsymbol{L}. \tag{XVIII.67}$$

---

[1]) If the spin-orbit coupling is small as compared with the rotational quanta, the presence of the spins will not sensibly modify the results and will be reflected simply in the appearance of fine structure as in the case of LS coupling for atoms. In the opposite case, the general form of the spectrum is rather considerably modified. Cf. L. D. Landau and E. M. Lifshitz, *loc. cit.*, note, p. 785.

Finally, we denote the unit vector along the molecular axis by $\boldsymbol{u}(\boldsymbol{u}=\mathbf{R}/R)$, and label vector components along this axis with the index u. In passing, we note the operator identity

$$\boldsymbol{G}\cdot\boldsymbol{R} = 0. \tag{XVIII.68}$$

$G_u(\equiv\boldsymbol{G}\cdot\boldsymbol{u})$ is therefore identically null and we have

$$K_u = L_u.$$

For the rest we retain the notation of the preceding paragraphs.

Consider first the motion of the electrons. The symmetries of $H^{(0)}$, considered as an operator acting on the electron variables alone, are the same as those of the Stark effect: $H^{(0)}$ is invariant under rotations about $\boldsymbol{u}$ and under reflections in planes passing through $\boldsymbol{u}$. If we have two identical nuclei, $H^{(0)}$ is also invariant under reflection proper $(x \to -x)$; we leave aside this particular case for the moment.

To classify the states, we need only to refer to the discussion of the Stark-Effect in § XV.14. Each level of $H^{(0)}$ corresponds to a given eigenvalue of L_u^2. The eigenvalues of L_u^2 may be written in the form $\hbar^2\Lambda^2$, where Λ is a quantum number taking all non-negative integral values. Following spectroscopic tradition, the terms corresponding to the first three values $\Lambda=0, 1, 2$, are denoted respectively by the greek capitals Σ, Π, Δ. If $\Lambda\neq 0$, the level is doubly degenerate and we can find two corresponding eigenvectors corresponding respectively to the values $\hbar\Lambda$ and $-\hbar\Lambda$ for the component of angular momentum along the molecular axis. The Σ levels $(\Lambda=0)$ are non-degenerate; they can be put into two categories, Σ^+ and Σ^-, according as their eigenvector is invariant or changes sign under reflection in a plane passing through the axis. In the great majority of diatomic molecules, the ground state is a Σ^+ state.

We now consider the total Hamiltonian. The appearance of degeneracy in the electronic levels is a complicating factor only in appearance. It can be shown, in fact, that the coupling introduced by T_{N} between the states $\hbar\Lambda$ and $-\hbar\Lambda$ is smaller than the separation between rotational levels; it is therefore simply neglected. In other words in addition to approximation (XVIII.50) we make the second approximation $L_u = Cst$.

On the other hand, although the mode of application of the variational method employed in § 14 and § 15 is well suited to a discussion of a general nature it does not permit the separation of rotations and vibrations to be easily exhibited. The difficulty stems from the correction $W_n'(\mathbf{R})$ being generally not invariant under rotation. It is preferable to take the rotational invariance of H and $H^{(0)}$ into account from the outset and to look for the eigenvectors of H having a given total angular momentum. The eigenvectors of $H^{(0)}$ can be characterized by:

(*i*) the quantum numbers of total angular momentum K and m_K (m_K, component of $\mathbf{K}$ along a *fixed* axis in space, not to be confused with K_u);

(*ii*) the quantum numbers specifying the state of the electrons, namely n, and when $\Lambda \neq 0$, s ($s \equiv$ sign of L_u);

(*iii*) the internuclear distance R.

The Schrödinger equation (XVIII.41) then reads

$$H^{(0)}|K m_K n\, s\, R\rangle = W_n(R)|K m_K n\, s\, R\rangle. \tag{XVIII.69}$$

The adiabatic approximation consists in looking for the eigenvectors of H in the subspace of vectors corresponding to well-defined values of K, m_K, n and s, i.e. among the vectors of the form

$$\int_0^\infty |K\, m_K\, n\, s\, R\rangle\, y(R)\, \mathrm{d}R \tag{XVIII.70}$$

[to be compared with the form (XVIII.51)]. The variational method is now applied as in § 14 and § 15 and leads to a Schrödinger equation for the radial function $y(R)$ whose eigenvalues are the molecular energy-levels corresponding to quantum numbers K and n (these levels are independent of m_K and s).

The Hamiltonian h of this radial equation is obtained by the method of § 15. From $H^{(0)}$ we have the contribution $W_n(R)$. To calculate the contribution from T_{N}, the kinetic energy of the nuclei, it is convenient to write this operator in the form

$$T_{\mathrm{N}} = \frac{P_{\mathrm{R}}^2}{2M} + \frac{G^2}{2MR^2} \tag{XVIII.71}$$

(M reduced mass of the nuclei; P_{R} radial momentum) and to separately treat the two terms on the right-hand side. It is easily shown that the first term gives

$$-\frac{\hbar^2}{2M}\frac{\mathrm{d}^2}{\mathrm{d}R^2}+w_n'(R), \tag{XVIII.72}$$

where $w_n'(R)$ is a small correction independent of K, m_K and s. The contribution from the second term, representing the kinetic energy of rotation, requires a more careful examination. It is equal to the product of $\hbar^2/2MR^2$ by the average value of the operator $\mathbf{G}^2$ in the subspace of the vectors given by (XVIII.70). With the aid of (XVIII.67) we can write

$$\begin{aligned}\langle \mathbf{G}^2\rangle &= \langle(\mathbf{K}-\mathbf{L})^2\rangle \\ &= \hbar^2K(K+1)-2\langle\mathbf{K}\cdot\mathbf{L}\rangle+\langle\mathbf{L}^2\rangle.\end{aligned}$$

Since $|Km_KnsR\rangle$ is an eigenstate of L_u, the average value of the component of $\mathbf{L}$ along an axis perpendicular to $\boldsymbol{u}$ is null; hence, taking (XVIII.68) into account,

$$\langle\mathbf{K}\cdot\mathbf{L}\rangle = \langle K_u L_u\rangle = \langle L_u{}^2\rangle = \hbar^2\Lambda^2.$$

$\langle\mathbf{L}^2\rangle$, on the other hand, is a certain positive quantity depending only on n. If we put $w_n''(R)\equiv(\langle\mathbf{L}^2\rangle-2\hbar^2\Lambda^2)/2MR^2$, we obtain for the contribution of the kinetic energy of rotation the expression

$$\frac{\hbar^2K(K+1)}{2MR^2}+w_n''(R). \tag{XVIII.73}$$

The small corrections $w_n'(R)$ and $w_n''(R)$ may be incorporated in the potential $W_n(R)$. The radial Hamiltonian then becomes

$$h\equiv-\frac{\hbar^2}{2M}\frac{\mathrm{d}^2}{\mathrm{d}R^2}+\frac{\hbar^2K(K+1)}{2MR^2}+W_n(R). \tag{XVIII.74}$$

This is the Hamiltonian for a particle of mass M and angular momentum K in the potential $W_n(R)$.

Note that the possible values for the integer K depend on n. By fixing n we fix Λ, and since $K\geqslant|K_u|$,

$$K\geqslant\Lambda. \tag{XVIII.75}$$

The energy levels E are the eigenvalues of h and are obtained by solving the radial equation

$$h\,y(R)=E\,y(R).$$

For given K and n, these are the levels of a particle of mass M and angular momentum K in the potential $W_n(R)$; to distinguish them one from another we shall use another quantum number which we denote v. n is the electronic quantum number, v the vibrational quantum number, K the rotational quantum number.

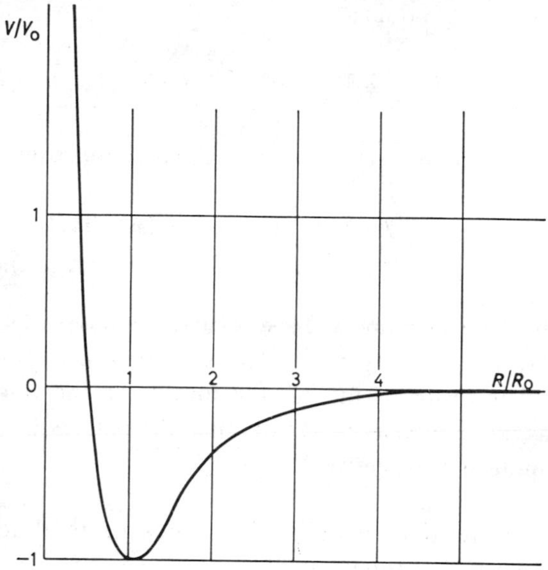

Fig. XVIII.2. The Morse potential: $V = V_0\,(e^{-2(R-R_0)/b} - 2e^{-(R-R_0)/b})$. R_0 is the equilibrium internuclear distance, V_0 the potential depth at the equilibrium position. The sharpness of the minimum varies as the smallness of the ratio b/R_0. The value adopted in the figure, $b/R_0 = 0.68$, corresponds to the hydrogen molecule.

The spectrum obtained owes its essential characteristics to the general form of $W_n(R)$; this function has a sharp minimum for a certain value R_0 of the internuclear distance corresponding to the position of stable equilibrium for the molecule. Experiment shows that $W_n(R)$ can most often be represented to a good approximation by a Morse potential about its position of equilibrium (cf. Fig. XVIII.2 and Problem XVIII.5). For the lowest levels the wave function $y(R)$ remains concentrated in a small domain about R_0 (approximate width $\varkappa R_0$) and represents vibrations of the nuclei about the point of equilibrium.

In a first (the harmonic) approximation, one can replace the R in the rotational energy term by R_0, and substitute for $W_n(R)$ the first two terms of its expansion in powers of $q \equiv R - R_0$. With the notations

$$B_n = \hbar^2/2MR_0^2, \quad W_n(R_0) = E_n, \quad W_n''(R_0) = M\omega_n^2,$$

this gives the radial equation

$$\left[-\frac{\hbar^2}{2M}\frac{\mathrm{d}^2}{\mathrm{d}q^2} + E_n + \tfrac{1}{2}M\omega_n^2 q^2 + B_n K(K+1)\right] y = E_{nvK}\, y.$$

This is the Schrödinger equation for a harmonic oscillator, so that we have

$$E_{nvK} = E_n + (v+\tfrac{1}{2})\,\hbar\omega_n + K(K+1)B_n \qquad \text{(XVIII.76)}$$
$$(v = 0, 1, 2, \ldots; \quad K = \Lambda, \Lambda+1, \Lambda+2, \ldots).$$

The energy is thus the sum of three terms: the energy of the electrons E_n, the vibrational energy $(v+\frac{1}{2})\hbar\omega_n$ and the rotational energy $K(K+1)B_n$. The order of magnitude found for the quanta $\hbar\omega_n$ and B_n confirms the analysis of § 12 and the subsequent deductions concerning molecular spectra [1]).

We shall not dwell here upon the necessary modifications of the theory due to the existence of spin.

We only mention one particularly striking effect due to spin and nuclear statistics. Since the coupling of the nuclear spins with the rest of the molecule is entirely negligible, the main effect is the existence of a spin degeneracy or multiplicity for each of the levels. The molecular eigenfunctions are of the form

$$\Psi = \Phi(\mathbf{R}, x)\,\chi(\mu_1, \mu_2)$$

and the order of degeneracy is equal to the number of linearly independent functions $\chi(\mu_1, \mu_2)$ that can be formed. If j_1 and j_2 are respectively

---

[1]) For the electronic ground state of the hydrogen atom (Σ^+ state), the first levels are accurately represented by this formula with $E_0 = -4.72$ eV, $\hbar\omega_0 = 0.54$ eV and $B_0 = 0.0074$ eV. These figures correspond to an internuclear distance: $R_0 = 0.74 \times 10^{-8}$ cm. A better representation of the vibration and rotation spectra is obtained by taking a Morse potential for $W_0(R)$ with $V_0 = 4.72$ eV, $R_0 = 0.74 \times 10^{-8}$ cm and $b = 0.68\,R_0$ (cf. Fig. XVIII.2 and Problem XVIII.5); the dissociation energy of the molecule is $V_0 - \frac{1}{2}\hbar\omega_0$.

the spins of the two nuclei, there exist in all $(2j_1+1)(2j_2+1)$ of these functions. If the two nuclei are different, there is no restriction on Ψ and the multiplicity of each level is just $(2j_1+1)(2j_2+1)$. If we have two identical nuclei of spin j $(j_1=h_2=j)$, Ψ must be symmetrical or antisymmetrical with respect to their exchange

$$(\mathbf{R} \leftrightarrow -\mathbf{R},\ \mu_1 \leftrightarrow \mu_2)$$

according as they are bosons or fermions, i.e. according as j is integral or half-integral. One can form $(j+1)(2j+1)$ symmetrical functions and $j(2j+1)$ antisymmetrical functions in the $(2j+1)^2$-dimensional space of the χ [Problem (XIII.13)]. The multiplicity g therefore depends on whether $\Psi(\mathbf{R}, x)$ is symmetrical or antisymmetrical, in other words it depends on the parity of Φ in a reflection of the nuclei alone. Denoting this parity by ϖ $(\varpi=\pm 1)$ we have

$$\begin{array}{lll} & (j \text{ integral}) & (j \text{ half-integral}) \\ g = \left\{ \begin{array}{l} \\ \\ \end{array} \right. \!\!\!\!\!\! & \begin{array}{l} (j+1)(2j+1) \\ j(2j+1) \end{array} & \begin{array}{ll} j(2j+1) & \text{if} \quad \varpi = +1 \\ (j+1)(2j+1) & \text{if} \quad \varpi = -1. \end{array} \end{array}$$

The interesting effect is due to the fact that ϖ depends on the parity of the total orbital angular momentum. It can be shown that

$$\varpi = (-)^K \varpi_e,$$

where ϖ_e $(=\pm 1)$ depends on the behavior under reflection of the electronic wave function corresponding to Φ. If $\Lambda \neq 0$ each level has two corresponding wave functions of opposite ϖ_e. For the Σ levels $(\Lambda=0)$ we have on the contrary only one electronic wave function, ϖ_e has a well-defined value, $+1$ or -1, and the multiplicity g varies in a characteristic manner from one rotational level to another [1]).

These features of the energy spectrum of the Σ levels of homonuclear diatomic molecules show up clearly in the "band spectra" of these molecules. Since the probabilities for optical transitions between states with different spin functions are very small, the transitions observed in practice all conserve the parity of K. In addition, under the usual conditions of observation the relative intensity of rays corresponding to even values of K and rays corre-

[1]) In particular, if $j = 0$ the levels with $\varpi = -1$ are absent and K can take only values of well-defined parity.

sponding to odd values of K is directly related to the ratio of the multiplicities calculated above, either $(j+1)/j$ or $j/(j+1)$ according to the sign of ϖ_e and according as the nuclei are bosons or fermions. This provides a particularly direct method for measuring nuclear spins.

EXERCISES AND PROBLEMS

1. E_0 and Ψ_0 are the ground-state energy and wave function respectively of a given quantum system. A variational calculation gives the energy E_{var} and the wave function Ψ_{var}. Ψ_0 and Ψ_{var} being supposed normalized to unity, we put $\varepsilon = 1-|\langle\Psi_0|\Psi_{\text{var}}\rangle|^2$. ε is the norm of the projection of Ψ_{var} onto the subspace orthogonal to Ψ_0, and is a measure of the square of the distance from the state Ψ_{var} to the state Ψ_0. Prove that

$$E_{\text{var}} - E_0 \geqslant \varepsilon(E_1 - E_0)$$

(E_1 energy of the first excited level). Verify that it is satisfied by the results of § 4. Discuss.

2. Supposing the ground-state wave function for the hydrogen atom known, calculate the level of the first excited state by taking as trial function that part of $u = \varrho\, \mathrm{e}^{-b\varrho}$ which is orthogonal to the ground-state wave function (notation of § 4). Compare with the exact eigenvalue and eigenfunction. Discuss.

3. Prove inequalities (XVIII.11) and (XVIII.12).

4. Taking the trial function $u = \varrho^{l+1}\, \mathrm{e}^{-b\varrho}$ (notation of § 4) calculate the lowest hydrogen atom level corresponding to angular momentum l. Compare with the exact results and comment.

5. Consider a particle in one dimension of mass M in the potential

$$V(q) = V_0[\mathrm{e}^{-2q/b} - 2\mathrm{e}^{-q/b}]$$

(*the Morse potential*). Determine the corresponding wave functions and energy levels.

N.B. The wave equation is taken over into a Laplace equation by the following changes of function and variable

$$\xi = 2K_0\, b\, \mathrm{e}^{-q/b}, \qquad w(\xi) = \mathrm{e}^{\frac{1}{2}\xi}\, \xi^{-\varkappa b}\, \psi(q),$$

where

$$K_0 = \sqrt{2MV_0}/\hbar \qquad \varkappa = \sqrt{-2ME}/\hbar.$$

We find a finite number of discrete levels depending on the index n in accordance with the formula:

$$E_n = -V_0\left(1 - \frac{n+\frac{1}{2}}{K_0\, b}\right)^2 \qquad (0 \leqslant n \leqslant K_0\, b - \tfrac{1}{2}).$$

CHAPTER XIX

COLLISION THEORY

1. Introduction

Up to the present, we have considered only the simplest collision problems, namely the scattering of an elementary particle by a potential (and notably by a central potential) and the mutual scattering of two elementary particles, the second problem reducing to the first when the relative and center-of-mass motions are separated. The treatment of this type of problem was described in Chapter X, and was complemented by a treatment of Coulomb scattering (Ch. XI, Section II) and of the mutual scattering of two identical particles (§ XIV.9–10). In addition, in § XVII.5 we obtained a particularly simple expression for the scattering of a particle by a potential $V(\boldsymbol{r})$ by treating $V(\boldsymbol{r})$ as a perturbation and considering only the first-order effect [eq. (XVII.54)]. However, the work of § XVII.5 is based on a somewhat questionable definition of the cross section and it is worth giving a rigorous derivation of this formula.

The object of this chapter is, on the one hand, to set up a formalism in which we can treat collisions between complex particles, and on the other, to extend the perturbation and variational methods of the preceding chapters to the calculation of collision cross sections.

These problems may be approached in two different ways. The first consists in giving a rigorous justification of the definition of § XVII.5 equating cross sections with probabilities per unit time and per unit incident flux, and then relating these quantities to the matrix elements of the evolution operator $U(t, t')$ in the limit when $t \to +\infty$ and $t' \to -\infty$. The second is a simple generalization of the treatment of Chapter X (Section I) in which the cross sections are directly related to the asymptotic behavior of the stationary solutions of the Schrödinger equation. It is the second of these clearly equivalent procedures that we adopt in the present chapter [1]).

[1]) For an account of the first approach, see B. Lippman and J. Schwinger, Phys. Rev. **79** (1949) 469 or M. Gell–Mann and M. L. Goldberger, Phys. Rev. **91** (1953) 398. The definitions of cross sections in both of these accounts are somewhat questionable: a discussion of this point and the possible remedies is given by S. Sunakawa, Prog. Theor. Phys. **14** (1955) 175.

This chapter has in all five sections. The first two are devoted to establishing the formalism and describing the perturbation method in the simple case of a particle in a potential $V(\mathbf{r})$. This is extended to complex collisions in Section III. Section IV is devoted to variational methods. In Section V we give a certain number of properties of the collision amplitudes that follow directly from general properties of the Hamiltonian such as Hermiticity, time-reversal invariance and other invariance properties.

I. FREE WAVE GREEN'S FUNCTION AND THE BORN APPROXIMATION

2. Integral Representations of the Scattering Amplitude

In this and the following sections we shall discuss the scattering of a particle of mass m by a potential $V(\mathbf{r})$. We denote the kinetic energy operator by H_0 and the total Hamiltonian by H:

$$H_0 \equiv -\frac{\hbar^2}{2m}\Delta \tag{XIX.1}$$

$$H \equiv -\frac{\hbar^2}{2m}\Delta + V(\mathbf{r}). \tag{XIX.2}$$

We shall suppose that the potential V tends asymptotically to 0 more rapidly than $1/r$. Potentials with the $1/r$ behavior will briefly be examined in § 15.

In what follows we shall introduce various types of waves which we wish to distinguish with suitable notations. The letter φ will be reserved for plane waves, the letter ψ for the stationary solutions of the Hamiltonian H. For a given propagation vector $\mathbf{k}$ we can define

(i) the plane wave $\varphi_{\mathbf{k}} \equiv \mathrm{e}^{i\mathbf{k}\cdot\mathbf{r}}$

(ii) the stationary waves $\psi_{\mathbf{k}}^{(+)}$ and $\psi_{\mathbf{k}}^{(-)}$ respectively characterized by the asymptotic behavior $\mathrm{e}^{i\mathbf{k}\cdot\mathbf{r}}+$ outgoing wave and $\mathrm{e}^{i\mathbf{k}\cdot\mathbf{r}}+$ incoming wave.

In particular, if $\mathbf{k}_a$ is the propagation vector of the incident particles and E their energy $[k_a = k = (2mE)^{\frac{1}{2}}]$, then the complete stationary scattering wave function (definition of § X.3) is $\psi_{\mathbf{k}_a}^{(+)}$. This wave and the corresponding scattering amplitude $f^{(+)}_{\mathbf{k}_a}$ are determined by the conditions:

$$H\psi^{(+)}_{\mathbf{k}_a} = E\psi^{(+)}_{\mathbf{k}_a} \qquad \psi^{(+)}_{\mathbf{k}_a} \underset{r\to\infty}{\sim} \mathrm{e}^{\mathrm{i}\mathbf{k}_a\cdot\mathbf{r}} + f^{(+)}_{\mathbf{k}_a}(\Omega)\,\frac{\mathrm{e}^{\mathrm{i}kr}}{r}. \tag{XIX.3}$$

We denote by $\mathrm{d}\sigma_{a\to b}/\mathrm{d}\Omega$ the scattering cross section in the direction Ω_b. In Chapter X we showed that

$$\mathrm{d}\sigma_{a\to b}/\mathrm{d}\Omega = |f^{(+)}_{\mathbf{k}_a}(\Omega_b)|^2. \tag{XIX.4}$$

Let $\mathbf{k}_b$ be a vector of length k pointing in the direction Ω_b. Throughout this section the only stationary waves to appear will be those defined by the vectors $\mathbf{k}_a$ and $\mathbf{k}_b$ so we shall simplify the writing by systematically replacing the indices $\mathbf{k}_a$ and $\mathbf{k}_b$ by a and b respectively.

We begin by establishing a very general property of the scattering amplitudes. Consider two potentials $U(\mathbf{r})$ and $\hat{U}(\mathbf{r})$ and denote by ξ and $\hat{\xi}$ the respective stationary solutions of the corresponding Hamiltonians. We are especially interested in the solutions $\hat{\xi}_b{}^{(-)}$ and $\xi_a{}^{(+)}$:

$$\left[-\frac{\hbar^2}{2m}\Delta + \hat{U}\right]\hat{\xi}_b{}^{(-)} = E\,\hat{\xi}_b{}^{(-)} \tag{XIX.5}$$

$$\left[-\frac{\hbar^2}{2m}\Delta + U\right]\xi_a{}^{(+)} = E\,\xi_a{}^{(+)} \tag{XIX.6}$$

$$\hat{\xi}_b{}^{(-)} \underset{r\to\infty}{\sim} \mathrm{e}^{\mathrm{i}\mathbf{k}_b\cdot\mathbf{r}} + \hat{f}_b{}^{(-)}(\Omega)\,\frac{\mathrm{e}^{-\mathrm{i}kr}}{r} \tag{XIX.7}$$

$$\xi_a{}^{(+)} \underset{r\to\infty}{\sim} \mathrm{e}^{\mathrm{i}\mathbf{k}_a\cdot\mathbf{r}} + f_a{}^{(+)}(\Omega)\,\frac{\mathrm{e}^{\mathrm{i}kr}}{r}. \tag{XIX.8}$$

It will now be shown that

$$\begin{aligned}\langle\hat{\xi}_b{}^{(-)}|(U-\hat{U})|\xi_a{}^{(+)}\rangle &\equiv \int \hat{\xi}_b{}^{(-)*}(\mathbf{r})\,[U(\mathbf{r})-\hat{U}(\mathbf{r})]\,\xi_a{}^{(+)}(\mathbf{r})\,\mathrm{d}\mathbf{r}\\ &= -\frac{2\pi\hbar^2}{m}\,[f_a{}^{(+)}(\Omega_b) - \hat{f}_b{}^{(-)*}(-\Omega_a)]\end{aligned} \tag{XIX.9}$$

(by convention, $-\Omega_a$ denotes the direction opposite to Ω_a).

The proof is analogous to the one used to obtain integral representations of the phase shifts in § X.17. There being no possibility of confusion, we shall sometimes omit the indices b and a and the symbol $\hat{}$. Multiply (XIX.6) by $\xi^{(-)*}$ and subtract the equation obtained by multiplying the complex conjugate of (XIX.5) by $\xi^{(+)}$. Since $\hat{U}$ is real, this gives

$$-\frac{\hbar^2}{2m}[\xi^{(-)*}(\Delta\xi^{(+)}) - (\Delta\xi^{(-)*})\,\xi^{(+)}] + \xi^{(-)*}(U-\hat{U})\,\xi^{(+)} = 0.$$

Integrating over the volume of a sphere of radius R centered at the origin, we get

$$\langle\xi^{(-)}|(U-\hat{U})|\xi^{(+)}\rangle = \frac{\hbar^2}{2m}\lim_{R\to\infty}\int_{r<R}[\xi^{(-)*}(\Delta\xi^{(+)}) - (\Delta\xi^{(-)*})\,\xi^{(+)}]\,\mathrm{d}\boldsymbol{r}. \qquad \text{(XIX.10)}$$

In spite of the Hermitean character of Δ, the integral on the right-hand side does not necessarily vanish in the limit since the ξ are not square-integrable functions. To calculate this integral, we use Green's theorem to transform it into a surface integral over the sphere of radius R.

If ξ_1 and ξ_2 are functions of $\boldsymbol{r}$, we shall denote the integral of the "radial Wronskian"

$$W[\xi_1, \xi_2] \equiv \xi_1\frac{\partial\xi_2}{\partial r} - \xi_2\frac{\partial\xi_1}{\partial r},$$

over the sphere by the notation $\{\xi_1, \xi_2\}$:

$$\begin{aligned}\{\xi_1, \xi_2\} &\equiv \int W[\xi_1, \xi_2]\,|_{r=R}\,R^2\,\mathrm{d}\Omega \\ &\equiv \int W[r\,\xi_1, r\,\xi_2]\,|_{r=R}\,\mathrm{d}\Omega.\end{aligned} \qquad \text{(XIX.11)}$$

Using Green's theorem,

$$\{\xi_1, \xi_2\} = \int_{r<R}[\xi_1(\Delta\xi_2)-(\Delta\xi_1)\xi_2]\,\mathrm{d}\boldsymbol{r}.$$

Equation (XIX.10) may then be written:

$$\langle\xi^{(-)}|(U-\hat{U})|\xi^{(+)}\rangle = \frac{\hbar^2}{2m}\lim_{R\to\infty}\{\xi^{(-)*}, \xi^{(+)}\}. \qquad \text{(XIX.12)}$$

The surface integral $\{\xi^{(-)*}, \xi^{(+)}\}$ tends asymptotically to a constant which may easily be determined by substituting for the ξ and their radial derivatives the first term in their asymptotic expansions in powers of $1/r$. Substituting from (XIX.7) and (XIX.8), we find:

$$\lim_{R\to\infty}\{\xi^{(-)*},\xi^{(+)}\} = \lim_{R\to\infty}\{\mathrm{e}^{-i\mathbf{k}_b\cdot\mathbf{r}},\mathrm{e}^{i\mathbf{k}_a\cdot\mathbf{r}}\} + \lim_{R\to\infty}\left\{\mathrm{e}^{-i\mathbf{k}_b\cdot\mathbf{r}}, f^{(+)}\frac{\mathrm{e}^{ikr}}{r}\right\} + \lim_{R\to\infty}\left\{f^{(-)*}\frac{\mathrm{e}^{ikr}}{r},\mathrm{e}^{i\mathbf{k}_a\cdot\mathbf{r}}\right\} + \lim_{R\to\infty}\left\{f^{(-)*}\frac{\mathrm{e}^{ikr}}{r}, f^{(+)}\frac{\mathrm{e}^{ikr}}{r}\right\}. \tag{XIX.13}$$

The asymptotic form of a plane wave is given by (Problem XIX.1):

$$\mathrm{e}^{i\mathbf{k}\cdot\mathbf{r}} \underset{r\to\infty}{\sim} \frac{2\pi}{ikr}\left[\delta(\Omega_r-\Omega_k)\,\mathrm{e}^{ikr}-\delta(\Omega_r+\Omega_k)\,\mathrm{e}^{-ikr}\right]+\mathrm{O}\left(\frac{1}{r^2}\right). \tag{XIX.14}$$

In the bracket on the right-hand side, Ω_r and Ω_k denote the directions of the vectors $\boldsymbol{r}$ and $\boldsymbol{k}$ respectively. The δ functions are defined by the property

$$\int \delta(\Omega'-\Omega)\,\varphi(\Omega')\,\mathrm{d}\Omega' = \varphi(\Omega)$$

for any function φ of the angles Ω. If we replace the plane waves in the right-hand side of (XIX.13) by their asymptotic expressions, the angular integrations are easily performed. As $\boldsymbol{k}_b$ and $\boldsymbol{k}_a$ have the same length, the first term vanishes (in agreement with the result of Problem XIX.2). In the second, the only non-vanishing contribution comes from the *incoming part* of the plane wave, and is equal to $-4\pi f^{(+)}(\Omega_b)$. The same is true for the third term, whose contribution is $4\pi f^{(-)*}(-\Omega_a)$. The fourth term is null. We have, therefore:

$$\lim_{R\to\infty}\{\xi^{(-)*},\xi^{(+)}\} = -\,4\pi[f^{(+)}(\Omega_b)-f^{(-)*}(-\Omega_a)].$$

Substituting this result in (XIX.12), we obtain relation (XIX.9). Q.E.D.

Property (XIX.9) is interesting chiefly because it is independent of the particular form of the potentials U and $\hat{U}$. It is required only that the latter be real and that they fall off asymptotically more rapidly than $1/r$.

As a first application, we take

$$U = V \qquad \hat{U} = 0.$$

Relation (XIX.9) gives:

$$\langle\varphi_b|V|\psi_a{}^{(+)}\rangle = -\frac{2\pi\hbar^2}{m}\,f_a{}^{(+)}(\Omega_b). \tag{XIX.15}$$

This integral representation of the scattering amplitude will be used in the next two paragraphs as a starting point for the Born approximation.

We next take

$$U = \hat{U} = V.$$

Since the left-hand side of (XIX.9) vanishes, the two amplitudes in the right-hand side are equal:

$$f_a^{(+)}(\Omega_b) = f_b^{(-)*}(-\Omega_a). \qquad \text{(XIX.16)}$$

Finally, let us take

$$U = 0, \qquad \hat{U} = V.$$

Relation (XIX.9) gives:

$$\langle \psi_b^{(-)} | V | \varphi_a \rangle = -\frac{2\pi\hbar^2}{m} f_b^{(-)*}(-\Omega_a). \qquad \text{(XIX.17)}$$

From (XIX.15–17) we obtain the important equality:

$$\langle \psi_b^{(-)} | V | \varphi_a \rangle = \langle \varphi_b | V | \psi_a^{(+)} \rangle. \qquad \text{(XIX.18)}$$

3. Cross Sections and the T Matrix. Microreversibility

If the scattering amplitude in (XIX.4) is replaced by its integral representation (XIX.15), we get

$$\frac{\mathrm{d}\sigma_{a\to b}}{\mathrm{d}\Omega} = \frac{m^2}{4\pi^2\hbar^4} |\langle \varphi_b | V | \psi_a^{(+)} \rangle|^2.$$

In order to have an expression resembling (XVII.54), we introduce the density of states at energy E

$$\varrho(E) = (2\pi\hbar)^{-3} p^2 (\mathrm{d}p/\mathrm{d}E) = m\hbar k/(2\pi\hbar)^3$$

in accordance with the definition of § XVII.5 [eq. (XVII.52)], and denote the initial velocity by $v = \hbar k/m$. The preceding equation then becomes [1]):

$$\frac{\mathrm{d}\sigma_{a\to b}}{\mathrm{d}\Omega} = \frac{2\pi}{\hbar v} |\langle \varphi_b | V | \psi_a^{(+)} \rangle|^2 \varrho(E). \qquad \text{(XIX.19)}$$

Since $|\psi_a^{(+)}\rangle$ and $|\varphi_b\rangle$ cannot be basis vectors in the same representa-

---

[1]) In the other formulation of collision theory (cf. reference, note, p. 801), this form follows in a natural way from the very definition of cross section.

tion, $\langle\varphi_b|V|\psi_a{}^{(+)}\rangle$ is not really a matrix element of the operator V. It is convenient to introduce a matrix T such that:

$$T_{a\to b} \equiv \langle\varphi_b|T|\varphi_a\rangle = \langle\varphi_b|V|\psi_a{}^{(+)}\rangle. \qquad \text{(XIX.20)}$$

T will be called the *transition matrix*, and the element $T_{a\to b}$ the *amplitude for the transition* $a \to b$. It is to be observed that these matrix elements are taken between plane waves of the same energy. One can obviously conceive of an operator T in Hilbert space satisfying condition (XIX.20); but it is not completely defined by this condition which merely determines certain of its matrix elements in a plane wave representation, namely the elements between waves corresponding to a specified energy. To completely define T we must also determine the matrix elements between waves corresponding to energies different to E. This will be done further on.

Formula (XIX.19) may now be written

$$\frac{\mathrm{d}\sigma_{a\to b}}{\mathrm{d}\Omega} = \frac{2\pi}{\hbar v}|T_{a\to b}|^2\,\varrho(E). \qquad \text{(XIX.19')}$$

Before going on, we mention the property of microreversibility. We label the various waves corresponding to momenta $-\boldsymbol{k}_a$ and $-\boldsymbol{k}_b$ by the indices Ka and Kb respectively. We have the obvious relation between plane waves:

$$\varphi_{-\boldsymbol{k}} = \varphi_{\boldsymbol{k}}{}^*.$$

In addition, since the Hamiltonian H is real,

$$\psi^{(\mp)}_{-\boldsymbol{k}} = \psi^{(\pm)*}_{\boldsymbol{k}}.$$

In particular

$$\varphi_a = \varphi^*_{Ka} \qquad \psi_b{}^{(-)} = \psi^{(+)*}_{Kb}$$

and, since V is real, the "matrix elements" $\langle\psi_b{}^{(-)}|V|\varphi_a\rangle$ and $\langle\varphi_{Ka}|V|\psi^{(+)}_{Kb}\rangle$ represent the same integral. Thus (XIX.18) may also be written

$$\langle\varphi_{Ka}|V|\psi^{(+)}_{Kb}\rangle = \langle\varphi_b|V|\psi_a{}^{(+)}\rangle$$

or again, from definition (XIX.20),

$$T_{Kb\to Ka} = T_{a\to b}. \qquad \text{(XIX.21)}$$

A fortiori, these two amplitudes have the same modulus. Returning to (XIX.19′), we obtain *the microreversibility property for elastic scattering* [1]:

$$\mathrm{d}\sigma_{Kb\to Ka}/\mathrm{d}\Omega = \mathrm{d}\sigma_{a\to b}/\mathrm{d}\Omega. \tag{XIX.22}$$

4. The Born Approximation

Formula (XIX.19) is *exact*. Like formula (X.2) from which it was derived, it relates the cross section to the stationary scattering solution $\psi_a^{(+)}$. In the present case the latter no longer appears in its asymptotic form but as a factor in an integral. If we replace it by an approximate solution we get an approximate expression for the cross section.

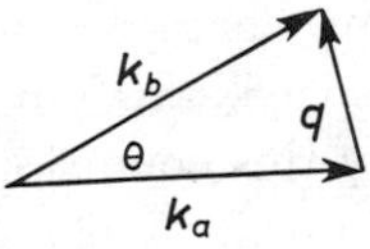

Fig. XIX.1.

In particular, for $V(\boldsymbol{r})$ sufficiently small, $\psi_a^{(+)}$ differs little from the incident plane wave φ_a, and may be replaced by the latter in the calculation of the transition amplitude. This gives the *Born approximation*:

$$T_{a\to b} \simeq T^{(\mathrm{B})}_{a\to b} = \langle \varphi_b | V | \varphi_a \rangle. \tag{XIX.23}$$

In this approximation (XIX.19) reduces to formula (XVII.54), justifying our conjecture that it gives an approximate expression for the cross section in the limit when $V(\boldsymbol{r})$ may be treated as a perturbation.

Put:

$$\boldsymbol{q} = \boldsymbol{k}_b - \boldsymbol{k}_a,$$

$\hbar \boldsymbol{q}$ is the momentum transferred to the particle in the course of the collision (Fig. XIX.1). The length of this vector depends on the scattering angle θ between the two vectors $\boldsymbol{k}_a$ and $\boldsymbol{k}_b$ as follows

$$q = 2k \sin \tfrac{1}{2}\theta \qquad (k = k_a = k_b). \tag{XIX.24}$$

From (XIX.23),

$$T^{(\mathrm{B})}_{a\to b} = \int \mathrm{e}^{-\mathrm{i}\boldsymbol{q}\cdot\boldsymbol{r}}\, V(\boldsymbol{r})\, \mathrm{d}\boldsymbol{r} \equiv \mathscr{V}(\boldsymbol{q}). \tag{XIX.25}$$

Thus in the Born approximation the scattering cross section takes the particularly simple form

$$\frac{\mathrm{d}\sigma^{(\mathrm{B})}_{a\to b}}{\mathrm{d}\Omega} = \frac{m^2}{4\pi^2\hbar^4}\, |\mathscr{V}(\boldsymbol{q})|^2. \tag{XIX.26}$$

It is proportional to the squared modulus of the Fourier component of

---

[1] For a central potential this property can also be deduced from rotational invariance. Here we see that it holds for non-central potentials as well.

$V(\boldsymbol{r})$ corresponding to the momentum transferred in the collision. Note that the dependence on energy and angle is entirely contained in the vector $\boldsymbol{q}$.

With a central potential the situation is simpler still. After integration over the angles the right-hand side of (XIX.25) becomes

$$\mathscr{V}(q) = \frac{1}{q}\int_0^\infty \sin qr\, V(r)\, r\, \mathrm{d}r. \qquad \text{(XIX.27)}$$

The differential cross section now depends only on the length $\hbar q$ of the momentum transfer. As for the total cross section σ_{tot}, if we take q as the variable of integration instead of θ, then

$$\sigma_{\text{tot}}^{(\text{B})} = \frac{m^2}{2\pi\hbar^4 k^2}\int_0^{2k} \mathscr{V}^2(q)\, q\, \mathrm{d}q. \qquad \text{(XIX.28)}$$

From these formulas, one can draw a certain number of general conclusions regarding the behavior of the cross sections at high energies. Denote the range of the potential $V(\boldsymbol{r})$ by a. Since the real function $V(\boldsymbol{r})$ takes appreciable values only in a region with linear dimensions a, its Fourier transform takes appreciable values only in a region of linear dimensions $1/a$ about the origin [1]).

The cross section is therefore relatively important only in the region $q \lesssim 1/a$. According to (XIX.24) this region corresponds to scattering angles such that

$$\sin \tfrac{1}{2}\theta \lesssim \frac{1}{2ka}.$$

At high energies ($ka \gg 1$), the scattering is *essentially concentrated in the forward direction*, in a cone with θ less than $1/ka$. These conclusions, based on the Born approximation, may be compared with the results of § X.13 for the high-energy scattering by a hard sphere.

The total cross section tends to zero like $1/E$. This result is evident from (XIX.28), whose asymptotic form is

$$\sigma_{\text{tot}}^{(\text{B})} \underset{k\to\infty}{\sim} \frac{m^2}{2\pi\hbar^4 k^2}\int_0^{\infty} \mathscr{V}^2(q)\, q\, \mathrm{d}q. \qquad \text{(XIX.29)}$$

It may be extended without difficulty to non-central potentials.

---

[1]) In the present discussion, a may be taken as a length of the order of the mean-square deviation of the distribution

$$\frac{V^2(\boldsymbol{r})}{\int V^2(\boldsymbol{r}')\, \mathrm{d}\boldsymbol{r}'}.$$

5. Integral Equation for Scattering

Up to the present, $\psi_a^{(+)}$ has been defined as a solution of the Schrödinger equation satisfying certain boundary conditions. It will now be shown that it is also the solution of a certain integral equation. With this new definition we shall be able to write $\psi_a^{(+)}$ as an expansion in powers of V and evaluate the corrections to the Born approximation.

To this end, we make use of the identity [1])

$$(\Delta + k^2)\, \frac{e^{ikr}}{r} = -\, 4\pi\delta(\mathbf{r}).$$

It follows that the function

$$\mathscr{G}(\mathbf{r}, \mathbf{r}') = -\,\frac{m}{2\pi\hbar^2}\, \frac{e^{ik|\mathbf{r}-\mathbf{r}'|}}{|\mathbf{r}-\mathbf{r}'|} \tag{XIX.30}$$

has the property

$$\frac{\hbar^2}{2m}\,(\Delta + k^2)\, \mathscr{G}(\mathbf{r}, \mathbf{r}') = \delta(\mathbf{r}-\mathbf{r}'). \tag{XIX.31}$$

$\mathscr{G}(\mathbf{r}, \mathbf{r}')$ is a free-particle Green's function for the energy $E = \hbar^2k^2/2m$. The complex conjugate function has the the same property.

The Schrödinger equation for $\psi_a^{(+)}$ may be written

$$\frac{\hbar^2}{2m}\,(\Delta + k^2)\, \psi = V\psi. \tag{XIX.32}$$

Suppose for the moment that the function $F(\mathbf{r}) \equiv V(\mathbf{r})\, \psi(\mathbf{r})$ is known. Equation (XIX.32) will then be an inhomogeneous partial differential equation for ψ. It follows from (XIX.31) that the function

$$\hat{\psi}(\mathbf{r}) \equiv \int \mathscr{G}(\mathbf{r}, \mathbf{r}')\, F(\mathbf{r}')\, d\mathbf{r}'$$

is a solution of this equation. The general solution is obtained by adding to $\hat{\psi}(\mathbf{r})$ the general solution of the homogeneous equation. In other words, if ψ obeys eq. (XIX.32), $\psi - \hat{\psi}$ is a free wave of the same energy:

$$\frac{\hbar^2}{2m}\,(\Delta + k^2)\,(\psi - \hat{\psi}) = 0 \tag{XIX.33}$$

and conversely.

---

[1]) Considered as a distribution (in the sense of Schwartz) e^{ikr}/r is differentiable in all orders. To obtain its Laplacian, we use the identity

$$\Delta(1/r) = -\, 4\pi\delta(\mathbf{r})$$

and the property

$$\Delta(fg) = (\Delta f)g + 2(\nabla f)\cdot(\nabla g) + f\Delta g.$$

To completely determine $\psi - \hat{\psi}$ we need only to find its asymptotic form. We first show that $\hat{\psi}$ tends asymptotically to an outgoing wave. Substituting in (XIX.30) the asymptotic expression

$$|\boldsymbol{r}-\boldsymbol{r}'| \equiv r\left[1 - 2\frac{\boldsymbol{r}\cdot\boldsymbol{r}'}{r^2} + \frac{r'^2}{r^2}\right]^{\frac{1}{2}} \underset{r\to\infty}{\sim} r - \frac{\boldsymbol{r}}{r}\cdot\boldsymbol{r}' + \mathrm{O}\left(\frac{r'}{r}\right),$$

we have, for $r \gg r'$,

$$\frac{\mathrm{e}^{\mathrm{i}k|\boldsymbol{r}-\boldsymbol{r}'|}}{|\boldsymbol{r}-\boldsymbol{r}'|} \underset{r\to\infty}{\sim} \frac{\mathrm{e}^{\mathrm{i}kr}}{r}\,\mathrm{e}^{-\mathrm{i}\boldsymbol{k}\cdot\boldsymbol{r}'} + \mathrm{O}\left(\frac{r'}{r}\right), \qquad \text{(XIX.34)}$$

$$(\boldsymbol{k} = k\boldsymbol{r}/r)$$

from which

$$\hat{\psi}(\boldsymbol{r}) \underset{r\to\infty}{\sim} -\frac{m}{2\pi\hbar^2}\frac{\mathrm{e}^{\mathrm{i}kr}}{r}\int \mathrm{e}^{-\mathrm{i}\boldsymbol{k}\cdot\boldsymbol{r}'}\,V(\boldsymbol{r}')\,\psi(\boldsymbol{r}')\,\mathrm{d}\boldsymbol{r}'. \qquad \text{(XIX.35)}$$

This expression is valid when r is very much larger than the range of the potential ($r \gg a$). Consequently, if the asymptotic form of ψ is given by (XIX.3), then $\psi - \hat{\psi}$ will also have the asymptotic form ($\mathrm{e}^{\mathrm{i}\boldsymbol{k}_a\cdot\boldsymbol{r}}$ + outgoing wave). Since it also satisfies eq. (XIX.33) it must be the plane wave $\mathrm{e}^{\mathrm{i}\boldsymbol{k}_a\cdot\boldsymbol{r}}$. Thus

$$\psi_a{}^{(+)} = \mathrm{e}^{\mathrm{i}\boldsymbol{k}_a\cdot\boldsymbol{r}} - \frac{m}{2\pi\hbar^2}\int \frac{\mathrm{e}^{\mathrm{i}k|\boldsymbol{r}-\boldsymbol{r}'|}}{|\boldsymbol{r}-\boldsymbol{r}'|}\,V(\boldsymbol{r}')\,\psi_a{}^{(+)}(\boldsymbol{r}')\,\mathrm{d}\boldsymbol{r}'. \qquad \text{(XIX.36)}$$

Eq. (XIX.36) is equivalent to (XIX.3). It is called the *scattering integral equation*.

With the aid of (XIX.34) the asymptotic behavior of $\psi_a{}^{(+)}$ may be read directly from the right-hand side of (XIX.36); property (XIX.15) can be proved in this way.

The preceding analysis may be repeated using in place of $\mathscr{G}(\boldsymbol{r}, \boldsymbol{r}')$ its complex conjugate $\mathscr{G}^*(\boldsymbol{r}, \boldsymbol{r}')$. The latter is also a free-particle Green's function, but corresponds to an incoming asymptotic behavior. This procedure leads to the integral equation:

$$\psi_a{}^{(-)} = \mathrm{e}^{\mathrm{i}\boldsymbol{k}_a\cdot\boldsymbol{r}} - \frac{m}{2\pi\hbar^2}\int \frac{\mathrm{e}^{-\mathrm{i}k|\boldsymbol{r}-\boldsymbol{r}'|}}{|\boldsymbol{r}-\boldsymbol{r}'|}\,V(\boldsymbol{r}')\,\psi_a{}^{(-)}(\boldsymbol{r}')\,\mathrm{d}\boldsymbol{r}'. \qquad \text{(XIX.37)}$$

6. The Born Expansion

Equations (XIX.36) and (XIX.37) can be solved by iteration. The method resembles the one used to solve eq. (XVII.13) of the time-dependent perturbation theory.

Consider eq. (XIX.36). Substituting the plane wave $e^{i\mathbf{k}_a\cdot\mathbf{r}}$ for $\psi_a^{(+)}$ in the integral on the right-hand side, we obtain

$$\psi_1^{(+)} = e^{i\mathbf{k}_a\cdot\mathbf{r}} + \int \mathscr{G}(\mathbf{r}, \mathbf{r}')\, e^{i\mathbf{k}_a\cdot\mathbf{r}'}\, d\mathbf{r}'.$$

Subsequently substituting $\psi_1^{(+)}$, we obtain

$$\psi_2^{(+)} = e^{i\mathbf{k}_a\cdot\mathbf{r}} + \int \mathscr{G}(\mathbf{r}, \mathbf{r}')\, \psi_1^{(+)}(\mathbf{r}')\, d\mathbf{r}'.$$

Substituting $\psi_2^{(+)}$, we obtain a new wave $\psi_3^{(+)}$, and so on. Under suitable conditions, the series given by this procedure converges to the exact solution $\psi_a^{(+)}$, which is then represented by an expansion in powers of V, namely

$$\psi_a^{(+)} = e^{i\mathbf{k}_a\cdot\mathbf{r}} + \sum_{n=1}^{\infty} \int K_n(\mathbf{r}, \mathbf{r}')\, e^{i\mathbf{k}_a\cdot\mathbf{r}'}\, d\mathbf{r}', \qquad \text{(XIX.38)}$$

where

$$K_n(\mathbf{r}, \mathbf{r}') = \int K_1(\mathbf{r}, \mathbf{r}'')\, K_{n-1}(\mathbf{r}'', \mathbf{r}')\, d\mathbf{r}'' \qquad (n > 1)$$
$$K_1(\mathbf{r}, \mathbf{r}') = \mathscr{G}(\mathbf{r}, \mathbf{r}')\, V(\mathbf{r}').$$

This is the *Born expansion* of the stationary scattering wave.

We can obtain an analogous expansion for $T_{a\to b}$ by substituting the above expansion of $\psi_a^{(+)}$ into the integral $\langle\varphi_b|V|\psi_a^{(+)}\rangle$. It is an expansion in powers of V and converges for V sufficiently small [1]). The Born approximation consists in keeping only the first term.

7. Validity Criterion for the Born Approximation

For the Born approximation to be justified the error made in calculating $T_{a\to b}$ by replacing $\psi_a^{(+)}$ by the plane wave φ_a must be negligible. We must therefore have the exact stationary wave differing little from the plane wave in the domain of the potential V. Putting

$$\psi'(\mathbf{r}) \equiv \psi_a^{(+)}(\mathbf{r}) - e^{i\mathbf{k}_a\cdot\mathbf{r}},$$

---

[1]) For the study of the convergence of the Born approximation see R. Jost and A. Pias, Phys. Rev. **82** (1951) 840; W. Kohn, Rev. Mod. Phys. **26** (1954) 292. The integral equation that occurs in the time-dependent perturbation method (Ch. XVII) is of the Volterra type; if $U^{(0)}$ and V were functions, and not operators, the expansion of U obtained from it by iteration would always converge; the only possible causes of divergence are due to $U^{(0)}$ and V being operators of Hilbert space. On the other hand, the integral equation with which we are concerned here is of the Fredholm type, and the Born expansion does not always converge.

we obtain the condition

$$|\psi'(\mathbf{r})| \ll 1 \tag{XIX.39}$$

(at any point $\mathbf{r}$ where V is relatively large).

We can estimate ψ' by taking the first term in its Born expansion. Taking the z axis along $\hat{\mathbf{k}}_a$ we thereby obtain after an obvious change of variable

$$\psi'(\mathbf{r}) \simeq -\frac{m}{2\pi\hbar^2}\, \mathrm{e}^{\mathrm{i}kz}\, I(\mathbf{r})$$

$$I(\mathbf{r}) \equiv \int \mathrm{e}^{\mathrm{i}k(R+Z)}\, V(\mathbf{R}+\mathbf{r})\, \mathrm{d}\mathbf{R}/R.$$

Due to the presence of k in the exponential, $|I|$ depends on the energy. However, we can obtain an energy-independent upper limit by replacing the quantity under the integral sign by its modulus:

$$|I| < \int |V(\mathbf{R}+\mathbf{r})|\, \mathrm{d}\mathbf{R}/R. \tag{XIX.40}$$

Denote the range of the potential by a [1]) and its average depth by V_0; in the relevant domain of the variable $\mathbf{r}$ this upper limit is approximately $2\pi V_0 a^2$, so that the Born approximation is justified at all energies if

$$V_0 \ll \hbar^2/ma^2. \tag{XIX.41}$$

This condition is obviously too restrictive. The integral $|I|$ attains the limit defined by (XIX.40) only for energy sufficiently low that the factor $\mathrm{e}^{\mathrm{i}k(R+Z)}$ is practically constant in the region of the potential [2]) i.e. when $ka \ll 1$. If instead we have $ka \gg 1$, this factor oscillates rapidly over the region of the potential, and the preceding evaluation is much too pessimistic. When $k \to \infty$ these oscillations become increasingly rapid and the integral $|I|$ tends to zero. We may therefore expect the Born approximation to be valid for sufficiently high energies.

The asymptotic behavior of I at high energies may be obtained by the method of stationary phases. The main contribution comes from the region surrounding the points where the oscillating phase factor is stationary, i.e. the region surrounding the half-line

---

[1]) Cf. note, p. 809.

[2]) If the sign of V is constant. To be exact, we have

$$I(\mathbf{r}) \underset{k\to 0}{\sim} \int V(\mathbf{R}+\mathbf{r})\, \mathrm{d}\mathbf{R}/R.$$

$X=Y=0$, $Z<0$. The details of the calculation will not be given here [1]). One obtains:

$$I \underset{k\to\infty}{\sim} \frac{2\pi \mathrm{i}}{k} \int_{-\infty}^{z} V(x, y, z')\, \mathrm{d}z' + \mathrm{O}(k^{-2}). \qquad \text{(XIX.42)}$$

Thus in the domain of $\boldsymbol{r}$ in which we are interested, $|I|$ is of order $2\pi V_0 a/k$ in this limit. Criterion (XIX.39) is therefore satisfied if we have

$$ka \gg 1 \qquad V_0 \ll \hbar^2 k/ma. \qquad \text{(XIX.43)}$$

In order to obtain a validity criterion for the Born approximation at intermediate energies when (XIX.41) is not satisfied, we must evaluate the integral I for each individual case. In practice, it is usually evaluated for a single suitably chosen point in the potential region, $\boldsymbol{r}=0$ say. With a central potential we find, after integration over the angles,

$$I(0) = \frac{2\pi \mathrm{i}}{k} \int_0^\infty (1-\mathrm{e}^{2\mathrm{i}kr})\, V(r)\, \mathrm{d}r,$$

in good agreement with properties (XIX.40) and (XIX.42); whence the criterion

$$\left|\int_0^\infty (1-\mathrm{e}^{2\mathrm{i}kr})\, V(r)\, \mathrm{d}r\right| \ll \hbar^2\, k/m. \qquad \text{(XIX.44)}$$

In a collision, a characteristic magnitude relating to the cross section is the *geometrical cross section* $4\pi a^2$ corresponding to the range a of the forces between the particles. When the Born approximation is valid, the total cross section is small compared to this quantity:

$$\sigma_{\text{tot}} \ll \text{geometric cross section.} \qquad \text{(XIX.45)}$$

Let us demonstrate this inequality for the two limiting cases $ka \ll 1$ and $ka \gg 1$. To this effect we make use of expression (XIX.28) for the total cross section. According to its definition [eq. (XIX.25)], the function $\mathscr{V}(q)$ is of order $(2\pi)^{3/2}\, V_0 a$ in a domain of linear dimensions $1/a$ surrounding the origin, and practically null elsewhere. Substituting these results in the right-hand side of (XIX.28), we obtain

$$\sigma_{\text{tot}}^{(\text{B})}/4\pi a^2 \approx 2\pi (V_0 m a^2/\hbar^2)^2 \qquad \text{if } ka \ll 1$$

$$\sigma_{\text{tot}}^{(\text{B})}/4\pi a^2 \approx \tfrac{1}{2}\pi (V_0 m a/\hbar^2 k)^2 \qquad \text{if } ka \gg 1.$$

---

[1]) See, for example: L. I. Schiff, Phys. Rev. **103** (1956) 443.

The conditions for the validity of the Born approximation are inequalities (XIX.41) in the first case, (XIX.43) in the second. In both cases: $\sigma_{\text{tot}}^{(B)}/4\pi a^2 \ll 1$.

Inequality (XIX.45) is a necessary, but not a sufficient condition for the validity of the Born approximation. It sometimes happens that due to resonance effects – such as the Ramsauer–Townsend effect in the scattering of slow electrons by atoms – the cross section is much smaller than the geometric cross section without the Born expansion having a rapid convergence. In actual practice, resonant effects can easily be recognized by their extreme sensitivity to variations of the incident energy. With these qualifications, inequality (XIX.45) is a most useful criterion for judging the validity of the Born approximation.

8. Elastic Scattering of Electrons by an Atom

As an application, let us consider the elastic scattering of a charged particle by an atom. In the simplified treatment to be given here the atom is treated as a distribution of electric charges, and we calculate in the Born approximation the cross section for the scattering of the charged particle in the potential created by this distribution. This method actually gives the correct cross section if we are in the region where the Born approximation is valid (see § 21). To be definite we shall suppose that the incident particle is an electron. We should then normally have to consider the exchange effect between the incident electron and the electrons of the atom, but since at energies where the Born approximation is valid this gives only a small correction, such effects will be ignored.

The atom, by hypothesis, is neutral. We denote the atomic number by Z and the density of the electrons by $\varrho(\boldsymbol{r})$:

$$\int \varrho \, \mathrm{d}\boldsymbol{r} = Z.$$

The electric potential satisfies the Poisson equation

$$\Delta\varphi = -4\pi e[Z\,\delta(\boldsymbol{r}) - \varrho(r)]. \tag{XIX.46}$$

The electron is subject to the potential

$$V(r) = -e\varphi(r),$$

which statisfies an analogous equation whose Fourier transform gives the relation

$$q^2\mathscr{V}(q) = 4\pi e^2[Z - F(q)] \tag{XIX.47}$$

between the function $\mathscr{V}(q)$ [definition (XIX.25) or (XIX.27)] and the function

$$F(q) \equiv \int \mathrm{e}^{-\mathrm{i}\mathbf{q}\cdot\mathbf{r}}\, \varrho(r)\, \mathrm{d}\mathbf{r} = q^{-1}\int_0^\infty \sin qr\, \varrho(r)\, r\mathrm{d}r. \tag{XIX.48}$$

With the aid of (XIX.47), the cross section in the Born approximation [eq. (XIX.26)] is

$$\frac{\mathrm{d}\sigma}{\mathrm{d}\Omega} = \frac{4[Z - F(q)]^2\, m^2\, e^4}{\hbar^4\, q^4}. \tag{XIX.49}$$

$F(q)$ is called the *form factor* for the electronic density. Its general form may easily be deduced from that of $\varrho(r)$. In particular, we have

$$F(0) = Z.$$

If a is the radius of the atom, i.e. the average distance of the electrons from the nucleus, the factor F has appreciable values only in the region $q \lesssim 1/a$.

If, for example, the electronic density is represented by the function

$$\varrho(r) = \frac{Z\mathrm{e}^{-r/a}}{2a^3},$$

the form factor is given by

$$F(q) = Z[1 + q^2a^2]^{-2}.$$

When $qa \gg 1$, i.e. for large scattering angles:

$$\sin \tfrac{1}{2}\theta \gg \frac{1}{2ka},$$

the form factor is practically null $[F(q) \ll Z]$ and formula (XIX.49) reduces essentially to the Rutherford formula giving the cross section for scattering by the nucleus alone: the effect of the electrons is negligible.

On the other hand, their effect becomes appreciable once $qa \lesssim 1$: the screening effect is therefore appreciable for small angles, i.e. for

$$\sin \tfrac{1}{2}\theta \lesssim \frac{1}{2ka}. \tag{XIX.50}$$

This is in agreement with the classical picture in which small scattering angles correspond to large impact parameters.

To conclude, let us examine the validity of the Born approximation.

The range of the potential is of the order of a. An estimate based on the Thomas–Fermi model gives

$$a \simeq \frac{Z^{-\frac{1}{3}}\,\hbar^2}{me^2}.$$

For the average value of the potential we may take the value at $r=a$ of the nuclear Coulomb potential:

$$V_0 \simeq \frac{Ze^2}{a}.$$

In what follows we use the familiar notations

$$v = \frac{\hbar k}{m}, \qquad \gamma = \frac{Ze^2}{\hbar v};$$

whence

$$ka = Z^{\frac{2}{3}}\,\gamma^{-1}.$$

Criterion (XIX.41) requires that $Z^{\frac{2}{3}} \ll 1$ and is therefore never realized. Hence the Born approximation is justified only for sufficiently high energies. In the high-energy domain ($ka \gg 1$), that is for $\gamma \ll Z^{\frac{2}{3}}$, criterion (XIX.43) requires $\gamma \ll 1$.

In summary, the Born approximation is justified only at energies sufficiently high that

$$\gamma \ll 1.$$

In this case the screening effect is appreciable only at very small angles, and becomes practically negligible outside the region defined by (XIX.50), i.e. outside the region

$$\theta \lesssim \gamma.$$

The form factor can be experimentally determined by making precise measurements of the angular distribution at small angles and high energies, and using formula (XIX.49) to interpret the results.

9. Central Potential. Calculation of Phase Shifts

When we have a central potential the amplitude $T_{a\to b}$ depends only on the scattering angle θ ($\cos\theta = \mathbf{k}_a \cdot \mathbf{k}_b/k^2$) and may be expanded as follows:

$$\begin{aligned} T_{a\to b} &= 16\pi^2 \textstyle\sum_{lm} T_l\, Y_l^{m*}(\widehat{\mathbf{k}}_b)\, Y_l^m(\widehat{\mathbf{k}}_a) \qquad \text{(XIX.51)} \\ &= 4\pi \textstyle\sum_l (2l+1)\, T_l\, P_l(\cos\theta). \end{aligned}$$

The coefficients T_l are easily related to the phase shifts by comparing this expansion with (X.31):

$$T_l = -\hbar^2 \mathrm{e}^{\mathrm{i}\delta_l} \sin \delta_l / 2mk. \tag{XIX.52}$$

On the other hand, expansion (XIX.51) can be directly obtained by expanding the waves φ_b and $\psi_a^{(+)}$ in the integral $\langle \varphi_b | V | \psi_a^{(+)} \rangle$ into spherical harmonics. The angular integrations are easily carried out with the aid of the orthonormality relations for the latter; the coefficients T_l appear as radial integrals. Putting

$$\psi_a^{(+)} = 4\pi \sum_{lm} \mathrm{i}^l \psi_l(r)\, Y_l^m(\hat{\mathbf{k}}_a)\, Y_l^{m*}(\hat{\mathbf{r}}), \tag{XIX.53}$$

we find:

$$T_l = \int_0^\infty j_l(kr)\, V(r)\, \psi_l(r)\, r^2\, \mathrm{d}r. \tag{XIX.54}$$

It is easily seen (Problem XIX.4) that:

$$\psi_l \underset{r\to\infty}{\sim} \mathrm{e}^{\mathrm{i}\delta_l} \sin (kr - \tfrac{1}{2} l\pi + \delta_l)/kr.$$

Comparing relations (XIX.52) and (XIX.54), we easily obtain the integral representation of $\sin \delta_l$ given in § X.17 [eq. (X.73)]; this reduces to the Born formula for the phase shifts [eq. (X.75)] in the limit when the l-wave is sufficiently close to the free wave.

From the scattering integral equation we obtain in the same way an integral equation for ψ_l. For this it is convenient to use the following expansion of the Green's function (Problem XIX.4):

$$\frac{\mathrm{e}^{\mathrm{i}k|\mathbf{r}-\mathbf{r}'|}}{|\mathbf{r}-\mathbf{r}'|} = 4\pi k \sum_{lm} j_l(kr_<)\, h_l^{(+)}(kr_>)\, Y_l^{m*}(\hat{\mathbf{r}}')\, Y_l^m(\hat{\mathbf{r}}). \tag{XIX.55}$$

In this formula $r_<$ and $r_>$ denote respectively the smaller and the larger of the two lengths r and r'. Substituting (XIX.53), (XIX.55) and the expansion of the plane wave into the integral equation (XIX.36), we obtain an integral equation for the outgoing partial wave:

$$\psi_l(r) = j_l(kr) - (2mk/\hbar^2) \int_0^\infty j_l(kr_<)\, h_l^{(+)}(kr_>)\, V(r')\, \psi_l(r')\, r'^2\, \mathrm{d}r'. \tag{XIX.56}$$

Iteration of this equation gives ψ_l as an expansion in powers of V.

10. Green's Function as an Operator. Relation to the Resolvent of H_0

In the preceding paragraphs the Green's function has appeared as a kernel in an integral equation. It may also be thought of as the matrix representative of a certain operator $G_0^{(+)}$ according to the definition:

$$\mathscr{G}(\boldsymbol{r}, \boldsymbol{r}') \equiv \langle \boldsymbol{r}|G_0^{(+)}|\boldsymbol{r}'\rangle. \qquad \text{(XIX.57)}$$

Thus, consider a vector $|u\rangle$ and denote by $u(\boldsymbol{r})$ the corresponding wave function; $u(\boldsymbol{r}) \equiv \langle \boldsymbol{r}|u\rangle$; the vector $G_0^{(+)}|u\rangle$ obtained by application of $G_0^{(+)}$ is represented by the function

$$\langle \boldsymbol{r}|G_0^{(+)}|u\rangle = \int \mathscr{G}(\boldsymbol{r}, \boldsymbol{r}')\, u(\boldsymbol{r}')\, \mathrm{d}\boldsymbol{r}'. \qquad \text{(XIX.58)}$$

We similarly define the operator $G_0^{(-)}$ by

$$\mathscr{G}^*(\boldsymbol{r}, \boldsymbol{r}') \equiv \langle \boldsymbol{r}|G_0^{(-)}|\boldsymbol{r}'\rangle. \qquad \text{(XIX.59)}$$

Since $\mathscr{G}(\boldsymbol{r}, \boldsymbol{r}')$ is symmetrical in $\boldsymbol{r}$ and $\boldsymbol{r}'$, one has

$$G_0^{(-)} = G_0^{(+)\dagger}. \qquad \text{(XIX.60)}$$

The index 0 indicates that these operators are related to the free-particle Hamiltonian H_0. The $(+)$ and $(-)$ indicate the respective asymptotic behavior, which from the asymptotic form of the Green's function [eq. (XIX.34)] is seen to be

$$\langle \boldsymbol{r}|G_0^{(\pm)}|u\rangle \underset{r\to\infty}{\sim} -\frac{m}{2\pi\hbar^2}\frac{\mathrm{e}^{\pm ikr}}{r}\int \mathrm{e}^{\mp i\boldsymbol{k}\cdot\boldsymbol{r}'}\, u(\boldsymbol{r}')\, \mathrm{d}\boldsymbol{r}'. \qquad \text{(XIX.61)}$$
$$(\boldsymbol{k} = k\boldsymbol{r}/r)$$

This result is valid for any vector $|u\rangle$ of finite norm (the latter condition guarantees the convergence of the integral on the right-hand side).

Note the extreme singularity of these operators. Unless the Fourier components of $u(\boldsymbol{r})$ relative to propagation vectors of length k all vanish, the fall-off of $\langle \boldsymbol{r}|G_0^{(\pm)}|u\rangle$ at infinity is not sufficiently rapid for it to be a square-integrable function. In other words, the application of $G_0^{(+)}$ or $G_0^{(-)}$ to a vector of Hilbert space gives a vector in general outside this space. Therefore, $G_0^{(+)}$ and $G_0^{(-)}$ are not, properly speaking, operators in Hilbert space.

They can, however, be defined as limits of operators in Hilbert space as follows:

$$G_0^{(\pm)} = \lim_{\varepsilon\to 0+} \frac{1}{E - H_0 \pm i\varepsilon} \qquad (\varepsilon > 0). \qquad \text{(XIX.62)}$$

On the right-hand side will be recognized the resolvent $(z-H_0)^{-1}$ (cf. Ch. XVI, Sec. III); it is a (bounded) operator of Hilbert space for all values of the complex variable z except for the eigenvalues of H_0, i.e. except for points on the positive real axis. The behavior of the resolvent in the neighborhood of this line is given by (XIX.62). If z tends to E from above the real axis ($\operatorname{Im} z>0$), $(z-H_0)^{-1}$ tends toward $G_0^{(+)}$; if it tends to E from below the real axis ($\operatorname{Im} z<0$), $(z-H_0)^{-1}$ tends toward $G_0^{(-)}$.

The demonstration of (XIX.62) proceeds as follows. Starting from the (diagonal) matrix of $(z-H_0)^{-1}$ in the $\{\boldsymbol{p}\}$ representation, we apply the well-known unitary transformation to obtain its matrix in the $\{\boldsymbol{r}\}$ representation:

$$\langle \boldsymbol{r}|(z-H_0)^{-1}|\boldsymbol{r}'\rangle = \frac{1}{(2\pi)^3}\int \mathrm{e}^{\mathrm{i}\boldsymbol{k}'\cdot(\boldsymbol{r}'-\boldsymbol{r})}\left(z-\frac{\hbar^2 k'^2}{2m}\right)^{-1} \mathrm{d}\boldsymbol{k}'.$$

The angular integrations are easily carried out. Introducing the quantity ζ defined by

$$z = \hbar^2\zeta^2/2m \qquad \operatorname{Re}\zeta>0$$

and writing

$$\boldsymbol{R} = \boldsymbol{r} - \boldsymbol{r}',$$

we find:

$$\langle \boldsymbol{r}|(z-H_0)^{-1}|\boldsymbol{r}'\rangle = \frac{m}{\pi^2\hbar^2 R}\int_0^\infty \frac{k'\sin k'R}{\zeta^2-k'^2}\,\mathrm{d}k'$$

$$= \frac{m}{\pi\hbar^2 R}\,\frac{1}{2\pi\mathrm{i}}\int_{-\infty}^{+\infty} \frac{k'\,\mathrm{e}^{\mathrm{i}k'R}}{\zeta^2-k'^2}\,\mathrm{d}k'.$$

The value of this last integral is not modified if we close the path of integration with a semi-circular contour at infinity in the upper half plane. The contour integral thus obtained is equal to $2\pi\mathrm{i}$ times the sum of the residues of the poles in the upper half-plane; in the present case there is just one pole, whose position depends on the sign of $\operatorname{Im}\zeta$, and therefore on the sign of $\operatorname{Im} z$ (Fig. XIX.2):

(*a*) $\operatorname{Im} z>0$. Pole for $k'=\zeta$ with residue $-\frac{1}{2}\mathrm{e}^{\mathrm{i}\zeta R}$;

(*b*) $\operatorname{Im} z<0$. Pole for $k'=-\zeta$ with residue $-\frac{1}{2}\mathrm{e}^{-\mathrm{i}\zeta R}$.

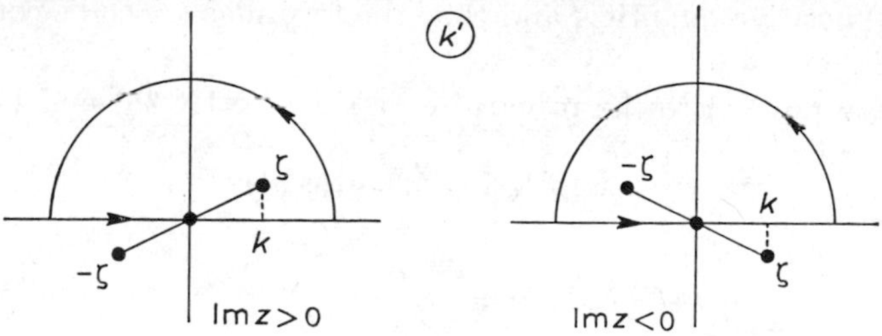

Fig. XIX.2.

Consequently:

$$\langle \boldsymbol{r}|(z-H)^{-1}|\boldsymbol{r}'\rangle = -\frac{m}{2\pi\hbar^2} \times \begin{cases} e^{i\zeta R}/R & \text{if} \quad \mathrm{Im}\, z > 0 \\ e^{-i\zeta R}/R & \text{if} \quad \mathrm{Im}\, z < 0. \end{cases}$$

These expressions are to be compared with those for $\mathscr{G}(\boldsymbol{r}, \boldsymbol{r}')$ [eq. (XIX.30)]. In the limit when z tends to E, ζ tends to k and the matrix element calculated above tends to $\mathscr{G}(\boldsymbol{r}, \boldsymbol{r}')$ or to $\mathscr{G}^*(\boldsymbol{r}, \boldsymbol{r}')$ according as the imaginary part of z is positive or negative in the passage to the limit. Q.E.D.

Operators are often more easily manipulated algebraically than their representative matrices. Thus there is frequently advantage in using the operators $G_0^{(+)}$ and $G_0^{(-)}$ rather than the Green's functions themselves. Nevertheless, these are singular operators, and their manipulation requires caution, and a certain flair [1]). In all rigor, they should be replaced by the regular operators $(E-H_0 \pm i\varepsilon)^{-1}$, and the passage to the limit $\varepsilon \to 0$ examined with care. These details of rigor will not be dwelt upon in what follows. When the $G_0^{(\pm)}$ are replaced by the operators $(E-H_0 \pm i\varepsilon)^{-1}$ it is always to be understood that

[1]) In particular, care must be taken that G acts only on vectors of *finite norm*. The kind of pitfall to which one is exposed if one forgets the singular character of these operators is illustrated by the following example. From relation (XIX.31) and the symmetry of the Green's function in $\boldsymbol{r}$ and $\boldsymbol{r}'$ we have

$$(E-H_0)\, G_0^{(\pm)} = 1, \qquad G_0^{(\pm)}(E-H_0) = 1.$$

These relations mean that the action of the left-hand side of each of these equations on a vector of finite norm gives the same vector, and nothing more. However, taking them literaly, one would be tempted to conclude that $E - H_0$ has an inverse, which is obviously false, and that $G_0^{(+)}$ and $G_0^{(-)}$ are both equal to that inverse and therefore equal to each other, which is also false.

ε is a real positive quantity, and that the formulas are to be considered in the limit $\varepsilon \to 0^+$.

We may now write the integral equations (XIX.36) and (XIX.37) in the form

$$\psi_a^{(\pm)} = \varphi_a + G_0^{(\pm)} V \psi_a^{(\pm)} \tag{XIX.63}$$

or

$$\psi_a^{(\pm)} = \varphi_a + \frac{1}{E - H_0 \pm i\varepsilon} V \psi_a^{(\pm)}. \tag{XIX.63$'$}$$

By iteration of these equations, we obtain the Born expansions:

$$\psi_a^{(\pm)} = \left[1 + \sum_{n=1}^{\infty} (G_0^{(\pm)} V)^n \right] \varphi_a. \tag{XIX.64}$$

In these expressions the symbols ψ and φ denote either the stationary waves themselves or the kets they represent (no confusion being possible, we drop the symbols $|\rangle$).

From these we obtain the conjugate equations by replacing the kets on both sides by their respective conjugate bras. Since H_0 is Hermitean, we have

$$G_0^{(+)\dagger} = G_0^{(-)} \qquad G_0^{(-)\dagger} = G_0^{(+)}. \tag{XIX.65}$$

From (XIX.63),

$$\langle \psi_a^{(\pm)} | = \langle \varphi_a | + \langle \psi_a^{(\pm)} | V G_0^{(\mp)} \tag{XIX.66}$$

and from (XIX.64) we have the Born expansions:

$$\langle \psi_a^{(\pm)} | = \langle \varphi_a | \left[1 + \sum_{n=1}^{\infty} (V G_0^{(\mp)})^n \right]. \tag{XIX.67}$$

II. GENERALIZATION TO DISTORTED WAVES

11. Generalized Born Approximation

It may happen that the potential $V(\mathbf{r})$ is too large for the Born approximation to be used but that we can exactly solve the scattering problem for a neighboring potential V. It is then useful to treat the difference as a perturbation, which may easily be done by a simple generalization of the treatment of Section I.

Let us put

$$\begin{aligned} V(\mathbf{r}) &= U_1(\mathbf{r}) + W_1(\mathbf{r}) \\ H_1 &= H_0 + U_1(\mathbf{r}). \end{aligned} \tag{XIX.68}$$

We therefore have:

$$H = H_1 + W_1. \qquad \text{(XIX.69)}$$

H_1 is the unperturbed Hamiltonian, W_1 the perturbation. We shall suppose that U_1 and V tend to 0 more rapidly than $1/r$; the generalization to $1/r$ potentials will be made in § 15. The stationary states of H_1 are assumed to be known. They will be denoted by the letter χ and the corresponding amplitudes by g; for the rest we follow the notation of § 2. $\chi_a^{(+)}$ and $g_a^{(+)}$ are defined by

$$H_1\, \chi_a^{(+)} = E\, \chi_a^{(+)} \qquad \chi_a^{(+)} \underset{r\to\infty}{\sim} \mathrm{e}^{\mathrm{i}\mathbf{k}_a\cdot\mathbf{r}} + g_a^{(+)}(\Omega)\, \mathrm{e}^{\mathrm{i}kr}/r.$$

All of the results of Section I relating to the Hamiltonian H are obviously true for H_1 as well. In particular we can define a transition matrix for collisions at energy E governed by the Hamiltonian H_1, which we shall denote by $T^{(1)}$

$$T^{(1)}_{a\to b} \equiv \langle\varphi_b|T^{(1)}|\varphi_a\rangle = \langle\varphi_b|U_1|\chi_a^{(+)}\rangle = \langle\chi_b^{(-)}|U_1|\varphi_a\rangle. \qquad \text{(XIX.70)}$$

Among the results of § 2, recall that:

$$g_b^{(-)*}(-\Omega_a) = g_a^{(+)}(\Omega_b) = -\frac{m}{2\pi\hbar^2}\, T^{(1)}_{a\to b}.$$

From (XIX.9) we can obtain an integral representation of the difference $T_{a\to b} - T^{(1)}_{a\to b}$. Taking

$$\hat{U} = U_1, \qquad U = V,$$

we obtain:

$$\begin{aligned} \langle\chi_b^{(-)}|W_1|\psi_a^{(+)}\rangle &= -\frac{2\pi\hbar^2}{m}\,[f_a^{(+)}(\Omega_b) - g_b^{(-)*}(-\Omega_a)] \\ &= -\frac{2\pi\hbar^2}{m}\,[f_a^{(+)}(\Omega_b) - g_a^{(+)}(\Omega_b)] \\ &= T_{a\to b} - T^{(1)}_{a\to b}. \end{aligned} \qquad \text{(XIX.71)}$$

In the same way, by taking $\hat{U} = V$ and $U = U_1$, we obtain:

$$\langle\psi_b^{(-)}|W_1|\chi_a^{(+)}\rangle = T_{a\to b} - T^{(1)}_{a\to b}. \qquad \text{(XIX.72)}$$

Note in passing the relation

$$\langle\psi_b^{(-)}|W_1|\chi_a^{(+)}\rangle = \langle\chi_b^{(-)}|W_1|\psi_a^{(+)}\rangle, \qquad \text{(XIX.73)}$$

an obvious consequence of (XIX.71) and (XIX.72) and a generalization of relation (XIX.18).

Either of these two integral representations can be used as a starting-point for the perturbation treatment. Let us take (XIX.71), which gives:

$$\boxed{T_{a\to b} = T^{(1)}_{a\to b} + \langle \chi_b^{(-)} | W_1 | \psi_a^{(+)} \rangle} \qquad \text{(XIX.74)}$$

This expression for the transition amplitude is exact. The first term is what it would be in the absence of W_1, the second the correction due to the latter. For W_1 sufficiently small, the exact stationary wave, $\psi_a^{(+)}$, differs little from $\chi_a^{(+)}$, and may be replaced by the latter in the correction term. We thereby obtain the transition amplitude to the first order in the perturbation W_1:

$$T_{a\to b} \simeq T^{(1)}_{a\to b} + \langle \chi_b^{(-)} | W_1 | \chi_a^{(+)} \rangle. \qquad \text{(XIX.75)}$$

This is the generalization of the Born approximation [cf. eq. (XIX.23)]. Note the simultaneous presence, and respective position, of the stationary solutions corresponding to outgoing and incoming waves in the perturbation integral:

$$\langle \chi_b^{(-)} | W_1 | \chi_a^{(+)} \rangle \equiv \int \chi_b^{(-)*}(\boldsymbol{r})\, W_1(\boldsymbol{r})\, \chi_a^{(+)}(\boldsymbol{r})\, \mathrm{d}\boldsymbol{r}. \qquad \text{(XIX.76)}$$

If we take $U_1 = 0$ we obtain the Born result. In the general case, when $U_1 \neq 0$, it is obviously more difficult to calculate this integral than the one appearing in the Born formula. The situation becomes somewhat simpler when U_1 and V are both spherically symmetrical. We may then use the expansions (Problem XIX.4):

$$\chi_{\mathbf{k}}^{(\pm)} = \frac{4\pi}{kr} \sum_{lm} \mathrm{i}^l\, \mathrm{e}^{\pm \mathrm{i}\eta_l}\, F_l(k;r)\, Y_l^{m*}(\hat{\mathbf{k}})\, Y_l^m(\hat{\boldsymbol{r}}), \qquad \text{(XIX.77)}$$

where $F_l(k;r)$ denotes the regular solution of the radial equation

$$\left[\frac{\mathrm{d}^2}{\mathrm{d}r^2} - \frac{l(l+1)}{r^2} - \frac{2m}{\hbar^2}\, U_1 + k^2\right] y = 0, \qquad \text{(XIX.78)}$$

whose asymptotic behavior is given by

$$F_l(k;r) \underset{r\to\infty}{\sim} \sin\left(kr - \tfrac{1}{2}l\pi + \eta_l\right). \qquad \text{(XIX.79)}$$

Here η_l is the phase shift of the l-wave in the potential U_1. Substituting the expansions of $\chi_a^{(+)}$ and $\chi_b^{(-)}$ into the integral (XIX.76) and integrating over the angles, we find

$$\langle \chi_b^{(-)} | W_1 | \chi_a^{(+)} \rangle = \frac{4\pi}{k^2} \sum_l (2l+1)\, P_l(\cos\theta)\, e^{2i\eta_l} \int_0^\infty F_l^2(k; r)\, W_1(r)\, dr.$$

The convergence of this expansion is obviously better the smaller the range of W_1

12. Generalization of the Born Expansion

To find the higher order corrections we must expand $\psi_a^{(+)}$ into powers of W_1. In analogy with the method of section I we do this by finding an integral equation for $\psi_a^{(+)}$ that can be iterated to give the desired expansion.

Denote by $G_1^{(+)}(\mathbf{r}, \mathbf{r}')$ the Green's function for the Hamiltonian H_1 corresponding to the energy $E = \hbar^2 k^2/2m$ and having the outgoing-wave asymptotic behavior. By definition, it is a symmetrical function of $\mathbf{r}$ and $\mathbf{r}'$ obeying the partial differential equation

$$(E - H_1)\, G_1^{(+)} \equiv \left[\frac{\hbar^2}{2m}(\Delta + k^2) - U_1\right] G_1^{(+)}(\mathbf{r}, \mathbf{r}') = \delta(\mathbf{r}' - \mathbf{r}) \quad \text{(XIX.80)}$$

and behaving asymptotically like e^{ikr}/r when $r \to \infty$, r' being kept fixed. It is the representative matrix of a certain operator $G_1^{(+)}$ according to the definition:

$$\langle \mathbf{r} | G_1^{(+)} | \mathbf{r}' \rangle \equiv G_1^{(+)}(\mathbf{r}, \mathbf{r}').$$

It will be shown in the next paragraph that there always exists one, and only one function $G_1^{(+)}(\mathbf{r}, \mathbf{r}')$ having these properties.

We obtain the integral equation by the method of § 5 using this function in place of the free-wave Green's function. We write the Schrödinger equation for $\psi_a^{(+)}$ in the form:

$$(E - H_1)\, \psi_a^{(+)} \equiv \left[\frac{\hbar^2}{2m}(\Delta + k^2) - U_1\right] \psi_a^{(+)} = W_1 \psi_a^{(+)}$$

and note that in view of eq. (XIX.80) the function

$$\psi_a^{(+)} - \int G_1^{(+)}(\mathbf{r}, \mathbf{r}')\, W_1(\mathbf{r}')\, \psi_a^{(+)}(\mathbf{r}')\, d\mathbf{r}'$$

satisfies the "homogeneous equation"

$$(E - H_1)\chi = 0.$$

Since this function has the same asymptotic form as $\chi_a^{(+)}$, it is necessarily equal to $\chi_a^{(+)}$. $\psi_a^{(+)}$ therefore satisfies the integral equation

$$\psi_a^{(+)} = \chi_a^{(+)}(\mathbf{r}) + \int G_1^{(+)}(\mathbf{r}, \mathbf{r}')\, W_1(\mathbf{r}')\, \psi_a^{(+)}(\mathbf{r}')\, \mathrm{d}\mathbf{r}'. \qquad \text{(XIX.81)}$$

The expansion of $\psi_a^{(+)}$ in powers of W_1 is easily obtained from eq. (XIX.81). Substituting this expansion into the "matrix element" in the right-hand side of (XIX.74) we obtain the expansion of $T_{a\to b}$ in powers of W_1. If we keep only the first two terms of this expansion we obtain the approximate expression (XIX.75).

The complex conjugate of $G_1^{(+)}(\mathbf{r}, \mathbf{r}')$ is also a Green's function of H_1 for the energy E: it is the function $G_1^{(-)}(\mathbf{r}, \mathbf{r}')$ which asymptotically has the incoming-wave behavior. From these properties we deduce by a similar method the integral equation

$$\psi_a^{(-)} = \chi_a^{(-)} + \int G_1^{(-)}(\mathbf{r}, \mathbf{r}')\, W_1(\mathbf{r}')\, \psi_a^{(-)}(\mathbf{r}')\, \mathrm{d}\mathbf{r}'. \qquad \text{(XIX.82)}$$

We could also obtain the expansion of $T_{a\to b}$ in powers of W_1 by starting from eq. (XIX.82), and using (XIX.73); the result would obviously be the same.

13. Green's Functions for Distorted Waves

The existence of the Green's functions $G_1^{(+)}$ and $G_1^{(-)}$ remains to be demonstrated. It will be shown that by a natural generalization of eq. (XIX.62) they can be defined as limits of the resolvent of H_1, *viz.*

$$G_1^{(\pm)} = \lim_{\varepsilon\to 0+} \frac{1}{E - H_1 \pm \mathrm{i}\varepsilon}. \qquad \text{(XIX.83)}$$

Similarly, for each value of E we associate with the Hamiltonian H the functions:

$$G^{(\pm)} = \lim_{\varepsilon\to 0+} \frac{1}{E - H \pm \mathrm{i}\varepsilon}. \qquad \text{(XIX.84)}$$

Let us first consider the operators $G^{(+)}$ and $G^{(-)}$ and show that

$$(E - H)G^{(\pm)} = 1, \qquad G^{(\pm)}(E - H) = 1. \qquad \text{(XIX.85)}$$

$|u\rangle$ being any vector of finite norm, we obviously have

$$(E - H)\frac{1}{E - H + \mathrm{i}\varepsilon}|u\rangle = |u\rangle - \frac{\mathrm{i}\varepsilon}{E - H + \mathrm{i}\varepsilon}|u\rangle. \qquad \text{(XIX.86)}$$

The norm of the second term on the right-hand side is

$$N(\varepsilon) = \varepsilon^2 \langle u| \frac{1}{(E-H)^2+\varepsilon^2} |u\rangle$$

$$= \varepsilon \int |u(E')|^2 \frac{\varepsilon}{(E-E')^2+\varepsilon^2} \, \mathrm{d}E'.$$

The second line is obtained by adopting a representation in which H is diagonal; $|u(E')|^2 \mathrm{d}E'$ is the norm of the component of $|u\rangle$ of energy E'. By a known property of the δ function [eq. (A.15*c*)], the integral tends to $\pi|u(E)|^2$ when $\varepsilon \to 0$. Thus the norm $N(\varepsilon)$ vanishes in this limit. Therefore, when $\varepsilon \to 0$ equation (XIX.86) gives:

$$(E-H)G^{(+)}|u\rangle = |u\rangle.$$

This being true for any $|u\rangle$ [*of finite norm* [1]], we have:

$$(E-H)G^{(+)} = 1.$$

The other relations of (XIX.85) may be demonstrated in the same way.

In similar fashion

$$(E-H_1)G_1^{(\pm)} = 1, \qquad G_1^{(\pm)}(E-H_1) = 1. \qquad \text{(XIX.87)}$$

Equations (XIX.85) and (XIX.87) show that $G^{(\pm)}$ and $G_1^{(\pm)}$ are respectively the Green's functions for H and H_1 for the energy E. In the $\{\boldsymbol{r}\}$ representation they give the partial differential equations characteristic of the Green functions: thus the first of eqs. (XIX.87) gives eq. (XIX.80).

In the preceding demonstration, we examined with some care the passage to the limit $\varepsilon \to 0^+$ since it plays an essential role. In what follows, we leave aside these points of rigor and, with the conventions of page 822, shall often replace $G^{(\pm)}$ by $[E-H \pm \mathrm{i}\varepsilon]^{-1}$ and $G_1^{(\pm)}$ by $[E-H_1 \pm \mathrm{i}\varepsilon]^{-1}$, where ε is a real, positive, infinitesimal quantity.

Proceeding as at the beginning of § XVI.16 we obtain the fundamental identities

$$\frac{1}{E-H\pm\mathrm{i}\varepsilon} - \frac{1}{E-H_0\pm\mathrm{i}\varepsilon} = \frac{1}{E-H\pm\mathrm{i}\varepsilon} V \frac{1}{E-H_0\pm\mathrm{i}\varepsilon} \qquad \text{(XIX.88}a\text{)}$$

$$= \frac{1}{E-H_0\pm\mathrm{i}\varepsilon} V \frac{1}{E-H\pm\mathrm{i}\varepsilon}. \qquad \text{(XIX.88}b\text{)}$$

[1] The remarks of note p. 821 fully apply here.

There are analogous identities with H_1 and U_1 in place of H and V respectively, and also with H_1 and W_1 in place of H_0 and V respectively.

As a first application of identities (XIX.88) we can deduce the relations [1])

$$(1 + G^{(\pm)}V)(1 - G_0{}^{(\pm)}V) = 1 \tag{XIX.89a}$$

$$(1 - G_0{}^{(\pm)}V)(1 + G^{(\pm)}V) = 1. \tag{XIX.89b}$$

Now eq. (XIX.63) may be written in the form

$$[1 - G_0{}^{(\pm)}V]\,\psi_a{}^{(\pm)} = \varphi_a.$$

Applying the operator $(1+G^{(\pm)}V)$ to both sides of this equation and using (XIX.89a) to simplify the left-hand side, we obtain the important formula:

$$\psi_a{}^{(\pm)} = \left(1 + \frac{1}{E - H \pm \mathrm{i}\varepsilon} V\right) \varphi_a. \tag{XIX.90}$$

Since H is Hermitean, we obviously have

$$G^{(\pm)\dagger} = G^{(\mp)}. \tag{XIX.91}$$

The conjugate equation to eq. (XIX.90) is therefore

$$\langle\psi_a{}^{(\pm)}| = \langle\varphi_a| \left(1 + V \frac{1}{E - H \mp \mathrm{i}\varepsilon}\right). \tag{XIX.92}$$

We are now in a position to obtain the asymptotic behavior of $G^{(+)}$ and $G^{(-)}$ from that of $G_0{}^{(+)}$ and $G_0{}^{(-)}$ respectively. If $|u\rangle$ is a vector with a sufficiently rapid fall-off at infinity, we have from (XIX.88b),

$$G^{(\pm)}|u\rangle = G_0{}^{(\pm)}|\mathscr{V}\rangle,$$

where

$$|\mathscr{V}\rangle = (1 + VG^{(\pm)})|u\rangle.$$

If the vector $|\mathscr{V}\rangle$ also falls off sufficiently rapidly at infinity [2]), we can apply (XIX.61), which gives

$$\langle \mathbf{r}|G^{(\pm)}|u\rangle \underset{r\to\infty}{\sim} -\frac{m}{2\pi\hbar^2}\frac{\mathrm{e}^{\pm\mathrm{i}kr}}{r}\langle\varphi_{\pm\mathbf{k}}|\mathscr{V}\rangle. \tag{XIX.93}$$

$$(\mathbf{k} = k\mathbf{r}/r).$$

---

[1]) From these identities we cannot conclude that $[1+G^{(\pm)}V]$ and $[1 - G_0^{(\pm)}V]$ are inverses of one another, nor even that each of them has an inverse. Cf. note, p. 821.

[2]) The following deductions are not valid if V behaves like $1/r$ at infinity.

$G^{(+)}$ acting on a vector of Hilbert space will therefore generally give a vector which asymptotically behaves as a purely outgoing wave, $G^{(-)}$ gives a vector which asymptotically behaves like a purely incoming wave. Replacing $|\mathscr{V}\rangle$ on the right-hand side of (XIX.93) by its definition, and using the fact [eq. (XIX.91)] that

$$\langle\varphi_{\pm\mathbf{k}}|(1 + VG^{(\pm)}) = \langle\psi^{(\mp)}_{\pm\mathbf{k}}|,$$

we find

$$\langle\mathbf{r}|G^{(\pm)}|u\rangle \underset{r\to\infty}{\sim} -\frac{m}{2\pi\hbar^2}\frac{\mathrm{e}^{\pm ikr}}{r}\langle\psi^{(\mp)}_{\pm\mathbf{k}}|u\rangle. \qquad \text{(XIX.94)}$$

It is to be observed that it is the wave $\psi^{(-)}_{\mathbf{k}}$ that appears in the asymptotic expression for $G^{(+)}$, and $\psi^{(+)}_{-\mathbf{k}}$ in that of $G^{(-)}$.

$G_1{}^{(+)}$ and $G_1{}^{(-)}$ are found to have analogous properties, and notably the asymptotic behavior

$$\langle\mathbf{r}|G_1{}^{(\pm)}|u\rangle \underset{r\to\infty}{\sim} -\frac{m}{2\pi\hbar^2}\frac{\mathrm{e}^{\pm ikr}}{r}\langle\chi^{(\mp)}_{\pm\mathbf{k}}|u\rangle. \qquad \text{(XIX.95)}$$

$$(\mathbf{k} = k\mathbf{r}/r).$$

When U_1 is spherically symmetrical, the Green functions $G_1{}^{(\pm)}$ are easily expressed in terms of the solutions of the radial equation (XIX.78). One finds (Problem XIX.4):

$$\langle\mathbf{r}|G_1{}^{(\pm)}|\mathbf{r}'\rangle = -\frac{2m}{\hbar^2 k}\frac{1}{rr'}\sum_{lm}\mathrm{e}^{\pm i\eta_l}F_l(k;r_<)\,u_l{}^{(\pm)}(k;r_>)\,Y_l{}^{m*}(\hat{\mathbf{r}}')\,Y_l{}^m(\hat{\mathbf{r}}). \qquad \text{(XIX.96)}$$

Here, $r_<$ and $r_>$ are respectively the smaller and the larger of the two lengths r and r'; η_l and F_l were defined in § 11; $u_l{}^{(\pm)}$ are the irregular solutions of eq. (XIX.78) having the asymptotic behavior

$$u_l{}^{(\pm)} \underset{r\to\infty}{\sim} \mathrm{e}^{\pm i(kr - \frac{1}{2}l\pi)}.$$

The explicit forms (XIX.96) are readily shown to have the characteristic properties of $G_1{}^{(+)}$ and $G_1{}^{(-)}$.

14. Applications. Definition and Formal Properties of T

By using the formal properties of the Green's functions given in § 13 we can obtain most of our previous results by a few simple algebraic manipulations. The advantage of such a procedure is that on the one hand it is formally very simple, and on the other it lends itself easily to generalization.

We obtain in particular the integral equations (XIX.81) and (XIX.82), which may be put in the form:

$$\psi_a{}^{(\pm)} = \chi_a{}^{(\pm)} + \frac{1}{E - H_1 \pm \mathrm{i}\varepsilon} W_1\, \psi_a{}^{(\pm)}. \tag{XIX.97}$$

By comparing the asymptotic behavior of both sides of (XIX.97) we obtain relation (XIX.74).

It can also be shown that

$$\chi_a{}^{(\pm)} = \left[1 + \frac{1}{E - H_1 \pm \mathrm{i}\varepsilon} U_1\right] \varphi_a, \tag{XIX.98}$$

$$\psi_a{}^{(\pm)} = \left[1 + \frac{1}{E - H \pm \mathrm{i}\varepsilon} W_1\right] \chi_a{}^{(\pm)}, \tag{XIX.99}$$

the proof of which is left to the reader.

We can also give a formal definition of T. Relation (XIX.20) gives its matrix elements only between plane waves of the same energy E. Taking equation (XIX.90) into account, this relation can be put in the form

$$\langle \varphi_b | T | \varphi_a \rangle = \langle \varphi_b | \left[V + V \frac{1}{E - H + \mathrm{i}\varepsilon} V \right] | \varphi_a \rangle. \tag{XIX.100}$$

We generalize this relation by putting:

$$T = V + V \frac{1}{E - H + \mathrm{i}\varepsilon} V. \tag{XIX.101}$$

In this definition, E plays the role of a simple parameter, T is the value taken by the function

$$T(z) = V + V \frac{1}{z - H} V$$

of the complex variable z in the limit when z tends towards the real value E while remaining in the upper half-plane ($\mathrm{Im}\, z > 0$).

Transforming the right-hand side of eq. (XIX.101) with the aid of identities (XIX.88*a*) and (XIX.88*b*), we easily obtain the following integral equations for the operator T:

$$T = V + T \frac{1}{E - H_0 + \mathrm{i}\varepsilon} V \tag{XIX.102a}$$

$$T = V + V \frac{1}{E - H_0 + \mathrm{i}\varepsilon} T. \tag{XIX.102b}$$

In practice, what usually appears are the matrix elements of T between free waves of energy E, and in particular between plane waves of energy E.

As an illustration we shall demonstrate the microreversibility relation (XIX.21) using the formal properties of T alone. Denote by K the (antilinear) time-reversal operator. H_0 is obviously invariant under time reversal, and furthermore:

$$\varphi_{Ka} = K\varphi_a, \qquad \varphi_{Kb} = K\varphi_b. \tag{XIX.103}$$

Let us suppose that H has this invariance property as well:

$$KHK^\dagger = H.$$

i.e.

$$KVK^\dagger = V.$$

From definitions (XIX.84) and (XIX.101) we successively obtain

$$KG^{(+)}K^\dagger = G^{(-)} = G^{(+)\dagger}$$

and

$$KTK^\dagger = T^\dagger. \tag{XIX.104}$$

From the above law for the transformation of T under time-reversal we deduce:

$$\begin{aligned} T_{Kb\to Ka} &= (\langle\varphi_a|K^\dagger)T(K|\varphi_b\rangle) \\ &= \langle\varphi_a|(K^\dagger TK)|\varphi_b\rangle^* \\ &= \langle\varphi_b|(K^\dagger T^\dagger K)|\varphi_a\rangle \\ &= \langle\varphi_b|T|\varphi_a\rangle = T_{a\to b}. \end{aligned}$$

This is the microreversibility relation.

15. Note on the $1/r$ Potentials

In the preceding sections, we have everywhere supposed that the potentials $V(r)$, $U_1(r)$ and $W_1(r)$ fall off at infinity more rapidly than $1/r$. This is a necessary condition for the various waves and Green's functions used to have the indicated asymptotic behavior. However, with a few modifications, the same treatment can be used when both $V(r)$ and $U_1(r)$ have a $1/r$ behavior provided that their difference $W_1(r)$ tends to 0 more rapidly than $1/r$. The asymptotic forms differ only through the presence of an additional term proportional to ln $2kr$ in the argument of the exponential; the arguments of the asymptotic forms of u_l and F_l undergo the same modification. Apart from these differences the method and the results are essentially the same. In particular, definitions (XIX.83) and (XIX.84) of the Green's functions are still valid, integral equation (XIX.97) is still satisfied as is the fundamental equation (XIX.74) and also formula (XIX.75) in the limit when W_1 can be treated as a small perturbation.

III. COMPLEX COLLISIONS AND THE BORN APPROXIMATION

16. Generalities. Cross Sections

In this section [1]), we extend the considerations of the two preceding sections to collisions between any two particles. We use the word "particle" in the general sense of the term where the particle may have an internal structure. The internal variables reduce to the spin variables alone in the case of the elementary particles such as electrons, protons and neutrons; but we shall also consider complex particles, ions, atoms, atomic nuclei, etc., made up of several elementary particles.

Suppose then that we have two particles, A and X, elementary or complex, entering into collision. In general, three types of effects may be observed:

(*a*) *elastic scattering*, where the particles are simply deviated without any change in their respective internal quantum states

$$A + X \to A + X$$

(*b*) *inelastic scattering*, where in addition to deviation, there is a change in the internal states of the particles [2]); they emerge, for example, in states A' and X' respectively:

$$A + X \to A' + X'$$

(*c*) a *rearrangement collision* (or, properly speaking, a *reaction*), where A and X exchange a certain number of their constituent elemen-

---

[1]) For more details concerning the terminology introduced in this section see J. Blatt and V. Weisskopf *Theoretical Nuclear Physics* Ch. VIII (Wiley, New York, 1952).

[2]) This could be a simple reversal of spin. The definition adopted here differs slightly from the usual one according to which a scattering process is inelastic or elastic according as there is a change in the internal energy of the particles or not.

tary particles in the course of the collision, or more generally, when the system $(A+X)$ splits into two or more different particles; for example when particles B and Y (different to A and X) emerge from the collision:

$$A+X \rightarrow B+Y.$$

A chemical reaction is a rearrangement collision between molecules, a nuclear reaction a rearrangement collision between atomic nuclei; several examples will be given in what follows.

The characteristic magnitude in the collision of two particles is the cross section. This notion has already been defined in Chapter X (§ 2) for elastic collisions. More generally, *the cross section for a certain type of event in a given collision is equal to the number of events of this type per unit time per target divided by the flux of incident particles relative to the target.*

To unambiguously define a cross section relating to the collision of A and X the initial conditions of the collision, that is, the quantum states and the respective velocities of particles A and X must be precisely specified. In the usual experimental conditions one of the velocities is null, that of X say: a target of particles of type X practically at rest is bombarded with a mono-ergic beam of particles of type A. However, since the motion of the center of mass can be completely separated from the motion of the relative coordinates, simple kinematic considerations relate cross sections corresponding to initial conditions differing only by a change of referential; in particular, by an evident generalization of the method of § X.7 (cf. Problem X.2), we can relate the cross sections in the laboratory system (velocity of X null) to the cross section in the center-of-mass system (velocity of the center of mass null). All the cross sections to be considered in what follows are with respect to the center-of-mass system.

In what follows E will denote the total incident energy in the center-of-mass system and H the Hamiltonian for the relative variables (one obtains the total Hamiltonian by adding the energy of the center of mass).

17. Channels

A concept that is very useful in the treatment of complex collisions is the concept of a *channel*. A channel is any possible mode of fragmentation of the system in the course of the collision. One of these modes is the two incident particles themselves: it is called the *entrance channel*. In an elastic collision, the two particles remain in the entrance channel; in the other two types of reaction, the out-going channel is different to the entrance channel: it is an inelastic collision or a rearrangement collision according as the particles which make up the channel are the same or are different to those of the entrance channel. We shall henceforth denote each channel by a particular Greek letter.

With each channel may be associated a certain number of parameters and magnitudes. For simplicity, we shall always suppose that the reaction channels are made up of two particles.

Consider then a channel γ made up of two particles, C and X. The vector $\mathbf{r}_\gamma$ fixes the position of C with respect to X, in other words, we have $\mathbf{r}_\gamma = \mathbf{r}_C - \mathbf{r}_Z$, where $\mathbf{r}_C$ and $\mathbf{r}_Z$ denote the respective positions of the centers of mass of C and X. We likewise define the relative momentum $\mathbf{p}_\gamma$ and the reduced mass M_γ:

$$M_\gamma = \frac{M_C M_Z}{M_C + M_Z};$$

The kinetic energy of channel γ is $\mathbf{p}_\gamma{}^2/2M_\gamma$.

The wave function φ_γ (of norm 1), describing the internal quantum state of the particles of the channel is the product of the wave functions φ_C and φ_Z of the particles C and Z respectively. If h_C and h_Z are the Hamiltonians of these particles, we have

$$h_C\,\varphi_C = e_C\,\varphi_C, \qquad h_Z\,\varphi_Z = e_Z\,\varphi_Z$$

$$\varphi_\gamma = \varphi_C\,\varphi_Z, \qquad e_\gamma = e_C + e_Z$$

e_γ is the total internal energy of the particles of channel γ.

Finally, let V_γ be the interaction between particles C and Z, that is, the sum of the interaction potentials between each elementary particle of C and each elementary particle of Z. V_γ tends to zero in the limit when $r_\gamma \to \infty$. In what follows, we shall always suppose that this decrease is more rapid than $1/r_\gamma$; the generalization to potentials in $1/r_\gamma$ is easily accomplished as indicated in § 15.

The Hamiltonian of the system is

$$H = H_\gamma + V_\gamma \tag{XIX.105}$$

with

$$H_\gamma = h_C + h_Z + \mathbf{p}_\gamma{}^2/2M_\gamma. \tag{XIX.106}$$

18. Calculation of Cross Sections. T Matrices

In the collision considered above, the entrance channel is the channel $(A+X)$ which we denote by the symbol α. To completely specify the initial conditions, we need to know the relative momentum $\hbar\mathbf{k}_a$ of the particles in the initial state. We shall represent the initial conditions by the letter or index $a \equiv (\alpha, \mathbf{k}_a)$. One has:

$$E = e_\alpha + \hbar^2 k_a{}^2/2M_\alpha. \tag{XIX.107}$$

Let us suppose that the reaction $A+X \to B+Y$ is possible. In this case one says that the channel $(B+Y)$, or the channel β, is an *open channel*. The particles of β emerge with a well-defined relative momentum of length $\hbar k_b$ given by the conservation of energy law

$$E = e_\beta + \hbar^2 k_b{}^2/2M_\beta. \tag{XIX.108}$$

For channel β to be open, it is obviously necessary that $E - e_\beta$ be positive.

One can associate a plane wave,

$$\Phi_a = \varphi_\alpha\, \mathrm{e}^{\mathrm{i}\mathbf{k}_a\cdot\mathbf{r}_\alpha}, \tag{XIX.109}$$

and two stationary waves $\Psi_a{}^{(+)}$ and $\Psi_a{}^{(-)}$ with each set of initial conditions a. $\Psi_a{}^{(+)}$ is the stationary solution of H corresponding to energy E having an ($\mathrm{e}^{\mathrm{i}\mathbf{k}_a\cdot\mathbf{r}_\alpha}+$ outgoing wave) asymptotic behavior in the entrance channel, and a purely outgoing-wave behavior in all other open channels. $\Psi_a{}^{(-)}$ is similarly defined for incoming waves. In accordance with these definitions we have

$$H_\alpha \Phi_a = E\Phi_a \tag{XIX.110}$$

$$H\Psi_a{}^{(\pm)} = E\Psi_a{}^{(\pm)} \tag{XIX.111}$$

and, for any open channel γ (we shall suppose that none of them has any more than two particles):

$$\begin{aligned} \Psi_a{}^{(\pm)} &\underset{r_\alpha\to\infty}{\sim} \varphi_\alpha \left[\mathrm{e}^{\mathrm{i}\mathbf{k}_a\cdot\mathbf{r}_\alpha} + f_{a\alpha}^{(\pm)}(\Omega_\alpha)\, \mathrm{e}^{\pm\mathrm{i}k_a r_\alpha}/r_\alpha\right] \\ &\underset{r_\gamma\to\infty}{\sim} \varphi_\gamma\, f_{a\gamma}^{(\pm)}(\Omega_\gamma)\, \mathrm{e}^{\pm\mathrm{i}k_c r_\gamma} \qquad (\gamma \neq \alpha). \end{aligned} \tag{XIX.112}$$

We assume that the stationary solutions $\Psi_a{}^{(+)}$ and $\Psi_a{}^{(-)}$ exist.

The cross sections are directly related to the asymptotic behavior of $\Psi_a^{(+)}$. Denote by $\mathrm{d}\sigma_{a\to b}/\mathrm{d}\Omega_\beta$ the cross section for emission of particle B in the direction Ω_b. One finds:

$$\frac{\mathrm{d}\sigma_{a\to b}}{\mathrm{d}\Omega_\beta} = \frac{v_b}{v_a} \mid f_{a\beta}^{(+)}(\Omega_b) \mid^2, \qquad \text{(XIX.113)}$$

where $v_a = \hbar k_a/M_\alpha$ is the incident velocity and $v_b = \hbar k_b/M_\beta$ the relative velocity of the particle B emerging from the collision. The demonstration of this result is a simple generalization of that given in § 4–6 of Chapter X [1]). It is left to the reader.

Generalizing the considerations of § 3, we are led to describing the phenomenon of collision at energy E by a certain transition matrix T defined such that

$$T_{a\to b} \equiv \langle b|T|a\rangle = -\frac{2\pi\hbar^2}{M_\beta} f_{a\beta}^{(+)}(\Omega_b). \qquad \text{(XIX.114)}$$

From (XIX.113) and (XIX.114),

$$\boxed{\frac{\mathrm{d}\sigma_{a\to b}}{\mathrm{d}\Omega_\beta} = \frac{2\pi}{\hbar v_a} |T_{a\to b}|^2 \varrho_b(E)} \qquad \text{(XIX.115)}$$

where $\varrho_b(E)$ denotes the density of final states in accordance with the definition of § XVII.5. Formula (XIX.115) is the generalization of formula (XIX.19′). $T_{a\to b}$ is the amplitude for the transition $a \to b$.

19. Integral Representations of the Transition Amplitude

In order to find the integral representations of $T_{a\to b}$ we generalize property (XIX.9).

Let H and $\hat{H}$ be two possible Hamiltonians for the quantum system in question: H and $\hat{H}$ have the same kinetic energy, but their potential energies may be different; we shall assume that any such difference is made up of terms tending asymptotically to zero more rapidly than $1/r$. The stationary solutions of H and $\hat{H}$ at energy E will be denoted by Ψ and $\hat{\Psi}$ respectively. It is to be noted that certain channels may be open to collisions governed by H and closed to collisions governed by $\hat{H}$, and *vice versa*. We shall suppose that channel β is open to collisions governed by $\hat{H}$. Therefore there exists a solution

[1]) This result can also be obtained by generalizing the argument of § X.2: the cross section is equal to the ratio of the flux of B particles, $v_b|f_{a\beta}^{(+)}(\Omega_b)|^2$ to the incident flux v_a.

$\hat{\Psi}_b^{(-)}$ corresponding to the initial conditions $b \equiv (\beta, \mathbf{k}_b)$. We thus have:

$$\hat{H}\hat{\Psi}_b^{(-)} = E\hat{\Psi}_b^{(-)} \qquad \text{(XIX.116)}$$

and, for any open channel δ (we shall suppose that no channel has any more than two particles),

$$\begin{aligned} \hat{\Psi}_b^{(-)} &\underset{r_\beta \to \infty}{\sim} \varphi_\beta \, [\mathrm{e}^{\mathrm{i}\mathbf{k}_b \cdot \mathbf{r}_\beta} + \hat{f}_{b\beta}^{(-)}(\Omega_\beta)\, \mathrm{e}^{-\mathrm{i}k_b r_\beta}/r_\beta] \\ &\underset{r_\delta \to \infty}{\sim} \varphi_\delta \, \hat{f}_{b\delta}^{(-)}(\Omega_\delta)\, \mathrm{e}^{-\mathrm{i}k_d r_\delta}/r_\delta \qquad (\delta \neq \beta). \end{aligned} \qquad \text{(XIX.117)}$$

One can show that

$$\langle \hat{\Psi}_b^{(-)} | (H - \hat{H}) | \Psi_a^{(+)} \rangle = -\frac{2\pi\hbar^2}{M_\beta} f_{a\beta}^{(+)}(\Omega_b) + \frac{2\pi\hbar^2}{M_\alpha} \hat{f}_{b\alpha}^{(-)*}(-\Omega_a). \quad \text{(XIX.118)}$$

The demonstration can be carried through the same way as that of property (XIX.9). Multiplying equation (XIX.111) by $\hat{\Psi}_b^{(-)*}$ and the complex conjugate of equation (XIX.116) by $\Psi_a^{(+)}$ and subtracting, we have

$$[\hat{\Psi}_b^{(-)*}(H\Psi_a^{(+)}) - (H\hat{\Psi}_b^{(-)})^*\Psi_a^{(+)}] + \hat{\Psi}_b^{(-)*}(H - \hat{H})\Psi_a^{(+)} = 0.$$

We obtain relation (XIX.118) by summing over the spin variables and integrating over the whole of configuration space. In spite of the Hermitean character of H, the contribution from the bracket does not necessarily vanish, since neither Ψ nor $\hat{\Psi}$ has a finite norm. To calculate this contribution, we calculate the integral over a finite volume of configuration space and then take the limit of that integral when this volume is extended to infinity. By use of Green's theorem the volume integral can be transformed into a surface integral [1]),

---

[1]) Recall that there are several ways to separate out the center of mass, but that the quantity

$$x \equiv (\textstyle\sum_j M_j \mathbf{r}_j^2)^{\frac{1}{2}}$$

is independent of the mode of reduction; $\mathbf{r}_1, \mathbf{r}_2, \ldots, \mathbf{r}_j, \ldots$ here denote the relative coordinates corresponding to this particular mode of reduction, and $M_1, M_2, \ldots, M_j, \ldots,$ the corresponding masses (cf. § IX,13). The volume of integration involved here can be defined by the condition $x \leqslant X$; where X is a positive quantity, large with respect to the range of the interactions entering into play. With Green's theorem we can transform the volume integral into an integral over the hypersurface $x = X$, which tends to the expression on the right hand side of (XIX.119) in the limit when $X \to \infty$.

which takes the form of a sum of terms relative to the different open channels ν common to Ψ and $\hat{\Psi}$. One finds

$$\langle \hat{\Psi}_b{}^{(-)}|(H-\hat{H})|\Psi_a{}^{(+)}\rangle = \sum_\nu \frac{\hbar^2}{2M_\nu} \lim_{R_\nu\to\infty} \{\hat{\Psi}_a{}^{(-)*}, \Psi_b{}^{(+)}\}_\nu, \quad \text{(XIX.119)}$$

The symbol $\{...\}_\nu$ is a generalization of the notation introduced in § 2. By definition

$$\{F_1, F_2\}_\nu = \langle \int \left(F_1 \frac{\partial F_2}{\partial r_\nu} - F_2 \frac{\partial F_1}{\partial r_\nu} \right) \Big|_{r_\nu = R_\nu} R_\nu{}^2 \, \mathrm{d}\Omega_\nu \rangle$$

the symbol $\langle \int \dots \mathrm{d}\Omega_\nu \rangle$ signifying summation or integration over all the variables except the relative distance r_ν. The different terms on the right-hand side of (XIX.119) may be evaluated by substituting for Ψ and $\hat{\Psi}$ and for their radial derivatives the respective asymptotic forms given by expressions (XIX.112) and (XIX.117). For any channel different to α and β, $\Psi_a{}^{(+)}$ is a purely outgoing wave, $\Psi_b{}^{(-)}$ a purely incoming wave, and therefore $\{...\}_\nu$ tends asymptotically to zero. For channels α and β, on the other hand the contribution from the bracket does not vanish, due to the presence of the plane-wave term in one of the two asymptotic forms. The calculation is identical to that of § 2 and gives the two terms on the right-hand side of relation (XIX.118). Q.E.D.

The fundamental relation (XIX.118) can be put in a more workable form. To this end we apply (XIX.118) in the special case where $\hat{H} = H$. The left-hand side being zero, we have

$$\frac{1}{M_\beta} f_{a\beta}^{(+)}(\Omega_b) = \frac{1}{M_\alpha} f_{b\alpha}^{(-)*}(-\Omega_a).$$

Comparing this with the relation defining T [eq. (XIX.114)], we obtain the equivalent definition

$$\langle b|T|a\rangle = -\frac{2\pi\hbar^2}{M_\alpha} f_{b\alpha}^{(-)*}(-\Omega_a). \quad \text{(XIX.114')}$$

These two definitions apply equally well to the transition matrix $\hat{T}$ associated with the Hamiltonian $\hat{H}$. Taking these into account, property (XIX.118) becomes

$$\langle b|T|a\rangle = \langle b|\hat{T}|a\rangle + \langle \hat{\Psi}_b{}^{(-)}|(H-\hat{H})|\Psi_a{}^{(+)}\rangle. \quad \text{(XIX.120)}$$

It is in this form that we shall make use of it.

This relation remains true when channel α is closed to wave $\hat{\Psi}_b^{(-)}$ if we put $\langle b|\hat{T}|a\rangle = 0$. Similarly, it remains true when channel β is closed to wave $\Psi_a^{(+)}$ if we put $\langle b|T|a\rangle = 0$.

In particular, if $\hat{H} = H_\beta$, $\hat{\Psi}_\beta^{(-)}$ reduces to the plane wave Φ_β, and since $H - H_\beta = V_\beta$, relation (XIX.120) gives

$$\langle b|T|a\rangle = \langle \Phi_b| V_\beta |\Psi_a^{(+)}\rangle. \qquad \text{(XIX.121)}$$

Similarly, if we replace H by H_α and $\hat{H}$ by H, (XIX.120) gives

$$\langle b|T|a\rangle = \langle \Psi_b^{(-)}| V_\alpha |\Phi_a\rangle. \qquad \text{(XIX.122)}$$

All of these properties are valid whatever the type of collision involved, elastic collision ($\alpha = \beta$), inelastic collision ($\alpha \neq \beta$, $V_\alpha = V_\beta$) or rearrangement collision ($V_\alpha \neq V_\beta$).

20. The Born Approximation and its Generalizations

By substituting the plane wave Φ_a for $\Psi_a^{(+)}$ in the right-hand side of equation (XIX.121), one obtains the *amplitude for the transition* $a \to b$ *in the Born approximation* [cf. eq. (XIX.23)]:

$$T_{a\to b} \simeq T^{(B)}_{a\to b} = \langle \Phi_b| V_\beta |\Phi_a\rangle. \qquad \text{(XIX.123)}$$

We obtain *the same* approximate value by replacing $\Psi_b^{(-)}$ by Φ_b in the right-hand side of equation (XIX.122). Indeed, if we replace H by H_α and $\hat{H}$ by H_β, (XIX.120) gives

$$\langle \Phi_b| V_\beta |\Phi_a\rangle = \langle \Phi_b| V_\alpha |\Phi_a\rangle. \qquad \text{(XIX.124)}$$

Thus we can also write

$$T^{(B)}_{a\to b} = \langle \Phi_b| V_\alpha |\Phi_a\rangle. \qquad \text{(XIX.123')}$$

The passage from (XIX.121) to (XIX.123) is justified if $\Psi^{(+)}$ differs sufficiently little from Φ_a in the region covered by the potential V_β; that from (XIX.122) to (XIX.123'), if $\Psi_b^{(-)}$ differs sufficiently little from Φ_b in the region covered by the potential V_α. These two conditions are obviously equivalent, although they appear different. They both suppose that $\Psi_a^{(+)}$ and $\Psi_b^{(-)}$ may be respectively replaced by the plane waves Φ_a and Φ_b.

More exact expressions may be obtained by using wave functions nearer to the exact stationary solutions $\Psi_a^{(+)}$ and $\Psi_b^{(-)}$ in place of the plane waves.

Suppose, for example, that V_α can be put in the form

$$V_\alpha = U_\alpha + W_\alpha$$

and that the stationary solutions of the Hamiltonian $H_\alpha + U_\alpha$ corresponding to the energy E are known. These solutions will be denoted by X and the corresponding transition matrix by $T^{(X)}$. In particular, $X_a^{(+)}$ will denote the "outgoing wave" solution corresponding to initial conditions a and we have

$$\begin{aligned} T^{(X)}_{a\to b} &= \langle \Phi_b|(H_\alpha + U_\alpha - H_\beta)|X_a^{(+)}\rangle \\ &= \langle \Phi_b|(V_\beta - W_\alpha)|X_a^{(+)}\rangle. \end{aligned} \tag{XIX.125}$$

If W_α is sufficiently small, $X_a^{(+)}$ will differ little from $\Psi_a^{(+)}$.

Similarly, suppose that V_β can be put in the form

$$V_\beta = U_\beta + W_\beta$$

and that the stationary solutions of the Hamiltonian $H_\beta + U_\beta$ corresponding to the energy E are known. We shall denote these solutions by Ξ and the associated transition matrix by $T^{(\Xi)}$. In particular, $\Xi_b^{(-)}$ is the "incoming wave" solution corresponding to the initial conditions b and we have

$$T^{(\Xi)}_{a\to b} = \langle \Xi_b^{(-)}|(V_\alpha - W_\beta)|\Phi_a\rangle. \tag{XIX.126}$$

If W_β is sufficiently small, $\Xi_b^{(-)}$ will differ little from $\Psi_b^{(-)}$.

Now according to (XIX.120)

$$T_{a\to b} = T^{(X)}_{a\to b} + \langle \Psi_b^{(-)}|W_\alpha|X_a^{(+)}\rangle \tag{XIX.127}$$

$$= T^{(\Xi)}_{a\to b} + \langle \Xi_b^{(-)}|W_\beta|\Psi_a^{(+)}\rangle. \tag{XIX.128}$$

These two expressions for $T_{a\to b}$ are exact. We obtain approximate expressions by replacing $\Psi_b^{(-)}$ by $\Xi_b^{(-)}$ in the first one and $\Psi_a^{(+)}$ by $X_a^{(+)}$ in the second

$$T_{a\to b} \simeq T^{(X)}_{a\to b} + \langle \Xi_b^{(-)}|W_\alpha|X_a^{(+)}\rangle \tag{XIX.129}$$

$$\simeq T^{(\Xi)}_{a\to b} + \langle \Xi_b^{(-)}|W_\beta|X_a^{(+)}\rangle. \tag{XIX.130}$$

Although formally different if $W_\alpha \neq W_\beta$, these two expressions are always equal, as may easily be seen by applying (XIX.120) with $H_\alpha + U_\alpha$ in place of H, and $H_\beta + U_\beta$ in place of $\hat{H}$.

These formulas constitute a generalization of the Born approximation [cf. eq. (XIX.75)]. They are better than the one obtained by simply replacing $\Psi_a^{(+)}$ by $X_a^{(+)}$ in expression (XIX.121). Indeed since one has [eq. (XIX.125)]

$$\langle \Phi_b | V_\beta | X_a^{(+)} \rangle = T^{(X)}_{a \to b} + \langle \Phi_b | W_\alpha | X_a^{(+)} \rangle,$$

this last approximation amounts to replacing $\Psi_b^{(-)}$ in expression (XIX.127) by Φ_b and not by $\Xi_b^{(-)}$. For similar reasons, formulas (XIX.129) and (XIX.130) are better than the expression obtained by replacing $\Psi_b^{(-)}$ by $\Xi_b^{(-)}$ in the right-hand side of (XIX.122).

21. Scattering of Fast Electrons by an Atom

As an illustration of the Born approximation proper, consider the scattering of fast electrons by an atom.

We shall suppose that the nucleus is infinitely heavy and fixed at the origin. The Hamiltonian of the system is

$$H = \frac{\mathbf{p}^2}{2m} + h + V(\mathbf{r}, A).$$

The first term is the kinetic energy of the incident electron, the second the Hamiltonian of the atom and the third the interaction energy

$$V(\mathbf{r}, A) = -\frac{Ze^2}{r} + \sum_{i=1}^{Z} \frac{e^2}{|\mathbf{r} - \mathbf{r}_i|}, \qquad \text{(XIX.131)}$$

where $\mathbf{r}$ is the position vector of the incident electron and

$$\mathbf{r}_1, \mathbf{r}_2, \ldots, \mathbf{r}_Z$$

the position vectors of the electrons of the atom. Finally, let

$$\varphi_0, \varphi_1, \ldots, \varphi_n, \ldots,$$

denote the eigenfunctions of h and

$$e_0, e_1, \ldots, e_n, \ldots,$$

the corresponding eigenvalues.

We consider an inelastic scattering process in which the momentum of the electron changes from $\hbar\mathbf{k}_0$ to $\hbar\mathbf{k}_n$ while the atom passes from the ground state φ_0 to the excited state φ_n. Energy being conserved in the collision we have

$$\hbar^2(k_0^2 - k_n^2) = 2m(e_n - e_0).$$

We denote the momentum transfer by $\hbar\mathbf{q}$,

$$\mathbf{q} = \mathbf{k}_n - \mathbf{k}_0.$$

Note that relation (XIX.24) does not apply here, but that

$$q^2 = (k_0 - k_n)^2 + 4k_0k_n \sin^2 \tfrac{1}{2}\theta. \qquad \text{(XIX.132)}$$

In addition to the direct process in which the incident electron is simply scattered with loss of a part of its kinetic energy, there may be an exchange of the incident electron with one of the electrons of the atom. This exchange effect can be important when the velocity of the scattered electron is of the same order of magnitude as the velocity of the electrons of the atom, i.e. when $k_n a \simeq 1$; it is small under conditions where the Born approximation is valid, and will be neglected here. In the same spirit, we shall treat the incident electron as a particle different from the electrons of the atom. Applying formula (XIX.123), we then obtain the transition amplitude in the Born approximation:

$$T_{0\to n} \simeq \int \mathrm{e}^{-\mathrm{i}\mathbf{q}\cdot\mathbf{r}}\, \varphi_n{}^*(A)\, V(\mathbf{r}, A)\, \varphi_0(A)\, \mathrm{d}\mathbf{r}\, \mathrm{d}A. \qquad \text{(XIX.133)}$$

This is the Born approximation transition amplitude for a particle undergoing the momentum transfer $\hbar\mathbf{q}$ in the potential

$$V_n(\mathbf{r}) \equiv \int \varphi_n{}^*(A)\, V(\mathbf{r}, A)\, \varphi_0(A)\, \mathrm{d}A. \qquad \text{(XIX.134)}$$

This result is true whatever n and applies equally well in the elastic scattering case $(n=0)$.

In order to put it in a form analogous to that obtained in § 8 we introduce the "electron density"

$$\varrho_n(\mathbf{r}) = Z \int \varphi_n{}^*(\mathbf{r}, \mathbf{r}_2, \ldots, \mathbf{r}_Z)\, \varphi_0(\mathbf{r}, \mathbf{r}_2, \ldots, \mathbf{r}_Z)\, \mathrm{d}\mathbf{r}_2 \ldots \mathrm{d}\mathbf{r}_Z \qquad \text{(XIX.135)}$$

and the corresponding form factor

$$F_n(\mathbf{q}) = \int \mathrm{e}^{-\mathrm{i}\mathbf{q}\cdot\mathbf{r}}\, \varrho_n(\mathbf{r})\, \mathrm{d}\mathbf{r}.$$

In the elastic scattering case $(n=0)$, we simply have the ground state electron density and the corresponding form factor [cf. eq. (XIX.48)]:

$$\varrho_0(\mathbf{r}) = \varrho(r), \qquad F_0(\mathbf{q}) = F(q).$$

If we substitute the explicit form of $V(\mathbf{r}, A)$ given by equation

(XIX.131) in the integral defining $V_0(\mathbf{r})$, we see that $V_0(\mathbf{r})$ is the Coulomb interaction potential for an electron in the field created by the charge distribution

$$e[Z\delta(\mathbf{r}) - \varrho(r)].$$

This is precisely the scattering potential adopted in § 8; thus the model adopted there is justified.

Consider now an inelastic collision ($n \neq 0$). We substitute the explicit form of $V(\mathbf{r}, A)$ given by equation (XIX.131) in the integral defining $V_n(\mathbf{r})$. Due to the orthogonality of the functions φ_0 and φ_n, the contribution of the term Ze^2/r vanishes. The other terms give a contribution equal to the Coulomb potential felt by an electron in the field created by the charge distribution $-e\varrho_n(\mathbf{r})$. Repeating the manipulations of § 8, we find

$$T_{0\to n} \simeq -4\pi\, e^2 F_n(\mathbf{q}) \qquad (n \neq 0)$$

whence the Born approximation result for the inelastic scattering cross section

$$\frac{\mathrm{d}\sigma_{0\to n}}{\mathrm{d}\Omega} = 4\,\frac{m^2e^4}{\hbar^4}\,\frac{k_n}{k_0}\,\frac{|F_n(\mathbf{q})|^2}{q^4}. \qquad \text{(XIX.136)}$$

Note the similarity of this formula and formula (XIX.49) for elastic scattering. The angular distribution depends on the factor $|F_n(\mathbf{q})|^2/q^4$. The form of $F_n(\mathbf{q})$ is easily deduced from that of $\varrho_n(\mathbf{r})$. In particular $F_n(0)=0$. Moreover, if a is the radius of the atom, the factor $F_n(\mathbf{q})$ is appreciably different to zero only in the region $qa \lesssim 1$. When the Born approximation is valid ($\gamma \ll 1$), we have $k_0 a \gg 1$; this corresponds to an incident energy much greater than the distance between atomic levels, which is of the order of $\hbar^2/ma^2$; it follows that $(k_0 - k_n)a$ is of the order of $1/k_0 a$. Since q varies from $k_0 - k_n$ to $k_0 + k_n$ when θ increases from zero to 2π, qa varies from $1/k_0 a$ to $2k_0 a$ in the same interval [cf. eq. (XIX.132)]. According to the foregoing discussion, the electron is most probably scattered into angles for which $qa \lesssim 1$, that is, into the domain of small angles:

$$\theta \lesssim \frac{1}{k_0 a}.$$

In principle, inelastic scattering can be used to measure the position of the electron. By hypothesis, the transversal dimensions of the incident wave packet are much greater than a, and the uncertainty in the transversal component of the momentum is therefore much smaller than $\hbar/a$. Immediately after the inelastic scattering, supposing that we can detect the change in quantum state of the atom, the position of the electron is known with an uncertainty of order a; however, the direction of its momentum being known only up to $1/k_0 a$, there is an uncertainty in the transversal component of the said momentum of order $\hbar/a$. This is in agreement with what was said in Chapter IV concerning position measurements (cf. in particular the discussion of measurements in the Wilson chamber, note, p. 142).

22. Coulomb Excitation of Nuclei

As an illustration of the generalized Born approximation, we take up again the problem treated in § XVII.3 with a view to avoiding the use of the classical approximation.

Unless otherwise indicated, we shall use the notation of § XVII.3. We shall suppose the incident energy sufficiently low that condition (XVII.28) is realized. On the other hand, conditions (XVII.29) and (XVII.30) upon which the classical treatment was founded will not necessarily be fulfilled. Since the incident energy is lower than the height Ze^2/R of the Coulomb barrier, the proton "penetrates" very little into the nucleus in the course of the collision. We therefore expect the effect of the specifically nuclear interactions to be small, and we neglect it for the moment. The collision is then governed by the Hamiltonian $H^{(0)} + V$.

We denote the initial and final conditions of the collision by a and b respectively and the corresponding eigensolutions of $H^{(0)}$ by $X_a^{(+)}$ and $X_b^{(-)}$. Since in $H^{(0)}$ the proton variables are completely separated from the nuclear variables, $X_a^{(+)}$ is the product of the nuclear wave-function in the initial state α by a Coulomb scattering wave $\xi_a^{(+)}(\boldsymbol{r})$ representing the stationary scattering state of a proton of energy E and initial momentum $\hbar \boldsymbol{k}_a$ by the potential Ze^2/r; similarly, $X_b^{(-)}$ is the product of the wave function of the nucleus in the state β by a Coulomb wave $\xi_b^{(-)}(\boldsymbol{r})$ of the "incoming wave" type [1]) representing the scattering of a proton of energy $(E - \Delta E)$ and of momentum

[1]) Its expansion into spherical harmonics is given by eq. (XIX.77), taking regular Coulomb solutions for F_l. Note that $\xi_b^{(-)} = \xi_{Kb}^{(+)*}$.

$\hbar\mathbf{k}_b$ by the potential Ze^2/r. Since $X_a^{(+)}$ gives no contribution to channel β the exact formula (XIX.127) gives

$$T_{a\to b} = \langle \Psi_b^{(-)}|V|X_a^{(+)}\rangle.$$

If V is treated as a small perturbation we can neglect its contribution to $\Psi_b^{(-)}$ and replace $\Psi_b^{(-)}$ by $X_b^{(-)}$, giving, in agreement with the generalized Born formula (XIX.129),

$$T_{a\to b} = \langle X_b^{(-)}|V|X_a^{(+)}\rangle.$$

Since the X-waves practically vanish for $r<R$, we may replace V by its expansion (XVII.34), giving

$$T_{a\to b} = \textstyle\sum_{lm}(-)^m R_l^{-m}\langle\beta J_\beta M_\beta|Q_l^m|\alpha J_\alpha M_\alpha\rangle$$

$$R_l^m = \frac{4\pi Ze}{2l+1}\int \xi_b^{(-)*}(\mathbf{r})\,\frac{Y_l^m(\Omega)}{r^{l+1}}\,\xi_a^{(+)}(\mathbf{r})\,\mathrm{d}\mathbf{r}. \qquad \text{(XIX.137)}$$

By applying relation (XIX.115) one obtains the Coulomb excitation cross section. The expression obtained is very similar to the one given by the semi-classical theory. The latter is obtained by replacing R_l^m by $A(\mathrm{d}\sigma_R/\mathrm{d}\Omega)^{\frac{1}{2}}S_l^m$, where A is the positive constant defined by relation (XIX.20): $A^2 = 4\pi^2\hbar^4 v_a/M^2 v_b$. Indeed in the limit when conditions (XVII.29–30) are fulfilled, the chief contribution to the integral R_l^m comes from the neighborhood of the classical trajectory and the semi-classical result can be obtained by applying the method of stationary phases.

The discussion of selection rules given at the end of § XVII.3 applies here without change. In particular, for experiments in which the target nuclei are not oriented and in which the polarization of the excited nuclei is not measured, we have

$$\frac{\mathrm{d}\sigma_{a\to b}}{\mathrm{d}\Omega} = \frac{1}{(2J_\alpha+1)(2l_0+1)}\,\frac{M^2 v_b}{4\pi^2\hbar^4 v_a}\,|\langle\beta\|Q^{(l_0)}\|\alpha\rangle|^2\,(\textstyle\sum_m |R_{l_0}^m|^2).$$

The above treatment can be extended to include the specifically nuclear interactions. Denote by V_{pA} the nuclear interaction potential between the proton and the nucleons of nucleus A. V_{pA} is very strong for $r<R$ and practically vanishes for $r>R$. We shall henceforth include V_{pA} in $H^{(0)}$. It is convenient to separate the external and the internal parts of V: $V = V_{\text{int}} + V_{\text{ext}}$, in accordance with the definition

$$V_{\text{ext}} = \begin{cases} V & \text{if} \quad r > R \\ 0 & \text{if} \quad r < R \end{cases}$$

and also to include V_{int} in $H^{(0)}$. With these modifications the separation of variables effected above is no longer possible and $X_a^{(+)}$ and $X_b^{(-)}$ are no longer pure elastic scattering waves. The generalized Born approximation now gives

$$T_{a\to b} \simeq T^{(X)}_{a\to b} + \langle X_b^{(-)}| V_{\text{ext}} | X_a^{(+)}\rangle.$$

The first term, $T^{(X)}_{a\to b}$ is the nuclear excitation term. It is the transition amplitude obtained when we replace the interaction between proton and nucleus in the external region ($r > R$) by a point Coulomb interaction; the excitation $\alpha \to \beta$ can then occur only if the proton penetrates into the nucleus. The second term is the Coulomb excitation term proper.

Due to the existence of the Coulomb barrier and the nature of nuclear forces (short range and strong), the $X_a^{(+)}$ and $X_b^{(-)}$ waves have narrow resonances at low energies analogous to the scattering resonances studied in Chapter X (Section IV). Knowing the parameters characteristic of these resonances – resonant energy and resonance width in the different open channels – one can construct these waves in the external region [1]), and calculate the two terms of the transition amplitude. Outside the resonances, the proton practically does not penetrate into the nucleus, $T^{(X)}_{a\to b}$ is negligible, and the Coulomb excitation amplitude is given to a very good approximation by formula (XIX.137), in which the X are pure Coulomb scattering waves. When passing through a resonance, the contribution from $T^{(X)}_{a\to b}$ ceases to be negligible and its energy-dependence has the typical resonant shape [cf. eq. (X.64)]; at the same time the Coulomb excitation amplitude departs significantly from formula (XIX.137); the two amplitudes contribute coherently to the total cross section.

23. Green's Functions and Integral Equations for Stationary Scattering Waves

The considerations of § 13 can easily be extended to include collisions of complex systems. To each of the Hamiltonians H, H_α, etc., we can associate the Green's function $[E-H \pm \mathrm{i}\varepsilon]^{-1}$, $[E-H_\alpha \pm \mathrm{i}\varepsilon]^{-1}$, etc. Except for a few changes in notation, the results of § 13 all remain valid here, and may be deduced in an analogous way, in particular

---

1) A detailed treatment of this question is given in the references of note 1, p. 832.

property (XIX.85), identities (XIX.88) and (XIX.89) and the asymptotic forms of these functions. One has, for example, for each open channel γ [cf. eq. (XIX.94)]

$$\langle \mathbf{r}_\gamma | \frac{1}{E-H\pm \mathrm{i}\varepsilon} |u\rangle \underset{r_\gamma\to\infty}{\sim} -\frac{M_\gamma}{2\pi\hbar^2}\,\varphi_\gamma\,\frac{\mathrm{e}^{\pm \mathrm{i}k_c r_\gamma}}{r_\gamma}\,\langle \Psi^{(\mp)}_{(\gamma,\pm\mathbf{k}_c)}|u\rangle$$

$$(\mathbf{k}_c = k_c \mathbf{r}_\gamma / r_\gamma).$$

Using these various properties of the Green's functions, one can deduce the integral equations

$$\Psi_a{}^{(\pm)} = \Phi_a + \frac{1}{E-H_\alpha \pm \mathrm{i}\varepsilon} V_\alpha \Psi_a{}^{(\pm)} \qquad \text{(XIX.138)}$$

$$\Psi_a{}^{(\pm)} = X_a{}^{(\pm)} + \frac{1}{E-H_\alpha - U_\alpha \pm \mathrm{i}\varepsilon} W_\alpha \Psi_a{}^{(\pm)} \qquad \text{(XIX.139)}$$

etc., and also the formulas

$$\Psi_a{}^{(\pm)} = \left(1+\frac{1}{E-H\pm \mathrm{i}\varepsilon} V_\alpha\right)\Phi_a \qquad \text{(XIX.140)}$$

$$= \left(1+\frac{1}{E-H\pm \mathrm{i}\varepsilon} W_\alpha\right) X_a{}^{(\pm)}. \qquad \text{(XIX.141)}$$

From these integral equations or from these formulas, it is easy to deduce the Born expansion for the transition amplitudes. Substituting formula (XIX.140) into (XIX.121) and expanding the Green's function, we obtain

$$\langle b|T|a\rangle = \langle \Phi_b | \left(V_\beta + V_\beta \frac{1}{E-H+\mathrm{i}\varepsilon} V_\alpha\right) |\Phi_a\rangle \qquad \text{(XIX.142)}$$

$$= \langle \Phi_b | \left(V_\beta + V_\beta \frac{1}{E-H_\alpha+\mathrm{i}\varepsilon} V_\alpha + \ldots\right) |\Phi_a\rangle. \qquad \text{(XIX.143)}$$

In the particular case of sections I and II, the transition amplitudes can all be defined as matrix elements of a certain operator T defined by equation (XIX.101), or else by one or the other of integral equations (XIX.102). When dealing with complex collisions, the definition of a unique operator is no longer possible. Nevertheless it will be seen from equation (XIX.142) that any transition amplitude from channel

α to channel β at energy E may be regarded as a matrix element of a certain operator $T^{\beta\alpha}$ defined by

$$T^{\beta\alpha} = V_\beta + V_\beta \frac{1}{E - H + \mathrm{i}\varepsilon} V_\alpha. \qquad \text{(XIX.144)}$$

Note that in the case of rearrangement collisions ($V_\beta \neq V_\alpha$), these matrix elements do not answer to the usual definition of the representation of operators by matrices, since the vectors $|\Phi_a\rangle$ and $\langle\Phi_b|$ occurring in the formula

$$T_{a\to b} = \langle\Phi_b|T^{\beta\alpha}|\Phi_a\rangle \qquad \text{(XIX.145)}$$

are not orthogonal.

24. Scattering of a Particle by Two Scattering Centers

The main interest of the formal considerations of the preceding paragraph is their generality and the fact that they provide a framework for the treatment of complex problems. To gain a certain familiarity with this formalism we shall apply it to a simple problem and prove in this way a certain number of familiar results.

We consider the scattering of a particle by two scattering centers, for example the scattering of an electron by two atoms. In what follows we neglect exchange effects but make no particular hypothesis about the wavelength of the incident particle.

We suppose the nuclei of the scattering atoms to be infinitely heavy and treat them as fixed centers. We take nucleus 1 as the origin of coordinates and denote by $\mathbf{R}$ the vector joining nucleus 1 to nucleus 2 (cf. Fig. XIX.3). The distance R is supposed large with respect to atomic dimensions: $a \ll R$. The collision is governed by the Hamiltonian

$$H = H_0 + V, \qquad \text{(XIX.146)}$$

where

$$H_0 = \frac{\mathbf{p}^2}{2m} + h_1 + h_2 \qquad \text{(XIX.146')}$$

$$V = V_1 + V_2. \qquad \text{(XIX.146'')}$$

h_1 and h_2 are the Hamiltonians of atoms 1 and 2 respectively and V_1 and V_2 their potentials of interaction with the incident particle. Finally, we denote the free-wave Green's function by G_0:

$$G_0 \equiv (E - H_0 + \mathrm{i}\varepsilon)^{-1}.$$

The transition matrix T associated with the (elastic or inelastic) scattering of the particle by the two atoms is represented by the Born expansion

$$T = V + VG_0V + VG_0VG_0V + \dots \qquad \text{(XIX.147)}$$

Replacing V by $V_1 + V_2$, we obtain the expansion of T in powers of V_1 and V_2

$$T = V_1 + V_2 + V_1G_0V_1 + V_1G_0V_2 + V_2G_0V_1 + V_2G_0V_2 + V_1G_0V_1G_0V_1 + V_1G_0V_1G_0V_2 + \dots$$

In what follows, we make no particular hypothesis about the strength of V_1 or V_2. This expansion is therefore not necessarily a rapidly converging one and thus cannot be taken, as it stands, as a starting point for an approximation method. However, it is possible to regroup its terms so as to form an expansion that is rapidly converging.

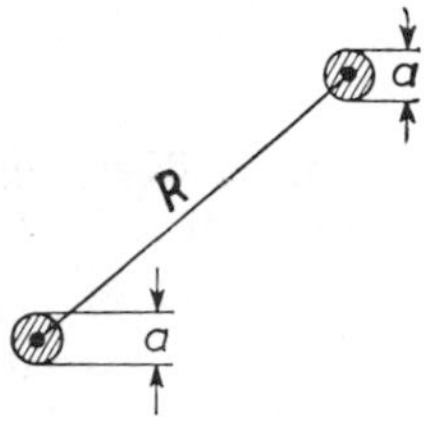

Fig. XIX.3.

The regroupment in question is based on the following remark. We consider the calculation of a matrix element of the second-order term $V_1G_0V_2$ in the representation where $\boldsymbol{r}$ is diagonal. Any matrix element of G_0, the free-wave Green's function, contains the factor $e^{ik|\boldsymbol{r}-\boldsymbol{r}'|}/|\boldsymbol{r}-\boldsymbol{r}'|$. Since V_1 is essentially localized in a small domain about the origin and V_2 in a small domain about the point $\boldsymbol{R}$, this factor is of order $1/R$. The same remark applies to the term $V_2G_0V_1$. Roughly speaking, the terms $V_1G_0V_2$ and $V_2G_0V_1$ are a/R times smaller than the terms $V_1G_0V_1$ and $V_2G_0V_2$. This remark applies equally well to higher-order terms. It suggests that we classify the various terms according to the number of times that G_0 appears between V_1 and V_2. Henceforth we shall say that a term is of the first order if G_0 never appears between V_1 and V_2, of the second order if this occurs once, ..., of the nth order if this occurs $(n-1)$ times, etc. In this terminology, $V_1G_0V_1$ and $V_2G_0V_2$ are of the first order, $V_1G_0V_2$ and $V_2G_0V_1$ of the second order.

We introduce the individual transition matrices T_1, T_2 defined by

$$\begin{aligned} T_i &= V_i + V_iG_0T_i \qquad (i = 1, 2) \qquad \text{(XIX.148)} \\ &= V_i + V_iG_0V_i + V_iG_0V_iG_0V_i + \dots \end{aligned}$$

T_1 is the transition matrix associated with scattering from atom 1 when we neglect the interaction of the incident particle with atom 2, T_2 that associated with scattering from atom 2 when we neglect the interaction with atom 1. The contributions of successive orders are simply expressed in terms of the operators T_1, T_2 and G_0. Such expressions are easily determined by simple inspection. The first order gives T_1+T_2, the second $T_1G_0T_2+T_2G_0T_1$, etc. We therefore have

$$T = (T_1 + T_2) + (T_1 G_0 T_2 + T_2 G_0 T_1) + (T_1 G_0 T_2 G_0 T_1 + T_2 G_0 T_1 G_0 T_2) + \dots \qquad \text{(XIX.149)}$$

Expansion (XIX.149) is the starting point of our treatment. The various terms are easy to interpret. The first-order terms represent simple scattering of the particle either by atom 1 (term T_1), or by atom 2 (term T_2). The second-order terms represent double scattering: $T_1G_0T_2$ represents the scattering of the incident particle by atom 2 (operator T_2), then propagation of the scattered particle from 2 to 1 (operator G_0) and finally the scattering of the particle by atom 1 (operator T_1). Similarily each nth order term represents n successive scatterings of the particle alternatively by atoms 1 and 2.

The mechanism thus associated with each term can be schematically represented by diagrams of the type used in the time dependent perturbation theory (Fig. XVII.1); two such diagrams are represented in Fig. XIX.4.

Expansion (XIX.149) relates the transition amplitudes of the two-scatterer problem to the amplitude of the single-scatterer problem.

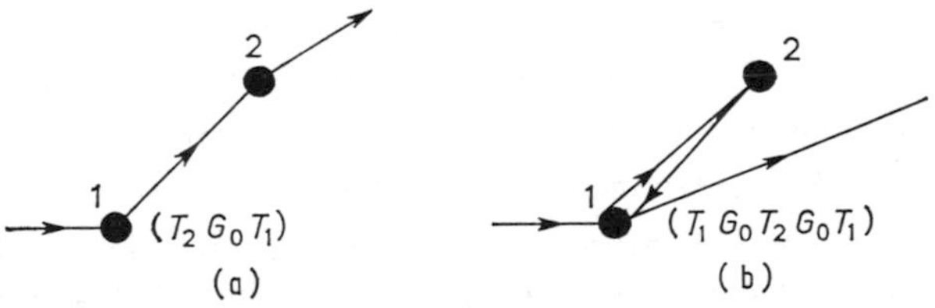

Fig. XIX.4. Diagrams representing two terms of expansion (XIX.149).

For simplicity, we shall suppose the two atoms identical and denote by $t(e)$ the transition matrix relative to energy e for the single-scatterer problem, that is, for the scattering of the particle by *one* of these atoms *placed at the origin*.

We denote the eigenvector of H_0 corresponding to the product of the plane wave $e^{i\mathbf{k}\cdot\mathbf{r}}$ representing the incident particle with momentum $\hbar\mathbf{k}$ by the wave function φ_m of atom 1 and the wave function φ_n of atom 2 by $|\mathbf{k}mn\rangle$:

$$H_0|\mathbf{k}mn\rangle = \left(\frac{\hbar^2k^2}{2m} + e_m + e_n\right)|\mathbf{k}mn\rangle.$$

With the normalization adopted here,

$$\langle \mathbf{k}'m'n'|\mathbf{k}mn\rangle = (2\pi)^3\,\delta(\mathbf{k}-\mathbf{k}')\delta_{mm'}\delta_{nn'}.$$

Similarly $|\mathbf{k}m\rangle$ denotes the product of the plane wave $e^{i\mathbf{k}\cdot\mathbf{r}}$ by the wave function φ_m of the atom in the single-scatterer problem.

From the definition (XIX.148) of T_1, one easily deduces that

$$\langle \mathbf{k}'m'n'|T_1(E)|\mathbf{k}mn\rangle = \delta_{nn'}\,\langle \mathbf{k}'m'|t(E-e_n)|\mathbf{k}m\rangle. \quad \text{(XIX.150)}$$

Similarily. one can relate the elements of the matrix T_2 to the elements of the transition matrix associated with the scattering by a single atom *placed at the point* $\mathbf{R}$; the latter is obtained from $t(e)$ by an overall translation of $\mathbf{R}$; it follows (Problem XIX.5) that

$$\langle \mathbf{k}'m'n'|T_2(E)|\mathbf{k}mn\rangle = \delta_{mm'}\,e^{i(\mathbf{k}-\mathbf{k}')\cdot\mathbf{R}}\langle \mathbf{k}'n'|t(E-e_m)|\mathbf{k}n\rangle. \quad \text{(XIX.151)}$$

Formulas (XIX.150) and (XIX.151) apply to any transition whatsoever; they are valid even if the states $|\mathbf{k}mn\rangle$ and $|\mathbf{k}'m'n'\rangle$ correspond to an energy different to E.

25. Simple Scattering. Interference

As a first application of expansion (XIX.149), we calculate the cross section for the elastic scattering of the particle by the two atoms.

Suppose that the atoms are, and remain, in their ground state φ_0, and denote by $\mathbf{k}_0$ and $\mathbf{k}$ the wave vectors of the incident and scattered waves respectively, i.e. we consider the transition $(\mathbf{k}_0 00) \to (\mathbf{k}00)$ and we have

$$k = k_0, \qquad E = \hbar^2k^2/2m + 2e_0.$$

To calculate the transition amplitude we shall take only the first-order terms in expansion (XIX.149):

$$T \simeq T_1 + T_2. \quad \text{(XIX.152)}$$

Taking (XIX.150) and (XIX.151) into account and putting

$$\boldsymbol{q} \equiv \boldsymbol{k} - \boldsymbol{k}_0$$
$$\langle \boldsymbol{k}0|t(E - e_0)|\boldsymbol{k}_0 0\rangle \equiv \langle \boldsymbol{k}|t|\boldsymbol{k}_0\rangle,$$

we find

$$\langle \boldsymbol{k}\,00|T|\boldsymbol{k}_0\,00\rangle \simeq [1 + \mathrm{e}^{-\mathrm{i}\boldsymbol{q}\cdot\boldsymbol{R}}]\,\langle \boldsymbol{k}|t|\boldsymbol{k}_0\rangle. \qquad \text{(XIX.153)}$$

This will be recognized as the relation giving the scattering amplitude in the elementary theory of interference. With the aid of (XIX.153) one can relate the cross section $\mathrm{d}\Sigma/\mathrm{d}\Omega$ for elastic scattering by the two atoms to the cross section $\mathrm{d}\sigma/\mathrm{d}\Omega$ for the transition $(\boldsymbol{k}_0 0) \to (\boldsymbol{k}0)$, that is, to the cross section for the same elastic scattering by a single atom. The first is obtained by multiplying the square of the modulus of $\langle \boldsymbol{k}00|T|\boldsymbol{k}_0 00\rangle$ by a suitable factor, the second by multiplying the square of the modulus of $\langle \boldsymbol{k}|t|\boldsymbol{k}_0\rangle$ by the same factor. Relation (XIX.153) thus leads to

$$\mathrm{d}\Sigma/\mathrm{d}\Omega \simeq 2I(\Omega)\,\mathrm{d}\sigma/\mathrm{d}\Omega \qquad \text{(XIX.154)}$$

$$I(\Omega) = 1 + \cos(\boldsymbol{q}\cdot\boldsymbol{R}). \qquad \text{(XIX.155)}$$

The presence of the factor $I(\Omega)$ in formula (XIX.154) is due to interference between the waves scattered by each atom. If this interference phenomenon did not occur, we would have $I(\Omega)=1$ and the cross section $\mathrm{d}\Sigma/\mathrm{d}\Omega$ would be simply the sum of the scattering cross sections of each of the atoms 1 and 2.

The usual results of interference theory are obtained when we examine the behavior of $I(\Omega)$ as a function of the scattering angle. We discuss only the two limiting cases when the wavelength $\lambda = 2\pi/k$ is very large or very small beside R.

If $\lambda \gg R$, then $\boldsymbol{q}\cdot\boldsymbol{R} \ll 1$ whatever the scattering angle, and therefore $I(\Omega)=2$. The cross section for scattering by the two atoms is therefore four times the individual cross section, that is, twice what it would be if the phenomenon of interference did not exist.

If $\lambda \ll R$, $I(\Omega)$ oscillates rapidly between the values 0 and 2 when the scattering angle is varied. Let the angles made by the vectors $\boldsymbol{k}_0$ and $\boldsymbol{k}$ with $\boldsymbol{R}$ be α_0 and α respectively:

$$\boldsymbol{q}\cdot\boldsymbol{R} = \frac{2\pi R\,(\cos\alpha_0 - \cos\alpha)}{\lambda}.$$

$I(\Omega)$ therefore vanishes each time that $(\cos\alpha - \cos\alpha_0)$ is a half-integral multiple of λ/R, and is equal to 2 each time that $(\cos\alpha - \cos\alpha_0)$ is an integral multiple of λ/R. The corresponding values of α give respectively the directions of minimum and maximum interference. The width of the interference fringes is of order λ/R. The possibility of observing these interferences depends on the angular resolving power of the detecting apparatus. The latter counts the particles admitted into a certain solid angle of *finite* dimensions $\delta\Omega \equiv (\delta\alpha)^2$. The counting rate is given by the integral of $\mathrm{d}\Sigma/\mathrm{d}\Omega$ over this finite domain. The angular dependence of $\mathrm{d}\Sigma/\mathrm{d}\Omega$ in this domain is essentially given by the factor $I(\Omega)$. If $\delta\alpha \gg \lambda/R$, $I(\Omega)$ has many oscillations in the domain in question and may be replaced by its average value: the results will be the same as if $I(\Omega)=1$ and as if the scattering from the two atoms was incoherent [1]). If, on the other hand, $\delta\alpha \ll \lambda/R$, $I(\Omega)$ is practically constant in this domain and the resolving power of the detector is sufficient for the observation of the interference phenomenon.

Let us now consider inelastic collisions in which one of the two atoms passes from its ground state to its nth excited state. Denote by $\mathbf{k}_n$ the wave vector for the scattered wave

$$E = \frac{\hbar^2 k_n{}^2}{2m} + e_0 + e_n.$$

The cross section $\mathrm{d}\Sigma_n/\mathrm{d}\Omega$ is the sum of the cross sections $\mathrm{d}\Sigma_{n0}/\mathrm{d}\Omega$ and $\mathrm{d}\Sigma_{0n}/\mathrm{d}\Omega$ corresponding to the transitions $(\mathbf{k}_0 00) \to (\mathbf{k}_n n0)$ and $(\mathbf{k}_0 00) \to (\mathbf{k}_n 0n)$ respectively. These are easily calculated in approximation (XIX.152) where we retain only the simple scattering terms in the expansion of T. In the transition $(\mathbf{k}_0 00) \to (\mathbf{k}_n n0)$, atom 1 is excited, atom 2 remains in its ground state; the contribution of T_2 obviously vanishes [cf. eq. (XIX.151)]; the contribution of T_1 gives $\mathrm{d}\sigma_n/\mathrm{d}\Omega$, the cross section of the process $(\mathbf{k}_0 0) \to (\mathbf{k}_n n)$, the elastic scattering of the particle by a single atom. The transition $(\mathbf{k}_0 00) \to (\mathbf{k}_n 0n)$ corresponds to the inverse situation: the contribution of T_1 vanishes, that of T_2 gives $\mathrm{d}\sigma_n/\mathrm{d}\Omega$. Finally

$$\frac{\mathrm{d}\Sigma_n}{\mathrm{d}\Omega} \equiv \frac{\mathrm{d}\Sigma_{n0}}{\mathrm{d}\Omega} + \frac{\mathrm{d}\Sigma_{0n}}{\mathrm{d}\Omega} = 2\frac{\mathrm{d}\sigma_n}{\mathrm{d}\Omega}.$$

[1]) This result is a confirmation and a more exact statement of the remarks of § X.2 regarding the conditions in which a target may be considered as formed of independent scatterers.

Contrary to what happens in elastic scattering, each atom acts as if it were alone: the waves scattered inelastically by atom 1 and by atom 2 correspond to different channels and cannot interfere.

26. Multiple Scattering

Consider now the transition $(\mathbf{k}_0 00) \rightarrow (\mathbf{k}pq)$ in which atoms 1 and 2 pass from their ground states to their pth and qth excited states respectively

$$E = \frac{\hbar^2 k^2}{2m} + e_p + e_q.$$

The cross section for this transition will be denoted by $\mathrm{d}\Sigma_{pq}/\mathrm{d}\Omega$.

Since both atoms change their quantum state in the transition, the contribution from the simple scattering terms T_1 and T_2 vanishes, and we must push the expansion of T to the second order. This gives

$$\langle \mathbf{k}\, pq|T|\mathbf{k}_0\, 00\rangle \simeq A_{12} + A_{21}, \tag{XIX.156}$$

where

$$A_{ij} \equiv \langle \mathbf{k}\, pq\,|\,T_i G_0 T_j\,|\,\mathbf{k}_0\, 00\rangle. \tag{XIX.157}$$

The diagrams for these two double scattering amplitudes are given in Figure XIX.5

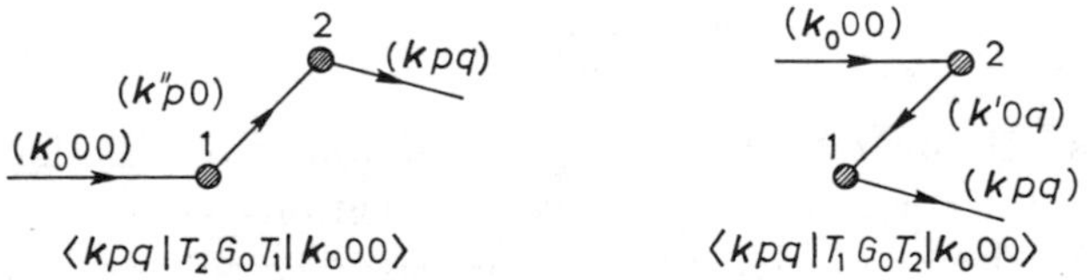

Fig. XIX.5. Diagram for the double scattering amplitudes.

We first calculate A_{21}. In order to take into account the condition $a \ll R$, we make the calculation in the $\{\mathbf{r}mn\}$ representation. Taking into account that G_0 commutes with h_1 and h_2, we find

$$A_{21} = \iint f_2(\mathbf{r}'')\, g(\mathbf{r}'', \mathbf{r}')\, f_1(\mathbf{r}')\, \mathrm{d}\mathbf{r}''\, \mathrm{d}\mathbf{r}', \tag{XIX.158}$$

where

$$f_1(\mathbf{r}') \equiv \langle \mathbf{r}'p0|T_1|\mathbf{k}_0 00\rangle = \frac{1}{(2\pi)^3} \int \mathrm{e}^{\mathrm{i}\mathbf{k}'\cdot\mathbf{r}'}\, \langle \mathbf{k}'p0|T_1|\mathbf{k}_0\, 00\rangle\, \mathrm{d}\mathbf{k}' \tag{XIX.159}$$

$$f_2(\mathbf{r}'') \equiv \langle \mathbf{k}pq|T_2|\mathbf{r}''p0\rangle = \frac{1}{(2\pi)^3} \int \mathrm{e}^{-\mathrm{i}\mathbf{k}''\cdot\mathbf{r}''}\, \langle \mathbf{k}pq|T_2|\mathbf{k}''\, p0\rangle\, \mathrm{d}\mathbf{k}'' \tag{XIX.160}$$

$$g(\mathbf{r}'', \mathbf{r}') \equiv \langle \mathbf{r}''p0|G_0|\mathbf{r}'p0\rangle = -\frac{m}{2\pi\hbar^2} \frac{\mathrm{e}^{\mathrm{i}K_p|\mathbf{r}''-\mathbf{r}'|}}{|\mathbf{r}''-\mathbf{r}'|}. \tag{XIX.161}$$

In the last expression, K_p is the positive quantity given by

$$E = \frac{\hbar^2 K_p^2}{2m} + e_p + e_0.$$

We shall also use the vector $\mathbf{K}_p$, defined by

$$\mathbf{K}_p \equiv K_p \mathbf{R}/R.$$

Owing to the properties of T_1, the function $f_1(\mathbf{r}')$ is appreciably different to zero only in a domain of radius a about the origin; owing to the properties of T_2, $f_2(\mathbf{r}'')$ is appreciably different to zero only in a domain of radius a about the point $\mathbf{R}$. We can therefore replace $g(\mathbf{r}'', \mathbf{r}')$ in the integral (XIX.158) by the first term in its expansion in powers of $\mathbf{r}'/R$ and $(\mathbf{r}''-\mathbf{R})/R$. In so doing we make an error of order a/R in the calculation of A_{21}. Since

$$|\mathbf{r}'' - \mathbf{r}'| \simeq R + \mathbf{R}\cdot(\mathbf{r}'' - \mathbf{R} - \mathbf{r}')/R + \dots,$$

this leads to

$$g(\mathbf{r}'', \mathbf{r}') \simeq -\frac{m}{2\pi\hbar^2} \frac{e^{i\mathbf{K}_p\cdot(\mathbf{r}''-\mathbf{r}')}}{R}. \tag{XIX.162}$$

Substituting expressions (XIX.159), (XIX.160) and (XIX.162) on the right-hand side of (XIX.158), and performing the integrations, we find:

$$A_{21} \simeq -(m/2\pi\hbar^2 R)\, \langle \mathbf{k}pq|T_2|\mathbf{K}_p p0\rangle\, \langle \mathbf{K}_p p0|T_1|\mathbf{k}_0 00\rangle. \tag{XIX.163}$$

Similarly if we denote by $\mathbf{K}_q$ the vector defined by

$$\mathbf{K}_q \equiv -K_q \mathbf{R}/R, \qquad E = \frac{\hbar^2 K_q^2}{2m} + e_0 + e_q$$

we obtain for A_{12}, with an error of order a/R, the expression

$$A_{12} \simeq -(m/2\pi\hbar^2 R)\, \langle \mathbf{k}pq|T_1|\mathbf{K}_q 0q\rangle\, \langle \mathbf{K}_q 0q|T_2|\mathbf{k}_0 00\rangle. \tag{XIX.164}$$

Note that the matrix elements of T_1 and T_2 occurring in expressions (XIX.163) and (XIX.164) correspond to transitions conserving the energy. By applying relations (XIX.150) and (XIX.151), we can therefore express A_{21} and A_{12} in terms of the transition amplitudes involved in the inelastic scattering by a single atom. This is also true for the cross section $d\Sigma_{pq}/d\Omega$ since

$$\frac{d\Sigma_{pq}}{d\Omega} = \frac{2\pi}{\hbar v_0} |A_{21} + A_{12}|^2 \varrho(E)$$

$$= \frac{2\pi}{\hbar v_0} |A_{21}|^2 \varrho(E) + \frac{2\pi}{\hbar v_0} |A_{12}|^2 \varrho(E) + \frac{2\pi}{\hbar v_0} (A_{21}^* A_{12} + A_{21} A_{12}^*)\, \varrho(E). \tag{XIX.165}$$

We obtain the result

$$\mathrm{d}\Sigma_{pq}/\mathrm{d}\Omega = (\mathrm{d}\sigma_p(\mathbf{k}_0 \to \mathbf{K}_p)/R^2\,\mathrm{d}\Omega)(\mathrm{d}\sigma_q(\mathbf{K}_p \to \mathbf{k})/\mathrm{d}\Omega) + (\mathrm{d}\sigma_q(\mathbf{k}_0 \to \mathbf{K}_q)/R^2\,\mathrm{d}\Omega)(\mathrm{d}\sigma_p(\mathbf{K}_q \to \mathbf{k})/\mathrm{d}\Omega) + \text{interference terms} \qquad \text{(XIX.166)}$$

We leave to the reader the calculation of the interference terms. In this expression, the symbol $\mathrm{d}\sigma_n(\mathbf{k} \to \mathbf{k}')/\mathrm{d}\Omega$ denotes the cross section for the inelastic scattering $(\mathbf{k}0) \to (\mathbf{k}'n)$ of the particle by a single atom.

The first two terms of formula (XIX.166) are precisely those given by an elementary classical treatment. Classically, one can imagine the double scattering taking place in two different ways: either the particle is first scattered inelastically by atom 1 towards atom 2 and then scattered inelastically by atom 2 into the final direction, or, it is first scattered by atom 2 towards atom 1 and then by atom 1 into the final direction. The cross sections for these two processes are given respectively by the first and second terms of expression (XIX.166). To these we must add terms coming from the interference between the two types of scattered waves. Remarks analogous to those of § 25 may be made with respect to these interference terms. To observe them, the resolving power of the detector must be sufficient to distinguish angles of order λ/R.

If $\lambda \ll a$, the individual cross sections are essentially concentrated in the forward direction, the scattering amplitudes practically vanish for deflections greater than λ/a. Therefore – as is easily seen from inspection of equations (XIX.163–165) – double scattering can only occur if the two atoms are aligned to within λ/a in the incident direction, that is if $\mathbf{k}_0 \| \mathbf{R}$, or if $\mathbf{k}_0 \| (-\mathbf{R})$. In the first case A_{12} is negligible but A_{21} is appreciable for small deflections, that is, for $\mathbf{k} \| \mathbf{k}_0$ to within λ/a: the particle is first scattered by atom 1 and then by atom 2 into a direction nearly parallel to its incident direction. In the second case, the roles of atoms 1 and 2 are interchanged. The observation of the "trajectories" of ionizing particles in a Wilson cloud chamber is based on these results (cf. note 1, p. 142).

IV. VARIATIONAL CALCULATIONS OF TRANSITION AMPLITUDES

27. Stationary Expressions for the Phase Shift

The variational method has already been used for the determination of energy levels (Ch. XVIII). In the present section we give a brief account of how it can be used to calculate phase shifts and, more generally, transition amplitudes. To do this, one must express these amplitudes as functionals of the scattering wave function which are stationary with respect to variations of this function about its correct value. The integral expressions for transition amplitudes given in the preceding section are not suitable for this purpose since they are not stationary. For example, expression (XIX.54) for T_l, considered as a functional of ψ_l, is not stationary when ψ_l is the correct solution of the radial equation; similarly, expression (XIX.127) for $T_{a\to b}$, considered as a functional of $\Psi_b^{(-)}$, is not stationary when $\Psi_b^{(-)}$ varies about its correct value. Several stationary expressions have been proposed for these quantities. Here we give the one, due to Schwinger [1]), which proves to be the most useful.

In this paragraph, we consider the case of a particle in a central potential and look for a stationary expression for the coefficient T_l of the expansion of the transition amplitude in spherical harmonics [expansion (XIX.51)]. Except for a few modifications to be described below we follow the notation of § 9.

If $\psi_a^{(+)}$ is the complete stationary scattering wave, the partial wave ψ_l satisfies the integral equation (XIX.56). With a view to later generalizations, we write the latter in the form

$$\psi_l(r) = j_l(kr) + g_l^{(+)} V \psi_l, \qquad \text{(XIX.167)}$$

where $g_l^{(+)}$ is the integral operator whose kernel is the Green's function

$$g_l^{(+)}(r, r') \equiv -(2mk/\hbar^2)\, j_l(kr_<)\, h_l^{(+)}(kr_>), \qquad \text{(XIX.168)}$$

in other words:

$$g_l^{(+)} V \psi_l \equiv \int_0^\infty g_l^{(+)}(r, r')\, V(r')\, \psi_l(r')\, r'^2\, \mathrm{d}r'.$$

We shall also use the notation $\langle \varphi_1, \varphi_2 \rangle$ to denote the scalar product of two radial functions φ_1, φ_2:

$$\langle \varphi_1, \varphi_2 \rangle \equiv \int_0^\infty \varphi_1^*(r)\, \varphi_2(r)\, r^2\, \mathrm{d}r.$$

---

[1]) See notably B. Lippmann and J. Schwinger, *loc. cit.*; a discussion of the respective merits of the different variational expressions proposed for the calculation of phase shifts is given by M. Moe and D. S. Saxon, Phys. Rev. **111** (1958) 950.

The integral form (XIX.54) for T_l can therefore be written

$$T_l = \langle j_l, V\psi_l \rangle. \qquad \text{(XIX.169)}$$

Let us now put

$$A[\psi] \equiv \langle j_l, V\psi \rangle = \langle \psi^*, Vj_l \rangle = \int_0^\infty j_l(kr)\, V(r)\, \psi(r)\, r^2\, \mathrm{d}r, \qquad \text{(XIX.170)}$$

$$B[\psi] \equiv \langle \psi^*, (V - Vg_l^{(+)}V)\,\psi \rangle \qquad \text{(XIX.171)}$$

$$= \int_0^\infty \psi^2(r)\, V(r)\, r^2\, \mathrm{d}r - \int_0^\infty \int_0^\infty (\psi(r)\, V(r)\, g_l^{(+)}(r, r')\, V(r')\, \psi(r'))\, r^2\, \mathrm{d}r\, r'^2\, \mathrm{d}r',$$

and consider the functional

$$\mathscr{T}_l[\psi] \equiv \frac{A^2}{B} \qquad \text{(XIX.172)}$$

depending on the function ψ. The domain of variation of ψ is defined only by the condition that $r^2|\psi|^2$ be locally integrable.

As an obvious consequence of (XIX.167) and (XIX.169) we have

$$\mathscr{T}_l\, [\psi_l] = T_l.$$

Note too that $\mathscr{T}_l$ *depends neither on the normalization of the function* ψ (it does not change when ψ is multiplied by an arbitrary constant), *nor on the value taken by* ψ *in regions where* $V(r) = 0$. $\mathscr{T}_l$ therefore takes the same value T_l for any function ψ_l satisfying the following less restrictive condition than eq. (XIX.167):

$$\psi_l\,(r) = Cj_l\,(kr) + g_l^{(+)}\, V\psi_l \quad \text{if} \quad V(r) \neq 0 \qquad \text{(XIX.167}a\text{)}$$

(C, arbitrary constant).

Let us calculate the variation of $\delta\mathscr{T}_l$ as a function of $\delta\psi$. From definition (XIX.172),

$$\delta\mathscr{T}_l = \frac{2A}{B}\,\delta A - \frac{A^2}{B^2}\,\delta B.$$

Now

$$\delta A = \int_0^\infty \delta\psi\, V(r)\, j_l(kr)\, r^2\, \mathrm{d}r = \langle \delta\psi^*, Vj_l \rangle$$

and, taking into account that V is real and $g_l^{(+)}(r, r')$ symmetrical in r and r',

$$\delta B = 2\,\langle \delta\psi^*, (V - Vg_l^{(+)}V)\,\psi \rangle.$$

We may therefore write

$$\delta \mathscr{T}_l = \frac{2A}{B^2} \langle \delta\psi^*, F \rangle,$$

where

$$F(r) = B[\psi] V(r) j_l(kr) - A[\psi] V(r) (\psi - g_l^{(+)} V\psi).$$

In order to have $\delta \mathscr{T}_l = 0$ for any $\delta\psi$, it is necessary and sufficient that $F(r)$ vanish. For this it is necessary that $j_l(kr)$ and $\psi - g_l^{(+)} V\psi$ be proportional at any point where $V(r)$ is not zero, that is, that ψ be one of the functions ψ_l obeying equation (XIX.167*a*). One easily verifies that this is also a sufficient condition. *Thus, the stationary value of $\mathscr{T}_l$ is equal to the amplitude that we wish to calculate*:

$$T_l = \mathscr{T}_l \big|_{\rm st} \tag{XIX.173}$$

In order to introduce only real functions into the calculation, we separate the real and imaginary parts of $g_l^{(+)}(r, r')$. The real part is the Green's function

$$g_l^{(1)}(r, r') \equiv -(2mk/\hbar^2) j_l(kr_<) n_l(kr_>)$$

and we have

$$g_l^{(+)}(r, r') = g_l^{(1)}(r, r') - \mathrm{i}(2mk/\hbar^2) j_l(kr) j_l(kr').$$

Substituting this expression in the definition of $\mathscr{T}_l$ (i.e. in expression (XIX.171) for $B[\psi]$), we can rewrite (XIX.171) in the equivalent form

$$T_l^{-1} = \mathscr{T}_l^{-1} \Big|_{\rm st} = \frac{\langle \psi^*, (V - V g_l^{(1)} V) \psi \rangle}{\langle j_l, V\psi \rangle^2} \Big|_{\rm st} + \mathrm{i} \frac{2mk}{\hbar^2}$$

and since from equation (XIX.52)

$$T_l^{-1} - \mathrm{i}(2mk/\hbar^2) = -2mk \cot \delta_l / \hbar^2,$$

we obtain the following stationary expression for $k \cot \delta_l$:

$$k \cot \delta_l = -\frac{\hbar^2}{2m} \frac{\langle \psi^*, (V - V g_l^{(1)} V) \psi \rangle}{\langle j_l, V\psi \rangle^2} \Big|_{\rm st}$$

$$= -\frac{\hbar^2}{2m} \frac{\int_0^\infty \psi^2 V r^2 \,\mathrm{d}r - \int_0^\infty \int_0^\infty (\psi(r) V(r) g_l^{(1)}(r, r') V(r') \psi(r')) r^2 \,\mathrm{d}r\, r'^2 \,\mathrm{d}r'}{[\int_0^\infty j_l(kr) V(r) \psi(r) r^2 \,\mathrm{d}r]^2} \Bigg|_{\rm st} \tag{XIX.174}$$

It can easily be shown that the function ψ_l for which the right-hand side of equation (XIX.174) is stationary can be taken to be real, and that this reality condition for the trial functions does not modify the variational property obtained.

28. The Variational Calculation of Phase Shifts. Discussion

Equation (XIX.174) is the starting point of a variational method for calculating the phase shifts. The functional on the right-hand side is calculated by substituting for ψ a trial function φ depending on several parameters and taking the stationary value of the function with respect to variations of these parameters. The closer the trial function φ to the exact solution ψ the closer will be the resulting approximate value for $k \cot \delta_l$ to the exact one. As has already been pointed out, and here we have one of the chief virtues of the Schwinger variational method, the result is independent of the normalization of φ and of the values taken by φ in regions where the potential V vanishes. For the method to be precise it is therefore sufficient to take a trial function whose general form is the same as the exact solution in the region of the potential. The estimate of the error is based essentially on these semi-quantitative considerations and is, as in the variational calculation of energy levels, largely empirical.

If we limit ourselves to substituting the free wave $j_l(kr)$ for ψ in the right-hand side of (XIX.174), we find

$$k \cot \delta_l \equiv -\frac{\hbar^2}{2m} \frac{1-\Delta_l}{\langle j_l, V j_l \rangle} \qquad \text{(XIX.175)}$$

putting

$$\Delta_l \equiv \frac{\langle j_l, V g_l^{(1)} V j_l \rangle}{\langle j_l, V j_l \rangle}. \qquad \text{(XIX.176)}$$

This formula is *a priori* more exact than the one given by the Born approximation [eq. (X.75)]. In the limit when $\Delta_l \ll 1$, it is equivalent to the second-order Born approximation, but when Δ_l ceases to be small it is often much better.

To illustrate the comparison between these two methods let us treat the s-wave scattering by a square well in the low energy limit. We take

$$V(r) = \begin{cases} -V_0 & r < r_0 \\ 0 & r > r_0. \end{cases} \qquad \text{(XIX.177)}$$

We shall calculate the scattering lengths

$$a = -\lim_{k\to 0} (k \cot \delta)^{-1}$$

by the different methods cited above and compare the results with those given by the exact calculation. The calculations are not difficult. If we put $b = (2m V_0 r_0^2/\hbar^2)^{\frac{1}{2}}$, the results are given by the following formulas:

exact calculation: $$a = -\left(\frac{\tan b}{b} - 1\right) r_0$$

variational calculation [formula (XIX.175)]: $$a_{\text{var}} = -\frac{\frac{1}{3}b^2}{1-\frac{2}{5}b^2} r_0$$

Born approximation: $$a_{\text{B}} = -\tfrac{1}{3} b^2 r_0$$

second-order Born approximation: $$a_{\text{B}}^{(2)} = -\left(\tfrac{1}{3} b^2 + \tfrac{2}{15} b^4\right) r_0.$$

TABLE XIX.1

Comparison of various calculations of the scattering length as a function of the parameter

$$b = (2m V_0 r^2{}_0/\hbar^2)^{\frac{1}{2}}.$$

r_0 has been taken as the unit of length.

b	Exact calculation a	Stationary formula (XIX.175) a_{var}	Born Approximation 2nd order $a_{\text{B}}^{(2)}$	Born Approximation 1st order $a_{\text{B}}^{(1)}$
0	0	0	0	0
$0.1\,\pi$	$-$ 0.034	$-$ 0.034	$-$ 0.034	$-$ 0.033
$0.2\,\pi$	$-$ 0.156	$-$ 0.156	$-$ 0.152	$-$ 0.132
$0.3\,\pi$	$-$ 0.460	$-$ 0.459	$-$ 0.401	$-$ 0.296
$0.4\,\pi$	$-$ 1.449	$-$ 1.428	$-$ 0.859	
$\frac{\pi}{2}$	∞ (*)	$-$ 63.2 (**)	$-$ 1.63	
$0.6\,\pi$	2.63	2.81	$-$ 2.9	
$0.7\,\pi$	1.63	1.72		
$0.8\,\pi$	1.29	1.38		
$0.9\,\pi$	1.11	1.21		
π	1.00	1.12		

(*) $a = \infty$ corresponds to the existence of a bound state of zero energy.
(**) a_{var} becomes infinite and changes sign for $b = 0.503\,\pi$.

The validity criterion for the Born approximation is given by inequality (XIX.43), namely:

$$b \ll 1$$

(b is the measure of the depth of the potential, that is, of the number of bound s-states). The numerical results corresponding to the four formulas above are given in Table (XIX.1). Note that a_{var} remains an excellent approximation for relatively large value of b, up to and including the region $\frac{1}{2}\pi < b < \pi$ in which the Born expansion certainly does not converge.

29. Extension to Complex Collisions

The preceding theory can be extended to more general collision problems. We shall not enter into the details of such possible extensions but shall limit ourselves to giving a stationary expression for the transition matrix in the case of the elastic or inelastic scattering of two complex particles.

Unless otherwise stated, we follow the notation of Section III. The amplitude for the transition $a \to b$ is given by

$$T_{a\to b} = \langle \Phi_b | V_\beta | \Psi_a^{(+)} \rangle = \langle \Psi_b^{(-)} | V_\alpha | \Phi_a \rangle.$$

These expressions are not stationary with respect to variations of $\Psi_a^{(+)}$ or $\Psi_b^{(-)}$. Since we are concerned with a scattering process, the unperturbed Hamiltonians are equal; we therefore put

$$H_\alpha = H_\beta = H_0 \qquad V_\alpha = V_\beta = V$$

$$G_0^{(+)} = G_0^{(-)\dagger} = [E - H_0 + \mathrm{i}\varepsilon]^{-1}.$$

One knows that

$$|\Phi_a\rangle = (1 - G_0^{(+)} V)\,|\Psi_0^{(+)}\rangle$$

$$\langle \Phi_b | = \langle \Psi^{(-)} |\, (1 - V G_0^{(+)}).$$

The amplitude $T_{a\to b}$ is also given by the expression

$$T_{a\to b} = \frac{\langle \Psi_b^{(-)} | V | \Phi_a \rangle \, \langle \Phi_b | V | \Psi_a^{(+)} \rangle}{\langle \Psi_b^{(-)} | (V - V\, G_0^{(+)}\, V) | \Psi_a^{(+)} \rangle}. \qquad \text{(XIX.178)}$$

This expression is stationary with respect to independent variations of the functions $\Psi_a^{(+)}$ and $\Psi_b^{(-)}$. It is the generalization of the stationary expression for T_l given in § 27.

Except in the simplest cases, such as the collision of two elementary particles, one encounters a major difficulty in the practical use of this expression, that of obtaining an explicit expression for the Green function $G_0{}^{(+)}$. However, it may sometimes be useful in arguments where an explicit use of $G_0{}^{(+)}$ is not required [1]). In any case its applications are rather limited.

V. GENERAL PROPERTIES OF THE TRANSITION MATRIX

Certain properties of the T matrix follow directly from the characteristic properties of the Hamiltonian governing the collision. Some of them have already been indicated in the preceding sections. However their character of great generality has not been stressed. This question will systematically be investigated in the present section.

30. Conservation of Flux. Unitarity of the S Matrix

Certain properties of the T matrix are a simple consequence of the Hermitean character of the Hamiltonian H governing the collision. Among these are the integral representations (XIX.121) and (XIX.122). By using the same method as in § 19 we shall obtain two new relations, called conservation of flux relations.

Following the notations of § 19 we consider two stationary waves $\Psi_a{}^{(+)}$, $\Psi_b{}^{(+)}$ corresponding to the *same* value E of the energy. We have

$$\Psi_b{}^{(+)*}\,(H\,\Psi_a{}^{(+)}) - (H\,\Psi_b{}^{(+)})^*\,\Psi_a{}^{(+)} = 0.$$

The quantity obtained by summing over the spins and integrating over a finite volume of configuration space therefore vanishes. By applying Green's theorem this quantity can be transformed into a surface integral, which takes the form of a sum of terms relative to the different channels in the limit when that surface tends to infinity (cf. note, p. 837). We thereby obtain

$$0 = \sum_\nu \frac{\hbar^2}{2M_\nu} \lim_{R_\nu\to\infty} \{\Psi_b{}^{(+)*}, \Psi_a{}^{(+)}\}_\nu. \qquad \text{(XIX.179)}$$

The right-hand side of this equation is to be compared with that of

---

1) Cf. B. Lippmann and J. Schwinger, *loc. cit.*

(XIX.119). It can be evaluated by replacing the functions $\Psi_b^{(+)}$, $\Psi_a^{(+)}$ by their asymptotic form in each channel, giving

$$0 = \frac{\hbar^2}{2M_\beta} \lim_{R_\beta \to 0} \left\{ \mathrm{e}^{-\mathrm{i}\mathbf{k}_b \cdot \mathbf{r}_\beta}, f_{a\beta}^{(+)}(\Omega_\beta) \frac{\mathrm{e}^{\mathrm{i}k_b r_\beta}}{r_\beta} \right\}_\beta$$
$$+ \frac{\hbar^2}{2M_\alpha} \lim_{R_\alpha \to 0} \left\{ f_{b\alpha}^{(+)*}(\Omega_\alpha) \frac{\mathrm{e}^{-\mathrm{i}k_a r_\alpha}}{r_\alpha}, \mathrm{e}^{\mathrm{i}\mathbf{k}_a \cdot \mathbf{r}_\alpha} \right\}_\alpha$$
$$+ \sum_\nu \frac{\hbar^2}{2M_\nu} \lim_{R_\nu \to 0} \left\{ f_{b\nu}^{(+)*}(\Omega_\nu) \frac{\mathrm{e}^{-\mathrm{i}k_n r_\nu}}{r_\nu}, f_{a\nu}^{(+)}(\Omega_\nu) \frac{\mathrm{e}^{\mathrm{i}k_n r_\nu}}{r_\nu} \right\}_\nu .$$

The evaluation of the contribution of the first two terms is patterned on the work of § 2. The third term is a sum over all the channels, α and β included, which is easily evaluated from the definition of the symbol $\{\ldots\}_\nu$; contrary to what occurs in the calculation of § 19, the contribution from this term does not vanish. We finally obtain

$$0 = -\frac{2\pi\hbar^2}{M_\beta} f_{a\beta}^{(+)}(\Omega_b) + \frac{2\pi\hbar^2}{M_\alpha} f_{b\alpha}^{(+)*}(\Omega_a) + \sum_\nu \frac{\mathrm{i}\hbar^2 k_n}{M_\nu} \int f_{b\nu}^{(+)*}(\Omega_\nu) f_{a\nu}^{(+)}(\Omega_\nu)\, \mathrm{d}\Omega_\nu .$$

Replacing the $f(\Omega)$ by the elements of the T matrix in accordance with definition (XIX.114), we obtain

$$0 = \langle b|T|a\rangle - \langle b|T^\dagger|a\rangle + 2\pi\mathrm{i} \sum_\nu \varrho_\nu(E) \int \langle b|T^\dagger|n\rangle \,\mathrm{d}\Omega_\nu \langle n|T|a\rangle . \quad \text{(XIX.180)}$$

Here we have denoted by n the plane wave in channel ν directed along Ω_ν and used the definition of the density of states

$$\varrho_\nu(E) = \frac{M_\nu k_n}{(2\pi)^3 \hbar^2} .$$

$T^\dagger$ is given by the usual definition of Hermitean conjugation:

$$\langle m|T^\dagger|n\rangle = \langle n|T|m\rangle^* .$$

The preceding work can also be carried through with the $\Psi^{(-)}$ in place of the $\Psi^{(+)}$. This gives the relation

$$0 = \sum_\nu \frac{\hbar^2}{2M_\nu} \lim_{R_\nu \to \infty} \{\Psi_a^{(-)}, \Psi_b^{(-)*}\}_\nu \quad \text{(XIX.179')}$$

which is obtained from relation (XIX.179) by exchanging a and b and replacing $\Psi^{(+)}$ by $\Psi^{(-)*}$. To evaluate the right-hand side, it suffices to make the necessary substitutions in the preceding calculation, and to use definition (XIX.114′) of the matrix elements of T in place of (XIX.114). One obtains:

$$0 = \langle b|T|a\rangle - \langle b|T^{\dagger}|a\rangle + 2\pi \mathrm{i} \sum_{\nu} \varrho_{\nu}(E) \int \langle b|T|n\rangle \,\mathrm{d}\Omega_{\nu} \langle n|T^{\dagger}|a\rangle. \quad \text{(XIX.180′)}$$

Let us give a second, more formal, demonstration of relations (XIX.180) and (XIX.180′). From the relations

$$\langle b|T|a\rangle = \langle \Phi_b|V_{\beta}|\Phi_a\rangle + \langle \Phi_b|V_{\beta} \frac{1}{E-H+\mathrm{i}\varepsilon} V_{\alpha}|\Phi_a\rangle$$

$$\langle b|T^{\dagger}|a\rangle = \langle \Phi_b|V_{\alpha}|\Phi_a\rangle + \langle \Phi_b|V_{\beta} \frac{1}{E-H-\mathrm{i}\varepsilon} V_{\alpha}|\Phi_a\rangle$$

we obtain, subtracting both sides and applying (XIX.124) and (A.15*c*):

$$\langle b|(T-T^{\dagger})|a\rangle = -2\pi \mathrm{i} \langle \Phi_b|V_{\beta}\delta(E-H)V_{\alpha}|\Phi_a\rangle. \quad \text{(XIX.181)}$$

We suppose that the set of stationary waves $\Psi_n^{(-)}$ *extended over the whole of the spectrum of H* – and complemented, if it exists, by a complete suitably normalized set of eigenvectors of the discrete spectrum – forms a complete orthogonal set of eigenvectors of H, and therefore that we have the closure relation

$$(2\pi)^{-3} \sum_{n} |\Psi_n^{(-)}\rangle\langle\Psi_n^{(-)}| = 1. \quad \text{(XIX.182)}$$

[The sum being extended to all the energies of the spectrum of H, discrete spectrum included.] We shall also suppose that the $\Psi_n^{(+)}$ satisfy the closure relation

$$(2\pi)^{-3} \sum_{n} |\Psi_n^{(+)}\rangle\langle\Psi_n^{(+)}| = 1. \quad \text{(XIX.182′)}$$

Using (XIX.182), we can put the scalar product on the right-hand side of (XIX.181) in the form

$$\langle \Phi_b|V_{\beta}\delta(E-H)V_{\alpha}|\Phi_a\rangle \equiv (2\pi)^{-3} \sum_{n} \langle \Phi_b|V_{\beta}|\Psi_n^{(-)}\rangle \delta(E-E_n) \langle \Psi_n^{(-)}|V_{\beta}|\Phi_a\rangle$$
$$= \sum_{\nu} \varrho_{\nu}(E) \int \langle b|T^{\dagger}|n\rangle \,\mathrm{d}\Omega_{\nu} \langle n|T|a\rangle$$

from which we deduce relation (XIX.180). Relation (XIX.180′) is obtained in the same way using (XIX.182′).

Equations (XIX.180) and (XIX.180′) are satisfied by the matrix elements of T and $T^{\dagger}$ for any a and b. They can be written more simply in the form:

$$T - T^{\dagger} + 2\pi i T^{\dagger} T = 0 \qquad \text{(XIX.183)}$$

$$T - T^{\dagger} + 2\pi i T T^{\dagger} = 0 \qquad \text{(XIX.183')}$$

with a suitable summation convention for the dummy indices in the matrix products $T^{\dagger}T$ and $TT^{\dagger}$, i.e. by weighting each index ν by the factor $\varrho_{\nu}(E)$ giving the density of states in the channel ν. Note that the matrix elements appearing here are all taken between states of energy E.

We now introduce the S matrix:

$$S \equiv 1 - 2\pi i T. \qquad \text{(XIX.184)}$$

This matrix is characteristic of collisions of energy E and its elements, like those of T, are defined between states of energy E. Expressing T and $T^{\dagger}$ in equations (XIX.180) and (XIX.180′) in terms of S and $S^{\dagger}$ we find:

$$S^{\dagger} S = S S^{\dagger} = 1. \qquad \text{(XIX.185)}$$

The S matrix is unitary.

It can also be shown that if $U(t, t')$ is the evolution operator for the system then

$$S = \lim_{\substack{t \to +\infty \\ t' \to -\infty}} U(t, t').$$

The demonstration of this requires great care in passing to the limit; it will not be given here [cf. references note p. 801].

31. The Bohr–Peierls–Placzek Relation (Optical Theorem)

Consider relation (XIX.180) in the particular case when $a = b$ [N.B. relations (XIX.180) and (XIX.180′) are identical when $a = b$]. We then have

$$\langle a|T|a\rangle - \langle a|T|a\rangle^* = -2\pi i \sum_{\nu} \int |\langle n|T|a\rangle|^2 \varrho_{\nu}(E)\, d\Omega_{\nu}. \qquad \text{(XIX.186)}$$

The integrand on the right-hand side is to within a factor $2\pi/\hbar v_a$ the cross section $d\sigma_{a\to n}/d\Omega_{\nu}$, and therefore

$$\sum_{\nu} \int |\langle n|T|a\rangle|^2 \varrho_{\nu}(E)\, d\Omega_{\nu} = \frac{\hbar v_a}{2\pi} \sum_{\nu} \int \frac{d\sigma_{a\to n}}{d\Omega_{\nu}}\, d\Omega_{\nu}$$

$$= \frac{\hbar v_a}{2\pi}\, \sigma_a^{\text{tot}},$$

where σ_a^{tot} is the total cross section for the collision corresponding to initial state a. Returning to (XIX.186) we have

$$\sigma_a^{\text{tot}} = -\frac{2}{\hbar v_a} \operatorname{Im} T_{aa}.$$

To put this expression in a more familiar form we express T_{aa} in terms of the scattering amplitude in the forward direction $f_{aa}^{(+)}(\Omega_a)$, which we denote simply by $f_a(0)$ [cf. eq. (XIX.114)]:

$$T_{aa} \equiv \langle a|T|a\rangle = -\frac{2\pi\hbar^2}{M_\alpha} f_a(0).$$

Thus

$$\boxed{\sigma_a^{\text{tot}} = \frac{4\pi}{k_a} \operatorname{Im} f_a(0)} \qquad \text{(XIX.187)}$$

This is the Bohr–Peierls–Placzek formula relating the total cross section to the imaginary part of the scattering amplitude in the forward direction.

32. Microreversibility

If H is invariant under time reversal, the T matrix satisfies the *microreversibility relation* (cf. § XV.20):

$$\boxed{T_{Kb\to Ka} = T_{a\to b}} \qquad \text{(XIX.188)}$$

The demonstration of this relation has already been given for the simple case of the scattering of a particle by a real potential (§ 3 and 14). The formal demonstration of § 14 can also be used in the general case with very little modification. K being the time-reversal operator, the initial and final states that are obtained from a and b by time reversal (reversal of momenta and spins) will be denoted by Ka and Kb respectively; more precisely

$$\Phi_{Kb} \equiv K\Phi_b \qquad \Phi_{Ka} \equiv K\Phi_a.$$

To prove relation (XIX.188), we make use of expression (XIX.142) giving the amplitude for a given transition:

$$\begin{aligned} T_{Kb\to Ka} &= \langle \Phi_{Ka}| \left[V_\alpha + V_\alpha \frac{1}{E - H + \mathrm{i}\varepsilon} V_\beta \right] |\Phi_{Kb}\rangle \\ &= (\langle \Phi_a|K^\dagger) \left[V_\alpha + V_\alpha \frac{1}{E - H + \mathrm{i}\varepsilon} V_\beta \right] (K|\Phi_b\rangle). \end{aligned}$$

Since K is antiunitary and commutes with H, V_α and V_β this gives

$$T_{Kb\to Ka} = \langle \Phi_b | \left[V_\alpha + V_\beta \frac{1}{E - H + \mathrm{i}\varepsilon} V_\alpha \right] | \Phi_a \rangle$$

$$= \langle \Phi_b | \left[V_\beta + V_\beta \frac{1}{E - H + \mathrm{i}\varepsilon} V_\alpha \right] \Phi_a \rangle .$$

The second line was obtained by applying (XIX.124), and is equal to the amplitude $T_{a\to b}$ as given by expression (XIX.142). Q.E.D.

By squaring both sides of (XIX.188) and expressing the result in terms of the cross sections $\mathrm{d}\sigma_{a\to b}/\mathrm{d}\Omega_\beta$ and $\mathrm{d}\sigma_{Kb\to Ka}/\mathrm{d}\Omega_\alpha$, we obtain the microreversibility relation for cross sections:

$$v_b \, \mathrm{d}\sigma_{Kb\to Ka}/\varrho_a(E)\, \mathrm{d}\Omega_\alpha = v_a \, \mathrm{d}\sigma_{a\to b}/\varrho_b(E)\, \mathrm{d}\Omega_\beta . \qquad \text{(XIX.189)}$$

Here we have used the fact that $v_{Kb} = v_b$, $\varrho_{Ka} = \varrho_a$. From the definition of velocity and density of states [eq. (XVII.52)] we have for each channel

$$v_n \varrho_n = p_n{}^2/(2\pi\hbar)^3 = k_n{}^2/(2\pi)^3 \hbar .$$

Therefore, relation (XIX.189) can be written, with the convention that $\mathrm{d}\Omega_\alpha = \mathrm{d}\Omega_\beta = \mathrm{d}\Omega$,

$$\boxed{k_b{}^2 \, \mathrm{d}\sigma_{Kb\to Ka} = k_a{}^2 \, \mathrm{d}\sigma_{a\to b}} \qquad \text{(XIX.190)}$$

33. Invariance Properties of the T Matrix

Let us now investigate the consequences of the invariance of H with respect to rotations, reflections and more generally with respect to transformations represented by unitary operators. We successively consider the consequences of invariance with respect to a given transformation and with respect to a specified group of transformations.

If H, H_α and H_β are invariant in a given unitary transformation X one has the relation (cf. § XV.13)

$$T_{Xa\to Xb} = T_{a\to b} . \qquad \text{(XIX.191)}$$

[N.B. This relation differs from the microreversibility relation by the sense of the reaction corresponding to the amplitude on the left-hand side.]

To prove (XIX.191), one needs only to observe that according to definition (XIX.144) the operator $T^{\beta\alpha}$ is also invariant in the transformation X:

$$X^{\dagger} T^{\beta\alpha} X = T^{\beta\alpha},$$

and therefore

$$T_{Xa\to Xb} \equiv \langle \Phi_b | X^{\dagger} T^{\beta\alpha} X | \Phi_a \rangle = \langle \Phi_b | T^{\beta\alpha} | \Phi_a \rangle \equiv T_{a\to b}.$$

From (XIX.191), one easily obtains the following relation between cross sections:

$$\mathrm{d}\sigma_{Xa\to Xb} = \mathrm{d}\sigma_{a\to b} \qquad \text{(XIX.192)}$$

to be compared with (XIX.190).

Suppose now that the total Hamiltonian H and the different "unperturbed" Hamiltonians H_α, H_β, ..., are invariant with respect to the transformations of a certain group G. As we shall see this results in certain properties of the T matrix analogous to those obtained in § XV.11 for the matrices representing observables invariant with respect to G.

To see this, we adopt the notation of § XV.11 and consider the two sets of observables J and M defined in that paragraph. Let ν be one of the channels open to collisions of energy E. H_ν, J and M form a set of commuting observables. Denote by $|\nu E_\nu \tau_\nu j \mu\rangle$ the vectors of a common basis (we shall assume that it is a standard basis suited to the group G, although this restriction is not essential). The index ν indicates the channel considered, E_ν is the eigenvalue of H_ν, j and μ denote the eigenvalues of J and M respectively, τ_ν is an additional quantum number which varies in a domain depending on the values of E_ν, j, and μ. These vectors are orthonormal:

$$\langle \nu E_\nu \tau_\nu j \mu | \nu E'_\nu \tau'_\nu j' \mu' \rangle = \delta(E_\nu - E'_\nu)\, \delta_{\tau_\nu \tau'_\nu}\, \delta_{jj'}\, \delta_{\mu\mu'}.$$

For simplicity we shall suppose the index τ_ν discrete. This is the case if we are dealing with a 2-particle channel and if the group G is the rotation group or contains the rotation group as a subgroup. τ_ν then takes a *finite* number of discrete values.

Consider now a collision at a fixed energy E and the transitions from a certain channel ν to another channel ν'; according to the hypotheses made above, the corresponding operator $T^{\nu\nu'}$ [definition (XIX.144)] is invariant with respect to the transformations of the group G. By an obvious generalization of property (XV.52) we have

$$\langle \nu E\tau_\nu j\mu | T^{\nu\nu'} | \nu' E\tau_{\nu'} j'\mu' \rangle = \delta_{jj'}\, \delta_{\mu\mu'}\, \langle \nu\tau_\nu | T^{(j)} | \nu'\tau_{\nu'} \rangle, \qquad \text{(XIX.193)}$$

where $\langle \nu\tau_\nu | T^{(j)} | \nu'\tau_{\nu'} \rangle$ depends on the quantum numbers j, τ_ν and $\tau_{\nu'}$, but not on μ. Equation (XIX.193) sums up all the consequences of the invariance with respect to the group G.

To each pair $(\nu\nu')$ of open channels, there therefore corresponds a certain number of coefficients $\langle \nu\tau_\nu | T^{(j)} | \nu'\tau_{\nu'} \rangle$. Those of these coefficients corresponding to a certain given value of j (j and E fixed; ν, τ_ν, ν' and $\tau_{\nu'}$ variable) form a certain square matrix which we denote by $T^{(j)}$. This matrix is analogous to the T matrix but the number of its dimensions is in general much smaller. In particular if G contains the rotation group and if none of the open channels has more than two particles, $T^{(j)}$ is a finite matrix; if in addition there is but one open channel and if the two particles have spin zero, $T^{(j)}$ has only one dimension, i.e. it is an ordinary number, equal to within an easily determined factor to the coefficient T_j defined by expansion (XIX.51).

It is easy to expand the transition amplitude $T_{a\to b}$ in a series of elements of the $T^{(j)}$ matrices. To this end we start from definition (XIX.145), which we transform using the closure relations for the standard bases corresponding to channels α and β, and make use of property (XIX.193). The coefficients of the expansion depend on the projections of the plane waves Φ_a and Φ_b on the basis vectors in question. Φ_n denoting a plane wave of energy E in channel ν, we can write

$$\langle \Phi_n | \nu E_\nu \tau_\nu j\mu \rangle = \delta(E - E_\nu)\, \langle \Phi_n | \nu\tau_\nu j\mu \rangle. \qquad \text{(XIX.194)}$$

With this notation, we find, after a brief calculation

$$T_{a\to b} = \sum_{j\mu} \sum_{\tau_\alpha \tau_\beta} \langle \Phi_b | \beta\tau_\beta j\mu \rangle\, \langle \beta\tau_\beta | T^{(j)} | \alpha\tau_\alpha \rangle\, \langle \alpha\tau_\alpha j\mu | \Phi_a \rangle. \qquad \text{(XIX.195)}$$

This expansion is the generalization of (XIX.51). Like the latter it is particularly useful when convergence is rapid; this usually occurs in nuclear collisions when the wavelength in the entrance and exit channels is large with respect to the range of nuclear forces, and it is here that it is most often used [cf. references note 1, p. 832].

EXERCISES AND PROBLEMS

1. Demonstrate the asymptotic property

$$\exp(\mathrm{i}\boldsymbol{q}\cdot\boldsymbol{r}) \underset{r\to\infty}{\sim} \frac{2\pi}{\mathrm{i}qr}\left[\delta(\Omega_r-\Omega_q)\,\mathrm{e}^{\mathrm{i}qr}-\delta(\Omega_r+\Omega_q)\,\mathrm{e}^{-\mathrm{i}qr}\right]+\mathrm{O}\left(\frac{1}{r^2}\right).$$

(*i*) using the expansion of the plane wave in spherical harmonics and the closure relations for the latter;

(*ii*) looking directly for the asymptotic form of

$$\int \exp(\mathrm{i}\boldsymbol{q}\cdot\boldsymbol{r})\,\varphi(\Omega_r)\,\mathrm{d}\Omega_r.$$

[$\varphi(\Omega)$, continuous function of the direction $\Omega \equiv (\theta\varphi)$; Ω_r and Ω_q, respective directions of the vectors $\boldsymbol{r}$ and $\boldsymbol{q}$.]

2. Show that for two plane waves $\exp(\mathrm{i}\boldsymbol{q}_1\cdot\boldsymbol{r})$, $\exp(\mathrm{i}\boldsymbol{q}_2\cdot\boldsymbol{r})$ of the same wavelength ($q_1 = q_2$), we have the exact relation

$$\{\exp(\mathrm{i}\boldsymbol{q}_1\cdot\boldsymbol{r}),\ \exp(\mathrm{i}\boldsymbol{q}_2\cdot\boldsymbol{r})\} = 0$$

whatever R. [definition of $\{\ldots\}$ of § 2].

3. Calculate the scattering cross section in the Born approximation

(*i*) for the square well of depth V_0 and radius a;

(*ii*) for the Gaussian potential

$$V = V_0 \exp(-r^2/a^2);$$

(*iii*) for the Yukawa potential

$$V = \frac{V_0 \exp(-Kr)}{Kr}.$$

Verify for these three particular cases the assertions of § 4 concerning the general form of the high energy angular distribution; determine the asymptotic form of the total cross section.

4. Consider the Hamiltonian of a particle of mass m in a short range potential $V(r)$, $(rV \underset{r\to\infty}{\to} 0)$

$$H \equiv -(\hbar^2/2m)\,\Delta + V(r).$$

At energy $E = \hbar^2k^2/2m$, the radial equation of order l is

$$\left[\frac{\mathrm{d}^2}{\mathrm{d}r^2} - \frac{l(l+1)}{r^2} - \frac{2m}{\hbar^2}V + k^2\right] y_l = 0.$$

The regular solution is denoted by $F_l(k;r)$, the "outgoing" and "incoming" solutions by $u_l^{(+)}(k;r)$ and $u_l^{(-)}(k;r)$ respectively. These solutions are normalized so that

$$F_l(k;r) \underset{r\to\infty}{\sim} \sin(kr - \tfrac{1}{2}l\pi + \delta_l)$$

$$u_l^{(\pm)}(k;r) \underset{r\to\infty}{\sim} \exp[\pm\, \mathrm{i}(kr - \tfrac{1}{2}l\pi)].$$

(*i*) Show that the stationary waves $\psi_{\mathbf{k}}^{(\pm)}$ (definitions of § 2) are given by the expansions

$$\Psi_{\mathbf{k}}^{(\pm)} = \frac{4\pi}{kr}\sum_{lm} \mathrm{i}^l \exp(\pm\, \mathrm{i}\delta_l)\, Y_l^{m*}(\hat{\mathbf{k}})\, Y_l^m(\hat{\mathbf{r}})\, F_l(k;r).$$

(*ii*) Show that the functions $G^{(\pm)}(\mathbf{r}, \mathbf{r}')$ defined by

$$\frac{\hbar^2}{2m} G^{(\pm)}(\mathbf{r}, \mathbf{r}') = -\frac{1}{krr'}\sum_{lm} \exp(\pm\, \mathrm{i}\delta_l) Y_l^{m*}(\hat{\mathbf{r}}) Y_l^m(\hat{\mathbf{r}}') F_l(k;r_<) u_l^{(\pm)}(k;r_>)$$

are the Green functions for the operator $E - H$, that is, functions symmetrical in $\mathbf{r}$ and $\mathbf{r}'$ satisfying the equation

$$(E - H)\, G^{(\pm)}(\mathbf{r}, \mathbf{r}') = \delta(\mathbf{r} - \mathbf{r}')$$

and that their asymptotic behavior is given by

$$G^{(\pm)}(\mathbf{r}, \mathbf{r}') \underset{r\to\infty}{\sim} -\frac{2m}{\hbar^2}\, \frac{\exp(\pm\, ikr)}{r}\, \psi^{(\mp)}_{\pm\mathbf{k}}(\mathbf{r}').$$

$$(\mathbf{k} = k\mathbf{r}/r)$$

[These formulas also apply when V behaves asymptotically like $1/r$ if we suitably re-define F_l and $u_l^{(\pm)}$; the asymptotic form of $G^{(\pm)}$ must be re-defined accordingly.]

5. Prove formula (XIX.151).

"I am black, but comely, . . ."
(*Song of Songs*, 1 : 5)

PART FIVE

ELEMENTS OF RELATIVISTIC QUANTUM MECHANICS

CHAPTER XX

THE DIRAC EQUATION

I. GENERAL INTRODUCTION

1. Relativistic Quantum Mechanics [1]

All of the applications made up to the present have been based on the Schrödinger equation. This equation, deduced by the correspondence principle from the Hamiltonian formalism of non-relativistic Classical Mechanics, has all the invariance properties of the Hamiltonian from which it derives. In particular, if the system is isolated, it is invariant under spatial rotations and translations. It can also be shown that it is invariant under Galilean transformations (cf. Problem XV.7). Therefore, the physical properties predicted by the Schrödinger theory are invariant in a Galilean change of referential, but they do not have the invariance under a Lorentz change of referential required by the principle of relativity. Since the Galilean transformation approximates to the Lorentz transformation only in the limit of small velocities, one expects – and experiment verifies – that this theory will correctly describe phenomena only when the velocities of the particles involved are negligible beside the velocity of light: $v \ll c$. In particular, all phenomena concerning the interaction between light and matter, such as emission, absorption or scattering of photons, is outside the framework of non-relativistic Quantum Mechanics.

One of the main difficulties in elaborating relativistic Quantum Mechanics comes from the fact that the *law of conservation of the number of particles ceases in general to be true*. Due to the equivalence of mass and energy, one of the most important consequences of relativity, there can be creation or absorption of particles whenever the interactions give rise to energy transfers equal or superior to the rest masses of these particles. To be a complete theory, Relativistic Quantum Mechanics must encompass in a single scheme dynamical

[1] Knowledge of Sections I and II of Appendix D is recommended for reading this chapter.

states differing not only by the quantum state, but also by the *number* and the *nature* of the elementary particles of which they are composed. For this, we must turn to the concept of the quantized field, whence the name of Quantum Field Theory currently given to Relativistic Quantum Mechanics. This theory, in its present form, is exempt neither of difficulties nor even of contradictions, but it accounts for a very large body of experimental facts.

The fifth and last part of this book is designed to serve as an introduction to Quantum Field Theory and at the same time to furnish elementary methods for calculating certain relativistic effects concerning the dynamics of the electron and the interaction between the electromagnetic field and charged particles.

It is made up of two chapters.

The present chapter, the first of the two, is devoted to one of the simplest problems in Relativistic Quantum Mechanics, the problem of a particle of spin $\frac{1}{2}$ in a given force field. One of the most important examples is the electron in an electromagnetic field. The field is not quantized and one tries to describe the evolution of the system with a wave equation having the invariance properties required by the principle of relativity. This equation must also satisfy the correspondence principle and give the Pauli theory in the non-relativistic approximation. Such an equation exists: it is called the Dirac equation. After reviewing the Lorentz Group and Classical Relativistic Dynamics (Section I) we establish the Dirac equation (Section II), and make a detailed study of its invariance properties (Section III). In the remainder of this chapter we discuss the physical significance of the theory, and, in the course of reviewing its principal applications, examine how it is situated with respect to Classical Dynamics (Section IV), non-relativistic Quantum Mechanics (Section V) and Quantum Field Theory (Section VI).

The second chapter is devoted to the concept of the quantized field, and to the elementary Quantum theory of electromagnetic radiation and its interaction with atomic and nuclear systems.

2. Notation, Various Conventions and Definitions

UNITS. Except for a few obvious exceptions, all expressions appearing in what follows are written with

$$\hbar = c = 1.$$

With this particular choice of units, time appears to have the dimension of a length; energies, momenta and masses the dimension of an inverse length; electric charges appear as dimensionless quantities ($e^2 \equiv e^2/\hbar c \simeq 1/137$). The general expressions may be re-established by simple considerations of homogeneity.

COORDINATES. Specification of an instant t and a point $\boldsymbol{r} \equiv (x, y, z)$ of ordinary space defines a point of space-time. We denote the coordinates of this point by x^0, x^1, x^2, x^3; $x^0 \equiv ct$ is the time coordinate; x^1, x^2, x^3 the three spatial coordinates: $x^1 \equiv x$, $x^2 \equiv y$, $x^3 \equiv z$. More generally, we use the indices 0, 1, 2, 3 to denote the components of four-vectors or tensors along the axes t, x, y, z respectively. Greek indices denote the space-time components of four-vectors or tensors and therefore take the four values 0, 1, 2, 3; roman indices are reserved for the components of ordinary space and therefore take the three values 1, 2, 3. Thus:

$$x^\mu \equiv (x^0, x^k) \equiv (x^0, x^1, x^2, x^3)$$
$$(\mu = 0, 1, 2, 3) \qquad (k = 1, 2, 3).$$

METRIC TENSOR, COVARIANT AND CONTRAVARIANT INDICES

The space-time metric is a pseudo-euclidian metric defined by the *metric tensor*

$$g_{\mu\nu} = \begin{pmatrix} 1 & 0 & 0 & 0 \\ 0 & -1 & 0 & 0 \\ 0 & 0 & -1 & 0 \\ 0 & 0 & 0 & -1 \end{pmatrix}$$

or again

$$g_{00} = 1, \quad g_{\lambda\lambda} = -1, \quad g_{\mu\nu} = 0 \text{ if } \mu \neq \nu \tag{XX.1}$$

We distinguish between *covariant* vectors (that transform like $\partial/\partial x^\mu$) and *contravariant* vectors (that transform like x^μ), and more generally between covariant tensor components and contravariant tensor components. Following the usual convention, covariant indices are placed as subscripts, contravariant indices as superscripts. Thus a^μ denotes a contravariant vector. The corresponding covariant vector a_μ is obtained by application of the metric tensor:

$$a_\mu = \sum g_{\mu\nu} a^\nu,$$

which gives

$$a_0 = a^0, \qquad a_k = -a^k.$$

We shall always follow *the convention of summing over repeated indices.* With this convention the preceding relation becomes simply

$$a_\mu = g_{\mu\nu} a^\nu.$$

Similarly, indices are raised by applying the tensor $g^{\mu\nu}$:

$$a^\mu = g^{\mu\nu} a_\nu.$$

In the present case, we also have

$$g^{\mu\nu} = g_{\mu\nu}.$$

In addition:

$$g_\mu^{\ \nu} = g_{\mu\varrho} g^{\varrho\nu} = g^\mu_{\ \nu} = \delta_\mu^{\ \nu},$$

where $\delta_\mu^{\ \nu}$ is the Kronecker symbol:

$$\delta_\mu^{\ \nu} = \begin{cases} 1 & \text{if} \quad \mu = \nu \\ 0 & \text{if} \quad \mu \neq \nu. \end{cases}$$

THREE-VECTORS, FOUR-VECTORS, SCALAR PRODUCT

For three-vectors, or vectors of ordinary space, we retain the usual notation; each of them is denoted by a bold-face letter and its length by the corresponding character in ordinary print.

The three space components of a contravariant four-vector a^μ form a three-vector. With the above notations, we therefore have

$$a^\mu \equiv (a^0, a^1, a^2, a^3) \equiv (a^0, \mathbf{a}) \qquad \mathbf{a} \equiv (a_x, a_y, a_z)$$

$$a^1 = a_x \qquad a^2 = a_y \qquad a^3 = a_z \qquad a \equiv (\mathbf{a}\cdot\mathbf{a})^{\frac{1}{2}} \equiv [a_x^2 + a_y^2 + a_z^2]^{\frac{1}{2}}.$$

When no confusion is possible with the length of the three-vector $\mathbf{a}$, we shall sometimes omit the index and denote the four-vector a^μ simply by a.

The scalar product of two four-vectors a^μ and b^μ is obtained by contracting the contravariant components of the one with the co-variant components of the other, i.e. it is given by either $a_\mu b^\mu$, or $a^\mu b_\mu$:

$$a_\mu b^\mu = a^\mu b_\mu = a^0 b^0 - \mathbf{a}\cdot\mathbf{b} \qquad \text{(XX.2)}$$

The *norm* of a^μ is $a_\mu a^\mu = (a^0)^2 - a^2$.

Classifications of the four-vectors

The four-vectors may be put into three classes, according to the sign of their norm

$$\begin{array}{ll} a_\mu a^\mu < 0 & a^\mu = \text{space-like vector} \\ a_\mu a^\mu = 0 & a^\mu = \text{null vector} \\ a_\mu a^\mu > 0 & a^\mu = \text{time-like vector} \end{array}$$

This classification corresponds to the position of the vector with respect to the light cone $x_\mu x^\mu = 0$. The two latter cases can be further classified according to the sign of the time component:

$a^0 > 0$ the vector points towards the future;
$a^0 < 0$ the vector points towards the past.

Gradient, differential operators

We retain the notation $\nabla \equiv (\partial/\partial x, \partial/\partial y, \partial/\partial z)$ and $\triangle \equiv \nabla \cdot \nabla$.

The four partial-differentiation operators $\partial/\partial x^\mu$ form a *covariant* vector, called the gradient operator, which we denote by the symbol ∂_μ:

$$\partial_\mu \equiv \partial/\partial x^\mu \equiv (\partial/\partial x^0, \partial/\partial x^1, \partial/\partial x^2, \partial/\partial x^3) \equiv (\partial/\partial ct, \nabla). \qquad \text{(XX.3)}$$

We shall also make use of the "contravariant gradient":

$$\partial^\mu \equiv g^{\mu\nu}\partial_\nu \equiv (\partial/\partial ct, -\nabla). \qquad \text{(XX.4)}$$

The Dalembertian $\Box$ is defined [1]) by (cf. § II.12):

$$\Box \equiv \frac{1}{c^2}\frac{\partial^2}{\partial t^2} - \triangle \equiv \partial_\mu \partial^\mu. \qquad \text{(XX.5)}$$

The $\varepsilon^{\lambda\mu\nu\varrho}$ tensor

$\varepsilon^{\lambda\mu\nu\varrho}$ denotes the completely antisymmetrical tensor with four indices, the components of which are equal to 0 if two of the indices are equal, to $+1$ if $(\lambda\mu\nu\varrho)$ is an even permutation of (0, 1, 2, 3), and to -1 if $(\lambda\mu\nu\varrho)$ is an odd permutation of (0, 1, 2, 3).

Electromagnetic field

The electromagnetic potential is made up of a vector term $\boldsymbol{A}(\boldsymbol{r}, t)$ and a scalar potential $\varphi(\boldsymbol{r}, t)$ which form a four-vector A^μ:

$$A^\mu \equiv (\varphi, \boldsymbol{A}). \qquad \text{(XX.6)}$$

---

[1]) Many authors use the symbol $\Box$ to denote the negative of the operator defined here.

The electric field $\mathscr{E}$ and the magnetic field $\mathscr{H}$ are given by

$$\mathscr{E} = -\nabla\varphi - \partial A/\partial x^0, \qquad \mathscr{H} = \operatorname{curl} \mathbf{A}. \tag{XX.7}$$

The components of $\mathscr{E}$ and $\mathscr{H}$ form an antisymmetrical space-time tensor, $F_{\mu\nu}$, according to the definition

$$F_{\mu\nu} = \frac{\partial A_\nu}{\partial x^\mu} - \frac{\partial A_\mu}{\partial x^\nu} \tag{XX.8}$$

giving

$$F_{\mu\nu} \equiv \begin{pmatrix} 0 & \mathscr{E}_x & \mathscr{E}_y & \mathscr{E}_z \\ -\mathscr{E}_x & 0 & -\mathscr{H}_z & \mathscr{H}_y \\ -\mathscr{E}_y & \mathscr{H}_z & 0 & -\mathscr{H}_x \\ -\mathscr{E}_z & -\mathscr{H}_y & \mathscr{H}_x & 0 \end{pmatrix} \tag{XX.9}$$

We shall also use the four-vector operator D_μ defined by

$$D_\mu \equiv \partial_\mu + \mathrm{i}eA_\mu \equiv \left(\frac{\partial}{\partial x^0} + \mathrm{i}e\varphi,\ \nabla - \mathrm{i}e\mathbf{A}\right). \tag{XX.10}$$

3. The Lorentz Group

A Lorentz change of referential is a *real*, *linear* transformation of the coordinates *conserving the norm* of the intervals between the different points of space-time. In such a transformation, the new coordinates x'^μ of a space-time point are obtained from the old ones x^μ by the relation

$$x'^\mu = \Omega^\mu{}_\nu x^\nu + a^\mu.$$

The real vector a^μ represents a simple translation of the space-time axes. In what follows, we shall treat the translations separately and give the name of Lorentz transformation to the homogeneous transformations $(a^\mu = 0)$ [1]:

$$x'^\mu = \Omega^\mu{}_\nu\, x^\nu. \tag{XX.11}$$

By raising or lowering the indices, we can obtain the matrices $\Omega_\mu{}^\nu$, $\Omega^{\mu\nu}$, $\Omega_{\mu\nu}$ from the matrix $\Omega^\mu{}_\nu$ (for example: $\Omega^{\mu\nu} = g^{\nu\varrho}\Omega^\mu{}_\varrho$). Specification of any one of these matrices defines the Lorentz trans-

[1]) The group formed by all of the Lorentz transformations including the translations is commonly called the *inhomogeneous Lorentz group*, or *Poincaré group*.

formation in question. The condition of reality and of invariance of the norm are written

$$\Omega_{\mu\nu}{}^{*} = \Omega_{\mu\nu} \tag{XX.12}$$

$$\Omega_{\mu\nu}\Omega^{\mu\lambda} = \Omega_{\nu\mu}\Omega^{\lambda\mu} = \delta_{\nu}{}^{\lambda}. \tag{XX.13}$$

It follows that

$$\det |\Omega^{\mu}{}_{\nu}| = \pm 1 \tag{XX.14}$$

and the inverse transformation is written

$$x^{\mu} = x'^{\nu}\Omega_{\nu}{}^{\mu}. \tag{XX.15}$$

These transformations form a group, *the complete Lorentz group*. It is the group of real linear transformations conserving scalar products between four-vectors.

If $\Omega^{00} > 0$, the transformation conserves the sense of time-like vectors, that is, it conserves the sign of the time component of these vectors; it is then called orthochronous, and the set of these particular Lorentz transformations is called *the orthochronous Lorentz group*.

If *in addition* $\det |\Omega^{\mu}{}_{\nu}| = +1$, the transformation also conserves the sense of Cartesian systems in ordinary space, it is then called a proper Lorentz transformation. The ensemble of these transformation forms a group, *the proper Lorentz group*, which we denote by $\mathscr{L}_0$.

All transformations of the proper group may be considered as a succession of infinitesimal transformations. The matrix $\Omega_{\mu\nu}$ of an *infinitesimal Lorentz transformation* is of the form

$$g_{\mu\nu} + \omega_{\mu\nu},$$

where the quantities $\omega_{\mu\nu}$ are infinitesimals. Conditions (XX.12) and (XX.13) give

$$\omega_{\mu\nu} = \omega_{\mu\nu}{}^{*}, \qquad \omega_{\mu\nu} + \omega_{\nu\mu} = 0. \tag{XX.16}$$

$\omega_{\mu\nu}$ is therefore a real antisymmetrical tensor.

Put

$$Z^{(\alpha\beta)}_{\mu\nu} = -\,Z^{(\beta\alpha)}_{\mu\nu} = g_{\mu\alpha}\,g_{\nu\beta} - g_{\mu\beta}g_{\nu\alpha}. \tag{XX.17}$$

$Z^{(\alpha\beta)}_{\mu\nu}$ is an antisymmetrical tensor whose only non-vanishing elements are the two elements $\mu = \alpha$, $\nu = \beta$ and $\mu = \beta$, $\nu = \alpha$; one of which is equal to $+1$, the other to -1. ε being an infinitesimal quantity,

$$g_{\mu\nu} - \varepsilon\, Z^{(\alpha\beta)}_{\mu\nu}$$

is the matrix of a particular infinitesimal Lorentz transformation, the "rotation" through an angle ε in the $x^\alpha x^\beta$ plane.

There exists in all six infinitesimal transformations of this type. The "rotations" in the planes x^1x^2, x^2x^3 and x^3x^1 are spatial rotations of angle ε about the axes Oz, Ox, Oy respectively, the "rotations" in the planes x^1x^0, x^2x^0, x^3x^0 are special Lorentz transformations of velocity ε in the directions Ox, Oy, Oz respectively [1]).

In addition to infinitesimal transformations, one can define different types of *reflection*, notably the spatial reflection s ($x^0 = x^0$, $x^k = -x^k$) and the time reflection t ($x^0 = -x^0$, $x^k = x^k$). The orthochronous group is made up of the transformations $\mathscr{L}_0$, of the reflection s and of their products $s\mathscr{L}_0$. The complete group is formed of the transformations $\mathscr{L}_0$, $s\mathscr{L}_0$, $t\mathscr{L}_0$, and $st\mathscr{L}_0$. The properties of these four sheets of the complete group are summed up in the following table:

<table>
<tr><th>Sheet</th><th>Det | $\Omega^\mu{}_\nu$ |</th><th>Ω^{00}</th><th colspan="3">group</th></tr>
<tr><td>$\mathscr{L}_0$</td><td>$+1$</td><td>> 0</td><td>proper</td><td rowspan="2">orthochronous</td><td rowspan="4">complete</td></tr>
<tr><td>$s\mathscr{L}_0$</td><td>-1</td><td>> 0</td><td></td></tr>
<tr><td>$t\mathscr{L}_0$</td><td>-1</td><td>< 0</td><td></td><td></td></tr>
<tr><td>$st\mathscr{L}_0$</td><td>$+1$</td><td>< 0</td><td></td><td></td></tr>
</table>

1) If the new referential is obtained from the old one by a rotation through a finite angle φ about Oz, one has:

$$x'^1 = x^1 \cos\varphi + x^2 \sin\varphi, \quad x'^2 = x^2 \cos\varphi - x^1 \sin\varphi, \quad x'^3 = x^3, \quad x'^0 = x^0.$$

If it is obtained by a special Lorentz transformation of velocity $v = \tanh\varphi$ directed along Ox, one has

$$x'^1 = x^1 \cosh\varphi - x^0 \sinh\varphi, \quad x'^0 = x^0 \cosh\varphi - x^1 \sinh\varphi, \quad x'^2 = x^2, \quad x'^3 = x^3.$$

The transformations considered above correspond to the case when $\varphi = \varepsilon \equiv$ infinitesimal.

4. Classical Relativistic Dynamics

Let us recall the dynamical properties of a classical particle of rest mass m and charge e in an electromagnetic field $(\varphi, \boldsymbol{A})$.

Let $\boldsymbol{v}$ be the velocity of the particle:

$$\boldsymbol{v} \equiv \frac{\mathrm{d}\boldsymbol{r}}{\mathrm{d}t}. \tag{XX.18}$$

We define the relativistic mass M and the mechanical momentum [1] $\boldsymbol{\pi}$ by:

$$M \equiv \frac{m}{\sqrt{1-v^2}}, \qquad \boldsymbol{\pi} \equiv M\boldsymbol{v} \tag{XX.19}$$

$(M, \boldsymbol{\pi})$ is a certain four-vector π^μ of norm m^2:

$$M^2 - \boldsymbol{\pi}^2 = m^2 \tag{XX.20}$$

and pointing into the future $(M > 0)$.

In the absence of a field, the particle follows a uniform rectilinear motion: $\boldsymbol{v} = Cst.$

In the presence of an electromagnetic field, the trajectory followed by the particle satisfies the equation

$$\frac{\mathrm{d}\boldsymbol{\pi}}{\mathrm{d}t} = e[\mathscr{E} + \boldsymbol{v} \times \mathscr{H}] \equiv \boldsymbol{F}. \tag{XX.21}$$

This is the fundamental equation of the relativistic dynamics of a material point. The vector $\boldsymbol{F}$ is called the *Lorentz force*.

From (XX.21) we have the equations

$$\frac{\mathrm{d}M}{\mathrm{d}t} = (\boldsymbol{v} \cdot \boldsymbol{F}) = e(\boldsymbol{v} \cdot \mathscr{E}), \tag{XX.21'}$$

$$\frac{\mathrm{d}}{\mathrm{d}t}(\boldsymbol{r} \times \boldsymbol{\pi}) = \boldsymbol{r} \times \boldsymbol{F} \tag{XX.22}$$

giving respectively the law of motion of the mass and of the moment of the mechanical momentum.

These relations can be put in covariant form by introducing the proper time τ of the particle, in accordance with the definition

$$\begin{aligned}\mathrm{d}\tau &= (\mathrm{d}x^\mu\, \mathrm{d}x_\mu)^{\frac{1}{2}} \\ &= \sqrt{1-v^2}\, \mathrm{d}t.\end{aligned}$$

---

[1] Not to be confused with the momentum which in this book means the Lagrange canonical conjugate of the coordinates (cf. note, p. 54, vol. I).

One defines the four-velocity

$$u^\mu \equiv \mathrm{d}x^\mu/\mathrm{d}\tau \equiv (\mathrm{d}t/\mathrm{d}\tau, \boldsymbol{v}\,\mathrm{d}t/\mathrm{d}\tau) \qquad (u^\mu u_\mu = 1)$$

whose product with m gives the mechanical four-momentum

$$\pi^\mu \equiv m u^\mu \equiv (M, \boldsymbol{\pi}).$$

Equations (XX.21) and (XX.21′) are equivalent to the formally covariant equation

$$\frac{\mathrm{d}\pi^\mu}{\mathrm{d}\tau} = eF^{\mu\nu} u_\nu, \tag{XX.23}$$

or

$$\frac{\mathrm{d}u^\mu}{\mathrm{d}\tau} = \frac{e}{m} F^{\mu\nu} u_\nu$$

$F^{\mu\nu}$ is the electromagnetic tensor [eqs. (XX.8–9)].

These laws of motion can be deduced from a Lagrangian or Hamiltonian formalism (cf. Problem I.5). The momentum $\boldsymbol{p}$ and the energy E form a four-vector p^μ, related to the four-vector π^μ by the relation

$$p^\mu = \pi^\mu + eA^\mu \tag{XX.24}$$

i.e.

$$E = M + e\varphi, \qquad \boldsymbol{p} = \boldsymbol{\pi} + e\boldsymbol{A}.$$

The Hamiltonian function is defined by

$$H \equiv e\varphi + \sqrt{(\boldsymbol{p} - e\boldsymbol{A})^2 + m^2} \tag{XX.25}$$

in accordance with relations (XX.24) and (XX.20). From (XX.25) we obtain Hamilton's canonical equations

$$\frac{\mathrm{d}\boldsymbol{r}}{\mathrm{d}t} = \frac{\boldsymbol{\pi}}{M}, \qquad \frac{\mathrm{d}\boldsymbol{p}}{\mathrm{d}t} = -\,e\,\mathrm{grad}\,(\varphi - \boldsymbol{v}\cdot\boldsymbol{A}).$$

The first of these is the definition of velocity. The second is equivalent to (XX.21) as may easily be verified using the definitions of $\mathscr{E}$ and $\mathscr{H}$ [eq. (XX.7)] and the fact that

$$\frac{\mathrm{d}\boldsymbol{A}}{\mathrm{d}t} = \left(\frac{\partial}{\partial t} + \boldsymbol{v}\cdot\mathrm{grad}\right)\boldsymbol{A}.$$

II. THE DIRAC AND KLEIN–GORDON EQUATIONS

5. The Klein–Gordon Equation

Since the problem of finding a relativistic wave equation for the electron is complicated by the existence of spin, we first look for a relativistic wave equation for a particle of spin 0, a π meson for example. Since such a particle has no internal degrees of freedom, its wave function Ψ depends only on the variables $\boldsymbol{r}$ and t. Let m be its mass and e its charge, and suppose that it is moving in the electromagnetic potential $A^\mu \equiv (\varphi, \boldsymbol{A})$.

To find the wave equation we proceed empirically using the correspondence principle; this will guarantee that we obtain the classical laws of motion when the classical approximation is valid.

We recall that the Schrödinger correspondence rule is given by

$$E \to \mathrm{i}\frac{\partial}{\partial t}, \qquad \boldsymbol{p} \to -\mathrm{i}\nabla. \tag{XX.26}$$

Putting $p^\mu \equiv (E, \boldsymbol{p})$, this rule can be written more simply:

$$p^\mu \to \mathrm{i}\partial^\mu. \tag{XX.26$'$}$$

From expression (XX.25) for the Hamiltonian we obtain

$$E = e\varphi + \sqrt{(\boldsymbol{p} - e\boldsymbol{A})^2 + m^2} \tag{XX.27}$$

from which we obtain, by rule (XX.26), the wave equation

$$\left(\mathrm{i}\frac{\partial}{\partial t} - e\varphi\right)\Psi = \left[\left(\frac{1}{\mathrm{i}}\nabla - e\boldsymbol{A}\right)^2 + m^2\right]^{\frac{1}{2}}\Psi.$$

This equation has two serious drawbacks. First, the dissymmetry between the space and time coordinates is such that relativistic invariance and its consequences are not clearly exhibited. Second, the operator on the right-hand side is a square root, which is practically untractable except when the field $\boldsymbol{A}$ vanishes.

One avoids these two difficulties by taking relation (XX.20) as the starting point of the correspondence operation, giving

$$(E - e\varphi)^2 - (\boldsymbol{p} - e\boldsymbol{A})^2 = m^2. \tag{XX.28}$$

This relation is not equivalent to (XX.27), but to the more general relation

$$E = e\varphi \pm \sqrt{(\boldsymbol{p} - e\boldsymbol{A})^2 + m^2}. \tag{XX.29}$$

Only the + sign corresponds to real classical solutions; the − sign represents solutions of negative mass without any physical significance. Thus by taking (XX.28) as a starting point we introduce *parasitic solutions of negative mass.*

The correspondence operation applied to (XX.28) gives the *Klein–Gordon equation*:

$$\left[\left(\mathrm{i}\frac{\partial}{\partial t} - e\varphi\right)^2 - \left(\frac{1}{\mathrm{i}}\nabla - e\boldsymbol{A}\right)^2\right]\Psi = m^2\Psi \qquad \text{(XX.30)}$$

which can also be written in the form

$$(D_\mu D^\mu + m^2)\Psi \equiv [(\partial_\mu + \mathrm{i}eA_\mu)(\partial^\mu + \mathrm{i}eA^\mu) + m^2]\Psi = 0, \quad \text{(XX.30')}$$

where its relativistic invariance is evident.

Let us briefly consider the interpretation of this equation [1]). To simplify the discussion we limit ourselves to the case when the field vanishes. We then have simply (cf. § II.12):

$$(\Box + m^2)\Psi = 0. \qquad \text{(XX.31)}$$

This is a second-order differential equation with respect to the time, and we must therefore know both Ψ and $\partial\Psi/\partial t$ at the initial time for Ψ to be completely determined at any later time. This difficulty is easily surmounted if we postulate that the dynamical state of the system at a given time is represented not by the single function Ψ but by the set of two functions Ψ and $\partial\Psi/\partial t$ or by the two linear combinations:

$$\Phi = \Psi + \frac{\mathrm{i}}{m}\frac{\partial\Psi}{\partial t}, \qquad \chi = \Psi - \frac{\mathrm{i}}{m}\frac{\partial\Psi}{\partial t}.$$

This is equivalent to postulating that the state of the system is represented by a wave function with two components, Φ and χ. This wave function must obey a differential equation of the first order with respect to time which is easily deduced from the Klein–Gordon equation. In the non-relativistic limit, the energy of the particle is nearly equal to its rest mass m, so that

$$\mathrm{i}\frac{\partial\Psi}{\partial t} \simeq m\Psi$$

and therefore, $\chi \ll \Phi$. One of the two components becoming negligible beside the other, we obtain the non-relativistic Schrödinger theory in which the dynamical state of a particle of spin 0 is represented by a one-component wave function.

[1]) For a more complete account, see H. Feshbach and F. Villars, Rev. Mod. Phys. **30** (1958) 24, where a list of the main references will also be found.

In order to interpret the wave function, we must define a position probability density P and a current probability density $\boldsymbol{j}$ satisfying the equation of continuity (cf. § IV.4):

$$\frac{\partial P}{\partial t} + \nabla \cdot \boldsymbol{j} = 0 \tag{XX.32}$$

or with the notation $j^\mu \equiv (P, \boldsymbol{j})$

$$\partial_\mu j^\mu = 0. \tag{XX.33}$$

Since Ψ and Ψ^* both satisfy equation (XX.31),

$$\Psi^* (\Box \Psi) - (\Box \Psi^*) \Psi = 0$$

which gives, using the definition of the Dalembertian,

$$\partial_\mu [\Psi^* (\partial^\mu \Psi) - (\partial^\mu \Psi^*) \Psi] = 0.$$

The equation of continuity is satisfied if we take j^μ proportional to the bracket on the left-hand side. The proportionality constant is fixed so as to recover the usual definition in the non-relativistic limit:

$$j^\mu = \frac{\mathrm{i}}{2m} [\Psi^* (\partial^\mu \Psi) - (\partial^\mu \Psi^*) \Psi],$$

i.e.

$$\begin{aligned} P(\boldsymbol{r}, t) &= \frac{\mathrm{i}}{2m} \left[\Psi^* \frac{\partial \Psi}{\partial t} - \frac{\partial \Psi^*}{\partial t} \Psi \right] \\ \boldsymbol{j}(\boldsymbol{r}, t) &= \frac{1}{2\mathrm{i}m} [\Psi^* (\nabla \Psi) - (\nabla \Psi^*) \Psi]. \end{aligned} \tag{XX.34}$$

Examining (XX.34) we see that *the density* $P(\boldsymbol{r}, t)$ *is not positive-definite*. Here we have one of the major difficulties with the Klein–Gordon equation.

Another difficulty, related to the preceding one, is due to the possibility of "negative energy solutions". If, for example, we look for the plane wave solutions of the equation in the absence of a field,

$$\Psi = \exp [-\mathrm{i}(Et - \boldsymbol{p} \cdot \boldsymbol{r})]$$

we obtain, substituting this expression in (XX.31), the condition:

$$E = \pm \sqrt{\boldsymbol{p}^2 + m^2}.$$

There therefore exist solutions of negative energy $-\sqrt{\boldsymbol{p}^2 + m^2}$. Their presence is obviously due to the above-mentioned introduction of negative masses into the theory (it would be more correct to call them negative mass solutions; however when the field is null, the distinction between mass and energy is illusory).

Following Pauli and Weisskopf [1]), we deal with these difficulties by modifying the interpretation of the four-vector j^μ and the definition of average values. According to this reinterpretation of the theory, ej^μ denotes the current-density four-vector; in particular $eP(\mathbf{r}, t)$ is the electric charge density. Equation (XX.33) is therefore an equation for the conservation of the charge. On the other hand, the number of particles is not conserved; this is explained by the possibility of annihilation and creation of pairs of particles of opposite charge, phenomena that only Field Theory accounts for in a satisfactory manner. When formulated in this way, *the theory is therefore a one-charge theory and not a one-particle theory*. In the Dirac theory, on the contrary, one is able to define a positive-definite density P, however, we shall see that the difficulty with negative energies remains, and that the Dirac theory cannot be considered in an entirely satisfying fashion as being a one-particle theory either (Section VI).

6. The Dirac Equation

Let us now attempt to form a relativistic wave equation for the electron. Following Dirac, we proceed by analogy with non-relativistic Quantum Mechanics.

Just as the electron of the non-relativistic theory is represented by a two-component spinor which transforms under rotation like an angular momentum of value $\frac{1}{2}$, the electron of the relativistic theory must be represented by a wave function of several components having a certain well-defined variance with respect to the larger group of Lorentz transformations. We denote the s component of the wave Ψ by $\psi_s(\mathbf{r}, t)$. Ψ may be written in the form of a column matrix:

$$\Psi = \begin{vmatrix} \psi_1 \\ \psi_2 \\ \vdots \\ \psi_N \end{vmatrix}$$

As in the non-relativistic case, one may equally well regard the wave Ψ at a given time as a function of the orbital variables $\mathbf{r}$ and

---

1) W. Pauli and V. Weisskopf, Helv. Phys. Acta 7 (1934) 709. See also H. Feshback and F. Villars *loc. cit.* note p. 886.

the intrinsic, or spin, variables s ($s=1, 2, \ldots, N$). Such a wave represents a certain state vector $|\psi(t)\rangle$; and the space of these states, $\mathscr{E}$, is the tensor product

$$\mathscr{E} = \mathscr{E}^{(0)} \otimes \mathscr{E}^{(s)}$$

of the orbital-variable space $\mathscr{E}^{(0)}$ by the spin-variable space $\mathscr{E}^{(s)}$; the wave Ψ represents this vector in a suitable representation:

$$\Psi(\mathbf{r}, s; t) \equiv \psi_s(\mathbf{r}, t) \equiv \langle \mathbf{r}s|\Psi(t)\rangle.$$

Continuing with the analogy, we define the position probability density by the formula

$$P(\mathbf{r}, t) = \sum_{s=1}^{N} |\psi_s|^2. \tag{XX.35}$$

With these hypotheses, the wave equation is necessarily of the form

$$\mathrm{i}\frac{\partial\Psi}{\partial t} = H_D\Psi, \tag{XX.36}$$

where H_D is a Hermitean operator of state-vector space. To see this, we note, on the one hand that since Ψ completely defines the dynamical state of the electron at each instant the wave equation must be of the first order with respect to time; on the other that H_D must be Hermitean in order to guarantee the self-consistency of our definition of $P(\mathbf{r}, t)$ (cf. § IV.3).

Since we are seeking a relativistic wave equation, we also require that it exhibit a certain formal symmetry between the spatial coordinates and the time namely that it also be of first order with respect to the spatial variables.

Let us first consider the case of an electron in the absence of field. The Hamiltonian must then be invariant under translation, thus independent of $\mathbf{r}$. Taking into account all the preceding hypotheses, it can therefore be written in the form

$$H_D = \boldsymbol{\alpha}\cdot\mathbf{p} + \beta m, \tag{XX.37}$$

where the operator $\mathbf{p}$ has the significance indicated by the correspondence rule (XX.26), i.e. $\mathbf{p} = -\mathrm{i}\nabla$, and where $\boldsymbol{\alpha} \equiv (\alpha_x, \alpha_y, \alpha_z)$ and β denote 4 Hermitean operators acting on the spin variables alone. If we adopt the notation $E \equiv \mathrm{i}\partial/\partial t$ the wave equation reads

$$[E - \boldsymbol{\alpha}\cdot\mathbf{p} - \beta m]\Psi = 0. \tag{XX.38}$$

To determine $\boldsymbol{\alpha}$ and β, we invoke the correspondence principle: we require the solutions of this equation to satisfy the Klein–Gordon equation, i.e. we require that

$$[E^2-\boldsymbol{p}^2-m^2]\Psi=0. \tag{XX.39}$$

Multiplying on the left by the operator $[E+\boldsymbol{\alpha}\cdot\boldsymbol{p}+\beta m]$, eq. (XX.38) gives the second-order equation

$$[E^2-\sum_k(\alpha^k)^2(p^k)^2-\beta^2m^2-\sum_{k<l}(\alpha^k\alpha^l+\alpha^l\alpha^k)\,p^kp^l \\ -\sum_k(\alpha^k\beta+\beta\alpha^k)\,mp^k]\,\Psi=0.$$

This equation and eq. (XX.39) are identical if the 4 operators β, $\boldsymbol{\alpha}$ anticommute and if their squares are equal to 1:

$$\begin{aligned} (\alpha^k)^2&=1 \qquad \alpha^k\alpha^l+\alpha^l\alpha^k=0 \qquad (k\neq l)\\ \beta^2&=1 \qquad \alpha^k\beta+\beta\,\alpha^k=0 \end{aligned} \tag{XX.40}$$

Equation (XX.38), in which the matrices β, $\boldsymbol{\alpha}$ are chosen to be Hermitean and to satisfy relation (XX.40), is called the Dirac equation.

From this equation for the free electron, we pass to the Dirac equation for an electron in the electromagnetic field (φ, $\boldsymbol{A}$) by making the substitution

$$E\to E-e\varphi, \qquad \boldsymbol{p}\to\boldsymbol{p}-e\boldsymbol{A} \tag{XX.41}$$

[e is the charge of the electron ($e<0$)]. One obtains:

$$[(E-e\varphi)-\boldsymbol{\alpha}\cdot(\boldsymbol{p}-e\boldsymbol{A})-\beta m]\,\Psi=0 \tag{XX.42}$$

i.e.

$$\left[\left(\mathrm{i}\frac{\partial}{\partial t}-e\varphi\right)-\boldsymbol{\alpha}\cdot(-\mathrm{i}\nabla-e\boldsymbol{A})-\beta m\right]\Psi=0. \tag{XX.43}$$

Comparing this with equation (XX.36) we find the following expression for the Dirac Hamiltonian in the presence of an external field:

$$H_D=e\varphi+\boldsymbol{\alpha}\cdot(\boldsymbol{p}-e\boldsymbol{A})+\beta m. \tag{XX.44}$$

7. Construction of the Space $\mathscr{E}^{(s)}$. Dirac Representation

It remains to construct $\mathscr{E}^{(s)}$. The operators of this space are the 4 basic operators β, α_x, α_y, α_z and all of the functions that can be formed with them. $\mathscr{E}^{(s)}$ must be irreducible with respect to this set of operators.

To construct $\mathscr{E}^{(s)}$ we shall make use of the Hermitean character of the four basic operators and of relations (XX.40) defining their algebraic properties.

These properties are analogous to those of the three operators $\sigma_1, \sigma_2, \sigma_3$ of the non-relativistic spin $\frac{1}{2}$ theory. In this case, the spin-variable space $\mathscr{E}^{(\sigma)}$ has two dimensions. It can be constructed in the following way. Since σ_3 is Hermitean and $\sigma_3{}^2 = 1$ its only possible eigenvalues are ± 1. Moreover, to each eigenvector of σ_3 one can associate another eigenvector corresponding to the opposite eigenvalue. Consider for example, a vector $|+\rangle$ such that: $\sigma_3 |+\rangle = |+\rangle$. Since σ_3 and σ_1 anticommute, the vector $|-\rangle \equiv \sigma_1 |+\rangle$ has the property $\sigma_3 |-\rangle = (-1) |-\rangle$. One has $\sigma_1 |\pm\rangle = |\mp\rangle$ and $\sigma_3 |\pm\rangle = (\pm 1) |\pm\rangle$. The space spanned by the vectors $|+\rangle$ and $|-\rangle$ is therefore invariant with respect to the operators σ_3 and σ_1 and with respect to functions of these operators (notably $\sigma_2 \equiv \mathrm{i}\sigma_1\sigma_3$). From the very fashion in which it was constructed, it is irreducible. It is therefore the sought-for space $\mathscr{E}^{(\sigma)}$. In the representation with basis vectors $|+\rangle$ and $|-\rangle$ the operators σ_1, σ_2 and σ_3 are represented by the Pauli matrices [cf. § XIII.19 or formula (VII.65)].

To construct $\mathscr{E}^{(s)}$ we reduce the problem to the preceding one. We introduce the operators σ_x, σ_y, σ_z and ϱ_1, ϱ_2, ϱ_3 defined by:

$$\sigma_z = -\mathrm{i}\alpha_x \alpha_y, \quad \sigma_x = -\mathrm{i}\alpha_y \alpha_z, \quad \sigma_y = -\mathrm{i}\alpha_z \alpha_x \qquad \text{(XX.45)}$$

$$\varrho_3 = \beta, \quad \varrho_1 = \sigma_z \alpha_z = -\mathrm{i}\alpha_x \alpha_y \alpha_z, \quad \varrho_2 = \mathrm{i}\varrho_1 \varrho_3 = -\beta\alpha_x \alpha_y \alpha_z; \qquad \text{(XX.46)}$$

the four basic operators are expressed in terms of the ϱ and the σ by the formulas

$$\beta = \varrho_3, \qquad \alpha^k = \varrho_1 \sigma^k. \qquad \text{(XX.47)}$$

The construction of $\mathscr{E}^{(s)}$ therefore consists in the construction of a space irreducible with respect to the ϱ and the σ. Now it is easy to see that:

(*i*) each ϱ commutes with each σ;

(*ii*) the σ are three anticommuting Hermitean operators whose square is unity;

(*iii*) the ϱ are three anticommuting Hermitean operators whose square is unity.

Consequently (cf. § VIII.7):

(*i*) $\mathscr{E}^{(s)}$ is the tensor product

$$\mathscr{E}^{(s)} = \mathscr{E}^{(\varrho)} \otimes \mathscr{E}^{(\sigma)}$$

of a space $\mathscr{E}^{(\varrho)}$ irreducible with respect to the ϱ and a space $\mathscr{E}^{(\sigma)}$ irreducible with respect to the σ;

(*ii*) $\mathscr{E}^{(\sigma)}$ is a 2-dimensional space that can be constructed following the method indicated above;

(*iii*) $\mathscr{E}^{(\varrho)}$ is also a 2-dimensional space that can be constructed by the same method.

The space $\mathscr{E}^{(s)}$ therefore has 4 dimensions.

In the following sections we show that the σ are related to the spin, and the ϱ to the sign of the energy, the Dirac equation having, like the Klein–Gordon – and for the same reasons – negative energy solutions. In particular we shall see that $\boldsymbol{\alpha}$ is a (polar) vector operator and that $\boldsymbol{\sigma} \equiv (\sigma_x, \sigma_y, \sigma_z)$ is an (axial) vector operator; in addition one formally has

$$\boldsymbol{\alpha} \times \boldsymbol{\alpha} = 2i\boldsymbol{\sigma}. \qquad \text{(XX.48)}$$

The spin of the electron is $\frac{1}{2}\boldsymbol{\sigma}$. The sign of the energy is roughly given by the eigenvalue of $\beta \equiv \varrho_3$.

The dynamical state of the electron is therefore represented by a function Ψ having 4 components, i.e. twice as many components as the wave of the non-relativistic spin $\frac{1}{2}$ theory. The representation in which the ϱ and the σ are the Pauli matrices [cf. eq. (VII.65–66)] is called the *Dirac representation*; in this representation, each component corresponds to a given orientation of the spin along the axis Oz, and roughly to a given sign of the energy.

8. Covariant Form of the Dirac Equation

Equation (XX.43) is the Dirac equation as originally proposed by Dirac himself. It is in this form that it lends itself most easily to physical interpretation and to the study of the passage to the non-relativistic limit. We now propose to obtain a second form, more symmetrical with respect to the space and time coordinates and therefore more convenient whenever questions of relativistic covariance play a preponderant role.

To this effect, we multiply both sides of (XX.43) on the left by β and put:

$$\begin{gathered}\gamma^\mu \equiv (\gamma^0, \gamma^1, \gamma^2, \gamma^3) \equiv (\gamma^0, \boldsymbol{\gamma}) \\ \gamma^0 \equiv \beta \qquad \boldsymbol{\gamma} \equiv \beta\boldsymbol{\alpha}.\end{gathered} \tag{XX.49}$$

We obtain

$$\boxed{[\mathrm{i}\gamma^\mu D_\mu - m]\,\Psi \equiv [\gamma^\mu(\mathrm{i}\partial_\mu - eA_\mu) - m]\,\Psi = 0} \tag{XX.50}$$

The properties of γ^μ are easily obtained from those of $\boldsymbol{\alpha}$ and β by applying definitions (XX.49). The ten relations (XX.40) give the ten equivalent relations

$$\gamma^\mu \gamma^\nu + \gamma^\nu \gamma^\mu = 2g^{\mu\nu}. \tag{XX.51}$$

The Hermitean conditions on the $\boldsymbol{\alpha}$ and β are equivalent to the conditions

$$\gamma^{0\dagger} = \gamma^0, \qquad \gamma^{k\dagger} = -\gamma^k \tag{XX.52}$$

that may be written in the condensed form

$$\gamma^{\mu\dagger} = \gamma^0 \gamma^\mu \gamma^0. \tag{XX.53}$$

It is convenient to extend the usual rule of raising and lowering of indices to the γ, and to put

$$\gamma_\mu = g_{\mu\nu}\gamma^\nu. \tag{XX.54}$$

Note that:

$$\gamma_0 = \gamma^0, \qquad \gamma_k = -\gamma^k \tag{XX.55}$$

$$\gamma^\mu = \gamma_\mu{}^\dagger = \gamma_\mu{}^{-1}. \tag{XX.56}$$

9. Adjoint Equation. Definition of the Current

We have defined a positive-definite position probability density [eq. (XX.35)]. As indicated above, the Hermitean character of the Dirac Hamiltonian guarantees that this definition is self-consistent. We shall now define a current density and show that the current defined with the solutions of the Dirac equation obeys an equation of continuity. We first give a complete discussion of this problem using the Dirac form, and then repeat the argument with the covariant form.

Suppose that we have chosen a particular representation of the β and $\boldsymbol{\alpha}$. The wave Ψ is then a certain column matrix with four lines

$$\Psi \equiv \begin{pmatrix} \psi_1 \\ \psi_2 \\ \psi_3 \\ \psi_4 \end{pmatrix}.$$

Denote its Hermitean conjugate by:

$$\Psi^\dagger \equiv (\psi_1^* \psi_2^* \psi_3^* \psi_4^*).$$

The operators of spin space are 4×4 matrices. One can define partial scalar products in which one sums over the spin variables alone. We shall indicate such scalar products by parentheses; thus the density P is written

$$P(\mathbf{r}, t) \equiv (\Psi^\dagger \Psi). \tag{XX.57}$$

As another illustration, denote by β_{st} the element in line s and column t of the matrix β $(s, t = 1, 2, 3, 4)$:

$$(\Psi^\dagger \beta \Psi) \equiv \sum_s \sum_t \psi_s^* \beta_{st} \psi_t.$$

Now if Ψ is a solution of the Dirac equation, that is, if

$$\begin{aligned} \mathrm{i} \frac{\partial \Psi}{\partial t} &= H_D \Psi \\ &= \left[e\varphi + \sum_k \alpha^k \left(-\mathrm{i} \frac{\partial}{\partial x^k} - eA^k \right) + \beta m \right] \Psi, \end{aligned} \tag{XX.58}$$

then $\Psi^\dagger$ is a solution of the Hermitean conjugate equation, that is of the equation obtained by taking the complex conjugate of (XX.58) and replacing each matrix by its transpose:

$$\begin{aligned} \mathrm{i} \frac{\partial \Psi^\dagger}{\partial t} &= -\Psi^\dagger H_D \\ &= -e\varphi \Psi^\dagger - \sum_k \left(\mathrm{i} \frac{\partial}{\partial x^k} - eA^k \right) \Psi^\dagger \alpha^k - m \Psi^\dagger \beta. \end{aligned} \tag{XX.59}$$

Scalar multiplication of (XX.58) on the left by $\Psi^\dagger$ and (XX.59) on the right by Ψ and then addition gives

$$\mathrm{i} \frac{\partial}{\partial t} (\Psi^\dagger \Psi) = -\mathrm{i} \sum_k \frac{\partial}{\partial x^k} (\Psi^\dagger \alpha^k \Psi). \tag{XX.60}$$

On the left-hand side we recognize the time derivative of the probability density, and on the right-hand side the divergence of a certain vector $\boldsymbol{j}(\boldsymbol{r}, t)$ defined by

$$\boldsymbol{j}(\boldsymbol{r}, t) \equiv (\Psi^\dagger \boldsymbol{\alpha} \Psi). \tag{XX.61}$$

$\boldsymbol{j}(\boldsymbol{r}, t)$ is the sought-for current density and (XX.60) is equivalent to the equation of continuity

$$\frac{\partial}{\partial t} P + \nabla \cdot \boldsymbol{j} = 0.$$

The above may be repeated starting from the covariant form of the Dirac equation [eq. (XX.50)]. The Hermitean conjugate of (XX.50) is

$$(-\mathrm{i}\partial_\mu - eA_\mu)\, \Psi^\dagger \gamma^{\mu\dagger} - m\, \Psi^\dagger = 0. \tag{XX.62}$$

[Here the symbol $\partial_\mu \Psi^\dagger \gamma^{\mu\dagger}$ represents the line matrix with four columns $(\partial \Psi^\dagger / \partial x^\mu) \gamma^{\mu\dagger}$.] It is convenient to put:

$$\overline{\Psi} = \Psi^\dagger \gamma^0, \qquad \Psi^\dagger = \overline{\Psi} \gamma^0. \tag{XX.63}$$

Taking relations (XX.53) into account, equation (XX.62) can then be put after multiplication on the left by γ^0 in the simpler form:

$$\boxed{(-\mathrm{i}\partial_\mu - eA_\mu)\, \overline{\Psi} \gamma^\mu - m \overline{\Psi} = 0} \tag{XX.64}$$

This equation is obviously equivalent to (XX.59). $\overline{\Psi}$ is called the *adjoint of* Ψ, and (XX.64) the *adjoint equation.*

Scalar multiplication of (XX.50) on the left by $\overline{\Psi}$ and (XX.64) on the right by Ψ and then subtraction, gives

$$\mathrm{i}\partial_\mu (\overline{\Psi} \gamma^\mu \Psi) = 0.$$

One defines the current density four-vector

$$j^\mu \equiv (\overline{\Psi} \gamma^\mu \Psi). \tag{XX.65}$$

The preceding equation is equivalent to the equation of continuity

$$\partial_\mu j^\mu = 0.$$

One easily verifies that $j^\mu \equiv (P, \boldsymbol{j})$. Thus, as expected, we obtain the equation of continuity written in its covariant form. In the next section, we show that the 4 components of j^μ indeed form a four-vector.

III. INVARIANCE PROPERTIES OF THE DIRAC EQUATION

10. Properties of the Dirac Matrices

As a preliminary to the study of the invariance properties of the Dirac equation we now make a systematic study of the properties of four 4×4 *matrices* $\gamma^\mu \equiv (\gamma^0, \gamma^1, \gamma^2, \gamma^3)$ satisfying the relations

$$\gamma^\mu \gamma^\nu + \gamma^\nu \gamma^\mu = 2g^{\mu\nu} I, \tag{XX.66}$$

where I is the unit matrix. The matrix relations (XX.66) are analogous to the operator relations (XX.51); however, the matrices introduced here do not necessarily verify the unitarity conditions (XX.53). All of the following properties are consequences of relation (XX.66) alone.

γ^A MATRICES. As the γ^μ anticommute, and as their square is equal to $+I$ or $-I$, any product of several γ^μ is equal, to within a sign, to one of the 16 particular γ^A matrices given in Table 1. These have been grouped in 5 classes denoted by (S), (V), (T), (A) and (P) and containing 1, 4, 6, 4 and 1 elements respectively; the reasons for this classification will become clear at the end of this section (cf. § 14).

TABLE XX.1

The γ^A matrices

	Matrix	Explicit form			
		$(\gamma^A)^2 = I$	$(\gamma^A)^2 = -I$		
(S)	$1 \equiv$	I			
(V)	$\gamma^\mu \equiv \{\gamma^0, \gamma^k\} \equiv$	γ^0	γ^1	γ^2	γ^3
(T)	$\gamma^{[\lambda\mu]} \equiv \{\gamma^k\gamma^0, \gamma^5\gamma^0\gamma^k\} \equiv$	$\gamma^1\gamma^0$ $\gamma^2\gamma^0$ $\gamma^3\gamma^0$	$\gamma^2\gamma^3$	$\gamma^3\gamma^1$	$\gamma^1\gamma^2$
(A)	$\gamma^{[\lambda\mu\nu]} \equiv \{\gamma^0\gamma^5, \gamma^k\gamma^5\} \equiv$	$\gamma^1\gamma^2\gamma^3$	$\gamma^0\gamma^2\gamma^3$	$\gamma^0\gamma^3\gamma^1$	$\gamma^0\gamma^1\gamma^2$
(P)	$\gamma^{[\lambda\mu\nu\varrho]} \equiv \gamma^5$			$\gamma^0\gamma^1\gamma^2\gamma^3$	

It is clear that $(\gamma^A)^2$ is equal, according to the case, to I or to $-I$; the six matrices whose square is equal to I are grouped in the left-hand column; the ten matrices whose square is equal to $-I$ in the right-hand column.

Of all these matrices, only I commutes with all of the others. If

$\gamma^A \neq I$, it anticommutes with 8 of these 16 matrices and commutes with the 8 others.

In particular the matrix γ^5, defined by [1])

$$\gamma^5 \equiv \gamma^0 \gamma^1 \gamma^2 \gamma^3 \qquad \text{(XX.67)}$$

anticommutes with the γ^μ:

$$\gamma^5 \gamma^\mu + \gamma^\mu \gamma^5 = 0 \qquad \text{(XX.68)}$$

and its square is

$$(\gamma^5)^2 = -I. \qquad \text{(XX.69)}$$

INVERSE MATRICES (γ_A). We define the γ_μ matrices by the relation:

$$\gamma_\mu = g_{\mu\nu} \gamma^\nu. \qquad \text{(XX.70)}$$

Obviously:

$$\gamma^\mu = [\gamma_\mu]^{-1}.$$

It follows that the inverse of a γ^A is obtained by reversing the order of the γ^μ involved and replacing each of them by the corresponding γ_μ; we denote the expression thereby obtained by γ_A:

$$\gamma_A \gamma^A = \gamma^A \gamma_A = I. \qquad \text{(XX.71)}$$

Following this method of constructing the inverse, one finds

$$\gamma_5 = \gamma_3 \gamma_2 \gamma_1 \gamma_0.$$

TRACE AND DETERMINANT

$$\operatorname{Tr} \gamma^A = \begin{cases} 4 & \text{if} \quad \gamma^A = I \\ 0 & \text{if} \quad \gamma^A \neq I. \end{cases} \qquad \text{(XX.72)}$$

To see this, suppose $\gamma^A \neq I$ and let γ^B be one of the 8 matrices which anticommute with γ^A:

$$\gamma^A = -\gamma^B \gamma^A \gamma_B.$$

We then have:

$$\operatorname{Tr} \gamma^A = -\operatorname{Tr} \gamma^B \gamma^A \gamma_B = -\operatorname{Tr} \gamma_B \gamma^B \gamma^A = -\operatorname{Tr} \gamma^A = 0.$$

We note in passing (Problem XX.3) that:

$$\det \gamma^A = 1.$$

REARRANGEMENT LEMMA. The following property may be verified by simple inspection:

If we multiply each matrix of the set of 16 γ^A matrices on the right

[1]) The index 4 is commonly used to denote the time component, according to the definition: $x^4 = ix^0 = ict$.

(or on the left) by a particular one of them, we obtain the same set of 16 matrices, except for possible changes in order and sign.

LINEAR INDEPENDENCE AND IRREDUCIBILITY. Using the rearrangement lemma and the properties of the trace, it can easily be shown that:

(*i*) The 16 γ^A matrices are linearly independent.

(*ii*) Any 4th order matrix M is a uniquely-defined linear combination of the γ^A:

$$M = \sum_A m_A \gamma^A \qquad m_A = \tfrac{1}{4}\,\mathrm{Tr}\,\gamma_A M.$$

(*iii*) Any matrix commuting with every γ^μ, and therefore with every γ^A, is a multiple of the unit matrix:

$$\text{if } [M, \gamma^\mu] = 0 \text{ for any } \mu, \; M = Cst. \times I.$$

FUNDAMENTAL THEOREM. *Let γ^μ and γ'^μ be two sets of 4 fourth-order matrices satisfying relation* (XX.66). *There exists a matrix S, non-singular* ($\det S \neq 0$) *and defined to within a constant, such that*

$$\gamma^\mu = S\gamma'^\mu S^{-1} \qquad (\mu = 0, 1, 2, 3). \tag{XX.73}$$

To demonstrate this theorem we proceed in the following way. To each set γ^μ, γ'^μ there corresponds a set of 16 matrices γ^A, γ'^A whose definition and principle properties were given above; thus to each particular γ^A there corresponds a certain matrix γ'^A, the index A taking all 16 distinct values. Let F be a certain matrix and denote by S the matrix defined by

$$S \equiv \sum_A \gamma'^A F \gamma_A,$$

the sum $\sum_A$ being extended over the 16 possible values of the index A.

Denote a particular matrix by γ^B, its inverse by γ_B and the corresponding matrix in the other system by γ'^B; in virtue of the rearrangement lemma,

$$\gamma'^B S \gamma_B \equiv \sum_A \gamma'^B \gamma'^A F \gamma_A \gamma_B = \sum_A \gamma'^A F \gamma_A \equiv S,$$

therefore

$$\gamma'^B S = S\gamma^B. \tag{XX.74}$$

For relation (XX.73) to be verified by S, it remains to show that S has an inverse. To this effect, we introduce the matrix T, defined by

$$T \equiv \sum_A \gamma^A G \gamma_A{}',$$

where G is an arbitrary matrix. Reasoning in an analogous way one shows that

$$\gamma^B T = T\gamma'^B.$$

Therefore

$$\gamma^B TS = T\gamma'^B S = TS\gamma^B,$$

whatever γ^B; since TS commutes with any matrix γ^B, it is a multiple of unity: $TS = c\times I$. The multiplication constant is given by the formula:

$$\begin{aligned} c &= \tfrac{1}{4}\operatorname{Tr} TS = \tfrac{1}{4}\sum_A\sum_B \operatorname{Tr}\gamma^A G\gamma'_A\gamma'^B F\gamma_B \\ &= \tfrac{1}{4}\operatorname{Tr} G(\sum_A\sum_B \gamma'_A\gamma'^B F\gamma_B\gamma^A) = 4\operatorname{Tr} GS. \end{aligned}$$

Now F can always be chosen so that S has at least one non-zero element, for clearly the 16 γ^A matrices would not be linearly independent if S vanished for every F. Thus it is always possible to choose G such that

$$\operatorname{Tr} GS \equiv \sum_s\sum_t G_{st}S_{ts} = \tfrac{1}{4};$$

one then has $c = 1$ and therefore $T = S^{-1}$. Thus S does have an inverse and property (XX.73) is obtained by multiplying both sides of (XX.74) on the right by S^{-1}.

If another matrix, S', has the same property, $S^{-1}S'$ commutes with all of the γ^μ and therefore: $S^{-1}S' = Cst\times I$. Conversely, if S has the property (XX.73), then so has any multiple of S. Thus we have shown that the non-singular matrix S exists, and that it is defined to within a constant. Q.E.D.

UNITARY γ^μ MATRICES. If the matrices obeying relations (XX.66) are unitary:

$$\gamma_\mu \equiv \gamma^0\gamma^\mu\gamma^0 = \gamma^{\mu\dagger}, \tag{XX.75}$$

all of the γ^A matrices are unitary and it follows that they are Hermitean or anti-Hermitean according as $(\gamma^A)^2$ is equal to $+I$ or $-I$.

The fundamental theorem is completed by the following corollary, the proof of which is left to the reader:

Let γ^μ and γ'^μ be two systems of 4 fourth-order unitary matrices satisfying relations (XX.66). *There exists a unitary matrix U, defined to within a phase, such that*: $\gamma'^\mu = U\gamma^\mu U^\dagger$ $(\mu = 0, 1, 2, 3)$.

COMPLEX CONJUGATION, B MATRIX. In particular, if the γ^μ are unitary and obey relations (XX.66), the 4 complex conjugate matrices

$\gamma^{\mu *}$ are also unitary and also obey relations (XX.66). The preceding corollary therefore applies: the γ^μ are obtained from the $\gamma^{\mu *}$ by a unitary transformation. We shall henceforth denote the matrix of that transformation by B (B is defined to within a phase):

$$\gamma^\mu = B\gamma^{\mu *} B^\dagger \qquad \gamma^{\mu *} = B^* \gamma^\mu \widetilde{B}. \tag{XX.76}$$

It can be shown (Problem XX.4) that B is antisymmetrical:

$$B = -\widetilde{B}$$

or, what amounts to the same, that

$$BB^* = B^* B = -I. \tag{XX.77}$$

If the γ matrices are those of the Dirac representation one has

$$\begin{aligned} B \equiv B_D &= \gamma^2\gamma^5 \\ &= -\mathrm{i}\varrho_3\sigma_y. \end{aligned}$$

Property (XX.77) is easily verified for this particular case.

11. Invariance of the Form of the Dirac Equation in an Orthochronous Change of Referential

In order to satisfy the relativity principle, the Dirac equation and the equation of continuity must have the same form in different Lorentz referentials. In actual fact, the principle requires this invariance of form only with respect to proper Lorentz transformations [1]), but it happens that the theory is formally invariant with respect to the complete group. We shall begin with a detailed study of invariance with respect to the orthochronous group. Time-reversal invariance will be examined at the end of this section along with other invariance properties characteristic of the Dirac equation but not directly related to Lorentz transformations.

---

[1]) And also with respect to space and time translations. This invariance can easily be demonstrated by an argument analogous to the one given in this paragraph. If the origin of axes is displaced by a four-vector a^μ, that is, if $x'^\mu = x^\mu + a^\mu$, then $A_\mu'(x') = A_\mu(x)$ and the law for the transformation of wave functions [that is, the analogue of (XX.85)] becomes simply:

$$\Psi'(x') = \Psi(x).$$

Let us therefore suppose that the dynamical state of the electron is represented in a referential (R) by a four-component wave function satisfying the Dirac equation:

$$[\gamma^\mu(\mathrm{i}\partial_\mu - eA_\mu(x)) - m]\,\Psi(x) = 0. \qquad \text{(XX.78)}$$

We suppose that a representation has been chosen once and for all for the operators of the space $\mathscr{E}^{(s)}$; the symbols γ^μ therefore denote well-defined matrices and relation (XX.78) represents 4 equations $(s=1, 2, 3, 4)$:

$$\sum_{t=1,2,3,4} \sum_\mu (\gamma^\mu)_{st} \left(\mathrm{i}\,\frac{\partial}{\partial x^\mu} - eA_\mu(x^0x^1x^2x^3)\right) \psi_t(x^0x^1x^2x^3) - m\,\psi_s(x^0x^1x^2x^3) = 0$$

satisfied by the 4 components $\psi_s(x)$ of the wave function.

Consider this same system in a new referential (R') obtained from the preceding one by a certain orthochronous Lorentz transformation $\mathscr{L}$:

$$(R') = \mathscr{L}(R).$$

$\mathscr{L}$ is characterized by a certain matrix $\Omega^\mu{}_\nu$ having properties (XX.12) and (XX.13) (in addition $\Omega^0{}_0 > 0$) and defining the linear correspondence between the coordinates x^μ of a given point in the referential (R) and the coordinates x'^μ *of the same point* in the referential (R') that is, the law for the transformation of contravariant vectors [eq. (XX.11) and (XX.15)]. We write symbolically

$$x' = \mathscr{L}x, \qquad x = \mathscr{L}^{-1}x'. \qquad \text{(XX.79)}$$

The partial-differentiation operators transform like covariant vectors:

$$\partial_\mu = \partial_\nu{}'\Omega^\nu{}_\mu. \qquad \text{(XX.80)}$$

If we denote the covariant components of the potential in the new referential by $A_\mu'(x')$, they too are related to the $A_\mu(x)$ by the law for the transformation of covariant vectors:

$$A_\mu(x) \equiv A_\mu(\mathscr{L}^{-1}x') = A_\nu'(x')\Omega^\nu{}_\mu. \qquad \text{(XX.81)}$$

Considered as a function of the new coordinates, $\Psi(x)$ obeys the equation obtained from (XX.78) by substituting into it from (XX.80) and (XX.81):

$$[\hat{\gamma}^\mu(\mathrm{i}\partial_\mu' - eA_\mu'(x')) - m]\,\Psi(\mathscr{L}^{-1}x') = 0, \qquad \text{(XX.82)}$$

where

$$\hat{\gamma}^\mu \equiv \Omega^\mu{}_\varrho\gamma^\varrho. \qquad \text{(XX.83)}$$

The four γ^μ matrices are unitary and satisfy relations (XX.66). The four $\hat{\gamma}^\mu$ matrices are not necessarily unitary, but, because of the orthogonality of the $\Omega^\mu{}_\nu$ [relations (XX.13)], they also verify relations (XX.66), i.e.

$$\hat{\gamma}^\mu\hat{\gamma}^\nu+\hat{\gamma}^\nu\hat{\gamma}^\mu = \Omega^\mu{}_\varrho\Omega^\nu{}_\varrho(\gamma^\varrho\gamma^\sigma+\gamma^\sigma\gamma^\varrho)$$
$$= 2\Omega^\mu{}_\varrho g^{\varrho\sigma}\Omega^\nu{}_\sigma = 2g^{\mu\nu}.$$

Therefore in virtue of the fundamental theorem of § 10, there exists a non-singular matrix Λ defined to within a constant which transforms the $\hat{\gamma}$ into the γ:

$$\hat{\gamma}^\mu \equiv \Omega^\mu{}_\varrho\gamma^\varrho = \Lambda^{-1}\gamma^\mu\Lambda \qquad (\mu = 0, 1, 2, 3). \tag{XX.84}$$

Substituting this relationship into (XX.82) and putting

$$\Psi'(x') = \Lambda\Psi(x) \equiv \Lambda\Psi(\mathscr{L}^{-1}x') \tag{XX.85}$$

one finds, after multiplying on the left by Λ:

$$[\gamma^\mu(\mathrm{i}\partial_\mu' - eA_\mu'(x'))]\,\Psi'(x') = 0.$$

This wave equation describes the evolution of the system in the new referential. It is seen to be formally identical with (XX.78). The Dirac equation is therefore formally invariant in an orthochronous change of referential and the law for the transformation of the wave function is given by equation (XX.85).

The matrix Λ, which is defined to within a constant, cannot in general be chosen to be unitary; however it will now be shown that the constant can always be chosen so as to have

$$\Lambda^\dagger = \gamma^0\Lambda^{-1}\gamma^0 \tag{XX.86}$$

Λ is then defined up to an arbitrary phase.

Since the $\Omega^\mu{}_\varrho$ are real and since the γ^μ are unitary and therefore verify (XX.75), the comparison of (XX.83) and its Hermitean conjugate gives

$$\hat{\gamma}^{\mu\dagger} = \gamma^0\hat{\gamma}^\mu\gamma^0.$$

Taking the Hermitean conjugate of (XX.84) and substituting the preceding relation one easily obtains

$$\hat{\gamma}^\mu = (\gamma^0\Lambda^\dagger\gamma^0)\gamma^\mu(\gamma^0\Lambda^\dagger\gamma^0)^{-1}.$$

Comparing with (XX.84), we see that the matrix $\Lambda\gamma^0\Lambda^\dagger\gamma^0$ commutes with the four γ^μ and is therefore a multiple of the unit matrix:

$$\Lambda^\dagger = c\gamma^0 \Lambda^{-1} \gamma^0. \qquad \text{(XX.87)}$$

Next we show that the constant c is necessarily real and positive. From (XX.87) and (XX.84),

$$\Lambda^\dagger \Lambda = c\gamma^0(\Lambda^{-1}\gamma^0\Lambda) = c(\Omega^0{}_0 + \sum_k \Omega^0{}_k \gamma^0\gamma^k)$$

whence, taking into account (XX.72), $\mathrm{Tr}\Lambda^\dagger\Lambda = 4c\Omega^0{}_0$. Now since the trace of the Hermitean-definite matrix $\Lambda^\dagger\Lambda$ is necessarily real and positive, and since $\Omega^0{}_0$ is also real and positive, then so also is c. Thus if one multiplies Λ by $\sqrt{c}$, the resulting matrix is also a Λ matrix and verifies equation (XX.86). Q.E.D.

From the law (XX.85) for the transformation of wave functions, we obtain the law for the transformation of the adjoint functions:

$$\overline{\Psi}' \equiv \Psi'^\dagger \gamma^0 = \Psi^\dagger \Lambda^\dagger \gamma^0 = \overline{\Psi} \gamma^0 \Lambda^\dagger \gamma^0$$

whence, taking into account (XX.86)

$$\overline{\Psi}'(x') = \overline{\Psi}(x)\Lambda^{-1}. \qquad \text{(XX.88)}$$

Using this transformation law, the reader may easily verify that the adjoint equation (XX.64) is also formally invariant in an orthochronous change of referential.

It remains to show that the equation of continuity is formally invariant or, better, that j^μ [definition (XX.65)] transforms like a contravariant four-vector [1].

This is easily verified; from (XX.85), (XX.88) and (XX.84),

$$\begin{aligned} j'^\mu(x') &\equiv (\overline{\Psi}'\gamma^\mu\Psi') = (\overline{\Psi}\Lambda^{-1}\gamma^\mu\Lambda\Psi) = \Omega^\mu{}_\varrho\,(\overline{\Psi}\gamma^\varrho\Psi) \\ &= \Omega^\mu{}_\varrho\, j^\varrho(x). \end{aligned}$$

For each Lorentz transformation, Λ is defined up to a phase by conditions (XX.84) and (XX.86). *In the present case, this phase has no physical significance.* In so far as possible it is desirable to remove the arbitrary in the phase, while preserving the property of the Λ to form a group homomorphic to the orthochronous Lorentz group (see the discussion of § XV.8).

[1]) Otherwise, the normalization of the wave function would depend on the reference system and the interpretation of j^0 as a position probability density would not be justified.

Now since the $\Omega^\mu{}_\nu$ are real, condition (XX.84) gives

$$\Omega^\mu{}_\nu \gamma^{\nu *} = (\Lambda^*)^{-1} \gamma^{\mu *} \Lambda^*,$$

whence, introducing the unitary matrix B [definition (XX.76)],

$$\Omega^\mu{}_\nu \gamma^\nu = (B\Lambda^* B^\dagger)^{-1} \gamma^\mu (B\Lambda^* B^\dagger).$$

Comparing this equation with (XX.84), we see that $B\Lambda^* B^\dagger \Lambda^{-1}$ commutes with the four γ^μ matrices and is therefore a multiple of the unit matrix; it is easy to see [for example by calculating $\det(B\Lambda^* B^\dagger \Lambda^{-1})$] that this multiple is a phase factor; in other words

$$\Lambda^* = e^{i\lambda} B^\dagger \Lambda B.$$

since Λ is determined up to a phase factor, one can always choose this phase so as to have $e^{i\lambda} = 1$. In what follows this will always be done; Λ is then defined up to a sign.

In conclusion, to each orthochronous Lorentz transformation there correspond *two* Λ matrices, differing by a sign, defined by the three conditions

$$\Omega^\mu{}_\nu \gamma^\nu = \Lambda^{-1} \gamma^\mu \Lambda \qquad \text{(XX.89}a\text{)}$$

$$\Lambda^\dagger = \gamma^0 \Lambda^{-1} \gamma^0 \qquad \text{(XX.89}b\text{)}$$

$$\Lambda^* = B^\dagger \Lambda B. \qquad \text{(XX.89}c\text{)}$$

It is clear that the set of Λ matrices thus defined forms a group and that this group is homomorphic to the orthochronous Lorentz group. We shall see in § 12 that the arbitrary in the sign of the Λ cannot be removed without violating this group property [1]).

[1]) Rather than condition (XX.89c), one could just as well take the more general condition: $\Lambda^* = \eta B^\dagger \Lambda B$, where η is a constant depending on the particular Lorentz transformation considered. The group property of the Λ is preserved if the η form an Abelian representation of the Lorentz group. Consequently, one necessarily has $\eta = 1$ for the transformations of the proper group $\mathscr{L}_0$, which gives back condition (XX.89c). For transformations of the reflection type that is for those of the sheet $s\mathscr{L}_0$, one may choose between the two following possibilities:

(a) $\eta = 1$ for any $s\mathscr{L}_0$; we obtain (XX.89c);

(b) $\eta = -1$ for any $s\mathscr{L}_0$, that is, $\Lambda^* = -B\Lambda B^\dagger$.

The physical content of the theory is obviously independent of this choice. The two groups, $G^{(a)}$ and $G^{(b)}$, which correspond respectively to (a) and (b) above, are both homomorphic to the orthochronous Lorentz group, but they are *not* isomorphic to each other. In particular, the two matrices which correspond to s have their square equal to I in $G^{(a)}$, and to $-I$ in $G^{(b)}$ [Cf. note 1, p. 908 below].

12. Transformation of the Proper Group

We shall now find explicit expressions for the Λ matrices defined by equation (XX.89). In this paragraph we limit ourselves to the transformations of the proper group.

Let us first consider the infinitesimal transformations. To each of the 6 infinitesimal "rotations" $g_{\mu\nu} - \varepsilon Z_{\mu\nu}^{(\alpha\beta)}$ there corresponds a matrix $\Lambda^{(\alpha\beta)}(\varepsilon)$ differing by an infinitesimal from the unit matrix and which may therefore be written in the form

$$\Lambda^{(\alpha\beta)}(\varepsilon) \simeq I + \mathrm{i}\varepsilon S_{\alpha\beta}, \qquad \text{(XX.90)}$$

where $S_{\alpha\beta}$ is a finite matrix to be determined. One has

$$[\Lambda^{(\alpha\beta)}(\varepsilon)]^{-1} \simeq \Lambda^{(\alpha\beta)}(-\varepsilon) \simeq I - \mathrm{i}\varepsilon S_{\alpha\beta}.$$

Property (XX.89*a*) therefore gives

$$-\varepsilon g^{\mu\nu} Z_{\nu\varrho}^{(\alpha\beta)} \gamma^{\varrho} = -\mathrm{i}\varepsilon [S_{\alpha\beta}, \gamma^{\mu}],$$

or, using (XX.17),

$$[S_{\alpha\beta}, \gamma^{\mu}] = \mathrm{i}(\delta^{\mu}{}_{\beta}\gamma_{\alpha} - \delta^{\mu}{}_{\alpha}\gamma_{\beta}).$$

$S_{\alpha\beta}$ satisfies the same commutation relations with the γ^{μ} as the matrix $\frac{1}{2}\mathrm{i}\gamma_{\alpha}\gamma_{\beta}$. The difference therefore commutes with the four γ^{μ} matrices and is thus a constant. One easily sees that conditions (XX.89*b*) and (XX.89*c*) are satisfied if, and only if, this constant vanishes. It is convenient to put

$$\begin{aligned} \sigma_{\mu\nu} &\equiv \tfrac{1}{2}\mathrm{i}[\gamma_{\mu}, \gamma_{\nu}] \\ &\equiv \mathrm{i}\gamma_{\mu}\gamma_{\nu} \qquad (\mu \neq \nu). \end{aligned} \qquad \text{(XX.91)}$$

One finds therefore:

$$\boxed{S_{\alpha\beta} = \tfrac{1}{2}\sigma_{\alpha\beta}} \qquad \text{(XX.92)}$$

The symbols $S_{\alpha\beta}$ and $\sigma_{\alpha\beta}$ will also be used for the operators represented by the matrices $S_{\alpha\beta}$ and $\sigma_{\alpha\beta}$ respectively. We shall see further on that $S_{\alpha\beta}$ is an antisymmetrical tensor operator (6 components) representing the intrinsic angular momentum or spin of the particle. To be exact, the spin is the spatial part (3 components) of this operator. $S_{\alpha\beta}$ is related to the operators $\boldsymbol{\sigma}$ and $\boldsymbol{\alpha}$ of § 6 and 7 by the relations

$$S_{10} = \tfrac{1}{2}\mathrm{i}\alpha_x \qquad S_{20} = \tfrac{1}{2}\mathrm{i}\alpha_y \qquad S_{30} = \tfrac{1}{2}\mathrm{i}\alpha_z \qquad \text{(XX.93}a\text{)}$$

$$S_{23} = \tfrac{1}{2}\sigma_x \qquad S_{31} = \tfrac{1}{2}\sigma_y \qquad S_{12} = \tfrac{1}{2}\sigma_z. \qquad \text{(XX.93}b\text{)}$$

Any finite transformation of the proper Lorentz group may be considered as the product of successive infinitesimal transformations. We can therefore construct the Λ matrices corresponding to a finite change of referential by taking the product of matrices for infinitesimal transformations as defined above. If we proceed in this way conditions (XX.89*b*) and (XX.89*c*) are automatically fulfilled and we obtain one of the two possible Λ matrices.

In particular, the "rotation" of angle φ in the plane $x^\alpha x^\beta$ is a product of infinitesimal rotation matrices in this plane, and the matrix $\Lambda^{(\alpha\beta)}(\varphi)$ representing the transformation is therefore

$$\Lambda^{(\alpha\beta)}(\varphi) = \mathrm{e}^{\mathrm{i}\varphi S_{\alpha\beta}} \tag{XX.94}$$

Thus (cf. note, p. 882), if it is a special Lorentz transformation of velocity $v = \tanh \varphi$ directed along the x axis, one finds, taking into account relations (XX.93*a*) and the properties of α_x:

$$\Lambda^{xt}(\varphi) = \mathrm{e}^{-\frac{1}{2}\alpha_x \varphi} = \cosh \tfrac{1}{2}\varphi - \alpha_x \sinh \tfrac{1}{2}\varphi. \tag{XX.95}$$

More generally let $\Lambda_{\mathrm{sp}}(v)$ be the matrix associated with the special Lorentz transformation of velocity $\mathbf{v}$; then

$$\Lambda_{\mathrm{sp}}(\mathbf{v}) = \cosh \tfrac{1}{2}\varphi - (\boldsymbol{\alpha}\cdot\boldsymbol{u}) \sinh \tfrac{1}{2}\varphi,$$

where:

$$\boldsymbol{u} \equiv \mathbf{v}/v, \qquad \varphi = \tanh^{-1}\mathbf{v}.$$

Let us put

$$b \equiv 1/\sqrt{1-v^2} = \cosh \varphi. \tag{XX.96}$$

After an elementary calculation, the preceding expression takes the form:

$$\Lambda_{\mathrm{sp}}(\mathbf{v}) = \frac{1}{\sqrt{2(1+b)}}\,[1 + b - (\boldsymbol{\alpha}\cdot\mathbf{v})\, b]. \tag{XX.97}$$

Consider now rotations in the ordinary sense of the word. Expression (XX.94) gives for rotations about Oz:

$$\Lambda^{(xy)}(\varphi) = \mathrm{e}^{\mathrm{i}S_{12}\varphi} = \mathrm{e}^{\frac{1}{2}\mathrm{i}\sigma_z\varphi} = \cos \tfrac{1}{2}\varphi + \mathrm{i}\sigma_z \sin \tfrac{1}{2}\varphi. \tag{XX.98}$$

More generally the matrix $\Lambda_{\boldsymbol{u}}(\varphi)$ associated with a rotation through an angle φ about the axis parallel to the unit vector $\boldsymbol{u}$ is

$$\Lambda_{\boldsymbol{u}}(\varphi) = \cos \tfrac{1}{2}\varphi + \mathrm{i}\sigma_u \sin \tfrac{1}{2}\varphi \tag{XX.99}$$

with:

$$\sigma_u \equiv (\boldsymbol{\sigma}\cdot\boldsymbol{u}).$$

We are now ready to discuss the spin of the particle described by the Dirac equation. The spin is defined by the transformation properties of the internal variables with respect to spatial rotations. Equation (XX.99) gives the general expression for the transformation matrices of the internal variables in a rotation. The only difference between this expression and the one given by equation (XIII.84) is the sign in front of σ_u; one passes from one to the other by changing φ into $-\varphi$; it follows that the two matrices are inverses one of the other. This difference is due to the fact that in Chapter XIII, we considered the rotation of the variables and of the states while keeping the axes fixed; here we have taken the opposite point of view. We now see that the Dirac wave function transforms under rotation like the wave function of *a particle of spin* $\frac{1}{2}$.

Note in particular that a rotation through 2π about any axis does not give back the unit matrix; indeed one finds that

$$\Lambda_u(2n\pi) = (-)^n I, \tag{XX.100}$$

property characteristic of half-integral spins. From this it is clear that the arbitrary in the sign of the Λ cannot be removed without violating their property of forming a group.

We shall henceforth call the wave functions of the Dirac theory *spinors*.

13. Spatial Reflection and the Orthochronous Group

Once the law of transformation of spinors in proper changes of referential has been determined, we need only to know the law of transformation in the reflection s to be able to determine the law of transformation in any orthochronous change of referential.

Denote by Λ_s the matrix corresponding to the reflection s of the referential. In this case (XX.85) becomes

$$\Psi'(t, \mathbf{r}) = \Lambda_s \Psi(t, -\mathbf{r}). \tag{XX.101}$$

Condition (XX.89*a*) gives

$$\Lambda_s^{-1} \gamma^0 \Lambda_s = \gamma^0 \qquad \Lambda_s^{-1} \gamma^k \Lambda_s = -\gamma^k,$$

whence

$$\Lambda_s = c_s \gamma^0.$$

The constant c_s is fixed by (XX.89*b*) and (XX.89*c*); one finds

$$c_s = \pm 1.$$

Therefore:

$$\Lambda_s = \pm \gamma^0 \tag{XX.102}$$

Λ_s is defined up to a sign in accordance with what was said above [1]).

14. Construction of Covariant Quantities

From the components of the spinor $\Psi(x)$ and those of its adjoint $\overline{\Psi}(x)$, one can form in all 16 linearly independent functions of x^0, x^1, x^2, x^3 that are bilinear in Ψ and $\overline{\Psi}$. They can be grouped into 5 fields of well-defined tensorial character, namely: a scalar S, a vector V^μ, an antisymmetrical tensor with two indices $T^{[\mu\nu]}$, an antisymmetrical tensor with three indices, or pseudovector $A^{[\lambda\mu\nu]}$ and an antisymmetrical tensor with four indices, or pseudoscalar P. These are given in Table XX.2.

The indicated tensorial characters can easily be demonstrated using the law for the transformation of the spinors Ψ and $\overline{\Psi}$ [eq. (XX.85) and (XX.88)] and relation (XX.89*a*) between the matrix Λ and the coefficients $\Omega^\mu{}_\nu$ of the corresponding Lorentz transformation.

Recall that the law for the transformation of a pseudoscalar differs from that of a scalar only by the presence of the additional factor det $|\Omega^\mu{}_\nu|$:

$$P(x') = \det |\Omega^\mu{}_\nu| \, P(x).$$

TABLE XX.2

Tensors bilinear in Ψ and $\overline{\Psi}$

Tensor	Number of Components	Nature
$S(x) = (\overline{\Psi}\Psi)$	1	Scalar
$V^\mu(x) = (\overline{\Psi}\gamma^\mu\Psi)$	4	Vector
$T^{[\mu\nu]}(x) = (\overline{\Psi}\gamma^\mu\gamma^\nu\Psi) \quad (\mu \neq \nu)$	6	Tensor of rank 2
$A^{[\lambda\mu\nu]}(x) = (\overline{\Psi}\gamma^\lambda\gamma^\mu\gamma^\nu\Psi) \quad (\lambda \neq \mu,\ \mu \neq \nu,\ \nu \neq \lambda)$	4	Pseudovector
$P(x) = (\overline{\Psi}\gamma^5\Psi)$	1	Pseudoscalar

[1]) Expression (XX.102) corresponds to choice (*a*) defined in note, p. 904. Choice (*b*) leads to:

$$\Lambda_s = \pm\, \mathrm{i}\gamma^0.$$

Thus a pseudoscalar field transforms like a scalar field in a proper Lorentz transformation, but changes sign in a reflection s. Similarly, the law for the transformation of a pseudovector differs from that of a vector only by the presence of the additional factor det $|\Omega^{\mu}{}_{\nu}|$.

The vector $V^{\mu}(x)$ has already been interpreted as the current-density four-vector:

$$V^{\mu}(x) \equiv j^{\mu}(x).$$

The other covariants are also capable of interpretation. Thus $T^{[\mu\nu]}$ is, to within a constant, equal to a tensor $S^{\mu\nu}$, which can be interpreted as a spin density:

$$T^{[\mu\nu]} = -2\mathrm{i}S^{\mu\nu}(x) \equiv -2\mathrm{i}(\overline{\Psi}S^{\mu\nu}\Psi).$$

15. A Second Formulation of the Invariance of Form: Transformation of States

In the preceding paragraph, each transformation is considered as an operation on the reference axes, and the physical system is not modified. Inversely, one may effect the transformation on the physical system and leave the axes fixed; this second point of view was systematically adopted in the third part (cf. in particular the remarks of § XIII.11). Although the results are expressed in different language, it is clear that the two points of view are equivalent.

In order to clarify this equivalence, let (S) be the state of the physical system represented in the referential (R) by the spinor $\Psi(x)$. Let (S') be the state obtained by effecting the transformation $\mathscr{L}$ on (S), and $(\hat{R})$ the referential which is taken into (R) by the same transformation (cf. Fig. (XX.1):

$$(S') = \mathscr{L}(S), \qquad (\hat{R}) = \mathscr{L}^{-1}(R).$$

We consider the following three spinors:

$\Psi(x)$	representing	(S)	in	referential	(R)
$\hat{\Psi}(\hat{x})$	,,	(S)	,,	,,	$(\hat{R})$
$\Psi'(x)$	,,	(S')	,,	,,	(R)

It is clear that $\hat{\Psi}$ and Ψ' are equal for equal values of their arguments:

$$\Psi'(x) = \hat{\Psi}(x). \tag{XX.103}$$

The correspondence between $\hat{\Psi}$ and Ψ was established in § 11. Since one passes from $(\hat{R})$ to (R) by the transformation $\mathscr{L}$, one has, applying

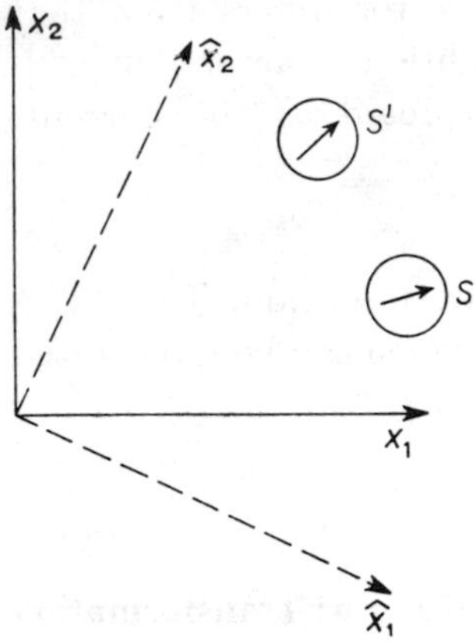

Fig. XX.1. The two ways of looking at a Lorentz transformation: change of referential ($\hat{x} \to x$) and transformation of the system ($S \to S'$).

(XX.85) and denoting the matrix associated with $\mathscr{L}$ by Λ:

$$\Psi(\hat{x}) = \Lambda \hat{\Psi}(\mathscr{L}^{-1}\hat{x}).$$

Therefore:

$$\Psi'(x) = \Lambda^{-1}\Psi(\mathscr{L}x). \qquad \text{(XX.104)}$$

Comparing with equation (XX.85), one sees that the transformation of states is realized by the inverse of the operator corresponding to the change of referential.

These remarks also apply to the electromagnetic field in which the Dirac particle moves. Denote this field by (A) and the field obtained by the transformation $\mathscr{L}$ by (A'):

$$(A') = \mathscr{L}(A).$$

We consider the following three (covariant) four-vectors:

$A_\mu(x)$ representing (A) in referential (R),
$\hat{A}_\mu(\hat{x})$,, (A) ,, ,, $(\hat{R})$,
$A_\mu'(x)$,, (A') ,, ,, (R).

We can repeat the argument given above for the spinors. One obviously has:

$$A_\mu'(x) = \hat{A}_\mu(x). \qquad \text{(XX.105)}$$

But, according to (XX.81):

$$\hat{A}_\mu(\mathscr{L}^{-1}x) = A_\nu(x)\Omega^\nu{}_\mu$$

whence

$$A_\mu'(x) = A_\nu(\mathscr{L}x)\Omega^\nu{}_\mu. \qquad \text{(XX.106)}$$

Suppose now that $\Psi(x)$ satisfies the Dirac equation in the potential $A_\mu(x)$:

$$[\gamma^\mu(\mathrm{i}\partial_\mu - eA_\mu) - m]\Psi = 0. \qquad \text{(XX.107)}$$

Taking into account equalities (XX.103) and (XX.105), the invariance of the form of the Dirac equation in the change of referential $(R) \to (\hat{R})$ gives

$$[\gamma^\mu(\mathrm{i}\partial_\mu - eA_\mu') - m]\Psi' = 0. \qquad \text{(XX.108)}$$

The invariance of form can therefore be expressed in the following way:

If $\Psi(x)$ satisfies the Dirac equation in a potential $A_\mu(x)$, the state $\Psi'(x)$ obtained by the transformation $\mathscr{L}$ satisfies the Dirac equation in the transformed potential $A_\mu'(x)$.

16. Invariance of the Law of Motion

Equations (XX.107) and (XX.108) are in general different. They are identical when the external potential (A) is invariant in the transformation $\mathscr{L}$, that is, when

$$A_\mu'(x) = A_\mu(x).$$

In this case, Ψ and Ψ' obey the *same* wave equation. Thus, *the law of motion of the dynamical states is invariant in any transformation $\mathscr{L}$ that conserves the external potential.*

In all of the preceding work $\mathscr{L}$ was any orthochronous Lorentz transformation. However, all that has been said can be repeated for space-time *translations* [cf. note, p. 900].

The two properties mentioned above – invariance of form and invariance of the law of motion – remain valid when $\mathscr{L}$ represents a space or time translation.

17. Transformation Operators. Momentum, Angular Momentum, Parity

To continue this analysis in accordance with the general scheme set forth in Chapter XV we write the transformation law (XX.104) in the form

$$\Psi' = T\Psi, \qquad \text{(XX.109)}$$

where T is an appropriate linear operator. The invariance of the Dirac equation in the transformation can then be expressed by the operator relation

$$T\,\mathscr{D}(A)\,T^{-1} = \mathscr{D}(A'), \tag{XX.110}$$

in which $\mathscr{D}(A)$ and $\mathscr{D}(A')$ denote the Dirac operators in the potentials A and A' respectively:

$$\mathscr{D}(A) \equiv \gamma^{\mu}(\mathrm{i}\partial_{\mu} - eA_{\mu}). \tag{XX.111}$$

The condition for the invariance of the law of motion under the transformation $\mathscr{L}$ is then expressed by the commutation relation

$$[T, \mathscr{D}(A)] = 0. \tag{XX.112}$$

The operator T is easily constructed. It is the product of an operator $T^{(s)}$ acting on the spin variables alone, and an operator $T^{(0)}$ acting on the orbital variables alone:

$$T = T^{(s)} \otimes T^{(0)}.$$

Comparing (XX.109) and (XX.104), one sees that

$$T^{(s)} = \Lambda^{-1}, \tag{XX.113}$$

where Λ denotes the *operator* represented by the matrix Λ defined in § 11.

Let us derive the explicit form of T for the infinitesimal Lorentz translations and "rotations", and for the reflection s.

For the translations one has $T^{(s)} = 1$. Let us introduce the differential operator

$$\boxed{p_{\mu} \equiv \mathrm{i}\partial_{\mu}} \tag{XX.114}$$

p_{μ} represents the *energy-momentum four-vector* (more precisely, the covariant components of the energy-momentum four-vector). For an infinitesimal translation ε along the direction of the axis x^{α}, one finds

$$T = 1 + \mathrm{i}\varepsilon p_{\alpha}.$$

Consider now an "infinitesimal rotation" of angle ε in the plane $x^{\alpha}x^{\beta}$. In this case one has

$$\begin{aligned}(\mathscr{L}x)^{\mu} &= x^{\mu} - \varepsilon\, Z^{(\alpha\beta)\mu}{}_{\nu}\, x^{\nu} \\ &= x^{\mu} - \varepsilon\,(\delta^{\mu}{}_{\alpha}\, x_{\beta} - \delta^{\mu}{}_{\beta}\, x_{\alpha}).\end{aligned}$$

If $\psi_s(x)$ is a particular component of the spinor $\Psi(x)$, then to the first order in ε:

$$\psi_s(\mathscr{L}x) \simeq \psi_s(x) + \varepsilon\left(x_\alpha \frac{\partial \psi_s}{\partial x^\beta} - x_\beta \frac{\partial \psi_s}{\partial x^\alpha} \right).$$

If we introduce the differential operator

$$L_{\alpha\beta} \equiv x_\alpha p_\beta - x_\beta p_\alpha \tag{XX.115}$$

the preceding equation takes the form

$$\psi_s(\mathscr{L}x) \simeq (1 - \mathrm{i}\varepsilon L_{\alpha\beta})\psi_s(x).$$

On the other hand, from (XX.90) and (XX.113),

$$T^{(s)} \simeq (1 - \mathrm{i}\varepsilon S_{\alpha\beta}),$$

where $S_{\alpha\beta}$ is defined by equation (XX.92). Finally, formula (XX.109) giving the law for the transformation of a spinor becomes in the "infinitesimal rotation" case

$$\begin{aligned} \Psi'(x) &\simeq (1 - \mathrm{i}\varepsilon S_{\alpha\beta})(1 - \mathrm{i}\varepsilon L_{\alpha\beta})\Psi(x) \\ &\simeq (1 - \mathrm{i}\varepsilon J_{\alpha\beta})\Psi(x), \end{aligned}$$

where

$$\boxed{J_{\alpha\beta} \equiv L_{\alpha\beta} + S_{\alpha\beta} \equiv x_\alpha p_\beta - x_\beta p_\alpha + \tfrac{1}{2}\sigma_{\alpha\beta}} \tag{XX.116}$$

The three spatial components J_{23}, J_{31} and J_{12} of $J_{\alpha\beta}$ are associated with infinitesimal rotations about the axes Ox, Oy and Oz respectively; they are the components of the total angular momentum $\boldsymbol{J}$ and one has

$$\begin{gathered} \boldsymbol{J} = \boldsymbol{L} + \boldsymbol{S} \\ \boldsymbol{L} = \boldsymbol{r} \times \boldsymbol{p}, \qquad \boldsymbol{S} - \tfrac{1}{2}\boldsymbol{\sigma}. \end{gathered} \tag{XX.117}$$

The components of $\boldsymbol{L}$ act on the orbital variables alone: $\boldsymbol{L}$ is the orbital angular momentum. The components of $\boldsymbol{S}$ act on the internal variables alone: $\boldsymbol{S}$ is the spin vector of the particle.

The reader will verify that $\boldsymbol{J}$, $\boldsymbol{L}$ and $\boldsymbol{S}$ satisfy the commutation relations characteristic of angular momenta and that $\boldsymbol{S}$ has the property

$$\boldsymbol{S}^2 = \tfrac{3}{4}$$

characteristic of a particle of spin $\tfrac{1}{2}$.

The operator associated with spatial reflection [1]) will be called the

---

[1]) See *Note added in proof*, p. 956.

parity operator and denoted by P. Let us denote by $P^{(0)}$ the "orbital parity" operator

$$P^{(0)}\Psi(t, \mathbf{r}) = \Psi(t, -\mathbf{r}).$$

According to (XX.113) we have for P the choice between two expressions differing by a sign, expressions easily obtained from the study of § 13 [cf. relation (XX.102)]. We adopt the most convenient one:

$$\boxed{P = \gamma^0 P^{(0)}} \tag{XX.118}$$

Note that P is Hermitean and that $P^2 = 1$.

18. Conservation Laws and Constants of the Motion

If the transformation depends on the time, the associated operator T explicitly brings in the time dependence of Ψ. This occurs notably in the case of the time translations and the special Lorentz transformations.

On the other hand, *for any transformation independent of the time, the action of T is defined independently of the law of motion of the state vector to which it is applied.* T can then be defined as a transformation operator acting on the state-vectors and observables of the system as was done in Chapter XV (Section II); the invariance properties of the law of motion of the states may then be expressed in the form of conservation laws.

For example, if $\mathscr{L}$ is a spatial transformation, T is a certain function of the operators of reflection, infinitesimal translation and infinitesimal rotation, that is, a certain function of P, $\boldsymbol{J}$ and $\boldsymbol{p}$; T therefore commutes with γ^0. And since

$$\gamma^0\left(\mathrm{i}\frac{\partial}{\partial t} - H_D\right) \equiv \mathscr{D}(A) - m,$$

the commutation relation (XX.112) is equivalent, in this case, to

$$[T, H_D] = 0.$$

This condition is the same as the one studied in § XV.12, and what was said there concerning the connection between the symmetries of the Hamiltonian and the laws of conservation may be applied here.

Thus, if $A_\mu(x)$ is invariant under translation, one obtains the commutation relations

$$[\boldsymbol{p}, H_D] = 0$$

and the conservation of momentum. If $A_\mu(x)$ is spherically symmetrical,

$$[\boldsymbol{J}, H_D] = 0$$

and the total angular momentum is conserved. If $A_\mu(x)$ is invariant under reflection in the origin,

$$[P, H_D] = 0$$

and the parity is conserved.

19. Time Reversal and Charge Conjugation

In this paragraph, we shall demonstrate the invariance of the form of the Dirac equation under two antilinear operations, time reversal and charge conjugation. It is convenient, for this, to introduce an antiunitary operator K [1]) of state-vector space having certain particularly simple general properties.

THE ANTIUNITARY OPERATOR K. K is by definition the antiunitary operator which transforms $\boldsymbol{p}$ into $-\boldsymbol{p}$ and conserves $\boldsymbol{r}$ and γ^μ:

$$K\boldsymbol{r}K^\dagger = \boldsymbol{r}, \qquad K\boldsymbol{p}K^\dagger = -\boldsymbol{p}. \tag{XX.119}$$

$$K\gamma^\mu K^\dagger = \gamma^\mu \qquad (\mu = 0, 1, 2, 3). \tag{XX.120}$$

It will be shown that such an operator exists, is defined to within a phase, and has the property

$$K^2 = -1. \tag{XX.121}$$

That K, if it exists, is defined to within a phase follows from relations (XX.119–120) and the fact that state-vector space is irreducible with respect to the basic operators $\boldsymbol{r}$, $\boldsymbol{p}$ and γ^μ. Let us now choose a particular representation, the Dirac representation for example. Each *operator* γ^μ is then represented by a certain matrix $\gamma_D{}^\mu$. Denote the operator represented by the "B matrix" which transforms the $\gamma_D{}^\mu$ into their respective complex conjugates by B_D. Here, B_D will be considered as a (unitary) operator of the total space and not as an operator of spin space alone; it is a unitary operator commuting with $\boldsymbol{r}$ and $\boldsymbol{p}$. Let K_D be the complex-conjugation operator associated with the representation (definition of § XV.5). Relations (XX.76) give:

$$\gamma^\mu = B_D(K_D\gamma^\mu K_D{}^\dagger)B_D{}^\dagger.$$

---

[1]) This operator *is not* the time reversal operator. The latter is denoted below by K_T.

Therefore, the antiunitary operator

$$K \equiv B_D K_D$$

satisfies relations (XX.120). Since B_D commutes with $\boldsymbol{r}$ and $\boldsymbol{p}$, and since from the definition of K_D,

$$K_D \boldsymbol{r} K_D = \boldsymbol{r}, \qquad K_D \boldsymbol{p} K_D = -\boldsymbol{p},$$

K also satisfies relations (XX.119). Finally, since $K_D = K_D^\dagger$, (XX.77) gives:

$$B_D(K_D B_D K_D) \equiv K^2 = -1.$$

This is just (XX.121); it obviously remains true if K is multiplied by any phase factor. Q.E.D.

CHARGE-CONJUGATION. Multiplying both sides of equation (XX.107) on the left by K and using the fact that K is antilinear and commutes with γ^μ, ∂_μ and $A_\mu(x)$, one finds:

$$[\gamma^\mu(-i\partial_\mu - eA_\mu(x)) - m]\, K\Psi(x) = 0. \qquad \text{(XX.122)}$$

$K\Psi$ therefore satisfies a wave equation differing from the Dirac equation only by the substitution of $-i$ for $+i$. Let us multiply both sides by γ^5. Since γ^5 anticommutes with γ^μ and commutes with all of the other operators in the bracket on the left-hand side, we obtain

$$[\gamma^\mu(i\partial_\mu + eA_\mu(x)) - m]\, \gamma^5 K\Psi(x) = 0. \qquad \text{(XX.123)}$$

Put:

$$\boxed{K_C \equiv \gamma^5 K} \qquad \text{(XX.124)}$$

$$\Psi^C(x) \equiv K_C \Psi(x). \qquad \text{(XX.125)}$$

Equation (XX.123) now becomes:

$$[\gamma^\mu(i\partial_\mu + eA_\mu(x)) - m]\, \Psi^C(x) = 0. \qquad \text{(XX.126)}$$

The equation satisfied by $\Psi^C(x)$ differs from the one satisfied by $\Psi(x)$ only in the sign of the charge. Thus, *if $\Psi(x)$ represents the motion of a Dirac particle of mass m and charge e in the potential $A_\mu(x)$, $\Psi^C(x)$ represents the motion of a Dirac particle of the same mass m and of opposite charge $(-e)$ in the same potential $A_\mu(x)$.*

The spinors Ψ and Ψ^C are called charge conjugates one of the other, and the transformation K_C is called *charge conjugation.*

It follows from the properties of K and γ^5 that

$$K_C{}^2 = 1. \tag{XX.127}$$

Thus the correspondence between Ψ and Ψ^C is reciprocal. It is easy to show that charge conjugation commutes with translations and orthochronous Lorentz transformations. More precisely, if $L\Psi$ is the transform of Ψ in one of these transformations, its charge-conjugate is $L\Psi^C$ in the case of a translation or a proper Lorentz transformation, and $-L\Psi^C$ in the case of a reflection (cf. Problem XX.5).

TIME REVERSAL. The time reversal invariance of the Dirac equation can be demonstrated directly, but it is just as simple to start from the preceding results on charge conjugation.

A given potential $A_\mu(t, \mathbf{r})$ is created by a certain number of charges in motion. The time-reversed potential $A_\mu'(t, \mathbf{r})$, is obtained by reversing the motion of these charges. In this operation the currents, and therefore the magnetic field, change their sign while electric charges, and therefore the electric field, remain unchanged

$$\mathscr{H}'(t, \mathbf{r}) = -\mathscr{H}(-t, \mathbf{r}), \qquad \mathscr{E}'(t, \mathbf{r}) = \mathscr{E}(-t, \mathbf{r}).$$

It follows that A_μ "transforms like a pseudovector":

$$\mathbf{A}'(t, \mathbf{r}) = -\mathbf{A}(-t, \mathbf{r}) \qquad A_0'(t, \mathbf{r}) = A_0(-t, \mathbf{r}).$$

If we change t into $-t$ in equation (XX.126), we therefore have

$$[-\gamma^0(\mathrm{i}\partial_0 - eA_0'(t, \mathbf{r})) + \sum_k \gamma^k(\mathrm{i}\partial_k - eA_k'(t, \mathbf{r})) - m]\,\Psi^C(-t, \mathbf{r}) = 0.$$

Let us multiply both sides by $\gamma^5\gamma^0$. Since this operator anticommutes with γ^0 and commutes with γ^k, we obtain:

$$[\gamma^\mu(\mathrm{i}\partial_\mu - eA_\mu'(t, \mathbf{r})) - m]\,\Psi'(t, \mathbf{r}) = 0 \tag{XX.128}$$

if we put:

$$\begin{aligned}\Psi'(t, \mathbf{r}) &\equiv \gamma^5\gamma^0\Psi^C(-t, \mathbf{r}) \\ &= \gamma^0 K\Psi(-t, \mathbf{r}).\end{aligned} \tag{XX.129}$$

Let us introduce the (antiunitary) time-reversal operator:

$$\boxed{K_T \equiv \gamma^0 K} \tag{XX.130}$$

$\Psi'(t, \mathbf{r})$ is by definition the time-reversal transform of $\Psi(-t, \mathbf{r})$. It satisfies equation (XX.128). Therefore, if Ψ satisfies the Dirac equation in the potential A_μ, its time-reversal transform Ψ' satisfies the Dirac equation in the potential A_μ' obtained from A_μ by time reversal.

In particular, if A_μ is invariant under time reversal (for example, if the particle is in a stationary electric field: $\mathbf{A}=0$, $\partial A_0/\partial t=0$), Ψ and Ψ' both obey the same Dirac equation.

From the properties of γ^0 and K, one obtains:

$$K_T{}^2 = -1. \tag{XX.131}$$

This result, characteristic of systems of half-integral angular momenta, has already been obtained in the non-relativistic case [eq. (XV.88)]. The consequences, in particular Kramers degeneracy, are also valid here.

Expressing B_D in terms of the ϱ and σ (cf. end of § 10), we easily obtain from definitions (XX.124) and (XX.130) the equivalent relations

$$K_C = \mathrm{i}\varrho_2\, \sigma_y\, K_D$$
$$K_T = \mathrm{i}\sigma_y\, K_D.$$

These are useful when manipulating the operators K_C and K_T in the Dirac representation.

20. Gauge Invariance

For completeness, we shall mention here the property of gauge invariance (cf. § XXI.20).

Changing the gauge of the electromagnetic potential means replacing the components $A_\mu(x)$ by

$$A_\mu'(x) \equiv A_\mu(x) - \partial_\mu G(x), \tag{XX.132}$$

where $G(x)$ is an arbitrary function of the space-time coordinates. This gives

$$A_0' = A_0 - \frac{\partial G}{\partial t}, \qquad \mathbf{A}' = \mathbf{A} + \nabla G.$$

The electric and magnetic fields are invariant in such a transformation.

If $\Psi(x)$ is a solution of the Dirac equation in the potential A_μ, then clearly

$$\Psi'(x) \equiv \mathrm{e}^{\mathrm{i}eG(x)}\Psi(x) \tag{XX.133}$$

is a solution of the Dirac equation in the potential A_μ'. This is called the gauge-invariance property of the Dirac equation.

IV. INTERPRETATION OF THE OPERATORS AND SIMPLE SOLUTIONS

21. The Dirac Equation and the Correspondence Principle

When the electromagnetic field is not zero, the solutions of the Dirac equation satisfy a second-order equation different to the Klein–Gordon equation but conforming with the correspondence principle.

To obtain this equation, one can start from the covariant form (XX.50) and write that the action of the operator $(-\mathrm{i}\gamma^\lambda D_\lambda - m)$ on the left-hand side gives zero:

$$[\gamma^\lambda\gamma^\mu D_\lambda D_\mu + m^2]\Psi = 0. \tag{XX.134}$$

From the algebraic properties of the γ^μ operators, one obtains

$$\gamma^\lambda\gamma^\mu \equiv g^{\lambda\mu} + \tfrac{1}{2}[\gamma^\lambda, \gamma^\mu]. \tag{XX.135}$$

By renaming the dummy indices, we have

$$[\gamma^\lambda, \gamma^\mu] D_\lambda D_\mu \equiv -[\gamma^\lambda, \gamma^\mu] D_\mu D_\lambda = \tfrac{1}{2}\,[\gamma^\lambda, \gamma^\mu]\,[D_\lambda, D_\mu]. \tag{XX.136}$$

and, from the definition of the operator D_μ [eq. (XX.10)]

$$\begin{aligned}[D_\lambda, D_\mu] &\equiv \mathrm{i}e[\partial_\lambda, A_\mu] + \mathrm{i}e[A_\lambda, \partial_\mu] \\ &\equiv \mathrm{i}e\left(\frac{\partial A_\mu}{\partial x^\lambda} - \frac{\partial A_\lambda}{\partial x^\mu}\right) \equiv \mathrm{i}eF_{\lambda\mu}.\end{aligned} \tag{XX.137}$$

Equations (XX.135–137) give

$$\gamma^\lambda\gamma^\mu D_\lambda D_\mu \equiv D_\mu D^\mu + eS^{\lambda\mu}F_{\lambda\mu}, \tag{XX.138}$$

where $S^{\lambda\mu}$ represents the spin of the particle [definition (XX.92)]. Equation (XX.134) can therefore be put in the form

$$[D_\mu D^\mu + eS^{\lambda\mu}F_{\lambda\mu} + m^2]\Psi = 0. \tag{XX.139}$$

Comparing (XX.139) with the form (XX.30′) of the Klein–Gordon equation, it is seen that it differs by the presence of the term

$$eS^{\lambda\mu}F_{\lambda\mu}, \tag{XX.140}$$

which is a term coupling the spin of the particle to the electromagnetic field. This term has no classical analogue and its contribution is negligible when the classical approximation is valid. The motion of a Dirac wave packet is then the same as the motion of a Klein–Gordon wave packet.

22. Dynamical Variables of a Dirac Particle

From time to time we have given the physical interpretation of a certain number of dynamical variables of the Dirac theory. We shall now take up this question in a more systematic way, and indicate, in particular, the variables of the Quantum Theory which correspond to the different classical quantities of § 4.

The relativistic invariance of the theory plays no essential role in this discussion. We adopt the same point of view as in non-relativistic Quantum Mechanics: the system is defined by giving a certain number of dynamical variables obeying a well-defined algebra, and the Dirac equation – in the Dirac form [eqs. (XX.36) and (XX.44)] – describes the evolution of the dynamical states in the Schrödinger "representation".

In what follows time is therefore treated as a simple parameter, while the spatial coordinates are included among the dynamical variables of the system. The fundamental variables are $\boldsymbol{r}$ and $\boldsymbol{p}$ together with the internal variables $\boldsymbol{\alpha}$ and β. The whole of representation theory applies here without change. In particular, in the Dirac representation, the state-vectors $|\Psi\rangle$, $|\Phi\rangle$, ..., are represented by four-component wave functions, $\Psi(\boldsymbol{r})$, $\Phi(\boldsymbol{r})$, ... of the coordinates x, y, z. In this representation the scalar product $\langle\Phi|\Psi\rangle$ is defined as a summation over the 4 possible values of the index representing the internal degree of freedom and an integration over the coordinates x, y, z:

$$\langle\Phi|\Psi\rangle = \sum_{s=1}^{4} \int \varphi_s^*(\boldsymbol{r})\, \psi_s(\boldsymbol{r})\, \mathrm{d}\boldsymbol{r}.$$

This definition of the scalar product is consistent with the definition of the position probability density given in § 6 [formula (XX.35)]. More generally, we shall adopt here without change the statistical interpretation of the theory as set forth in the first part of this book; in particular, the average value of an operator Q for a given state of the system is given by

$$\langle Q\rangle = \langle u|Q|u\rangle,$$

where $|u\rangle$ is the normalized ket representing that state.

The observables of the theory that do not act on the internal degree of freedom have an obvious interpretation; in particular we have:

$\boldsymbol{r}$, the position vector,

$\boldsymbol{p}$, the (Lagrange canonical) momentum, called the momentum in this book.

$\boldsymbol{\pi} \equiv \boldsymbol{p} - e\boldsymbol{A}(\boldsymbol{r}, t)$, the mechanical momentum.

Among the functions of $\boldsymbol{r}$ we have the operator

$$\delta(\boldsymbol{r} - \boldsymbol{r}_0),$$

which is the projector onto the subspace of the eigenvalue $\boldsymbol{r}_0$; it represents the position probability density at the point $\boldsymbol{r}_0$.

Among the observables depending on the internal degree of freedom we define [1]:

the energy:

$$H \equiv e\varphi + \boldsymbol{\alpha} \cdot \boldsymbol{\pi} + \beta m; \qquad \text{(XX.141)}$$

the relativistic mass:

$$M \equiv H - e\varphi \equiv \boldsymbol{\alpha} \cdot \boldsymbol{\pi} + \beta m; \qquad \text{(XX.142)}$$

the current density at $\boldsymbol{r}$:

$$\boldsymbol{j}(\boldsymbol{r}_0) \equiv \boldsymbol{\alpha} \delta(\boldsymbol{r} - \boldsymbol{r}_0); \qquad \text{(XX.143)}$$

the total angular momentum:

$$\boldsymbol{J} \equiv (\boldsymbol{r} \times \boldsymbol{p}) + \tfrac{1}{2}\boldsymbol{\sigma}; \qquad \text{(XX.144)}$$

the spin:

$$\boldsymbol{S} \equiv \tfrac{1}{2}\boldsymbol{\sigma}; \qquad \text{(XX.145)}$$

the parity:

$$P \equiv \beta P^{(0)}. \qquad \text{(XX.146)}$$

The definitions of H and M are based on the correspondence with classical mechanics; that of $\boldsymbol{j}(\boldsymbol{r}_0)$ follows from the equation of continuity; those of $\boldsymbol{J}$ and $\boldsymbol{S}$ are related to the transformations of the states under rotation and that of P to the transformations under reflection.

Finally, *the correspondence principle leads to the interpretation of* $\boldsymbol{\alpha}$ *as the velocity of the particle.* This interpretation is also suggested by the expression for the current density. To establish it, we compare the classical equations (XX.18), (XX.19) and (XX.21) with the corresponding quantum equations, and to do this we must obviously pass

---

[1]) Note that $\boldsymbol{p}$ depends on the choice of gauge; only the momentum of the total system (particle + electromagnetic field) is independent of this choice. The same remarks apply to the energy H and to the angular momentum $\boldsymbol{J}$ (cf. § XXI.23).

over to the Heisenberg "representation". The Heisenberg equations for the variables $\boldsymbol{r}$ and $\boldsymbol{\pi}$ (in the Heisenberg "representation") are written:

$$\frac{\mathrm{d}\boldsymbol{r}}{\mathrm{d}t} = -\,\mathrm{i}[\boldsymbol{r}, H]$$

$$\frac{\mathrm{d}\boldsymbol{\pi}}{\mathrm{d}t} = -\,\mathrm{i}[\boldsymbol{\pi}, H] + \frac{\partial \boldsymbol{\pi}}{\partial t}.$$

Replacing H and $\boldsymbol{\pi}$ on the right-hand side by the expressions given above and using the commutation or anti-commutation relations for the operators $\boldsymbol{r}$, $\boldsymbol{p}$, $\boldsymbol{\alpha}$ and β, one finds, after a rather long but straightforward calculation (Problem XX.6),

$$\frac{\mathrm{d}\boldsymbol{r}}{\mathrm{d}t} = \boldsymbol{\alpha} \tag{XX.147}$$

$$\frac{\mathrm{d}\boldsymbol{\pi}}{\mathrm{d}t} = e(\mathscr{E} + \boldsymbol{\alpha} \times \mathscr{H}). \tag{XX.148}$$

Also, from (XX.142) and the properties of $\boldsymbol{\alpha}$, one has the identity

$$\boldsymbol{\pi} = \tfrac{1}{2}(M\boldsymbol{\alpha} + \boldsymbol{\alpha}M). \tag{XX.149}$$

Equations (XX.147–149) between dynamical variables in the Heisenberg "representation" may be identified respectively with equations (XX.18), (XX.21) and (XX.19) between the classical dynamical variables if one treats $\boldsymbol{\alpha}$ as the classical velocity $\boldsymbol{v}$.

Note that the components of the velocity $\boldsymbol{\alpha}$ do not commute, and that each of them has in all two eigenvalues, $+c$ and $-c$ ($+1$ and -1 in the units used here). Here we have no difficulty of principle, but simply an additional indication that the classical picture of the phenomena should not be taken too seriously. We shall return to this question in § 37.

23. The Free Electron. Plane Waves

In the rest of this section we examine the solutions of the Dirac equation, first in the absence of a field, then in a static central potential. Solving the Dirac equation is then equivalent to finding the eigensolutions of the Hamiltonian H_D. Unless otherwise indicated, the calculations will be made in the Dirac representation, and we shall frequently make use of the operators ϱ_1, ϱ_2, ϱ_3 and σ_x, σ_y, σ_z introduced in § 7.

We first suppose the field null. The Hamiltonian H_D then commutes with the three components of the momentum. We therefore wish to find the eigensolutions of H_D corresponding to a well-defined value $\boldsymbol{p}$ for the momentum. Such solutions are plane waves, that is, functions of the form

$$u(\boldsymbol{p})\,\mathrm{e}^{\mathrm{i}\boldsymbol{p}\cdot\boldsymbol{r}},$$

where $u(\boldsymbol{p})$ is a four-component spinor independent of $\boldsymbol{r}$. It is determined by the eigenvalue equation

$$Hu(\boldsymbol{p}) = Eu(\boldsymbol{p}), \tag{XX.150}$$

where H is the following operator of $\mathscr{E}^{(s)}$ space:

$$H \equiv \boldsymbol{\alpha}\cdot\boldsymbol{p}+\beta m \equiv \varrho_1(\boldsymbol{\sigma}\cdot\boldsymbol{p})+\varrho_3 m. \tag{XX.151}$$

A simple calculation gives:

$$H^2 = p^2+m^2.$$

The only possible eigenvalues of H are therefore the two values $\pm\sqrt{p^2+m^2}$, i.e.:

$$\begin{aligned} E &= \varepsilon E_p \qquad\qquad (\varepsilon = \pm 1) \\ E_p &= \sqrt{p^2+m^2}. \end{aligned} \tag{XX.152}$$

It is easy to show — for example by using the fact that ϱ_2 anticommutes with H — that these two values are doubly degenerate.

The *component* $\boldsymbol{\sigma}\cdot\boldsymbol{p}/2p$ *of the spin in the direction of* $\boldsymbol{p}$ *commutes with* H. This can be seen from the last of expressions (XX.151); (the other spin components do not commute with H). We are therefore led to look for the common eigensolutions of H and $\boldsymbol{\sigma}\cdot\boldsymbol{p}/2p$. We obtain the following 4 pairs of eigenvalues:

$$(+E_p,+\tfrac{1}{2}) \quad (+E_p,-\tfrac{1}{2}) \quad (-E_p,+\tfrac{1}{2}) \quad (-E_p,-\tfrac{1}{2}).$$

To each of these pairs there corresponds a single eigenstate. The corresponding eigenspinor is easily determined from the two eigenvalue equations. An alternative method for finding this spinor will be given in the following paragraph.

The components of the 4 eigenspinors (normalized to unity) are given in Table XX.3 for the particularly simple case when $\boldsymbol{p}$ is directed along the z axis. Recall that, in the Dirac representation, β and σ_z are represented by diagonal matrices.

TABLE XX.3

Components of the spinors corresponding to the wave of momentum $\boldsymbol{p} \equiv (0, 0, p)$ *in the Dirac representation* ($E_p = \sqrt{m^2 + p^2}$).

Energy $E =$		Positive $+E_p$		Negative $-E_p$	
Spin $\boldsymbol{\sigma}\cdot\boldsymbol{p}/2p \equiv \frac{1}{2}\sigma_z$		↺ $+\frac{1}{2}$	↷ $-\frac{1}{2}$	↺ $+\frac{1}{2}$	↷ $-\frac{1}{2}$
$\left(\frac{2E_p}{E_p+m}\right)^{\frac{1}{2}} \times$	$u_1 =$	1	0	$-\frac{p}{E_p+m}$	0
	$u_2 =$	0	1	0	$\frac{p}{E_p+m}$
	$u_3 =$	$\frac{p}{E_p+m}$	0	1	0
	$u_4 =$	0	$-\frac{p}{E_p+m}$	0	1

The 4 spinors are normalized to unity: $u^\dagger u = 1$.

24. Construction of the Plane Waves by a Lorentz Transformation

When $A_\mu = 0$, any Lorentz transform of a solution of the Dirac equation is another solution of the Dirac equation. In particular, any plane wave of momentum $\boldsymbol{p}$ can be obtained by a Lorentz transformation from a plane wave of momentum zero. We shall now describe a method based on this remark for constructing the spinors $u(\boldsymbol{p})$ of the preceding paragraph.

For a zero momentum, equation (XX.150) becomes

$$\beta m u(0) = E u(0).$$

The two possible eigenvalues are $+m$ and $-m$. To the eigenvalue $\varepsilon m (\varepsilon = \pm 1)$ there corresponds the spinor $u^{(\varepsilon)}(0)$; it is an eigenvector of the operator β. We shall suppose it normalized to unity, and we fix the direction of the spin in an arbitrary way; $u^{(\varepsilon)}(0)$ is then defined up to a phase.

The plane wave

$$\Psi_0{}^{(\varepsilon)} = u^{(\varepsilon)}(0) \mathrm{e}^{-\mathrm{i}\varepsilon m t}$$

is a solution of the Dirac equation corresponding to a momentum zero and an energy εm, that is, to the energy-momentum four-vector $(\varepsilon m, 0)$.

Consider the same solution in a new referential having a velocity

$\boldsymbol{v} = -\boldsymbol{p}/\varepsilon\sqrt{m^2+p^2} = -\boldsymbol{p}/\varepsilon E_p$ with respect to the preceding one. In this new referential, the energy-momentum of the particle is

$$p^\mu \equiv (\varepsilon E_p, \boldsymbol{p}). \tag{XX.153}$$

The solution is there represented by the plane wave:

$$\begin{aligned}\Psi_{\boldsymbol{p}}^{(\varepsilon)} &= \Lambda_{\text{sp}}(\boldsymbol{v})\, u^{(\varepsilon)}(0) \exp(-\mathrm{i}p^\mu x_\mu) \\ &= [\Lambda_{\text{sp}}(\boldsymbol{v})\, u^{(\varepsilon)}(0)] \exp[-\mathrm{i}(\varepsilon E_p t - \boldsymbol{p}\cdot\boldsymbol{r})].\end{aligned}$$

The term in brackets is therefore proportional to one of the sought-for spinors $u(\boldsymbol{p})$ which we shall henceforth denote by $u^{(\varepsilon)}(\boldsymbol{p})$. Its norm is the time component of the associated current four-vector; it may be obtained from the current four-vector associated with $u^{(\varepsilon)}(0)$ by a Lorentz transformation; it is therefore equal to:

$$b \equiv (1-v^2)^{-\frac{1}{2}} = E_p/m.$$

We therefore adopt the definition:

$$u^{(\varepsilon)}(\boldsymbol{p}) \equiv b^{-\frac{1}{2}}\Lambda_{\text{sp}}(\boldsymbol{v})\, u^{(\varepsilon)}(0).$$

Substituting (XX.97) into this definition with the values of $\boldsymbol{v}$ and b given above, one finds

$$u^{(\varepsilon)}(\boldsymbol{p}) = [2E_p(m+E_p)]^{-\frac{1}{2}}[m+E_p+\varepsilon\boldsymbol{\alpha}\cdot\boldsymbol{p}]u^{(\varepsilon)}(0), \tag{XX.154}$$

which is the required expression. In particular if $u^{(\varepsilon)}(0)$ is an eigenstate of $(\boldsymbol{\sigma}\cdot\boldsymbol{p})$, then so is $u^{(\varepsilon)}(\boldsymbol{p})$, which is therefore in this case one of the spinors defined in the preceding paragraph. In particular one obtains the results of Table 3 when $\boldsymbol{p}$ is directed along the z axis.

Expression (XX.154) may also be put in the form

$$u^{(\varepsilon)}(\boldsymbol{p}) = [2E_p(m+E_p)]^{-\frac{1}{2}}[m+\gamma^\mu p_\mu]u^{(\varepsilon)}(0), \tag{XX.155}$$

in which p_μ represents the energy-momentum four-vector defined by equation (XX.153).

25. Central Potential

We now look for the eigensolutions of a Dirac particle in a static central potential $V(r)$. The Dirac Hamiltonian is then

$$H_D \equiv \boldsymbol{\alpha}\cdot\boldsymbol{p}+\beta m+V(r). \tag{XX.156}$$

It is invariant under rotation and reflection:

$$[H_D, \boldsymbol{J}] = 0, \qquad [H_D, P] = 0.$$

We therefore look for eigensolutions of well-defined angular momentum and parity.

It is convenient to write the solutions Ψ in the form

$$\Psi = \begin{pmatrix} \Phi \\ \chi \end{pmatrix}, \tag{XX.157}$$

where

$$\Phi \equiv \begin{pmatrix} \psi_1 \\ \psi_2 \end{pmatrix}, \qquad \chi \equiv \begin{pmatrix} \psi_3 \\ \psi_4 \end{pmatrix}. \tag{XX.158}$$

Projecting Ψ onto the subspaces $\beta = +1$ and $\beta = -1$, one finds

$$\tfrac{1}{2}(1+\beta)\,\Psi = \begin{pmatrix} \Phi \\ 0 \end{pmatrix}, \qquad \tfrac{1}{2}(1-\beta)\,\Psi = \begin{pmatrix} 0 \\ \chi \end{pmatrix}. \tag{XX.159}$$

Φ and χ are functions of $\boldsymbol{r}$ and of the spin component μ along the z axis; they may also be considered as functions of the radial variable r and of the "angular variables" (θ, φ, μ): in this they are entirely analogous to the wave functions of the Pauli theory.

Let us now suppose that Ψ is a simultaneous eigenfunction of $\boldsymbol{J}^2$, J_z and P. We denote the angular momentum quantum numbers by (JM). For convenience, we indicate the parity with the aid of the quantum number ϖ such that:

$$\varpi = \begin{cases} +1 \text{ for states of parity } (-)^{J+\frac{1}{2}} \\ -1 \text{ for states of parity } (-)^{J-\frac{1}{2}} \end{cases} \tag{XX.160}$$

Thus, by hypothesis:

$$\begin{gathered} \boldsymbol{J}^2 \begin{pmatrix} \Phi \\ \chi \end{pmatrix} = J(J+1) \begin{pmatrix} \Phi \\ \chi \end{pmatrix}, \qquad J_z \begin{pmatrix} \Phi \\ \chi \end{pmatrix} = M \begin{pmatrix} \Phi \\ \chi \end{pmatrix} \\ P^{(0)} \begin{pmatrix} \Phi \\ \chi \end{pmatrix} = (-)^{J+\frac{1}{2}\varpi} \begin{pmatrix} \Phi \\ -\chi \end{pmatrix}. \end{gathered} \tag{XX.161}$$

Let $\mathscr{Y}_{LJ}^{M}(\theta, \varphi, \mu)$ be the function of total angular momentum (JM) formed by the composition of a spin $\frac{1}{2}$ with the spherical harmonics of order L. The parity of this function is $(-)^L$. Also, according to the rules for the composition of angular momenta, L can take only the two values

$$L = l \equiv J + \tfrac{1}{2}\varpi \qquad L = l' \equiv J - \tfrac{1}{2}\varpi \tag{XX.162}$$

and the two functions $\mathscr{Y}_{lJ}^{M}$ and $\mathscr{Y}_{l'J}^{M}$ are of opposite parity, that of the first being $(-)^{J+\frac{1}{2}\varpi}$ and that of the second $(-)^{J-\frac{1}{2}\varpi}$. According to equations (XX.161), Φ is a function of $(r, \theta, \varphi, \mu)$ of angular momentum (JM) and of parity $(-)^{J+\frac{1}{2}\varpi}$; it is therefore necessarily equal to the product of a function of r by $\mathscr{Y}_{lJ}^{M}$. A similar argument shows that χ is equal to the product of a function of r by $\mathscr{Y}_{l'J}^{M}$.

In conclusion, if $\Psi_{\varpi J}^{M}$ represents a state of angular momentum (JM) and of parity $(-)^{J+\frac{1}{2}\varpi}$, it can be written in the form

$$\Psi_{\varpi J}^{M} = \frac{1}{r}\begin{pmatrix} F\ \mathscr{Y}_{lJ}^{M} \\ \mathrm{i}G\ \mathscr{Y}_{l'J}^{M} \end{pmatrix}, \tag{XX.163}$$

where l and l' are given by equations (XX.162), and F and G are arbitrary functions of r.

Consider now the eigenvalue problem

$$H_D \Psi_{\varpi J}^{M} = E \Psi_{\varpi J}^{M}. \tag{XX.164}$$

To solve this equation we separate the "angular" variables from the radial variables in the operator H_D. The method to be followed is wholly analogous to the one of Chapter IX.

We introduce the radial momentum p_r and the "radial velocity" α_r:

$$p_r \equiv -\mathrm{i}\frac{1}{r}\frac{\partial}{\partial r} r \tag{XX.165}$$

$$\alpha_r \equiv \boldsymbol{\alpha}\cdot\hat{\boldsymbol{r}} = \varrho_1 (\boldsymbol{\sigma}\cdot\boldsymbol{r})/r. \tag{XX.166}$$

From identity (XIII.83), one obtains

$$\begin{aligned}(\boldsymbol{\alpha}\cdot\boldsymbol{r})(\boldsymbol{\alpha}\cdot\boldsymbol{p}) &= (\boldsymbol{\sigma}\cdot\boldsymbol{r})(\boldsymbol{\sigma}\cdot\boldsymbol{p}) = \boldsymbol{r}\cdot\boldsymbol{p}+\mathrm{i}\boldsymbol{\sigma}\cdot\boldsymbol{L} \\ &= rp_r+\mathrm{i}(1+\boldsymbol{\sigma}\cdot\boldsymbol{L}).\end{aligned}$$

Whence, multiplying on the left by α_r/r and using the obvious property $\alpha_r^2=1$, the identity:

$$\boldsymbol{\alpha}\cdot\boldsymbol{p} \equiv \alpha_r\left(p_r+\frac{\mathrm{i}}{r}(1+\boldsymbol{\sigma}\cdot\boldsymbol{L})\right). \tag{XX.167}$$

Let us examine the operator $1+\boldsymbol{\sigma}\cdot\boldsymbol{L}$. One easily shows that

$$1+\boldsymbol{\sigma}\cdot\boldsymbol{L} = \boldsymbol{J}^2+\tfrac{1}{4}-\boldsymbol{L}^2.$$

Further, from (XX.163), it is clear that the action of $\mathbf{L}^2$ on $\Psi_{\varpi J}^M$ is equivalent to that of the operator

$$(J+\tfrac{1}{2}\varpi\beta)(J+\tfrac{1}{2}\varpi\beta+1) \equiv J(J+1)+\tfrac{1}{4}+\tfrac{1}{2}\varpi\beta(2J+1).$$

Therefore:

$$(1+\boldsymbol{\sigma}\cdot\mathbf{L})\Psi_{\varpi J}^M = -\tfrac{1}{2}\varpi(2J+1)\beta\Psi_{\varpi J}^M. \qquad \text{(XX.168)}$$

Substituting relations (XX.167) and (XX.168) into equation (XX.164), one obtains

$$\left[\alpha_r\left(p_r - \frac{\mathrm{i}\varpi(J+\frac{1}{2})}{r}\beta\right)+m\beta+V(r)\right]\Psi_{\varpi J}^M = E\Psi_{\varpi J}^M.$$

By replacing the eigenfunction by expression (XX.163), the operators p_r and α_r by their definitions (XX.165) and (XX.166) and using the identites (cf. Problem XX.8):

$$\begin{aligned}(\boldsymbol{\sigma}\cdot\hat{\mathbf{r}})\,\mathscr{Y}_{lJ}^M &= -\,\mathscr{Y}_{l'J}^M\\ (\boldsymbol{\sigma}\cdot\hat{\mathbf{r}})\,\mathscr{Y}_{l'J}^M &= -\,\mathscr{Y}_{lJ}^M\end{aligned} \qquad \text{(XX.169)}$$

this equation leads to two coupled differential equations for the radial functions $F(r)$ and $G(r)$, namely

$$\left[-\frac{\mathrm{d}}{\mathrm{d}r}+\frac{\varpi(J+\frac{1}{2})}{r}\right]G = (E-m-V)\,F \qquad \text{(XX.170}a\text{)}$$

$$\left[\frac{\mathrm{d}}{\mathrm{d}r}+\frac{\varpi(J+\frac{1}{2})}{r}\right]F = (E+m-V)\,G. \qquad \text{(XX.170}b\text{)}$$

These equations here play the role of equation (IX.20) in the non-relativistic theory.

After integration over the angles, the norm of $\Psi_{\varpi J}^M$ is given by the expression:

$$\langle\Psi_{\varpi J}^M|\Psi_{\varpi J}^M\rangle = \int_0^\infty (|F|^2+|G|^2)\,\mathrm{d}r \qquad \text{(XX.171)}$$

to be compared with expression (IX.21).

The discussion of the regularity of F and G is in all ways analogous to the discussion of the regularity of $y_l(r)$ in the non-relativistic theory. We shall not go into the details here.

26. Free Spherical Waves

For $V=0$, the method of the preceding paragraph gives the stationary solutions of the Dirac equation of the free electron which correspond to well-defined angular momentum and parity; these are the Dirac free spherical waves.

In this case, eq. (XX.170*b*) gives,

$$G = \frac{1}{E+m}\left[\frac{\mathrm{d}}{\mathrm{d}r} + \frac{\varpi(J+\frac{1}{2})}{r}\right] F. \qquad \text{(XX.172)}$$

Substituting this expression into (XX.170*a*), one finds:

$$\begin{aligned}(E^2-m^2)\,F &= \left[-\frac{\mathrm{d}}{\mathrm{d}r} + \frac{\varpi(J+\frac{1}{2})}{r}\right]\left[\frac{\mathrm{d}}{\mathrm{d}r} + \varpi\frac{(J+\frac{1}{2})}{r}\right] F \\ &= \left[-\frac{\mathrm{d}^2}{\mathrm{d}r^2} + \frac{(J+\frac{1}{2})\,(J+\varpi+\frac{1}{2})}{r^2}\right] F.\end{aligned}$$

It can easily be shown that

$$(J+\tfrac{1}{2})(J+\varpi+\tfrac{1}{2}) = l(l+1),$$

where l is the integer defined by equation (XX.162). The preceding equation is therefore identical with the free wave radial equation of the non-relativistic theory if one substitutes for (E^2-m^2) the product of $2m$ by the non-relativistic energy. It has one and only one regular solution for any positive value of (E^2-m^2). If one puts

$$k = \sqrt{E^2-m^2} \qquad (|E| \geqslant m)$$

it becomes

$$\left[\frac{\mathrm{d}^2}{\mathrm{d}r^2} - \frac{l(l+1)}{r^2} + k^2\right] F = 0.$$

Its regular solution (defined up to a constant) is given by

$$F = r j_l(kr).$$

The corresponding G function is obtained by applying relation (XX.172). Using the recursion relations (B.42) and (B.43) [the first for $\varpi = 1$, the second for $\varpi = -1$, both being written with $\gamma = 0$], one finds

$$G = \frac{\varpi k}{E+m}\, r j_{l'}(kr).$$

In conclusion, for any value of the energy E situated outside the interval $(-m, +m)$, there exists a free spherical wave of angular momentum (JM) and parity $(-)^{J+\frac{1}{2}\varpi}$. In the form (XX.163), it is written

$$Cst.\times\begin{pmatrix} |E+m|^{\frac{1}{2}}\, j_l(\sqrt{E^2-m^2}\,r)\, \mathscr{Y}_{lJ}^{M} \\ \mathrm{i}\varpi\varepsilon|E-m|^{\frac{1}{2}}\, j_{l'}(\sqrt{E^2-m^2}\,r)\, \mathscr{Y}_{l'J}^{M} \end{pmatrix} \qquad \text{(XX.173)}$$

where: $\varepsilon = E/|E|$.

27. The Hydrogen Atom

As a second example, let us look for the bound states of an electron in the Coulomb field of an atomic nucleus. The nucleus will be treated as a point charge equal to $(-Z)$ times the charge of the electron, and fixed at the origin [1]. We must therefore find *the bound states* of a Dirac particle in the central potential

$$V = -\frac{Ze^2}{r}.$$

This eigenvalue problem can be exactly solved. Here we shall give only the broad outline of the method, which is a simple extension of the one set forth in § XI.4.

It is clear from an examination of the asymptotic behavior of the solutions of the set of radial equations (XX.170) that E must be contained in the interval $(-m, +m)$. The desired eigenvalues are those for which the solutions that are regular at the origin behave asymptotically like $\exp(-\sqrt{m^2-E^2}\,r)$.

Put:

$$\varkappa = \sqrt{m^2-E^2} \qquad \nu = \sqrt{\frac{m-E}{m+E}} \qquad \text{(XX.174)}$$

$$\zeta = Ze^2 \qquad \tau = \varpi(J+\tfrac{1}{2}) \qquad \text{(XX.175)}$$

and introduce the variable

$$\varrho \equiv \varkappa r. \qquad \text{(XX.176)}$$

The set (XX.170) is equivalent to

$$\left(-\frac{\mathrm{d}}{\mathrm{d}\varrho}+\frac{\tau}{\varrho}\right)G = \left(-\nu+\frac{\zeta}{\varrho}\right)F \qquad \text{(XX.177}a\text{)}$$

$$\left(\frac{\mathrm{d}}{\mathrm{d}\varrho}+\frac{\tau}{\varrho}\right)F = \left(\nu^{-1}+\frac{\zeta}{\varrho}\right)G. \qquad \text{(XX.177}b\text{)}$$

---

[1] This supposes the nucleus infinitely heavy. The error thus made cannot be neglected, for it is of the order of magnitude of the relativistic effects. It is largely compensated for if the mass of the electron m is everywhere replaced by the reduced mass.

We look for solutions of the form

$$F(\varrho) = \varrho^s e^{-\varrho}(a_0 + a_1\varrho + a_2\varrho^2 + \dots) \quad (a_0 \neq 0) \qquad \text{(XX.178}a\text{)}$$

$$G(\varrho) = \varrho^s e^{-\varrho}(b_0 + b_1\varrho + b_2\varrho^2 + \dots) \quad (b_0 \neq 0). \qquad \text{(XX.178}b\text{)}$$

Substituting these expansions into equations (XX.177) and equating terms of successive orders one obtains a series of equations of which the first fixes s and the subsequent ones permit the determination of the coefficients $a_0, b_0, a_1, b_1, \dots, a_n, b_n \dots$ by recurrence. The equation in s has the two roots $\pm\sqrt{\tau^2 - \zeta^2}$. A necessary and sufficient condition for F and G to fulfil the conditions of regularity at the origin $F(0) = G(0) = 0$, is that $s > 0$. Thus only the positive root is to be kept [1]:

$$s = \sqrt{\tau^2 - \zeta^2}.$$

Thus for each value of E there is one solution that is regular at the origin. In general it behaves like $\varrho^s e^{\varrho}$ at infinity unless the two expansions (XX.178) have only a finite number of terms. This can only happen for certain particular values of E; these are the required energy levels. The calculation shows that they are given by the expression

$$m\left[1 + \frac{\zeta^2}{(n' + s)^2}\right]^{-\frac{1}{2}},$$

where n', the radial quantum number, is the degree of the polynomials figuring in expressions (XX.178). For each positive value of n' there exists a regular solution for each of the two values of ϖ; for $n' = 0$ there exists a regular solution for $\varpi = -1$, but no solution for $\varpi = +1$.

Let us introduce the principal quantum number

$$n = J + \tfrac{1}{2} + n'.$$

The preceding results may then be reformulated in the following way. The levels of the discrete spectrum depend on the two quantum numbers n and J according to the formula

$$E_{nJ} = m\left[1 + \frac{Z^2e^4}{(n - \varepsilon_J)^2}\right]^{-\frac{1}{2}} \qquad \text{(XX.179)}$$

$$\varepsilon_J = J + \tfrac{1}{2} - \sqrt{(J + \tfrac{1}{2})^2 - Z^2e^4}, \qquad \text{(XX.179')}$$

[1] We suppose $\zeta < |\tau|$, i.e. $Ze^2 < (J + \frac{1}{2})$. This condition is always fulfilled if $Z < 137$, which is always the case in practice. If it were not, the discussion of the regularity conditions at the origin would be much more delicate.

where n can take all positive integral values and J all half-integral values in the interval $(0, n)$:

$$n = 1, 2, \ldots, \infty; \qquad J = \tfrac{1}{2}, \tfrac{3}{2}, \ldots, n - \tfrac{1}{2}.$$

To each value of J there correspond two series of $(2J+1)$ solutions of opposite parities, except for the value $J = n - \frac{1}{2}$ to which there corresponds a single series of $(2J+1)$ solutions of parity $(-)^{n-1}$. Rather than specify the parities, one may instead specify the values of l, the orbital angular momentum of the first two components of the spinor; recall that the parity of the spinor is $(-)^l$.

The spectroscopic notation nl_J is generally used to distinguish these different series of solutions one from another. The following table lists the first few levels in increasing order, with the corresponding spectroscopic terms [each term has a degeneracy of order $2J+1$]:

$n=1$	$J=\frac{1}{2}$	$1s_{1/2}$			$(n'=0)$
$n=2$	$J=\frac{1}{2}$	$2s_{1/2}$	$2p_{1/2}$		$(n'=1)$
	$J=\frac{3}{2}$		$2p_{3/2}$		$(n'=0)$
$n=3$	$J=\frac{1}{2}$	$3s_{1/2}$	$3p_{1/2}$		$(n'=2)$
	$J=\frac{3}{2}$		$3p_{3/2}$	$3d_{3/2}$	$(n'=1)$
	$J=\frac{5}{2}$			$3d_{5/2}$	$(n'=0)$.

If expression (XX.179) is expanded into a power series in Z^2e^4 one finds

$$E_{nJ} = m\left[1 - \frac{Z^2e^4}{2n^2} - \frac{(Z^2e^4)^2}{2n^4}\left(\frac{n}{J+\frac{1}{2}} - \frac{3}{4}\right) + \ldots\right].$$

The first term is the mass term. The second, $-Z^2e^4/2n^2$, is exactly equal to the quantity given by the non-relativistic theory. The third and following terms give the relativistic corrections. These corrections partially remove the "accidental degeneracy" of the non-relativistic levels: for n fixed, the binding energy $m-E$ of each term is slightly increased; the increase depends only on J, and is larger for smaller J.

The experimental results on the fine structure of the hydrogen atom and hydrogen-like atoms (notably He^+) are in broad agreement with these predictions.

However, the agreement is not perfect. The largest discrepancy is observed in the fine structure of the $n=2$ levels of the hydrogen atom [1]). In the non-relativistic approximation, the three levels $2s_{1/2}$,

1) W. E. Lamb and R. C. Retherford, Phys. Rev. 72 (1947) 241.

$2p_{1/2}$ and $2p_{3/2}$ are equal. In the Dirac theory, the levels $2s_{1/2}$ and $2p_{1/2}$ are still equal, while the $2p_{3/2}$ level is slightly lower (the separation is of the order of 10^{-4}eV). The level distance $2p_{3/2} - 2p_{1/2}$ agrees with the theory but the level $2s_{1/2}$ is lower than the level $2p_{1/2}$ and the distance $2s_{1/2} - 2p_{1/2}$ is equal to about a tenth of the distance $2p_{3/2} - 2p_{1/2}$. This effect is known as the Lamb shift. To explain it, we need a rigorous treatment of the interaction between the electron, the proton and the quantized electromagnetic field; in the Dirac theory one retains only the Coulomb potential which is the main term in that interaction; the Lamb shift represents "radiative corrections" to this approximation [1]).

V. NON-RELATIVISTIC LIMIT OF THE DIRAC EQUATION

28. Large and Small Components

Consider the positive energy plane waves whose components are given in Table XX.3. Let us suppose that the energy E_p differs little from the rest energy:

$$W \equiv E_p - m \ll m.$$

The non-relativistic approximation is then valid, for the kinetic energy W is nearly equal to $\frac{1}{2}mv^2$ and we have

$$\frac{W}{m} \simeq \tfrac{1}{2}v^2 \ll 1.$$

It will be seen that the non-vanishing component corresponding to $\beta = +1$ is then much larger than the one corresponding to $\beta = -1$:

$$\sigma_z = +1 \qquad \frac{u_3}{u_1} = \left(\frac{W}{W+2m}\right)^{\frac{1}{2}} \simeq \mathrm{O}\left(\frac{v}{c}\right) \ll 1$$

$$\sigma_z = -1 \qquad \frac{u_4}{u_2} = -\left(\frac{W}{W+2m}\right)^{\frac{1}{2}} \simeq \mathrm{O}\left(\frac{v}{c}\right) \ll 1.$$

A similar observation applies for the free spherical waves [cf. expression (XX.173)] or for the eigenfunctions of the hydrogen atom (cf.

---

[1]) The most recent measurements give 1057.77 ± 0.70 Mc/s (Mc/s $\equiv$ Megacycle per second) for the separation $2s_{1/2} - 2p_{1/2}$; the theoretical value obtained when the "radiative corrections" predicted by Quantum Electrodynamics are taken into account is 1057.99 ± 0.2 Mc/s [C. M. Sommerfield, Phys. Rev. **107** (1957) 328].

notably the particular eigensolutions defined in Problem XX.10). This suggests that in the non-relativistic approximation two of the components of the spinor Ψ, the components Ψ_3 and Ψ_4 corresponding to the eigenvalue -1 of β, are very small and may be neglected, and that the Dirac theory is then equivalent to a two-component theory.

In order to put this point properly in evidence, we write the Dirac spinor Ψ in the form (XX.157), Φ and χ being defined by equations (XX.158) or (XX.159). As has already been noted in § 25, Φ and χ may be regarded as vectors of the state-vector space of the two component non-relativistic theory.

With these notations the Dirac equation relative to a stationary state of energy E is written, in the Dirac form and representation:

$$(\boldsymbol{\sigma}\cdot(\mathbf{p}-e\mathbf{A}))\,\chi+(e\varphi+m)\,\Phi = E\Phi \qquad \text{(XX.180}a\text{)}$$

$$(\boldsymbol{\sigma}\cdot(\mathbf{p}-e\mathbf{A}))\,\Phi+(e\varphi-m)\,\chi = E\chi. \qquad \text{(XX.180}b\text{)}$$

Let us put:

$$\begin{aligned} \boldsymbol{\pi} &= \mathbf{p}-e\mathbf{A}, \qquad M = E-e\varphi \\ W = E-m, &\qquad M' = \tfrac{1}{2}(m+M) = m+\tfrac{1}{2}(W-e\varphi). \end{aligned} \qquad \text{(XX.181)}$$

Solving equation (XX.180b) for χ and then substituting into equation (XX.180a), we obtain

$$\chi = \frac{1}{2M'}\,(\boldsymbol{\sigma}\cdot\boldsymbol{\pi})\,\Phi \qquad \text{(XX.182)}$$

$$\left[(\boldsymbol{\sigma}\cdot\boldsymbol{\pi})\,\frac{1}{2M'}\,(\boldsymbol{\sigma}\cdot\boldsymbol{\pi})+e\varphi\right]\Phi = W\Phi. \qquad \text{(XX.183)}$$

The set of equations (XX.182–183) is *exactly equivalent* to the Dirac equation.

In the non-relativistic limit

$$W,\ e\varphi,\ \mathbf{p},\ e\mathbf{A} \ll m, \qquad M' \simeq m. \qquad \text{(XX.184)}$$

It is clear from equation (XX.182) that

$$\chi \ll \Phi$$

and that the ratio of these two quantities is of the order of p/m, i.e. v/c. χ and Φ are known as the *small and large* components respectively.

In the rest of this section, we shall make use of the concept of "*even*" and "*odd*" operators. By definition:

(*i*) an operator $\mathscr{P}$ is "even" if it has no matrix element linking small and large components (examples: $\mathbf{p}$, $\mathbf{r}$, $\mathbf{L}$, $\boldsymbol{\sigma}$, $\mathbf{J}$, $P(\mathbf{r}_0)$, β);

(*ii*) an operator $\mathscr{I}$ is "odd" if its non-vanishing matrix elements link small and large components (examples: $\boldsymbol{\alpha}$, $\beta\boldsymbol{\alpha}$, γ^5, $\mathbf{j}(\mathbf{r}_0)$).

It is equivalent to say that $\mathscr{P}$ is an operator that commutes with β, $\mathscr{I}$ an operator that anticommutes with β:

$$\mathscr{P} = \beta\mathscr{P}\beta, \qquad \mathscr{I} = -\beta\mathscr{I}\beta. \tag{XX.185}$$

Any operator Q is the sum of an "even" and an "odd" operator, and furthermore this decomposition is unique:

$$Q = \tfrac{1}{2}[Q+\beta Q\beta]+\tfrac{1}{2}[Q-\beta Q\beta].$$

The product of two "even" or of two "odd" operators is an "even" operator; the product of an "even" operator by an "odd" operator is an "odd" operator.

29. The Pauli Theory as the Non-relativistic Limit of the Dirac Theory

We now return to the system of equations (XX.182–183). In neglecting the small components, one makes an error of order v^2/c^2 in the normalization of the wave function. An error of the same order is made in replacing the operator M' in equation (XX.183) by the mass m. In this approximation equation (XX.183) takes the form of an eigenvalue equation [1]:

$$H_{n.r.}\Phi = W\Phi \tag{XX.186}$$

of a certain Hamiltonian

$$H_{n.r.} \equiv \frac{1}{2m}(\boldsymbol{\sigma}\cdot\boldsymbol{\pi})(\boldsymbol{\sigma}\cdot\boldsymbol{\pi}) + e\varphi \tag{XX.187}$$

acting on the two-component wave function Φ. Equation (XX.186) defines the energy W to within v^2/c^2.

In order to put $H_{n.r.}$ in a more familiar form we apply identity (XIII.83), noting that the components of $\boldsymbol{\pi}$ do not commute, and that therefore:

$$\boldsymbol{\pi}\times\boldsymbol{\pi} = ie \operatorname{curl} \mathbf{A} = ie\mathscr{H}.$$

One then obtains

$$H_{n.r.} \equiv \frac{1}{2m}(\mathbf{p}-e\mathbf{A})^2 - \frac{e}{2m}(\boldsymbol{\sigma}\cdot\mathscr{H}) + e\varphi. \tag{XX.188}$$

---

[1] Equation (XX.183) is not a true eigenvalue equation since the operator in brackets on the left-hand side depends on the "eigenvalue" W through M'.

This will be recognized as the Hamiltonian of the Pauli theory corresponding to a particle of mass m, charge e and intrinsic angular momentum:

$$\boldsymbol{\mu} = \mu_B \boldsymbol{\sigma} \qquad (\mu_B \equiv \text{Bohr magneton} \equiv e/2m).$$

Not only does the Dirac theory predict the existence of an intrinsic magnetic moment for the electron, but it gives its correct value (§ XIII.18). This is one of the major successes of the theory [1]).

In order to prove that the Dirac theory in the approximation considered here is equivalent to the two-component Pauli theory, we must be able to find operators corresponding to the operators in the Dirac theory but acting only on the large components.

This can actually be done provided that the said operators enter into the calculations only through their matrix elements between states Ψ', Ψ'' whose energy is positive and sufficiently close to that of the rest mass for the non-relativistic approximation to be valid.

If we are concerned with an even operator $\mathscr{P}$, the matrix element $\langle\Psi''|\mathscr{P}|\Psi'\rangle$ takes the form

$$\langle\Phi''|\mathscr{P}|\Phi'\rangle + \langle\chi''|\mathscr{P}|\chi'\rangle.$$

The second term is $(v/c)^2$ times smaller than the first, and may be neglected in the approximation discussed here. $\mathscr{P}$ may then be replaced by its projection on the space of the large components: this projection represents in the non-relativistic Pauli theory the physical quantity represented by $\mathscr{P}$ in the Dirac theory.

---

[1]) In actual fact, the experimental value μ_{exp} differs slightly from this theoretical value for the magnetic moment of the electron [P. Kusch and H. M. Foley, Phys. Rev. **72** (1947) 1256]. More recent measurements give

$$\Delta\mu_{\text{exp}} \equiv \mu_{\text{exp}} - \mu_B = (1.165 \pm 0.011) \times 10^{-3}\, \mu_B.$$

The "radiative corrections" of Quantum Electrodynamics account for the existence of this anomalous magnetic moment; they give (Sommerfield, *loc. cit.*):

$$\Delta\mu_{\text{th}} = 1.163 \times 10^{-3}\, \mu_B.$$

Note in passing that the equation obtained by adding the term $\varkappa\mu_B\sigma_{\mu\nu}F^{\mu\nu}$ to the Dirac operator has all the invariance properties of the Dirac equation, and this for any given value of the numerical constant $\varkappa$; such an equation describes a particle of mass m, of charge e and of intrinsic magnetic moment $(1 + \varkappa)\, \mu_B$.

If we are concerned with an odd operator, $\mathscr{I}$, one has

$$\langle\Psi''|\mathscr{I}|\Psi'\rangle = \langle\Phi''|\mathscr{I}|\chi'\rangle + \langle\chi''|\mathscr{I}|\Phi'\rangle.$$

Here the small components are involved explicitly in each term on the right-hand side. In the approximation in question however equation (XX.182) gives

$$|\chi\rangle = \varrho_1 \frac{\boldsymbol{\sigma}\cdot\boldsymbol{\pi}}{2m} |\Phi\rangle$$

from which

$$\langle\Psi''|\mathscr{I}|\Psi'\rangle = \frac{1}{2m} \langle\Phi''|[\mathscr{I} \varrho_1(\boldsymbol{\sigma}\cdot\boldsymbol{\pi}) + (\boldsymbol{\sigma}\cdot\boldsymbol{\pi}) \varrho_1 \mathscr{I}]|\Phi'\rangle.$$

$\mathscr{I}$ may therefore be replaced by the projection on the space of the large components of the operator

$$\frac{1}{2m} [\mathscr{I} \varrho_1(\boldsymbol{\sigma}\cdot\boldsymbol{\pi}) + (\boldsymbol{\sigma}\cdot\boldsymbol{\pi}) \varrho_1 \mathscr{I}].$$

Thus the "velocity" $\boldsymbol{\alpha} = \varrho_1\boldsymbol{\sigma}$ may be replaced by the operator in the space of the large components

$$\frac{\boldsymbol{\pi}}{m} \equiv \frac{\boldsymbol{\sigma}(\boldsymbol{\sigma}\cdot\boldsymbol{\pi}) + (\boldsymbol{\sigma}\cdot\boldsymbol{\pi})\,\boldsymbol{\sigma}}{2m}.$$

Similarly, the current density at the point $\boldsymbol{r}_0$:

$$\boldsymbol{j}(\boldsymbol{r}_0) \equiv \varrho_1\boldsymbol{\sigma}\delta(\boldsymbol{r}-\boldsymbol{r}_0)$$

may be replaced by the operator in the space of the large components:

$$(\boldsymbol{j}(\boldsymbol{r}_0))_{n.r.} \equiv \delta(\boldsymbol{r}-\boldsymbol{r}_0)\,\boldsymbol{\sigma} \left(\frac{\boldsymbol{\sigma}\cdot\boldsymbol{\pi}}{2m}\right) + \left(\frac{\boldsymbol{\sigma}\cdot\boldsymbol{\pi}}{2m}\right) \boldsymbol{\sigma}\,\delta(\boldsymbol{r}-\boldsymbol{r}_0)$$

or again, applying identity (XIII.83):

$$(\boldsymbol{j}(\boldsymbol{r}_0))_{n.r.} \equiv \boldsymbol{j}^{(\mathrm{I})} + \boldsymbol{j}^{(\mathrm{II})} \tag{XX.189}$$

$$\boldsymbol{j}^{(\mathrm{I})} \equiv \frac{\delta(\boldsymbol{r}-\boldsymbol{r}_0)\,\boldsymbol{\pi} + \boldsymbol{\pi}\,\delta(\boldsymbol{r}-\boldsymbol{r}_0)}{2m} \tag{XX.190a}$$

$$\boldsymbol{j}^{(\mathrm{II})} \equiv \mathrm{i}\,\frac{\delta(\boldsymbol{r}-\boldsymbol{r}_0)\,(\boldsymbol{p}\times\boldsymbol{\sigma}) - (\boldsymbol{p}\times\boldsymbol{\sigma})\,\delta(\boldsymbol{r}-\boldsymbol{r}_0)}{2m}. \tag{XX.190b}$$

In this limit, the Dirac electric current $e\boldsymbol{j}$ is therefore made up of two terms. The first, $e\boldsymbol{j}^{(\mathrm{I})}$, is identical with the current of the Schrödinger theory (cf. Problem IV.1). In order to interpret the second we consider its matrix element between the large components Φ' and Φ''. The calculation shows that

$$\langle \Phi'' | e\boldsymbol{j}^{(\mathrm{II})} | \Phi' \rangle = \frac{e}{2m} \operatorname{curl} \langle \Phi'' | \delta(\boldsymbol{r} - \boldsymbol{r}_0)\, \boldsymbol{\sigma} | \Phi' \rangle .$$

This is a magnetic current term, and the quantity

$$\frac{e}{2m} \langle \Phi'' | \delta(\boldsymbol{r} - \boldsymbol{r}_0)\, \boldsymbol{\sigma} | \Phi' \rangle \equiv \langle \Phi'' | \delta(\boldsymbol{r} - \boldsymbol{r}_0)\, \boldsymbol{\mu} | \Phi' \rangle$$

may be interpreted as a magnetic moment density. It will be seen that the divergence of this magnetic current vanishes, and therefore that it gives no contribution to the equation of continuity.

30. Application: Hyperfine Structure and Dipole-Dipole Coupling

We now consider an electron in the electric field of an atom, described by a certain electrostatic potential $\varphi(r)$, and examine the effect of the field created by the magnetic moment $\boldsymbol{M}$ of the nucleus. The field created by a magnetic dipole $\boldsymbol{M}$ situated at the origin of coordinates may be represented by the vector potential:

$$\boldsymbol{A} \equiv \frac{\boldsymbol{M} \times \boldsymbol{r}}{r^3} \tag{XX.191}$$

$$\equiv \operatorname{curl} (\boldsymbol{M}/r). \tag{XX.191'}$$

The presence of this field leads to an additional term $-e\boldsymbol{\alpha}\cdot\boldsymbol{A}$ in the Dirac Hamiltonian.

To determine the effect of this field in the non-relativistic approximation we can calculate the non-relativistic limit of the operator $-e\boldsymbol{\alpha}\cdot\boldsymbol{A}$ by the method of the preceding paragraph. We can equally well directly examine the modifications of the Pauli Hamiltonian (XX.188) due to the presence of $\boldsymbol{M}$. These two methods are equivalent. We shall adopt the second one here.

If we retain only terms linear in $\boldsymbol{M}$, the Pauli Hamiltonian contains the two supplementary terms:

$$I_a = -\frac{e}{2m} (\boldsymbol{p}\cdot\boldsymbol{A} + \boldsymbol{A}\cdot\boldsymbol{p})$$

$$I_b = -\frac{e}{2m} (\boldsymbol{\sigma}\cdot\mathscr{H}) = -\boldsymbol{\mu}\cdot\mathscr{H} ;$$

where $\mathscr{H}$ is the field created by the dipole $\boldsymbol{M}$.

I_a is a spin-orbit coupling term (spin of the nucleus, orbit of the electron). Clearly, [cf. eq. (XX.191′)] div $\mathbf{A}=0$ whence:

$$I_a = -\frac{e}{m}\,\mathbf{A}\cdot\mathbf{p}$$

Substituting expression (XX.191) onto the right-hand side, and introducing the orbital angular momentum of the electron $\mathbf{L} \equiv \mathbf{r}\times\mathbf{p}$, one finds:

$$I_a = -\frac{e\mathbf{M}\cdot\mathbf{L}}{mr^3}. \tag{XX.192}$$

I_b is the spin-spin or dipole-dipole coupling term. It can be calculated with the aid of (XX.191′):

$$\begin{aligned} I_b &= -\boldsymbol{\mu}\cdot(\nabla\times\mathbf{A}) = -\boldsymbol{\mu}\cdot\left[\nabla\times\left(\nabla\times\frac{\mathbf{M}}{r}\right)\right] \\ &= (\boldsymbol{\mu}\cdot\mathbf{M})\,\triangle\left(\frac{1}{r}\right) - [(\boldsymbol{\mu}\cdot\nabla)\,(\mathbf{M}\cdot\nabla)]\left(\frac{1}{r}\right). \end{aligned} \tag{XX.193}$$

When $r\neq 0$, I_b can easily be calculated by performing the differentiation, which gives:

$$-\frac{3(\mathbf{M}\cdot\mathbf{r})\,(\boldsymbol{\mu}\cdot\mathbf{r}) - (\mathbf{M}\cdot\boldsymbol{\mu})\,r^2}{r^5}.$$

Considered as a simple function, expression (XX.193) has a singularity in $1/r^3$ at the origin. To determine the action of the operator I_b, it is convenient to examine the result of integration of the product of this quantity by a regular function $f(\mathbf{r})$ in a small domain about the point $r=0$. To this effect, we write I_b in the form

$$I_b = \tfrac{2}{3}\,(\boldsymbol{\mu}\cdot\mathbf{M})\,\triangle\left(\frac{1}{r}\right) - [(\boldsymbol{\mu}\cdot\nabla)\,(\mathbf{M}\cdot\nabla) - \tfrac{1}{3}\,(\boldsymbol{\mu}\cdot\mathbf{M})\,\triangle]\left(\frac{1}{r}\right). \tag{XX.193′}$$

The second term in this expression is a second order tensor operator in the space of functions of $\mathbf{r}$; if, to effect the integration mentioned above, $f(\mathbf{r})$ is expanded into spherical harmonics. Only coefficients of spherical harmonics of order 2 will contribute to the integration over the angles; these vanish at the origin at least as rapidly as r^2; the contribution of the second term of (XX.193′) also vanishes at the origin in spite of the singularity in $1/r^3$. With the aid of identity

(A.12), the first term may be put in the form $-(\frac{8}{3}\pi)\,(\boldsymbol{\mu}\cdot\boldsymbol{M})\delta(\boldsymbol{r})$. Thus, for any $\boldsymbol{r}$, including the origin:

$$I_b = -\frac{8\pi}{3}\,(\boldsymbol{M}\cdot\boldsymbol{\mu})\,\delta(\boldsymbol{r}) - \frac{1}{r^3}\left[3\left(\boldsymbol{M}\cdot\frac{\boldsymbol{r}}{r}\right)\left(\boldsymbol{\mu}\cdot\frac{\boldsymbol{r}}{r}\right) - (\boldsymbol{M}\cdot\boldsymbol{\mu})\right]. \qquad \text{(XX.194)}$$

Expressions (XX.192) and (XX.194) are valid in the non-relativistic imit and allow the determination of the hyperfine structure of atomic levels to within v^2/c^2. In particular, the contribution of the s-electrons to the hyperfine structure is given by the contact term $-(\frac{8}{3}\pi)\,(\boldsymbol{\mu}\cdot\boldsymbol{M})\delta(\boldsymbol{r})$.

31. Higher-order Corrections and the Foldy–Wouthuysen Transformation

To the lowest order in v/c, the Dirac theory is equivalent to the two-component Pauli theory. It is possible to obtain higher-order relativistic corrections by starting as before from equations (XX.182–183). To this effect, one replaces $1/M'$ by its expansion in powers of $[(W-e\varphi)/2m]$:

$$\frac{1}{M'} = \frac{1}{m}\left[1 - \frac{W-e\varphi}{2m} + \left(\frac{W-e\varphi}{2m}\right)^2 - \dots\right].$$

Since:

$$\left\langle\frac{W-e\varphi}{2m}\right\rangle \simeq \left\langle\frac{\boldsymbol{\pi}^2}{4m^2}\right\rangle \simeq \mathrm{O}\left(\frac{v^2}{c^2}\right),$$

this is essentially a power series expansion in v^2/c^2. If this expansion is stopped at the first term one obtains the Pauli theory, as in § 29. Higher-order relativistic corrections are obtained by taking the expansion beyond the first term. However, once corrections of the order of v^2/c^2 are taken into account, the Dirac theory in the form (XX.182–183) ceases to be formally equivalent to a two-component theory. This is because:

(*i*) the contribution from the small components can no longer be neglected, neither in the normalization, nor in the calculation of matrix elements of even operators;

(*ii*) equation (XX.183) is properly speaking no longer an eigenvalue equation (cf. note, p. 935).

Although the method is not thereby absolutely condemned, its application and the interpretation of the results becomes rather delicate. Foldy and Wouthuysen [1]) have proposed another method which allows one to approximate to the Dirac theory by a two-component theory to any given order in v/c. It essentially consists in effecting a suitably chosen unitary transformation on the wave functions and operators of the Dirac theory. In the new "representation" – which we shall call the FW "representation" – the Dirac Hamiltonian is an "even" operator to the given order in v/c, so that in this approximation the small and the large components are completely decoupled in the wave equation. One may therefore simply ignore the small components, thereby obtaining the desired two-component theory. The operators of the two-component theory are then obtained from the "even" operators of the FW "representation" and not from the operators of the old "representation". One is thus led to a new interpretation of the operators of non-relativistic mechanics, notably of the position operator, an interpretation in many ways more satisfying than the old one.

The rest of this section is devoted to the FW transformation and to its application to the non-relativistic approximation of the Dirac equation.

32. FW Transformation for a Free Particle

In the case of a free particle, the small and large components can be completely decoupled in all orders of v/c.

We consider the Dirac Hamiltonian

$$H_0 \equiv \boldsymbol{\alpha}\cdot\boldsymbol{p}+\beta m.$$

Let Γ_+ and Γ_- be the projectors onto the positive and negative energy solutions respectively:

$$\Gamma_\pm \equiv \frac{1}{2}\left[1 \pm \frac{H_0}{E_p}\right] = \frac{1}{2}\left[1 \pm \frac{\boldsymbol{\alpha}\cdot\boldsymbol{p}+\beta m}{E_p}\right]. \qquad \text{(XX.195)}$$

$$E_p \equiv \sqrt{m^2+\boldsymbol{p}^2}.$$

---

[1]) L. L. Foldy and S. A. Wouthuysen, Phys. Rev. **78** (1958) 29.

Denote by B_+ and B_- the projectors onto the spaces of the large and small components respectively:

$$B_\pm \equiv \tfrac{1}{2}(1 \pm \beta).$$

By definition, the operator U, which takes us over to the FW "representation", transforms Γ_+ into B_+ and Γ_- into B_-. With primes denoting the vectors and operators of the FW "representation", we therefore have:

$$U^\dagger U = UU^\dagger = 1$$
$$\Gamma'_\pm \equiv U\Gamma_\pm U^\dagger = B_\pm.$$

We also require that U be invariant under translation, rotation and reflection. It is left to the reader to show that U is then defined to within a phase factor. Fixing this phase one obtains

$$U = \sqrt{\frac{2E_p}{m+E_p}}\,\frac{1}{2}\left[1+\beta\,\frac{H_0}{E_p}\right] \qquad \text{(XX 196)}$$

$$= \sqrt{\frac{m+E_p}{2E_p}} + \beta\,\frac{\boldsymbol{\alpha}\cdot\boldsymbol{p}}{\sqrt{2E_p(m+E_p)}}. \qquad \text{(XX.196')}$$

It will easily be verified that this expression has all the desired properties.

Since U is time-independent, the Hamiltonian H_{F} which governs the evolution of the states in the FW "representation" is given by the equation

$$H_{\mathrm{F}} = UH_D U^\dagger,$$

which gives, with the aid of (XX.196),

$$H_{\mathrm{F}} = \beta E_p \equiv \beta(m^2+\boldsymbol{p}^2)^{\frac{1}{2}}. \qquad \text{(XX.197)}$$

Since H_{F} is an even operator, the large components Φ' and the small components χ' are completely decoupled in the equation of motion:

$$\mathrm{i}\,\frac{\partial\Phi'}{\partial t} = E_p\,\Phi' \qquad \text{(XX.198}a\text{)}$$

$$\mathrm{i}\,\frac{\partial\chi'}{\partial t} = -\,E_p\,\chi'. \qquad \text{(XX.198}b\text{)}$$

If we limit ourselves to positive energy solutions – *a fortiori* to non-relativistic energies – the Dirac theory is exactly equivalent to the two-component theory represented by equation (XX.198*a*) to all orders in v/c.

The operator U commutes with $\boldsymbol{p}$, $\boldsymbol{J}$ and the parity operator P, but not with $\boldsymbol{r}$. In a representation with $\boldsymbol{r}$ diagonal, it is an integral operator with matrix element:

$$\langle \boldsymbol{r}|U|\boldsymbol{r}'\rangle = \int\int \langle \boldsymbol{r}|\boldsymbol{p}\rangle \,\mathrm{d}\boldsymbol{p}\, \langle \boldsymbol{p}|U|\boldsymbol{p}'\rangle \,\mathrm{d}\boldsymbol{p}'\, \langle \boldsymbol{p}'|\boldsymbol{r}'\rangle,$$

whence, with use of (XX.196′),

$$\langle \boldsymbol{r}|U|\boldsymbol{r}'\rangle = (2\pi)^{-3} \int \left[\sqrt{\frac{m+E_p}{2E_p}} + \beta \frac{\boldsymbol{\alpha}\cdot\boldsymbol{p}}{\sqrt{2E_p(m+E_p)}}\right] \mathrm{e}^{\mathrm{i}\boldsymbol{p}\cdot(\boldsymbol{r}-\boldsymbol{r}')}\,\mathrm{d}\boldsymbol{p}$$

$\langle \boldsymbol{r}|U|\boldsymbol{r}'\rangle$ is a function of $(\boldsymbol{r}-\boldsymbol{r}')$ that practically vanishes for $|\boldsymbol{r}-\boldsymbol{r}'| \gg 1/m$, but which takes non-negligible values when $|\boldsymbol{r}-\boldsymbol{r}'|$ is smaller or of the order of $1/m$. The FW transformation is therefore a non-local transformation in which the spinor $\Psi'(\boldsymbol{r})$, the transform of $\Psi(\boldsymbol{r})$, is obtained by taking a certain average over the values taken by Ψ in a volume about $\boldsymbol{r}$ whose linear dimensions are of the order of $1/m$, the Compton wavelength of the particle.

The position of the particle is represented in the FW "representation" by the operator

$$\boldsymbol{r}' \equiv U\boldsymbol{r}U^{\dagger}.$$

This operator is different to $\boldsymbol{r}$. Following Foldy and Wouthuysen, we shall call the quantity represented by $\boldsymbol{r}$ in the FW "representation" the *average position*. In the ordinary "representation", it is represented by a certain operator $\boldsymbol{R}$ and one has $\boldsymbol{R}' \equiv \boldsymbol{r}$, therefore:

$$\boldsymbol{R} \equiv U^{\dagger}\boldsymbol{r}U.$$

In the Dirac representation, $\boldsymbol{R}$ is a non-local operator whose action on the spinor $\Psi(\boldsymbol{r})$ consists, roughly, in multiplying by $\boldsymbol{r}$ and replacing the value at each point by a certain average over the values of the spinor in a domain of order $1/m$ about the point, whence the name of average position given above.

If Q' is an "even" operator of the FW "representation", the corresponding observable $Q_{n.r.}$ in the above-defined two-component theory is obtained by keeping only the matrix elements of Q' between vectors of the space of the large components: $Q_{n.r.} \equiv B_+Q'B_+$. In particular, the observable $\boldsymbol{r}$ representing the position in the two-component theory corresponds to the "average position" $\boldsymbol{R}$ and not to the position operator of the Dirac theory proper [1]).

33. FW Transformation for a Particle in a Field

In the presence of a field the Dirac Hamiltonian takes the form:

$$H = \beta m + \mathscr{I} + \mathscr{P}$$
$$\mathscr{I} \equiv \boldsymbol{\alpha}\cdot\boldsymbol{\pi} = \boldsymbol{\alpha}\cdot(\boldsymbol{p} - e\boldsymbol{A}), \qquad \mathscr{P} \equiv e\varphi.$$

In general, there exists no "representation" in which the Hamiltonian is exactly "even" but by applying successive unitary transformations one may obtain "representations" in which the respective Hamiltonians have an "odd" part of higher and higher order in v/c.

To see this, let us make the unitary transformation

$$U = \exp(\beta\mathscr{I}/2m).$$

The Hamiltonian H_1 which governs the evolution of states in the new representation is given by the equation

$$H_1 = UHU^\dagger - \mathrm{i}U\,\partial U^\dagger/\partial t.$$

By making use of the fact that $\beta\mathscr{I}$ anticommutes with $(\beta m + \mathscr{I})$ and that $U^\dagger = \exp(-\beta\mathscr{I}/2m)$, one obtains:

$$\begin{aligned} U(\beta m+\mathscr{I})U^\dagger &= U^2(\beta m+\mathscr{I}) \\ &= \beta m[\cos(\mathscr{I}/m) + (\mathscr{I}/m)\sin(\mathscr{I}/m)] \\ &\qquad + m[(\mathscr{I}/m)\cos(\mathscr{I}/m) - \sin(\mathscr{I}/m)]. \end{aligned}$$

The terms $U\mathscr{P}U^\dagger$ and $\mathrm{i}U\,\partial U^\dagger/\partial t$ may be expanded into a power series

---

1) In accordance with the interpretation given here, the orbital angular momentum $\boldsymbol{r}\times\boldsymbol{p}$ and the spin $\boldsymbol{\sigma}$ of the two-component theory do not correspond to the orbital angular momentum and spin of the Dirac theory, but to the "average angular momentum" $\boldsymbol{R}\times\boldsymbol{p}$ and the "average spin" $\boldsymbol{\Sigma}$. Here $\boldsymbol{\Sigma}$ is the operator whose correspondent in the FW "representation" is $\boldsymbol{\sigma}$; $\boldsymbol{\Sigma}' \equiv \boldsymbol{\sigma}$. The reader may verify that each of the components of the average spin and each of the components of the average angular momentum commutes with the free particle Hamiltonian; the spin and the orbital angular momentum proper do not have this property. Note also that:

$$\boldsymbol{J} \equiv (\boldsymbol{r}\times\boldsymbol{p}) + \tfrac{1}{2}\boldsymbol{\sigma} = (\boldsymbol{R}\times\boldsymbol{p}) + \tfrac{1}{2}\boldsymbol{\Sigma}.$$

in $\mathscr{I}/m$ by using the following operator identity, valid for any two operators A and B (cf. Problem VIII.4):

$$\mathrm{e}^{A}B\mathrm{e}^{-A} = B + [A, B] + \frac{1}{2}[A, [A, B]] + \ldots + \frac{1}{n!}\underbrace{[A, [A, \ldots [A, [A, B]] \ldots]]}_{n \text{ brackets}} + \ldots$$

We shall only give the result of the calculation of H' when $\mathscr{I}$ is time-independent. Since we are concerned with a first approximation, we put: $H' = H_1$. One finds:

$$H_1 = \beta m + \mathscr{P}_1 + \mathscr{I}_1$$

$$\mathscr{P}_1 = \mathscr{P} + \beta\frac{\mathscr{I}^2}{2m} - \frac{1}{8}m\left[\frac{\mathscr{I}}{m}, \left[\frac{\mathscr{I}}{m}, \frac{\mathscr{P}}{m}\right]\right] - \frac{1}{8}\beta m\left(\frac{\mathscr{I}}{m}\right)^4 + \ldots$$

$$\mathscr{I}_1 = m\left(\frac{1}{2}\beta\left[\frac{\mathscr{I}}{m}, \frac{\mathscr{P}}{m}\right] - \frac{1}{3}\left(\frac{\mathscr{I}}{m}\right)^3\right) + \ldots$$

The terms given in these expansions of the "even" and "odd" parts of H_1 allow the determination of $\mathscr{P}_1$ to within $(\mathscr{I}/m)^6$ or $(\mathscr{P}/m)\,(\mathscr{I}/m)^4$ whichever is the larger and the determination of $\mathscr{I}_1$ to within $(\mathscr{I}/m)^5$ or $(\mathscr{P}/m)\,(\mathscr{I}/m)^3$ whichever is the larger. The "odd" part of H_1 is therefore smaller than that of H by a factor of the order of the larger of $\mathscr{P}/m$ or $(\mathscr{I}/m)^2$; in the non-relativistic limit, $\mathscr{P}/m$ and $\mathscr{I}/m$ are of the order of $(v/c)^2$ and v/c respectively: $\mathscr{I}_1$ is therefore of the order of $(v/c)^3$.

We now effect upon H_1 the operation that we have effected upon H; i.e. we make a new unitary transformation with the operator

$$U_1 = \exp\,(\beta\mathscr{I}_1/2m),$$

and denote the new Hamiltonian by H_2. Its "odd" part $\mathscr{I}_2$ is smaller than that of H_1 by a factor of the order of $\mathscr{P}_1/m$ or $(\mathscr{I}_1/m)^2$, whichever is the larger: in the non-relativistic limit, $\mathscr{P}_1/m$ is of the order of $(v/c)^2$, $(\mathscr{I}_1/m)^2$ of the order of $(v/c)^6$ and $\mathscr{I}_2$ is therefore of the order of $(v/c)^5$. If one neglects terms of this order, H_2 is an "even" operator given by the formula:

$$\begin{aligned} H_2 &\simeq \beta m + \mathscr{P}_2 + \mathrm{O}(v^5) \\ &\simeq \beta m + \mathscr{P} + \beta\frac{\mathscr{I}^2}{2m} - \frac{1}{8}m\left[\frac{\mathscr{I}}{m}, \left[\frac{\mathscr{I}}{m}, \frac{\mathscr{P}}{m}\right]\right] - \frac{1}{8}\beta m\left(\frac{\mathscr{I}}{m}\right)^4 + \mathrm{O}(v^5) \\ &\simeq \beta m + e\varphi + \frac{1}{2m}\beta(\boldsymbol{\sigma}\cdot\boldsymbol{\pi})^2 - \frac{e}{8m^2}[(\boldsymbol{\sigma}\cdot\boldsymbol{\pi}), [(\boldsymbol{\sigma}\cdot\boldsymbol{\pi}), \varphi]] - \frac{1}{8m^3}\beta(\boldsymbol{\sigma}\cdot\boldsymbol{\pi})^4 + \mathrm{O}(v^5). \end{aligned}$$

Similarly, if one neglects terms of order $(v/c)^3$, H_1 is the "even" operator given by

$$H_1 \simeq \beta m + e\varphi + \frac{1}{2m}\beta(\boldsymbol{\sigma}\cdot\boldsymbol{\pi})^2 + \mathrm{O}(v^3).$$

We may now pass over to the two-component theory as in the case of the free particle. To within $(v/c)^5$, the positive energy solutions are represented by the wave functions Φ' of the space of the large components which obey the equation

$$\mathrm{i}\frac{\partial\Phi'}{\partial t} = (m + H'_{n.r.})\,\Phi',$$

where $(m+H'_{n.r.})$ is the projection of the above approximate expression for H_2 onto the space of the large components; i.e.

$$H'_{n.r.} = e\varphi + \frac{1}{2m}(\boldsymbol{\sigma}\cdot\boldsymbol{\pi})^2 - \frac{e}{8m^2}[(\boldsymbol{\sigma}\cdot\boldsymbol{\pi}), [(\boldsymbol{\sigma}\cdot\boldsymbol{\pi}), \varphi]] - \frac{1}{8m^3}(\boldsymbol{\sigma}\cdot\boldsymbol{\pi})^4. \quad \text{(XX.199)}$$

The first two terms are the Hamiltonain $H_{n.r.}$ of Pauli theory. The last two terms are relativistic corrections of order $(v/c)^2$ to the non-relativistic energy $H_{n.r.}$.

A simple calculation gives

$$(\boldsymbol{\sigma}\cdot\boldsymbol{\pi})^4 = (\boldsymbol{\pi}^2 - e(\boldsymbol{\sigma}\cdot\mathscr{H}))^2 \quad \text{(XX.200)}$$

$$[(\boldsymbol{\sigma}\cdot\boldsymbol{\pi}), [(\boldsymbol{\sigma}\cdot\boldsymbol{\pi}), \varphi]] = \operatorname{div}\mathscr{E} + 2\boldsymbol{\sigma}\cdot(\mathscr{E}\times\boldsymbol{\pi}), \quad \text{(XX.201)}$$

which allows $H'_{n.r.}$ to be put in a more familiar form.

By successive application of a sufficient number of these unitary transformations, one may thus construct a two-component theory giving the positive energy states to any desired order in v/c. Each new transformation reduces the error by a factor of $(v/c)^2$. The study of the convergence of the series is rather delicate; it is very likely that it is an asymptotic expansion in most cases. Roughly speaking, it is a power series expansion in the operators $\mathbf{p}/m$, that is $(\hbar/mc)$ grad [and in $\partial/m\partial t$, that is, $(\hbar/mc^2)\partial/\partial t$]. The rate of convergence of the series therefore depends on the smallness of the variation of the potential $(\mathbf{A}, \varphi)$ over a distance of the order of $\hbar/mc$ [and over a time interval of the order of $\hbar/mc^2$, the interval necessary to travel one Compton wave length at the velocity of light].

34. Electron in a Central Electrostatic Potential

As an application of the technique described in the preceding paragraph, consider an electron in a central electrostatic potential $V(r) \equiv e\varphi(r)$. In this case, $A(\boldsymbol{r})=0$ and the Hamiltonian of the Pauli theory is just the Hamiltonian of the ordinary Schrödinger theory:

$$H_{n.r.} = \frac{\boldsymbol{p}^2}{2m} + V(r).$$

If one wishes to continue the calculations to the order immediately above v^2/c^2, one must replace $H_{n.r.}$ by $H'_{n.r.}$. This amounts to adding the last two terms of (XX.199) to $H_{n.r.}$. In the present case

$$e\mathscr{E} = -\operatorname{grad} V = -\frac{\boldsymbol{r}}{r}\frac{\mathrm{d}V}{\mathrm{d}r}$$

$$e \operatorname{div} \mathscr{E} = -\triangle V$$

which gives, taking into account relation (XX.200) and (XX.201),

$$H'_{n.r.} = H_{n.r.} - \frac{p^4}{8m^3c^2} + \frac{\hbar^2}{4m^2c^2}\frac{1}{r}\frac{\mathrm{d}V}{\mathrm{d}r}(\boldsymbol{\sigma}\cdot\boldsymbol{L}) + \frac{\hbar^2}{8m^2c^2}\triangle V. \quad \text{(XX.202)}$$

The first correction term, $-p^4/8m^3c^2$, is the relativistic correction to the kinetic energy $p^2/2m$. The second is a spin-orbit coupling term [cf. formula (XIII.95)]. The third term, $\hbar^2 \triangle V/8m^2c^2$, is a correction to the central potential known as the Darwin term; if $V(r) = -Ze^2/r$ (pure Coulomb potential), the Darwin term is equal to

$$(\pi Z e^2 \hbar^2/2m^2c^2)\,\delta(\boldsymbol{r})$$

and affects only the s-states.

35. Discussions and Conclusions

In the presence, as in the absence, of a field, the operators of the two component non-relativistic theory are the projections of operators of the FW "representation" on the space of the large components. In particular, the operator $\boldsymbol{r}$ of the non-relativistic theory can be identified with what we have called the "average position" $\boldsymbol{R}$. In the Dirac theory, the interaction of the particle with the electromagnetic potential is a local interaction, in other words the particle interacts with the electromagnetic potential at its position $\boldsymbol{r}$. When we pass to the "FW representation", where $\boldsymbol{r}$ represents the "average position", this interaction is transformed into a non-local interaction which has contributions from the values taken by the electromagnetic potential in a domain about the particle of approximate dimensions $\hbar/mc$; if the potential ($\mathbf{A}, \varphi$) varies little in this domain, this interaction can be represented by a Taylor expansion involving the value of the potential and its successive derivatives at the point $\mathbf{r}$. A Hamiltonian such as $H'_{n.r.}$ [eqs. (XX.199) or (XX.202)] contains the first terms of this expansion.

Thus in the non-relativistic limit, the Dirac electron appears not as a point charge, but as a distribution of charge and current extending over a domain of linear dimensions $\hbar/mc$. This explains the appearance of interaction terms characteristic of the presence of a magnetic moment (interaction $-\boldsymbol{\mu}\cdot\mathscr{H}$, spin-orbit interaction) and of an extended charge distribution (Darwin term).

Finally, we note that the application of the non-relativistic approximation to potentials that are singular at the origin such as $\mathbf{A}=\mathbf{M}\times\mathbf{r}/r^3$ or $\varphi=-Ze/r$ is not rigorously justified since in the neighborhood of the point $r=0$ the quantities $e\mathbf{A}/m$ and $e\varphi/m$ cease to be small. If the method of successive approximations described in this section was continued sufficiently far, terms sufficiently singular in the origin to give an infinite contribution to the energy would make their appearance in the non-relativistic Hamiltonian. The solution to this difficulty is suggested by the preceding discussion. In the non-relativistic Hamiltonian, $\mathbf{A}$ and φ are replaced by a certain average of these quantities over a domain of linear dimensions of the order of $\hbar/mc$. If the non-relativistic approximation is really justified, this amounts to effecting a cut-off of the singularity at a distance $\hbar/mc$ from the origin in all the singular expressions encountered in the calculation. In order for the non-relativistic approximation to be applicable to the two cases mentioned above, it suffices that [1]:

$$e|\mathbf{A}| \ll mc^2, \qquad e\varphi \ll mc^2$$

at the point $r=\hbar/mc$.

---

[1] If m_N is the mass of the atomic nucleus $|\mathbf{M}| \simeq Ze\hbar/m_N c$; the quantity eA/mc^3 is of the order of $(e^2/\hbar c)(Zm/m_N)$ at the point $r = \hbar/mc$, i.e. 10^{-5} to 10^{-6}; our calculation of the hyperfine coupling is therefore entirely justified. With regard to the example of § 34, the quantity $e\varphi/mc^2$ being of the order of $Ze^2/\hbar c$, the calculation is valid if $Z \ll 137$.

VI. NEGATIVE ENERGY SOLUTIONS AND POSITRON THEORY

Θαλασσα! θαλασσα! (*Anabasis*, IV.8).

36. Properties of Charge Conjugate Solutions

The concept of charge conjugation defined in § 19 will be useful to us in the following discussion. Charge conjugation is an antilinear and reciprocal correspondence between wave functions representing the evolution of two different particles in the same electromagnetic potential $(\boldsymbol{A}, \varphi)$: these particles have the same mass m but opposite charges $+e$ and $-e$.

If a physical quantity associated with the first particle is represented by $Q(e)$ the same quantity associated with the second particle is represented by $Q(-e)$. Thus the momentum is represented in both cases by $\boldsymbol{p} \equiv -\mathrm{i}\nabla$, and the energy is represented by

$$H(e) \equiv \boldsymbol{\alpha}\cdot(\boldsymbol{p}-e\boldsymbol{A})+\beta m+e\varphi$$

in the one case and by

$$H(-e) \equiv \boldsymbol{\alpha}\cdot(\boldsymbol{p}+e\boldsymbol{A})+\beta m-e\varphi$$

in the other.

Consider a solution $\Psi(\boldsymbol{r}, t)$ and the charge-conjugate solution $\Psi^C(\boldsymbol{r}, t)$. We wish to compare the physical properties of the states represented by these solutions. One knows that

$$\Psi^C = K_C \Psi, \tag{XX.203}$$

where K_C is the antilinear operator defined by equation (XX.124). The notation $\langle Q\rangle$ will be used to denote the average value of Q in the state Ψ and the notation $\langle Q\rangle_C$ to denote the average value of the same operator in the state Ψ^C. Ψ and Ψ^C being supposed normalized to unity, we have

$$\langle Q\rangle = \langle \Psi|Q|\Psi\rangle$$
$$\langle Q\rangle_C = \langle \Psi^C|Q|\Psi^C\rangle.$$

From relation (XX.203),

$$\begin{aligned}\langle Q\rangle_C &= (\langle \Psi|K_C{}^\dagger)(QK_C|\Psi\rangle)\\ &= \langle \Psi|(K_C{}^\dagger QK_C)|\Psi\rangle^* = \langle \Psi|(K_C{}^\dagger Q^\dagger K_C)|\Psi\rangle\end{aligned}$$

from which we obtain the relation between average values

$$\langle Q\rangle_C = \langle (K_C{}^\dagger Q^\dagger K_C)\rangle. \tag{XX.204}$$

By applying this relation and making use of the properties of the antiunitary transformation K_C, one finds the following relations between average values in the state Ψ and in the charge conjugate state:

$$\begin{array}{lll} \langle\beta\rangle_C = -\langle\beta\rangle & \langle\boldsymbol{\alpha}\rangle_C = \langle\boldsymbol{\alpha}\rangle & \langle\boldsymbol{\sigma}\rangle_C = -\langle\boldsymbol{\sigma}\rangle \\ \langle\mathbf{r}\rangle_C = \langle\mathbf{r}\rangle & \langle\mathbf{p}\rangle_C = -\langle\mathbf{p}\rangle & \langle\mathbf{L}\rangle_C = -\langle\mathbf{L}\rangle \\ \langle P(\mathbf{r}_0)\rangle_C = \langle P(\mathbf{r}_0)\rangle & \langle\mathbf{j}(\mathbf{r}_0)\rangle_C = \langle\mathbf{j}(\mathbf{r}_0)\rangle & \langle\mathbf{J}\rangle_C = -\langle\mathbf{J}\rangle \\ & \langle H(-e)\rangle_C = -\langle H(e)\rangle. & \end{array} \qquad \text{(XX.205)}$$

It is seen that the two charge-conjugate solutions have the *same probability density and the same current density at all points* — thus opposite charge densities and electric-current densities — *but opposite energies*: charge conjugation changes the sign of the energy.

37. Abnormal Behavior of the Negative Energy Solutions

After these preliminaries, we are in a position to discuss the question of negative energies in detail.

We first consider the free particle case. The solutions of the Dirac equation were given in § 23. The energy spectrum is made up of two continuous bands $(-\infty, -mc^2)$ and $(mc^2, +\infty)$ separated by an interval of $2mc^2$ (Fig. XX.2*a*). The first of these bands corresponds to negative energy states: $E = -E_p = -\sqrt{m^2+p^2}$, and the second to positive energy states.

We propose to study the motion of a packet of free waves. It will be shown that in general it is only in the average that the center of the packet follows the classical trajectory. To this effect, we integrate the equations of motion in the Heisenberg "representation" which in this case are:

$$\frac{\mathrm{d}\mathbf{r}}{\mathrm{d}t} = \mathrm{i}[H, \mathbf{r}] = \boldsymbol{\alpha} \qquad \text{(XX.206)}$$

$$\begin{aligned} \frac{\mathrm{d}\boldsymbol{\alpha}}{\mathrm{d}t} &= \mathrm{i}[H, \boldsymbol{\alpha}] = \mathrm{i}(H\boldsymbol{\alpha} + \boldsymbol{\alpha}H) - 2\mathrm{i}\boldsymbol{\alpha}H \\ &= 2\mathrm{i}\mathbf{p} - 2\mathrm{i}\boldsymbol{\alpha}H, \end{aligned} \qquad \text{(XX.207)}$$

$\mathbf{p}$ and H being constant in time, equation (XX.207) is easily integrated to give

$$\boldsymbol{\alpha}(t) = \left(\boldsymbol{\alpha}(0) - \frac{\mathbf{p}}{H}\right) \mathrm{e}^{-2\mathrm{i}Ht} + \frac{\mathbf{p}}{H}.$$

The dependence of $\mathrm{d}\boldsymbol{r}/\mathrm{d}t$ on t being thus explicitly given, equation (XX.206) can easily be integrated to give:

$$\boldsymbol{r}(t) = \boldsymbol{r}(0) + \frac{\boldsymbol{p}}{H}t + \mathrm{i}\left(\boldsymbol{\alpha}(0) - \frac{\boldsymbol{p}}{H}\right)\frac{\mathrm{e}^{-2\mathrm{i}Ht}}{2H}. \qquad \text{(XX.208)}$$

Equation (XX.208) gives the operator $\boldsymbol{r}$ of the Heisenberg "representation" at time t as a function of the values taken by the operators $\boldsymbol{r}$ and $\boldsymbol{\alpha}$ at the initial time $t=0$. From it we can obtain the law of motion of the center $\langle \boldsymbol{r} \rangle$ of any wave packet, which it will be instructive to compare with the classical law:

$$\boldsymbol{r}_{\mathrm{cl}}(t) = \boldsymbol{r}_{\mathrm{cl}}(0) + \left(\frac{\boldsymbol{p}}{H}\right)_{\mathrm{cl}} t.$$

Instead of the classical uniform rectilinear motion, the free wave packet follows a complicated motion resulting from the addition of a uniform rectilinear motion of velocity $\langle \boldsymbol{p}/H \rangle$ and a rapidly oscillatory motion,

$$\left\langle \mathrm{i}\left(\boldsymbol{\alpha}(0) - \frac{\boldsymbol{p}}{H}\right)\frac{\mathrm{e}^{-2\mathrm{i}Ht}}{2H}\right\rangle,$$

whose amplitude and period are of the order of $\hbar/2mc$ and $\hbar/2mc^2$ respectively. This oscillatory motion is called "Zitterbewegung".

The "Zitterbewegung" term vanishes if the packet is a superposition of only positive or only negative energy waves. To see this it suffices to show that

$$\Gamma_\pm\left(\boldsymbol{\alpha} - \frac{\boldsymbol{p}}{H}\right)\frac{\mathrm{e}^{-2\mathrm{i}Ht}}{2H}\Gamma_\pm = 0;$$

where Γ_+ and Γ_- are the projectors onto the states of positive and negative energies respectively [definition (XX.195)]. One finds successively

$$[H, \boldsymbol{\alpha}] = 2\boldsymbol{p} - 2\boldsymbol{\alpha}H$$

$$[\Gamma_\pm, \boldsymbol{\alpha}] = \pm\frac{\boldsymbol{p}}{E_p} \mp \boldsymbol{\alpha}\frac{H}{E_p},$$

and since $H\Gamma_\pm = \pm E_p\Gamma_\pm$, it can be deduced that

$$0 \equiv \Gamma_\pm[\Gamma_\pm, \boldsymbol{\alpha}]\,\Gamma_\pm = \Gamma_\pm\left(\frac{\boldsymbol{p}}{H} - \boldsymbol{\alpha}\right)\Gamma_\pm,$$

from which we obtain the enunciated property by using the fact that H commutes with Γ_+ and Γ_-. "The Zitterbewegung" is therefore caused by interference between the positive and negative energy components of the wave packet.

The "Zitterbewegung" is a curious effect related to negative energies but does not, in itself, constitute a difficulty. The difficulty appears when one studies the motion of a wave packet formed exclusively of negative energy states. In this case, the "Zitterbewegung" disappears; the center of the packet describes a uniform rectilinear motion of velocity:

$$\mathbf{v} = \left\langle \frac{\mathbf{p}}{H} \right\rangle = -\left\langle \frac{\mathbf{p}}{E_p} \right\rangle$$

in the opposite direction to its momentum $\langle \mathbf{p} \rangle$. In particular, in a non-relativistic limit ($H \simeq -mc^2$), one has the relation $\mathbf{v} = -\langle \mathbf{p} \rangle / m$, i.e. the particle behaves as if it had a negative mass $-m$.

This type of difficulty is even more apparent when one studies the motion of wave packets in a static field.

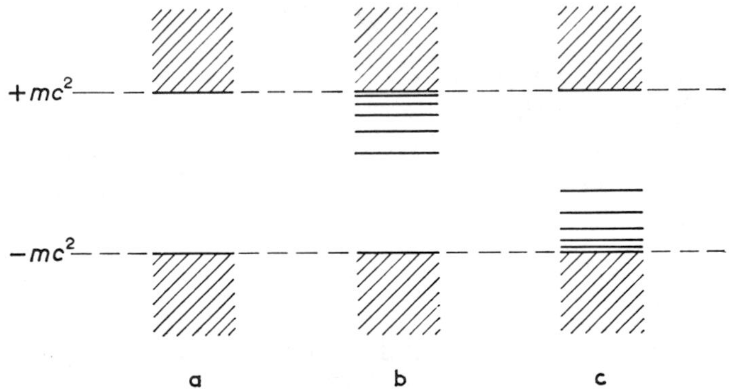

Fig. XX.2. Energy spectrum of a Dirac electron: (*a*) free; (*b*) in the attractive potential $-Ze^2/r$; (*c*) in the repulsive potential Ze^2/r.

Consider, for example, an electron in the attractive Coulomb potential $-Ze^2/r$. The spectrum (cf. Fig. XX.2*b*) is made up of a continuous positive energy band from mc^2 to ∞, a series of positive energy levels smaller than mc^2 and a continuous negative energy band from $-mc^2$ to $-\infty$. To picture the negative energy states, recall that they correspond by charge conjugation to the states of a particle of the same mass and of opposite charge (that is, a positron) in the same potential or, what amounts to the same, to the states of an electron in the repulsive potential Ze^2/r. In this correspondence the energy changes sign and the small and large components are interchanged, but the densities and the current densities remain the same [cf. eq. (XX.205)]. The spectrum of the electron in the repulsive potential Ze^2/r is shown in Figure XX.2*c*. The positive energy continuum in the repulsive potential corresponds to the negative energy continuum in the attractive potential.

Let us consider the motion of a packet of negative energy waves in the potential $-Ze^2/r$, assuming that the non-relativistic approximation is valid ($Ze^2 \ll 1$, energies near $-mc^2$); the motion is the same as that of the packet of positive energy waves that corresponds by charge conjugation. In particular, in the limit of very small velocities, the classical approximation may be applied (cf. § VI.5) and the motion at the center of the packet is essentially that of a classical electron in the potential with the opposite sign, that is, of *a particle of negative mass* $-m$ in the potential $-Ze^2/r$: the velocity points in the opposite direction to the momentum, the acceleration in the opposite direction to the force. Such a situation has never been observed experimentally.

38. Reinterpretation of the Negative Energy States. Theory of "Holes" and Positrons

As they stand, the negative energy solutions have no physical significance. If it were possible to completely decouple the positive and negative energy states the latter could simply be ignored. Such, however, is not the case.

Consider, for example, a free electron in a positive energy state E_+, and subject it during a time interval $(0, t)$ to a radio-frequency field of frequency ω. If t is sufficiently long and the intensity of the field not too strong, the resulting effect can be calculated by the method of § XVII.6; one finds a non-vanishing probability for the electron to make a transition to a state of energy $E_+ + \hbar\omega$ or $E_+ - \hbar\omega$. In particular if

$$\hbar\omega > E_+ + mc^2,$$

the second transition is made to a state of negative energy.

As another example, consider the complete spectrum of the hydrogen atom (Fig. XX.2*b*). Owing to the coupling of the electron with the electromagnetic field, there is always a certain probability of a radiative transition from a given state of the atom to a state of lower energy. Consequently an electron in one of the bound states of the hydrogen atom can, even if isolated, make quantum jumps to states of negative energy with emission of one or several photons; further, since the spectrum has no lower bound, the hydrogen atom has no stable state [1]).

In order to avoid these difficulties Dirac has made the following suggestion. In what one calls the "vacuum", all of the states of negative energy are occupied by an electron. If an electron is added to this "vacuum", it will necessarily be in a positive energy state since all of the negative energy states are occupied and electrons obey Fermi–Dirac statistics.

The "vacuum" therefore appears as a completely degenerate Fermi gas of infinite density. In addition, it is supposed that it is completely unobservable, giving rise to no gravitational or electromagnetic effects. The observable physical properties of a given state will be the deviations of that state from this "vacuum". Thus the observable charge of the system (electron+"vacuum") is the difference between the total charge of the system and the charge of the "vacuum", i.e. the charge of the electron. Similarly the observable energy of this system is the difference between its total energy and the energy of the "vacuum", and is therefore the energy of the electron. Up to the present, therefore, the only effect of redefining the vacuum in this way, and reinterpreting measurable quantities accordingly, is to forbid transitions to the negative energies, owing to the exclusion principle [2]).

Let us now consider what will be observed when an electron of the negative energy "sea" is missing. Applying the above convention concerning observable physical properties, we can conclude that this "hole" will have a charge opposite to that of the missing electron. It will also have an energy of opposite sign, that is a positive energy, and a momentum in the opposite direction. These considerations are valid whether or not the missing electron is in an eigenstate of the Hamiltonian. If, in particular, the missing electron forms a wave packet moving with velocity $\mathbf{v}$, the "hole" moves with the same

---

1) O. Klein has formulated a celebrated paradox which exhibits in another way the existence of a non-vanishing probability of transition to negative energy states. Klein's paradox is expounded in many treatises, for example, in M. Born, *loc. cit.*, note 1, p. 4, Vol. I.

2) In particular, the Zitterbewegung effect is automatically eliminated.

velocity but opposite momentum: the "hole" therefore acts like a particle of positive mass $+m$ and charge $-e$. Such particles have been observed in nature: they are called *positrons*.

Under the action of an electromagnetic field or any other suitable perturbation, an electron from the negative energy "sea" can make a transition to a state of positive energy. The "hole" of negative energy appears as a positron. In such a transformation, a pair of particles of opposite sign is thus formed. The creation of positron-electron pairs has been observed experimentally.

Similarly, if there is a "hole" in the negative energy "sea", an electron in a positive energy state can make a transition to this unoccupied negative energy state with emission of photons. This phenomenon of annihilation of an electron-positron pair with emission of photons has also been observed experimentally.

39. Difficulties with the "Hole" Theory

The "hole" theory which was briefly outlined above, permits the reconciliation of the Dirac theory with the experimental facts: non-existence of negative energy states, existence of positrons, creation and annihilation of pairs. It therefore constitutes a considerable step forward. However, it has a number of limitations and difficulties.

First of all, it is incomplete. By postulating the occupation of the quasi-totality of negative energy states, *the theory ceases to be a one-particle theory*, even when it sets out to describe a single electron. The formalism of the Dirac theory of a single particle, as set forth in this chapter, is therefore insufficient for describing such a situation, and it is only in the framework of Field Theory that one can hope to obtain a self-consistent description.

The hole theory is only a first step in the direction of a correct theory of the quantized electron field. It has the merit of providing simple pictures and can therefore serve as a guide in the elaboration of the correct theory. But pitfalls and contradictions appear when it is pushed too far.

For example, having defined the "vacuum" as composed of an infinite number of electrons, it is inconsistent to assume that these electrons do not interact.

Another weak point of the theory is the apparently very unsymmetrical role played by the electrons and the positrons. One can also construct a corresponding charge-conjugate theory where the positrons play the role of the particles and the electrons that of the holes without any of the physical consequences being changed. All of these difficulties can be avoided in the Field Theory formalism by starting from equations invariant with respect to charge conjugation.

Finally, we note that even the definition of the negative energy states depends on the applied electromagnetic potential. In the two cases considered in § 37, namely the free particle and the particle in a Coulomb field, the space of the negative energy states is not the same. If, for example, the ground-state wave function for the hydrogen atom is expanded in a series of plane waves, one finds a weak but non-vanishing contribution from plane waves of negative energy. In the above definition of the "vacuum", the states of negative energy considered are those of the free particle; indeed it is natural to define the vacuum in the absence of a field. The introduction of an external electromagnetic field modifies this state of the "vacuum" (pair creation), the latter acting like a polarizable medium, in such a way that an electric charge in the "vacuum" seems smaller than it really is. Such effects are also found in field theory. Hole theory predicts these effects but gives no reliable and self-consistent method for their calculation.

Note Added in Proof (cf. p. 913).

To be entirely correct, one should state the parity question as follows. To the transformation s of the orthochronous Lorentz group, there correspond two transformations, s' and s'', of the group $G^{(a)}$ of Lorentz transformation operators. These are respectively represented by the *two* parity operators P' and P'' given by $P' = c' \gamma^0 P^{(0)}$ and $P'' = c'' \gamma^0 P^{(0)}$, with $c' = -c''$. The set (c', c'') defines the *intrinsic parity* of the particle. According to the discussion of § 13, there are two possible intrinsic parities, $(+1, -1)$ and $(-1, +1)$. They correspond to two inequivalent irreducible representations of the group $G^{(a)}$. Since we are dealing here with a single particle, this notion of intrinsic parity is academic. However, it is relevant in Quantum Field Theory when the interaction between several different particles is considered.

A similar treatment applies if $G^{(b)}$ instead of $G^{(a)}$ is chosen as the group of Lorentz transformation operators (cf. notes, p. 904 and p. 908). One again finds two possible values of the intrinsic parity, namely $(+i, -i)$ and $(-i, +i)$.

It should be noted that, contrary to what is often stated in the literature, the number of possible intrinsic parities for spinors *is not four but two.*

EXERCISES AND PROBLEMS

1. Show that if Ψ satisfies the Klein–Gordon equation with a field A^μ, the equation of continuity is satisfied by the four-current:

$$j^\mu = \frac{i}{2m}[\Psi^*(D^\mu\Psi) - \Psi(D^\mu\Psi)^*] \equiv \frac{i}{2m}[\Psi^*(\partial^\mu\Psi) - \Psi(\partial^\mu\Psi^*)] - \frac{e}{m}A^\mu\Psi^*\Psi$$

(cf. Problem IV.1).

2. Consider a hydrogen atom in which the electron is replaced by a particle of the same mass and the same charge obeying the Klein–Gordon equation. The levels E of the discrete spectrum are then given by the eigenvalue equation:

$$\left[\Delta + m^2 - \left(E - \frac{e^2}{r}\right)^2\right]\Psi(\mathbf{r}) = 0.$$

Show that this equation can be solved exactly by separating the angular and radial variables, and that the levels of the discrete spectrum depend on the quantum numbers n and l according to the formula:

$$E^{nl} = m\left(1 + \frac{e^4}{(n-\varepsilon_l)^2}\right)^{-\frac{1}{2}} \qquad \varepsilon_l = l + \tfrac{1}{2} - [(l+\tfrac{1}{2})^2 - e^4]^{\frac{1}{2}}$$

$$[n = 1, 2, \ldots, \infty; \qquad l = 0, 1, \ldots, n-1].$$

Compare this spectrum with that given by the non-relativistic Schrödinger theory.

3. Show that all of the (not necessarily unitary) γ^A matrices defined in Table 1 (§ 10), have a determinant equal to 1.

4. If B is the matrix defined at the end of § 10, show that $BB^* = B^*B = -I$. [Show first that

(*i*) BB^* is a multiple of the unit element, and therefore that $BB^* = B^*B = \pm I$;

(*ii*) the matrix BB^* is the same whatever the system of 4 unitary matrices γ^μ used to define B.]

5. Prove the following properties of the (antiunitary) charge conjugation operator K_C defined in § 19

$$K_C\, p_\mu\, K_C^\dagger = -\, p_\mu, \qquad K_C\, J_{\alpha\beta}\, K_C^\dagger = -\, J_{\alpha\beta}$$
$$K_C\, P\, K_C^\dagger = -\, P, \qquad K_C\, K_T\, K_C^\dagger = -\, K_T.$$

From these, deduce that with the choice made for the phase of the transformation operators in § 17, K_C commutes with the operators of translation and of the proper Lorentz transformations and that it anticommutes with the spatial reflections and time reversal. How must the choice of phases be modified in order to have K_C commute with all of these transformations.

6. From the Dirac Hamiltonian deduce the equation of motion (XX.147) and (XX.148) for the operators $\boldsymbol{r}$ and $\boldsymbol{\pi}$ in the Heisenberg representation. Similarly deduce the equations

$$\frac{\mathrm{d}}{\mathrm{d}t}\left[(\boldsymbol{r}\times\boldsymbol{\pi})+\frac{1}{2}\boldsymbol{\sigma}\right]=\boldsymbol{r}\times\boldsymbol{F}, \qquad \frac{\mathrm{d}M}{\mathrm{d}t}=\boldsymbol{\alpha}\cdot\boldsymbol{F}\equiv e\boldsymbol{\alpha}\cdot\mathscr{E},$$

where $\boldsymbol{F}$ is the "Lorentz force": $\boldsymbol{F}\equiv e(\mathscr{E}+\boldsymbol{\alpha}\times\mathscr{H})$; compare these with equations (XX.22) and (XX.21′) from classical dynamics.

7. In the absence of a field, any solution of the Dirac equation is a solution of the Klein–Gordon equation. Show by giving a counter example that the converse is not true.

8. Prove identities (XX.169).

9. Expand a Dirac plane wave of momentum $\boldsymbol{p}$ directed along the z axis into free spherical waves.

10. Make a systematic search for the wave functions of the hydrogen atom such that the radial functions F and G are multiples of each other. Verify that the levels found correspond to $n'=0$ (therefore $J=n-\frac{1}{2}$) and $l=n-1$. One finds (notations of § 27):

$$E_{n,n-\frac{1}{2}}=m\left(1-\frac{e^4}{n^2}\right)^{\frac{1}{2}}$$

$$F=Cst.\times\varrho^s\,\mathrm{e}^{-\varrho}, \qquad G=-\,\nu F$$

with

$$s=\sqrt{n^2-e^4}, \qquad \varkappa=me^2/n, \qquad \varrho=\varkappa r, \qquad \nu=\varkappa/(E+m)\simeq e^2/2n.$$

11. Following the method described in § 27, calculate the levels of the hydrogen atom predicted by the Dirac theory.

12. Compare the fine structure of the levels of the hydrogen atom as given by the Dirac theory and as given by the Klein–Gordon theory of a particle of the same mass and same charge in the same Coulomb field (cf. Problem XX.2).

13. Calculate the relativistic corrections of order v^2/c^2 given by expression (XX.202) for the levels $2s_{1/2}$, $2p_{1/2}$ and $2p_{3/2}$ of the hydrogen atom. Verify that in this approximation the states $2s_{1/2}$ and $2p_{1/2}$ remain at the same level and compare the results with those given by the exact treatment of § 27.

CHAPTER XXI

FIELD QUANTIZATION. RADIATION THEORY

Se non è vero, è bene trovato

1. Introduction

The purpose of this last chapter is twofold: on the one hand to familiarize the reader with the concept of a quantized field and provide an introduction to the Quantum Theory of fields, its physical significance, its successes and its limitations; on the other, to give an elementary treatment of the Quantum Theory of electromagnetic radiation and the coupling of radiation with atomic and nuclear systems.

We shall establish the Quantum Theory of a field by the same method as was used for the non-relativistic Quantum Theory of particle systems. The method is based on the correspondence principle and starts from Hamilton's canonical formalism for the classical field. The only difference is that here it is applied to a system with an infinite number of degrees of freedom. The resulting formalism is called the Hamiltonian formalism.

The main shortcoming of this formalism is that it is not formally covariant [1]). It is possible to put the theory in a completely covariant form by starting from covariant equations for the classical field and adopting a quantization method that preserves their covariant character. Such a formalism has indisputable advantages, both practical and conceptual. Many calculations then have a simple character owing to the fact that the expressions automatically conserve a condensed and symmetrical form. On the other hand, the covariant formalism requires the construction of an elaborate mathematical framework. The Hamiltonian formalism uses more familiar concepts and is better suited for an introduction.

The chapter is divided into four sections, of which the first two are devoted to the simplest type of field, the real scalar field. Section I is devoted to the free field; in it we give the method of quantizing the classical field and its variants, the definition of state-vector space

[1]) This obviously does not imply that the relativity principle is violated. However, the relativistic invariance of the theory is not *a priori* evident and must be demonstrated. The demonstration will not be given here.

and the interpretation of the corresponding quantum states. In section II, we consider the coupling of such a field with a system of particles, and with the aid of this simple model examine the characteristic properties of a field in interaction with an atomic or nuclear system; the applications treated in this section have been chosen to illustrate the methods, the physical significance and the difficulties of Quantum Field Theory. The last two sections are devoted to electromagnetic radiation. In section III we recall the classical theory and in section IV we briefly treat the quantum theory and its applications. Most of the techniques and discussions relating to the scalar field are easily extended to radiation; they are repeated very briefly for this latter case, with special attention to the differences, which are due to the vector character of the electro-magnetic potential and to the fact that the mass of the photon is null [1]).

I. QUANTIZATION OF A REAL SCALAR FIELD

2. Classical Free Field. Normal Vibrations

A real classical scalar field is defined at each instant t by giving its amplitude $\Phi(\mathbf{r}, t)$ at each point $\mathbf{r}$ of space. It can be regarded as

[1]) There exist many treatises on Quantum Electrodynamics. We cite in particular: W. Heitler, *The Quantum Theory of Radiation* (Oxford University Press, second edition, 1944); A. I. Akhiezer and V. B. Berestetsky, *Quantum Electrodynamics* (translated from the Russian by Consultants Bureaux Inc. (1956)); J. M. Jauch and F. Röhrlich, *The Theory of Photons and Electrons* (Addison Wesley, Cambridge, 1956); N. N. Bogoliubov and D. V. Shirkov, *Introduction to the Theory of Quantized Fields* (translated from the Russian by G. M. Volkoff; Interscience Publishers Inc., New York, 1959); S. S. Schweber, *An Introduction to Relativistic Quantum Field Theory* (Row, Peterson and Company, 1961); W. E. Thirring, *Principles of Quantum Electrodynamics* (translated from the German by J. Bernstein; Academic Press, New York, 1958). Heitler uses the Hamiltonian formalism and treats the principal applications of the theory to atomic physics. Akhiezer and Berestetsky, and Jauch and Röhrlich give a very complete account of the covariant formalism and also a very complete review of its applications. Bogoliubov and Shirkov, and in a more complete way, Schweber, give a unified exposition of Quantum Field Theory in the covariant formalism including a thorough discussion of the renormalization problem and of the implications of causality in Field Theory. Thirring gives an overall view of the covariant formalism and a detailed discussion of its physical significance and its difficulties. For the measurability of field operators, one may also consult the classical articles of N. Bohr and L. Rosenfeld, Det. Klg. Danske Viddenskab. Selskab. **12**, no. 8 (1933) and Phys. Rev. **78** (1950) 794.

a dynamical system with an infinite number of degrees of freedom. To each point of space there corresponds a particular coordinate of the system, namely the amplitude of the field at that point.

The dynamics of such a system is not essentially different to that of a system with a finite number of degrees of freedom. However, since the coordinates are labelled with the aid of *continuous* parameters – for example the three components x, y, z, of the point $\boldsymbol{r}$ – differentiation with respect to time is replaced by partial differentiation. The evolution of the system is determined by an equation of motion of the form:

$$\ddot{\Phi}(\boldsymbol{r}, t) \equiv \frac{\partial^2 \Phi}{\partial t^2} = F[\Phi(\boldsymbol{r}, t), \dot{\Phi}(\boldsymbol{r}, t)],$$

where F is a functional of the amplitude $\Phi(\boldsymbol{r}, t)$ and of its partial derivative: $\dot{\Phi} \equiv \partial\Phi/\partial t$, both taken at the same instant t. The dynamical state of the system is determined for any given time if we are given its position and its velocity at an initial time t_0, i.e. its coordinates $\Phi(\boldsymbol{r}, t_0)$ and their respective derivatives with respect to the time:

$$\dot{\Phi}(\boldsymbol{r}, t_0) \equiv \left.\frac{\partial \Phi(\boldsymbol{r}, t)}{\partial t}\right|_{t=t_0}.$$

Of all the equations of motion invariant with respect to the transformations of the inhomogeneous Lorentz group, the simplest is the Klein–Gordon equation:

$$[\square + \mu^2]\Phi \equiv \ddot{\Phi} - \triangle\Phi + \mu^2\Phi = 0. \qquad \text{(XXI.1)}$$

This equation is linear and homogeneous in Φ; it is the law of motion for a free field. μ is a constant. We shall see further along that μ is the mass of the corpuscles associated with the quantized field (§ XXI.6).

If the term $\triangle\Phi$ did not appear in the left-hand side of eq. (XXI.1) the motion of the different coordinates of the system would be independent, and each would effect a harmonic oscillation of frequency μ with amplitude and phase depending on the initial conditions. The term $\triangle\Phi$ couples these harmonic oscillations.

Such a set of coupled oscillators can be transformed into a set of independent oscillators by the introduction of normal coordinates, as will now be shown.

We denote by $f_1, f_2, \ldots, f_i, \ldots$, a complete orthonormal set of real functions of $\boldsymbol{r}$ satisfying the eigenvalue equation of the Hermitean operator $(-\triangle)$. The corresponding eigenvalue spectrum extends from 0 to $+\infty$. We denote the eigenvalue corresponding to the function f_i by k_i^2. One has, therefore

$$(\Delta + k_i^2) f_i = 0 \tag{XXI.2}$$

$$\int f_i(\boldsymbol{r})\, f_j(\boldsymbol{r})\, \mathrm{d}\boldsymbol{r} = \delta_{ij} \tag{XXI.3}$$

$$\sum_i f_i(\boldsymbol{r})\, f_i(\boldsymbol{r}') = \delta(\boldsymbol{r} - \boldsymbol{r}'). \tag{XXI.4}$$

From the orthogonality and closure relations (XXI.3) and (XXI.4), we obtain the expansions

$$\Phi(\boldsymbol{r}, t) = \sum_i q_i(t)\, f_i(\boldsymbol{r}) \tag{XXI.5}$$

$$q_i(t) = \int f_i(\boldsymbol{r})\, \Phi(\boldsymbol{r}, t)\, \mathrm{d}\boldsymbol{r}. \tag{XXI.6}$$

The quantities $q_1, q_2, \ldots, q_i, \ldots$ are the desired normal coordinates. From equations (XXI.6) and (XXI.1),

$$\ddot{q}_i + \omega_i^2 q_i = 0, \tag{XXI.7}$$

where

$$\omega_i = (k_i^2 + \mu^2)^{\frac{1}{2}}. \tag{XXI.8}$$

Thus the equation of motion of each q_i is indeed that of an independent harmonic oscillator and the corresponding frequency is ω_i. In accordance with equation (XXI.5), the field amplitude is a linear superposition of these independent oscillators.

In all of this, we have supposed that the basis functions f were labelled with a discrete index. In fact, since the operator $(-\triangle)$ has a continuous spectrum (extending from 0 to $+\infty$), these functions depend on a set of indices, at least one of which is continuous. It is easy to repeat the above analysis with continuous indices; apart from a few obvious modifications, the details of which will not be given here, the results remain essentially the same. However, the existence of continuous indices complicates somewhat the quantum treatment. In order to avoid these inessential complications, we shall suppose that the field is defined in a finite volume of space and satisfies convenient boundary conditions on the surface of this volume, and that the physical quantities we wish to calculate may be deduced from the quantities which we actually do calculate by increasing this volume indefinitely. This type of artifice has already been described in § V.11. It obviously is not rigorous. It should also be noted that it partly destroys, in an artificial way, the invariance properties of the theory.

3. Quantization of the Free Field

The passage to normal coordinates suggest a very simple method for quantizing the real scalar field. It consists in associating with each mode of normal vibration of the classical field a quantum oscillator of the same frequency (see Chapter XII).

Let us write the classical Hamiltonian in normal coordinates. Let p_i be the momentum conjugate to q_i. Equation (XXI.7) is then equivalent to the Hamilton equations:

$$\dot{q}_i = p_i, \qquad \dot{p}_i = -\omega_i^2 q_i.$$

These can be obtained by taking the following Hamiltonian for the ith degree of freedom:

$$h_i = \tfrac{1}{2}(p_i^2 + \omega_i^2 q_i^2), \tag{XXI.9}$$

whence the following expression for the total Hamiltonian:

$$H = \sum_i h_i. \tag{XXI.10}$$

The corresponding quantized field is obtained by replacing the real dynamical variables q_i and p_i by observables obeying the commutation relations ($\hbar = 1$):

$$[q_i, p_j] = \mathrm{i}\delta_{ij}. \tag{XXI.11}$$

To each mode of vibration there corresponds a series of discrete equidistant levels according to the formula:

$$E_{n_i} = (n_i + \tfrac{1}{2})\omega_i \qquad (n_i = 0, 1, 2, \ldots, \infty). \tag{XXI.12}$$

Here it is convenient to introduce annihilation and creation operators, which we denote by b_i and $b_i^\dagger$ respectively:

$$\left.\begin{aligned} b_i &= (2\omega_i)^{-\frac{1}{2}}(\omega_i q_i + \mathrm{i}p_i) \\ b_i^\dagger &= (2\omega_i)^{-\frac{1}{2}}(\omega_i q_i - \mathrm{i}p_i). \end{aligned}\right. \tag{XXI.13}$$

The commutation rules (XXI.11) between observables are equivalent to the commutation rules between Hermitean conjugate operators:

$$[b_i, b_j^\dagger] = \delta_{ij} \tag{XXI.14}$$

and the eigenvectors of h_i are obtained by the repeated action of $b_i^\dagger$ on the eigenvector of the ground state [see eq. (XII.20)].

A complete set of eigenstates of H is obtained by taking the tensor product of the eigenstates of the partial Hamiltonians $h_1, h_2, \ldots, h_i, \ldots$. Each state is labelled with the quantum numbers $n_1, n_2, \ldots, n_i, \ldots$; its energy is the sum of the partial energies

$$E_{n_1 n_2 \ldots n_i \ldots} = \sum_i (n_i + \tfrac{1}{2})\, \omega_i. \qquad \text{(XXI.15)}$$

Its eigenvector, normalized to unity, is obtained from the vector $|0\rangle$ representing the ground state by the formula

$$|n_1 n_2 \ldots n_i \ldots\rangle = \prod_i \frac{(b_i^\dagger)^{n_i}}{(n_i!)^{\frac{1}{2}}} |0\rangle. \qquad \text{(XXI.16)}$$

The field at the point $\mathbf{r}$ is a certain Hermitean operator $\Phi(\mathbf{r})$, defined by the expression

$$\Phi(\mathbf{r}) = \sum_i q_i\, f_i(\mathbf{r}) \qquad \text{(XXI.17)}$$

deduced by correspondence from the classical relation (XXI.5). It is useful to express it in terms of the b_i and $b_i^\dagger$; from equations (XXI.13) and (XXI.17),

$$\Phi(\mathbf{r}) = \sum_i (2\omega_i)^{-\frac{1}{2}} (b_i + b_i^\dagger)\, f_i. \qquad \text{(XXI.18)}$$

Up to now the field has appeared as a set of quantized oscillators. In the stationary state considered above, each quantum number n represents the number of vibrational quanta relative to a particular normal mode of vibration. But one may also give the eigenstates of H, and more generally the operators of the system, a corpuscular interpretation of which the essential was set forth in § XII.6. n_i then represents the number of corpuscles in the state f_i of energy ω_i; it is the eigenvalue of a certain operator N_i, the "number of corpuscles in the state f_i" operator, defined by

$$N_i = b_i^\dagger b_i. \qquad \text{(XXI.19)}$$

b_i is the annihilation operator for a corpuscle in the state f_i, $b_i^\dagger$ the creation operator for a corpuscle in the state f_i.

The interpretation is self-consistent only if the total energy of a given dynamical state is the sum of the energies of the corpuscles present in that state. As has already been noted in § XII.6, it is sufficient for this to subtract the constant $\frac{1}{2}\omega_i$ from each term h_i of the sum on the right-hand side of (XXI.10). This modification of the Hamiltonian obviously has no effect on the equations of motion, and the new Hamiltonian has the desired property, i.e.,

$$H = \sum_i N_i\, \omega_i. \tag{XXI.20}$$

In particular, the vacuum is the state of zero energy namely the state represented by the ket vector $|0\rangle$. Similarly, the vector $b_i^\dagger\,|0\rangle$ represents a state having a single corpuscle and its energy is the energy ω_i of that corpuscle.

The corpuscles considered here are indistinguishable and the dynamical state of the total system is completely determined by giving the numbers $n_1, n_2, \ldots, n_i, \ldots$ of these corpuscles in each of the individual states $f_1, f_2, \ldots, f_i, \ldots$ that can be occupied. These "occupation numbers" can take any integral value from 0 to $+\infty$. The corpuscles therefore obey Bose–Einstein statistics (cf. § XIV.6) and the quantized field represents a *system of bosons* of undetermined number.

We conclude with a remark concerning the ground state of the system. This vacuum of the quantized field differs profoundly from the classical vacuum. In the case of a classical field, the vacuum, or state of minimum energy, is a state for which the field vanishes at every point. In the case of the quantized field, the field at a given point $\Phi(\boldsymbol{r})$ is an operator which does not commute with the Hamiltonian. Its vacuum expectation value vanishes as may easily be seen using the properties of the b_i and the $b_i^\dagger$, but its mean square deviation does not. Indeed, using expression (XXI.18) of the field, one finds,

$$\langle \Phi^2(\boldsymbol{r})\rangle_0 = \sum_i \sum_j \tfrac{1}{2}(\omega_i\, \omega_j)^{-\frac{1}{2}} \langle 0|\, (b_i + b_i^\dagger)\, (b_j + b_j^\dagger)\, |0\rangle\, f_i(\boldsymbol{r})\, f_j(\boldsymbol{r}),$$

and since

$$\langle 0|(b_i + b_i^\dagger)(b_j + b_j^\dagger)|0\rangle = \langle 0|b_i b_j^\dagger|0\rangle = \delta_{ij},$$

we have

$$\langle \Phi^2\rangle_0 = \sum_i \frac{f_i^2(\boldsymbol{r})}{2\omega_i}.$$

The right-hand side is a series of positive terms, and is therefore a non-zero positive quantity. In fact it can be shown that this series is divergent [1]). The appearance of divergent quantities is characteristic of systems with an infinite number of degrees of freedom and is a source of serious difficulties in Quantum Field Theory. We shall have occasion to return to this point in section II.

4. Lagrangian of the Field. Momentum Conjugate to $\Phi(\mathbf{r})$

Before we continue, let us return to the classical field and briefly describe the generalization of the Lagrangian and Hamiltonian formalisms to this type of system having an infinite number of degrees of freedom. If the coordinates are labelled by a set of discrete indices, the generalization is obvious; it is the one that we used with the normal coordinates. The situation is more delicate if the coordinates depend on a continuous index, in particular if the "position" of the field is defined by specifying its amplitude at each point of space. It is precisely this choice of coordinates that interests us here.

The Lagrangian function L is a function of the coordinates of the system and of the components of its velocity; in the present case, it is a functional of Φ and $\dot{\Phi}$. We assume that it may be represented by an expression of the form

$$L = \int \mathscr{L}\, \mathrm{d}\mathbf{r}. \tag{XXI.21}$$

The Lagrangian density $\mathscr{L}$ depends on $\mathbf{r}$ and t through Φ, through the three components of its gradient and through $\dot{\Phi}$:

$$\mathscr{L} \equiv \mathscr{L}\left(\Phi, \frac{\partial \Phi}{\partial x^k}, \dot{\Phi}\right).$$

Knowing L, one defines the action integral

$$I = \int_{t_1}^{t_2} L\, \mathrm{d}t = \int_{t_1}^{t_2} \mathrm{d}t \int \mathrm{d}\mathbf{r}\, \mathscr{L}. \tag{XXI.22}$$

I is a certain functional of $\Phi(\mathbf{r}, t)$. The equations of motion are given by the principle of least action [eq. (I.12)]:

$$\delta I = 0 \qquad \text{(supposing } \delta\Phi(t_1) = \delta\Phi(t_2) = 0\text{)}. \tag{XXI.23}$$

---

[1]) On the other hand, the integral of the field over a finite volume has a finite fluctuation; this fluctuation increases with the smallness of the volume of integration, becoming infinite in the limit where this volume vanishes (cf. Problem XXI.1).

From relation (XXI.22), it is clear that this law of motion obeys the relativity principle *if $\mathscr{L}$ transforms like a scalar in the transformations of the Lorentz group*. This condition on $\mathscr{L}$ makes it much easier to find the Lagrangian function.

Lagrange's equations are replaced in the present case by a partial differential equation for the amplitude $\Phi(\mathbf{r}, t)$ that is easily deduced from the principle of least action. One finds:

$$\frac{\partial}{\partial t}\frac{\partial \mathscr{L}}{\partial \dot{\Phi}} + \sum_k \frac{\partial}{\partial x^k}\frac{\partial \mathscr{L}}{\partial(\partial \Phi/\partial x^k)} - \frac{\partial \mathscr{L}}{\partial \Phi} = 0. \tag{XXI.24}$$

This equation is the equation of motion for the field.

To rigorously define the field coordinates, one must imagine the whole of space divided into infinitesimal cells. To each cell $(\mathbf{r}, \mathbf{r}+\mathrm{d}\mathbf{r})$ there corresponds a coordinate of the system, namely the quantity $\Phi(\mathbf{r}, t)\,\mathrm{d}\mathbf{r}$. The law of motion fixes the variation of these coordinates as a function of time. In accordance with the usual definition, the conjugate momentum $\Pi(\mathbf{r}, t)$ of the coordinate $\Phi(\mathbf{r}, t)\,\mathrm{d}\mathbf{r}$ is given by the functional derivative of L with respect to the velocity component $\dot{\Phi}(\mathbf{r}, t)\,\mathrm{d}\mathbf{r}$, i.e.:

$$\Pi(\mathbf{r}, t) \equiv \frac{\delta L}{\delta \dot{\Phi}(\mathbf{r}, t)\,\mathrm{d}\mathbf{r}} = \frac{\partial \mathscr{L}}{\partial \dot{\Phi}}. \tag{XXI.25}$$

The concept of a functional derivative used here is a natural generalization of the concept of a partial derivative; δL is the variation of L when $\dot{\Phi}$ varies by the infinitesimal quantity $\delta\dot{\Phi}$ in a small volume of extension $\mathrm{d}\mathbf{r}$ about the point $\mathbf{r}$, while at the same time remaining constant in the rest of space.

Having defined the conjugate momentum for each coordinate, one obtains the Hamiltonian function H by applying the usual definition [eq. (I.13)]; it is a functional of Φ and Π:

$$H \equiv H[\Phi, \Pi] \equiv \int \Pi \dot{\Phi}\,\mathrm{d}\mathbf{r} - L,$$

or again

$$H = \int \mathscr{H}\,\mathrm{d}\mathbf{r}$$

$$\mathscr{H} \equiv \mathscr{H}\left(\Phi, \frac{\partial \Phi}{\partial x^k}, \Pi\right) = \Pi\dot{\Phi} - \mathscr{L}. \tag{XXI.26}$$

$\mathscr{H}$ is called the Hamiltonian density. Hamilton's canonical equations are given by [cf. eq. (I.14)]:

$$\begin{aligned} \dot{\Phi} &= \frac{\partial \mathscr{H}}{\partial \Pi} \\ \dot{\Pi} &= -\frac{\partial \mathscr{H}}{\partial \Phi} + \sum_k \frac{\partial}{\partial x^k} \frac{\partial \mathscr{H}}{\partial(\partial \Phi / \partial x^k)}. \end{aligned} \tag{XXI.27}$$

In the case of the free scalar field, the function

$$\begin{aligned} \mathscr{L} &= \tfrac{1}{2} \left[(\partial_\mu \Phi)(\partial^\mu \Phi) - \mu^2 \Phi^2 \right] \\ &= \tfrac{1}{2} \left[\dot{\Phi}^2 - (\nabla \Phi)^2 - \mu^2 \Phi^2 \right] \end{aligned} \tag{XXI.28}$$

can be taken as the Lagrangian density since substitution of this expression in equation (XXI.24) gives equation (XXI.1).

In this case the momentum conjugate to Φ is:

$$\Pi = \dot{\Phi}. \tag{XXI.29}$$

Applying definition (XXI.26), one obtains for the Hamiltonian function:

$$H = \tfrac{1}{2} \int (\Pi^2 + (\text{grad } \Phi)^2 + \mu^2 \Phi^2) \, \mathrm{d}\mathbf{r}. \tag{XXI.30}$$

The function H defined above is the same as the one given in terms of the normal coordinates by equation (XXI.10). To show this, we need only to replace Φ and Π by their expansions in terms of the q_i and the p_i, and to make use of the properties of the f. The expansion of Φ is given by equation (XXI.5). As for Π, from (XXI.25) one obtains:

$$\begin{aligned} \Pi(\mathbf{r}, t) \, \mathrm{d}\mathbf{r} &= \frac{\delta L}{\delta \dot{\Phi}(\mathbf{r}, t)} \\ &= \sum_i \frac{\partial L}{\partial \dot{q}_i} \frac{\delta \dot{q}_i}{\delta \dot{\Phi}(\mathbf{r}, t)} \end{aligned}$$

and, since by definition $p_i = \partial L / \partial \dot{q}_i$ and since, according to equation (XXI.6)

$$\dot{q}_i = \int f_i(\mathbf{r}) \, \dot{\Phi}(\mathbf{r}, t) \, \mathrm{d}\mathbf{r},$$

from which

$$\frac{\delta \dot{q}_i}{\delta \dot{\Phi}(\mathbf{r}, t)} = f_i(\mathbf{r}) \, \mathrm{d}\mathbf{r},$$

we have:

$$\Pi(\mathbf{r}, t) = \sum_i p_i f_i(\mathbf{r}). \tag{XXI.31}$$

The substitutions mentioned above therefore give:

$$H = \tfrac{1}{2} \sum_i \sum_j [p_i p_j \int f_i f_j \, \mathrm{d}\mathbf{r} + q_i q_j \int (\nabla f_i \cdot \nabla f_j) \, \mathrm{d}\mathbf{r} + \mu^2 q_i q_j \int f_i f_j \, \mathrm{d}\mathbf{r}]. \qquad \text{(XXI.32)}$$

Integrating by parts and applying equation (XXI.2), we obtain

$$\int (\nabla f_i \cdot \nabla f_j) \, \mathrm{d}\mathbf{r} = - \int f_i \triangle f_j \, \mathrm{d}\mathbf{r} = k_i^2 \int f_i f_j \, \mathrm{d}\mathbf{r}.$$

Substituting this last expression into the right-hand side of (XXI.32) and using the orthogonality relations for the f [eq. (XXI.3)] and the definition of ω_i [eq. (XXI.8)] we finally obtain the stated result:

$$H = \tfrac{1}{2} \sum_i (p_i^2 + \omega_i^2 \, q_i^2).$$

[Recall that this expression differs from expression (XXI.20) by an infinite constant.]

In order to quantize the field, it makes no difference whether we take the q_i and the p_i, the b_i and the $b_i^\dagger$ or the $\Phi(\mathbf{r})$ and the $\Pi(\mathbf{r})$ as our fundamental variables. The commutation relations for the Φ and the Π have a particularly simple form. They can be obtained from the commutation relations for the b and the $b^\dagger$. Equations (XXI.13) give:

$$p_i = \tfrac{1}{2} \mathrm{i} \sqrt{2\omega_i} (b_i^\dagger - b_i).$$

Substituting this expression in expansion (XXI.31), one finds

$$\Pi(\mathbf{r}) = \sum_i \tfrac{1}{2} \mathrm{i} \sqrt{2\omega_i} \, (b_i^\dagger - b_i) f_i. \qquad \text{(XXI.33)}$$

The commutation relations are obtained by using expansions (XXI.18) and (XXI.33), the commutation relations of the b and the $b^\dagger$ and the closure relation (XXI.4). One obtains

$$\begin{aligned} [\Phi(\mathbf{r}), \Phi(\mathbf{r}')] &= [\Pi(\mathbf{r}), \Pi(\mathbf{r}')] = 0 \\ [\Phi(\mathbf{r}), \Pi(\mathbf{r}')] &= \mathrm{i}\delta(\mathbf{r} - \mathbf{r}'). \end{aligned} \qquad \text{(XXI.34)}$$

5. Complex Basis Functions

We have seen in the preceding paragraph how the field can be quantized without having to make use of the normal coordinates. Nevertheless, the use of normal coordinates usually simplifies the calculations and also the interpretation of the theory of the quantized field. Since the eigenvalues of $(-\triangle)$ are degenerate, there is a large arbitrary in the choice of the basis functions and normal coordinates.

Furthermore, it is possible, by making a very simple generalization, to quantize the field with the aid of complex basis functions. In this paragraph, we shall first give an account of this more general method of quantization, and then show that the quantized field obtained is independent of the choice of the basis functions.

Denote by $u_1, u_2, \ldots, u_s, \ldots$ a complete orthonormal set of basis functions and by ω_s the corresponding energy. Thus [cf. eq. (XXI.2–4) and (XXI.8)],

$$\int u_s^* \, u_t \, \mathrm{d}\mathbf{r} = \delta_{st} \qquad \sum_s u_s(\mathbf{r}) \, u_s^*(\mathbf{r}') = \delta(\mathbf{r}-\mathbf{r}') \tag{XXI.35}$$

$$(\triangle + k_s^2) u_s = 0 \tag{XXI.36}$$

$$\omega_s = (k_s^2 + \mu^2)^{\frac{1}{2}}. \tag{XXI.37}$$

To each mode u_s there are associated two Hermitean conjugate operators a_s and $a_s^\dagger$. These operators obey the commutation rules [cf. eq. (XXI.14)]:

$$\begin{aligned} [a_s, a_t] &= [a_s^\dagger, a_t^\dagger] = 0, \\ [a_s, a_t^\dagger] &= \delta_{st}, \end{aligned} \tag{XXI.38}$$

which permit the construction of the space of the dynamical states of the system. A quantized harmonic oscillator is thus associated with each mode u_s. a_s and $a_s^\dagger$ are to be interpreted respectively as annihilation and creation operators of a corpuscle in the state u_s. The observables of the system are functions of the annihilation and creation operators. In particular, the observable

$$N_s \equiv a_s^\dagger a_s$$

represents the number of corpuscles in the state u_s. The field $\Phi(\mathbf{r})$ is given by the expansion [cf. eq. (XXI.18)]:

$$\Phi(\mathbf{r}) = \sum_s (2\omega_s)^{-\frac{1}{2}} \, (a_s \, u_s(\mathbf{r}) + a_s^\dagger \, u_s^*(\mathbf{r})), \tag{XXI.39}$$

the conjugate momentum, $\Pi(\mathbf{r})$, by the expansion [cf. eq. (XXI.33)]:

$$\Pi(\mathbf{r}) = \sum_s \tfrac{1}{2} \, \mathrm{i}(2\omega_s)^{+\frac{1}{2}} \, (a_s^\dagger \, u_s^*(\mathbf{r}) - a_s \, u_s(\mathbf{r})), \tag{XXI.40}$$

and the Hamiltonian H governing the evolution of the system by [cf. eq. (XXI.20)]

$$H = \sum_s a_s^\dagger \, a_s \, \omega_s. \tag{XXI.41}$$

We shall now establish the relation between the a and $a^\dagger$ and the operators b and $b^\dagger$ of § 3 and show that the system defined here is indeed the same as the quantum system defined in § 3.

We have used s to denote the set of quantum numbers that distinguish between the u functions. By convention, this set contains a quantum number that determines the energy and a set σ of additional quantum numbers that distinguish between functions corresponding to the same value of the energy; we shall use the wave number k to label the energy:

$$\omega = (k^2+\mu^2)^{\frac{1}{2}}. \tag{XXI.42}$$

Thus: $s \equiv (k, \sigma)$.

Similarly the set i of quantum numbers distinguishing between the f functions contains the wave number k fixing the energy and also a certain set ϱ of additional quantum numbers: $i \equiv (k, \varrho)$.

We pass from the $f_{k\varrho}$ functions corresponding to a given value of k to the $u_{k\sigma}$ functions corresponding to the same value of k by a unitary transformation:

$$u_{k\sigma} = \sum_{\varrho} T_{\sigma\varrho}\, f_{k\varrho}, \qquad f_{k\varrho} = \sum_{\sigma} (T^\dagger)_{\varrho\sigma}\, u_{k\sigma} \tag{XXI.43}$$

$$(T \equiv \text{unitary matrix}).$$

All of the quantities appearing in what follows will relate to a well-defined value of k and we shall henceforth drop the index k.

A necessary and sufficient condition for expansions (XXI.18) and (XXI.39) to represent the same operator $\Phi(\boldsymbol{r})$, and for expansions (XXI.33) and (XXI.40) to represent the same operator $\Pi(\boldsymbol{r})$, is that for any value of k:

$$\sum_{\sigma} a_\sigma u_\sigma = \sum_{\varrho} b_\varrho f_\varrho .$$

Taking into account the second of relations (XXI.43), this is equivalent to writing

$$a_\sigma = \sum_{\varrho} T^*_{\sigma\varrho}\, b_\varrho \tag{XXI.44}$$

or:

$$a_\sigma^\dagger = \sum_{\varrho} T_{\sigma\varrho}\, b_\varrho^\dagger. \tag{XXI.44†}$$

Thus we have established the correspondence between the a and the b on the one hand, and the $a^\dagger$ and the $b^\dagger$ on the other. This correspondence is linear. More precisely, the linear correspondence between the creation operators $b^\dagger$ and $a^\dagger$ [relation (XXI.44†)] is identical with the linear correspondence between the f and the u [eq. (XXI.43)].

It results from relations (XXI.44) and (XXI.44†) that expansions (XXI.18) and (XXI.39) represent the same field $\Phi(\boldsymbol{r})$. In order that the two methods of quantizing this field be equivalent, it is necessary that the a and the $a^\dagger$ thus defined obey commutation relations (XXI.38), and that the Hamiltonian H defined by equation (XXI.20) be expressed in term of these operators by expansion (XXI.41). These two results can easily be proved using the unitarity of the T matrix. From this latter property we have that for each value of k:

$$\begin{aligned}[a_\sigma, a_{\sigma'}^\dagger] &= \sum_{\varrho\varrho'} T_{\sigma\varrho}^* T_{\sigma'\varrho'} [b_\varrho, b_{\varrho'}^\dagger] \\ &= \sum_{\varrho\varrho'} T_{\sigma\varrho}^* T_{\sigma'\varrho'} \delta_{\varrho\varrho'} = \delta_{\sigma\sigma'},\end{aligned}$$

from which:

$$[a_s, a_{s'}^\dagger] = \delta_{ss'}.$$

Similarly for each value of k:

$$\begin{aligned}\sum_\sigma a_\sigma^\dagger a_\sigma &= \sum_{\varrho\varrho'} \sum_\sigma T_{\sigma\varrho} T_{\sigma\varrho'}^* b_\varrho^\dagger b_{\varrho'} \\ &= \sum_{\varrho\varrho'} \delta_{\varrho\varrho'} b_\varrho^\dagger b_{\varrho'} = \sum_\varrho b_\varrho^\dagger b_\varrho,\end{aligned}$$

from which we obtain the desired expression for H.

6. Plane Waves. Definition of the Momentum

Among the different sets of complex basis functions one has notably the plane waves. They correspond, as will be shown below, to individual states of well-defined momentum.

In order to introduce discrete indices, we shall suppose the field enclosed in a cube of side L, and require the functions u_s to be periodic at the edges of the cube, i.e.:

$$u_s(\tfrac{1}{2}L, y, z) = u_s(-\tfrac{1}{2}L, y, z)$$

with two similar equations for the arguments y and z. These conditions are a simple generalization of the periodicity condition described in § V.11.

As basis functions we may then take the plane waves:

$$u_{\boldsymbol{k}} = L^{-3/2} e^{i\boldsymbol{k}\cdot\boldsymbol{r}} \qquad \text{(XXI.45)}$$

whose wave vector has components that are multiples of $2\pi/L$:

$$k_x = \frac{2\pi n_x}{L}, \qquad k_y = \frac{2\pi n_y}{L}, \qquad k_z = \frac{2\pi n_z}{L}.$$

A complete orthonormal system of basis functions is obtained by giving each of the numbers n_x, n_y, n_z all possible integral values:

$$n_x, n_y, n_z = 0, \pm 1, \pm 2, \pm 3, \ldots.$$

With each of these plane waves, we associate an annihilation operator $a_{\boldsymbol{k}}$ and a creation operator $a_{\boldsymbol{k}}^\dagger$. The field $\Phi(\boldsymbol{r})$ is represented by the expansion [cf. eq. (XXI.39)]:

$$\Phi(\boldsymbol{r}) = \sum_{\boldsymbol{k}} (2\omega_{\boldsymbol{k}} L^3)^{-\frac{1}{2}} (a_{\boldsymbol{k}}\, \mathrm{e}^{\mathrm{i}\boldsymbol{k}\cdot\boldsymbol{r}} + a_{\boldsymbol{k}}^\dagger\, \mathrm{e}^{-\mathrm{i}\boldsymbol{k}\cdot\boldsymbol{r}}) \qquad \text{(XXI.46)}$$

its conjugate moment [cf. eq. (XXI.40)] by:

$$\Pi(\boldsymbol{r}) = \sum_{\boldsymbol{k}} \mathrm{i}\left(\frac{\omega_{\boldsymbol{k}}}{2L^3}\right)^{\frac{1}{2}} (a_{\boldsymbol{k}}^\dagger\, \mathrm{e}^{-\mathrm{i}\boldsymbol{k}\cdot\boldsymbol{r}} - a_{\boldsymbol{k}}\, \mathrm{e}^{\mathrm{i}\boldsymbol{k}\cdot\boldsymbol{r}}) \qquad \text{(XXI.47)}$$

and the Hamiltonian [cf. eq. (XXI.41)] by:

$$H = \sum_{\boldsymbol{k}} (a_{\boldsymbol{k}}^\dagger a_{\boldsymbol{k}})\, \omega_{\boldsymbol{k}}, \qquad \text{(XXI.48)}$$

the sums being extended over all possible values of k i.e., over all possible values of n_x, n_y, n_z.

As was explained in § V.11, the correct results are obtained by letting L increase indefinitely. In this limit the summations are replaced by integrations. In a small band $(\boldsymbol{k}, \boldsymbol{k}+\delta\boldsymbol{k})$, there are $(L/2\pi)^3\, \delta\boldsymbol{k}$ possible sets of values for the three numbers n_x, n_y, n_z. If we assume – in the spirit of the passage to the limit $L \to \infty$ – that the terms over which we sum may be treated as continuous functions of $\boldsymbol{k}$, each symbol $\sum$ may be replaced by the symbol

$$\int \left(\frac{L}{2\pi}\right)^3 \mathrm{d}\boldsymbol{k}.$$

$(L/2\pi)^3$ is the density of individual states in wave vector space. One commonly reserves the term *level density* for the number of individual states per unit solid angle and per unit energy; the level density is a certain function $\varrho_L(\omega)$ of the energy. The number $\varrho_L\, \mathrm{d}\Omega\, \mathrm{d}\omega$ of states with wave vector in the solid angle $(\Omega, \Omega+\mathrm{d}\Omega)$, and energy in the band $(\omega, \omega+\mathrm{d}\omega)$ is given by

$$\varrho_L \,\mathrm{d}\Omega\, \mathrm{d}\omega = \left(\frac{L}{2\pi}\right)^3 k^2 \frac{\mathrm{d}k}{\mathrm{d}\omega}\, \mathrm{d}\omega\, \mathrm{d}\Omega$$

$$= \left(\frac{L}{2\pi}\right)^3 \omega k \,\mathrm{d}\omega\, \mathrm{d}\Omega.$$

Therefore,

$$\varrho_L(\omega) = \left(\frac{L}{2\pi}\right)^3 \omega k \qquad \text{(XXI.49)}$$

[cf. eq. (XVII.52)].

In actual fact, it is possible to completely avoid the artifice of the cube, and from the beginning use plane waves extending over all space. The wave vector $\mathbf{k}$ may then take all values without restriction and the waves in question depend on the 3 *continuous indices* k_x, k_y, k_z. Normalization with Kronecker symbols is then replaced by normalization with δ functions.

One then takes as basis functions the functions:

$$u(\mathbf{k}) \equiv u(\mathbf{k};\mathbf{r}) = \frac{\mathrm{e}^{\mathrm{i}\mathbf{k}\cdot\mathbf{r}}}{(2\pi)^{3/2}}$$

and associates with each of them the Hermitean conjugate operators $a(\mathbf{k})$ and $a^\dagger(\mathbf{k})$. The different formulas are obtained from the preceding ones by everywhere replacing $u_\mathbf{k}$ by $(2\pi/L)^{3/2}u(\mathbf{k})$, $a_\mathbf{k}$ by $(2\pi/L)^{3/2}a(\mathbf{k})$ and the symbol $\sum$ by $\int (L/2\pi)^3\, \mathrm{d}\mathbf{k}$. Thus the characteristic properties of the basis functions [cf. eq. (XXI.35–37)] are written:

$$\int u^*(\mathbf{k};\mathbf{r})\, u(\mathbf{k}';\mathbf{r})\, \mathrm{d}\mathbf{r} = \delta(\mathbf{k}-\mathbf{k}') \qquad \int u(\mathbf{k};\mathbf{r})\, u^*(\mathbf{k};\mathbf{r}')\, \mathrm{d}\mathbf{k} = \delta(\mathbf{r}-\mathbf{r}')$$

$$(\triangle + k^2)\, u(\mathbf{k};\mathbf{r}) = 0$$

$$\omega(k) = (k^2+\mu^2)^{\frac{1}{2}}.$$

The commutation relations for the operators a and $a^\dagger$ are [cf. eq. (XXI.38)]:

$$[a(\mathbf{k}), a(\mathbf{k}')] = [a^\dagger(\mathbf{k}), a^\dagger(\mathbf{k}')] = 0$$

$$[a(\mathbf{k}), a^\dagger(\mathbf{k}')] = \delta(\mathbf{k}-\mathbf{k}').$$

The fields $\Phi(\mathbf{r})$ and $\Pi(\mathbf{r})$ are represented by the integrals [cf. eq. (XXI.39) and (XXI.40)]:

$$\Phi(\mathbf{r}) = (2\pi)^{-3/2} \int \frac{\mathrm{d}\mathbf{k}}{\sqrt{2\omega}} \left(a(\mathbf{k})\, \mathrm{e}^{\mathrm{i}\mathbf{k}\cdot\mathbf{r}} + a^\dagger(\mathbf{k})\, \mathrm{e}^{-\mathrm{i}\mathbf{k}\cdot\mathbf{r}}\right)$$

$$\Pi(\mathbf{r}) = (2\pi)^{-3/2}\, \mathrm{i} \int \sqrt{\frac{\omega}{2}}\, \mathrm{d}\mathbf{k} \left(a^\dagger(\mathbf{k})\, \mathrm{e}^{-\mathrm{i}\mathbf{k}\cdot\mathbf{r}} - a(\mathbf{k})\, \mathrm{e}^{\mathrm{i}\mathbf{k}\cdot\mathbf{r}}\right)$$

and the Hamiltonian [cf. eq. (XXI.41)] by:

$$H = \int a^\dagger(\mathbf{k})\, a(\mathbf{k})\, \omega(k)\, \mathrm{d}\mathbf{k}.$$

It remains to establish the relation between the momentum $\mathbf{W}$ of the field and the expansion in plane waves.

By definition the vector operator $\mathbf{W}$ is related to infinitesimal transformations by formula (XV.41). In a finite translation $\mathscr{T}(\mathbf{a})$ (notations of § XV.9), the operator $\Phi(\mathbf{r}_0)$ giving the field amplitude at a given point $\mathbf{r}=\mathbf{r}_0$ is transformed into the operator $\Phi(\mathbf{r}_0+\mathbf{a})$ giving the field amplitude at the point obtained from $\mathbf{r}_0$ in the translation [1]). Similarly $\Pi(\mathbf{r}_0)$ is transformed into $\Pi(\mathbf{r}_0+\mathbf{a})$. Applying this law for the transformation of observables to the case when $\mathbf{a}$ is equal to an infinitesimal vector $\boldsymbol{\epsilon}$, one finds:

$$\begin{aligned} [\boldsymbol{\epsilon}\cdot \mathbf{W}, \Phi(\mathbf{r}_0)] &= \mathrm{i}\boldsymbol{\epsilon}\cdot \nabla\Phi|_{\mathbf{r}=\mathbf{r}_0} \\ [\boldsymbol{\epsilon}\cdot \mathbf{W}, \Pi(\mathbf{r}_0)] &= \mathrm{i}\boldsymbol{\epsilon}\cdot \nabla\Pi|_{\mathbf{r}=\mathbf{r}_0}. \end{aligned} \qquad \text{(XXI.50)}$$

Since these commutation rules must be satisfied for any $\mathbf{r}_0$, they define $\mathbf{W}$ to within a constant additive vector. Thus the component W_x along the x axis is the operator defined to within a constant by the commutation relations

$$[W_x, \Phi(\mathbf{r}_0)] = \mathrm{i}\left.\frac{\partial\Phi}{\partial x}\right|_{\mathbf{r}=\mathbf{r}_0} \qquad \text{(XXI.51)}$$

$$[W_x, \Pi(\mathbf{r}_0)] = \mathrm{i}\left.\frac{\partial\Pi}{\partial x}\right|_{\mathbf{r}=\mathbf{r}_0}. \qquad \text{(XXI.52)}$$

The preceding relations are satisfied if

$$W_x = -\int \Pi\, \frac{\partial\Phi}{\partial x}\, \mathrm{d}\mathbf{r} + Cst. \qquad \text{(XXI.53)}$$

An integration by parts gives the equivalent expression

$$W_x = \int \frac{\partial\Pi}{\partial x}\, \Phi\, \mathrm{d}\mathbf{r} + Cst. \qquad \text{(XXI.54)}$$

Substituting expression (XXI.53) into the left-hand side of equation

[1]) Note the difference with the law for the transformation of the observable x defined in § XV.9 (cf. note, p. 645). Here $\mathbf{r}_0$ is a parameter fixing the point in space where the field amplitude is measured.

(XXI.51) one finds, taking into account commutation relations (XXI.34):

$$\left[-\int \Pi(\mathbf{r})\,\frac{\partial\Phi(\mathbf{r})}{\partial x}\,\mathrm{d}\mathbf{r},\,\Phi(\mathbf{r}_0)\right] = -\int\,[\Pi(\mathbf{r}),\,\Phi(\mathbf{r}_0)]\,\frac{\partial\Phi(\mathbf{r})}{\partial x}\,\mathrm{d}\mathbf{r}$$

$$= \mathrm{i}\int \delta(\mathbf{r}-\mathbf{r}_0)\,\frac{\partial\Phi(\mathbf{r})}{\partial x}\,\mathrm{d}\mathbf{r}$$

$$= \mathrm{i}\,\frac{\partial\Phi}{\partial x}\bigg|_{\mathbf{r}=\mathbf{r}_0}.$$

One similarly shows that relation (XXI.52) is satisfied if we substitute for W_x expression (XXI.54).

Analogous expressions can be written down for W_y and W_z. The three components of $\mathbf{W}$ are thereby obtained to within a constant that is fixed by requiring that $\mathbf{W}$ be a vector operator. We thus find for the momentum of the field the following equivalent expressions:

$$\mathbf{W} = -\int \Pi(\nabla\Phi)\,\mathrm{d}\mathbf{r} \tag{XXI.55}$$

$$= +\int (\nabla\Pi)\,\Phi\,\mathrm{d}\mathbf{r}. \tag{XXI.56}$$

[*N.B.* The classical theory leads to a formally identical definition of the momentum.]

Let us now express $\mathbf{W}$ in terms of the $a_{\mathbf{k}}$ and $a_{\mathbf{k}}^{\dagger}$ operators. To this effect, we substitute for Φ and Π in the right-hand side of equation (XXI.55) their respective expansions [eqs. (XXI.46) and (XXI.47)] and make use of the orthogonality relations for the plane waves. We obtain:

$$\mathbf{W} = \tfrac{1}{2}\sum_{\mathbf{k}} \mathbf{k}(a_{\mathbf{k}}^{\dagger}\,a_{\mathbf{k}} + a_{\mathbf{k}}\,a_{\mathbf{k}}^{\dagger} - a_{\mathbf{k}}\,a_{-\mathbf{k}} - a_{-\mathbf{k}}^{\dagger}\,a_{\mathbf{k}}^{\dagger})$$

or, taking into account the commutation relations for the a and $a^{\dagger}$,

$$\mathbf{W} = \sum_{\mathbf{k}} (a_{\mathbf{k}}^{\dagger}\,a_{\mathbf{k}})\,\mathbf{k} + \tfrac{1}{2}\sum_{\mathbf{k}} \mathbf{k}(1 - a_{-\mathbf{k}}\,a_{\mathbf{k}} - a_{-\mathbf{k}}^{\dagger}\,a_{\mathbf{k}}^{\dagger}).$$

The symbols $\sum_{\mathbf{k}}$ indicate summations over all possible values of $\mathbf{k}$. In the second sum, the expression in parentheses does not change when one changes $\mathbf{k}$ to $-\mathbf{k}$; therefore, the two terms that correspond to a given value of $\mathbf{k}$ and its negative differ by a sign and the second sum vanishes. Thus:

$$\mathbf{W} = \sum_{\mathbf{k}} (a_{\mathbf{k}}^{\dagger}\,a_{\mathbf{k}})\,\mathbf{k}. \tag{XXI.57}$$

From this expression one easily obtains the commutation relations of $\boldsymbol{W}$ with the a and the $a^\dagger$:

$$[\boldsymbol{W}, a_{\boldsymbol{k}}] = -\boldsymbol{k} a_{\boldsymbol{k}} \tag{XXI.58}$$

$$[\boldsymbol{W}, a_{\boldsymbol{k}}^\dagger] = +\boldsymbol{k} a_{\boldsymbol{k}}^\dagger. \tag{XXI.59}$$

Expressions (XXI.57–59) have a simple interpretation if we postulate that a corpuscle in state $u_{\boldsymbol{k}}$ has momentum $\boldsymbol{k}$. Since $(a_{\boldsymbol{k}}^\dagger a_{\boldsymbol{k}})$ is the number of corpuscles in the state $u_{\boldsymbol{k}}$, formula (XXI.57) means simply that the total momentum $\boldsymbol{W}$ of the field is equal to the sum of the momenta of each of its constituent corpuscles. Similarly, relations (XXI.58) and (XXI.59) are consistent with the interpretation of $a_{\boldsymbol{k}}$ and $a_{\boldsymbol{k}}^\dagger$ respectively as operators of annihilation and creation of a corpuscle of momentum $\boldsymbol{k}$. Indeed if $|\boldsymbol{w}\rangle$ is an eigenvector of the total momentum corresponding to the eigenvalue $\boldsymbol{w}$; then from equation (XXI.58) the vector $a_{\boldsymbol{k}}|\boldsymbol{w}\rangle$ (if it is not a null vector, that is, if the field contains at least one corpuscle of momentum $\boldsymbol{k}$) satisfies the eigenvalue equation:

$$\begin{aligned}\boldsymbol{W} a_{\boldsymbol{k}} |\boldsymbol{w}\rangle &= a_{\boldsymbol{k}}(\boldsymbol{W}-\boldsymbol{k}) |\boldsymbol{w}\rangle = a_{\boldsymbol{k}}(\boldsymbol{w}-\boldsymbol{k}) |\boldsymbol{w}\rangle \\ &= (\boldsymbol{w}-\boldsymbol{k}) a_{\boldsymbol{k}} |\boldsymbol{w}\rangle.\end{aligned}$$

In the same way we obtain from equation (XXI.59):

$$\boldsymbol{W} a_{\boldsymbol{k}}^\dagger |\boldsymbol{w}\rangle = (\boldsymbol{w}+\boldsymbol{k}) a_{\boldsymbol{k}}^\dagger |\boldsymbol{w}\rangle.$$

It will be noted that the corpuscles of momentum $\boldsymbol{k}$ contained in the field have an energy $\omega = (k^2+\mu^2)$. *They are therefore corpuscles of mass* μ.

7. Spherical Waves. Definition of the Angular Momentum

The plane waves are the basis functions most often used. However, one can just as well use spherical waves. The basis functions are then of the form

$$u_{klm} \equiv Cst.\ j_l(kr)\, Y_l^m(\theta, \varphi) \tag{XXI.60}$$

and depend on the continuous index k and the two discrete indices l and m. In order to have only discrete indices, we can enclose the field in a sphere of radius R and require that the basis functions vanish at the surface; the correct results are obtained by letting R become indefinitely large.

The entire analysis of the preceding paragraph can be repeated with these new basis functions. One thus introduces the annihilation and creation operators a_{klm} and $a^{\dagger}_{klm}$ of a corpuscle in the state represented by the spherical wave u_{klm}. It can be shown that the spherical waves are related to individual states of well-defined angular momentum just as the plane waves are related to individual states of well-defined momentum. For the total angular momentum $\mathbf{l}$ of the field, one obtains the expression:

$$\mathbf{l} = -\int \Pi(\mathbf{l}\Phi)\,\mathrm{d}\mathbf{r} \tag{XXI.61}$$

$\mathbf{l}$ here represents the operator $-\mathrm{i}(\mathbf{r}\times\nabla)$ and acts on the function Φ to its right:

$$\mathbf{l}\Phi = -\mathrm{i}\mathbf{r}\times(\nabla\Phi).$$

We can also use the equivalent expression:

$$\mathbf{l} = \int (\mathbf{l}\Pi)\,\Phi\,\mathrm{d}\mathbf{r}.$$

The a_{klm} and $a^{\dagger}_{klm}$ are respectively interpreted as annihilation and creation operators of a corpuscle of energy $\omega=(k^2+\mu^2)^{\frac{1}{2}}$ and of angular momentum (lm). In addition the $(2l+1)$ operators $a^{\dagger}_{klm}$ corresponding to a given value of l and of k are the standard components of an irreducible tensor operator of order l; the $(2l+1)$ operators a_{klm} are, except for order and sign, the standard components of the Hermitean conjugate tensor operator (definition of § XIII.30).

8. Space and Time Reflections

Among the transformations which leave the equations of motion invariant one also has the space and time reflections. Each of these is completely defined by giving the law for the transformation of the field $\Phi(\mathbf{r})$ and its conjugate momentum $\Pi(\mathbf{r})$; the corresponding (unitary or antiunitary) transformation operator is then determined up to a phase.

In the case of the *space reflection*, the law in question is

$$\Phi(\mathbf{r}) \rightarrow \Phi(-\mathbf{r}), \qquad \Pi(\mathbf{r}) \rightarrow \Pi(-\mathbf{r}). \tag{I}$$

This law is characteristic of the scalar field. The operator S_0 corresponding to this transformation is *unitary* (the commutation relations for the fields are therefore conserved in the transformation). Since all of the operators of the theory are functions of Φ and Π, it is easy to deduce from (I) their law of transformation in the space reflection. In particular, for the a and $a^{\dagger}$ operators associated with the plane waves, one finds, in accordance with the interpretation given to these operators:

$$S_0 a_{\boldsymbol{k}} S_0^{\dagger} = a_{-\boldsymbol{k}} \qquad \text{(II)}$$
$$S_0 a_{\boldsymbol{k}}^{\dagger} S_0^{\dagger} = a_{-\boldsymbol{k}}^{\dagger}.$$

In the case of *time reversal*, the field Φ is conserved and its velocity changes sign, the law is therefore:

$$\Phi(\boldsymbol{r}) \rightarrow \Phi(\boldsymbol{r}), \qquad \Pi(\boldsymbol{r}) \rightarrow -\Pi(\boldsymbol{r}). \qquad \text{(I')}$$

The operator K corresponding to this transformation is *antiunitary*, since the commutation relations for the fields change sign in the transformation. The law for the transformation of the a and $a^{\dagger}$ operators associated with the plane waves can be obtained without difficulty from (I′); one obtains, in accordance with the interpretation given to these operators:

$$K a_{\boldsymbol{k}} K^{\dagger} = a_{-\boldsymbol{k}} \qquad \text{(II')}$$
$$K a_{\boldsymbol{k}}^{\dagger} K^{\dagger} = a_{-\boldsymbol{k}}^{\dagger}.$$

These creation and absorption operators therefore transform in an identical way in space reflection and time reversal. One must take care, however, not to confuse these two transformations the one of which is unitary, the other antiunitary.

Relations (I) or (II) and relations (I′) or (II′) respectively define S_0 and K to within a phase. To remove the arbitrary in the phase, we shall require the vector $|0\rangle$ to be invariant in each of these transformations:

$$S_0 |0\rangle = |0\rangle, \qquad K |0\rangle = |0\rangle.$$

II. COUPLING WITH AN ATOMIC SYSTEM

9. Coupling to a System of Particles

We now consider the field in interaction with a particle. Most of what follows would not be modified if this single particle were replaced by a system of several particles.

The dynamical variables of the whole system, particle+field, are functions of the fundamental variables of each subsystem. For the particle, which we assume spinless for simplicity, we shall take as fundamental variables its position vector $\boldsymbol{R}$ and its momentum $\boldsymbol{P}$. For the fundamental variables of the field, we may take $\Phi(\boldsymbol{r})$ and $\Pi(\boldsymbol{r})$ or we may take a complete set of creation and annihilation operators like those defined in the preceding paragraph; in what follows we shall often use the operators $a_{\mathbf{k}}$ and $a_{\mathbf{k}}^{\dagger}$ associated with the decomposition into plane waves (cf. § 6).

The states of the whole system span a space that is the product of the space $\mathscr{E}_{\text{part}}$ of the states of the particle alone and the space $\mathscr{E}_{\text{field}}$ of the states of the free field:

$$\mathscr{E} = \mathscr{E}_{\text{part}} \otimes \mathscr{E}_{\text{field}}$$

The Hamiltonian H of the total system is the sum of the three terms

$$H = H_{\text{part}} + H_{\text{field}} + H'. \tag{XXI.62}$$

The first two terms are those which would govern the evolution of each of the two subsystems if they were completely decoupled, the last represents the interaction energy.

Thus H_{field} is the Hamiltonian for the free field; several equivalent expressions have been given above; we note in particular equation (XXI.48). H_{part} is the Hamiltonian which would govern the evolution of the particle in the absence of the field Φ. Let us suppose that the particle in question is placed in a potential and denote its mass by M. We assume that

$$M \gg \mu$$

and that the motion of the particles may be treated in the non-relativistic approximation, i.e.:

$$H_{\text{part}} = \frac{\mathbf{P}^2}{2M} + V(R). \tag{XXI.63}$$

It remains to define H'. The simplest possible expression for H' is obtained by assuming the interaction proportional to the value taken by the field amplitude at the position of the particle $\mathbf{R}$:

$$H' = g\Phi(\mathbf{R}) \tag{XXI.64}$$

$$= gL^{-3/2} \sum_{\mathbf{k}} \frac{1}{\sqrt{2\omega_{\mathbf{k}}}} (a_{\mathbf{k}}\, \mathrm{e}^{i\mathbf{k}\cdot\mathbf{R}} + a_{\mathbf{k}}^{\dagger}\, \mathrm{e}^{-i\mathbf{k}\cdot\mathbf{R}}). \tag{XXI.64'}$$

g is a dimensionless constant called the *coupling constant*. The second expression for H' is obtained from the first by using expansion (XXI.46).

This particular form of the interaction is almost uniquely determined by considerations of relativistic invariance. However, the theory to be investigated here contains from the start a non-relativistic approximation. This is implied not only because the term H_{part} lacks the covariant properties required by the relativity principle, but also because the very concept of a material system of a single particle – and more generally that of a system made up of a definite number of particles – ceases to be justified in Relativistic Quantum Mechanics. These two limitations of the theory must be kept in mind in choosing H'. The study made in Chapter XX of the non-relativistic approximation of the Dirac equation can here be used as a guide. It suggests that the interaction between a non-relativistic particle of mass M and a field is not a local interaction like that given by equation (XXI.64) but an interaction involving the values taken by the field in a domain of extension $1/M$ about the position of the particle. This suggests that we replace expression (XXI.54) for H' by the expression:

$$H' = g \int \Phi(\mathbf{r})\, \varrho(|\mathbf{r}-\mathbf{R}|)\, \mathrm{d}\mathbf{r}, \tag{XXI.65}$$

where $\varrho(\mathbf{r}) \equiv \varrho(r)$ is a real, spherically symmetrical function obeying the normalization condition

$$\int \varrho(\mathbf{r})\, \mathrm{d}\mathbf{r} \equiv 4\pi \int_0^\infty \varrho(r) r^2\, \mathrm{d}r = 1,$$

and concentrated in a domain of radius $1/M$ about the origin (cf. Fig. XXI.1*a*). We obtain (XXI.64) by substituting $\delta(\mathbf{r}-\mathbf{R})$ for this function in the right-hand side of equation (XXI.65).

We shall give the name of cut-off function to the function $C(k)$ defined by

$$C(k) = \int \mathrm{e}^{+i\mathbf{k}\cdot\mathbf{r}}\, \varrho(\mathbf{r})\, \mathrm{d}\mathbf{r}.$$

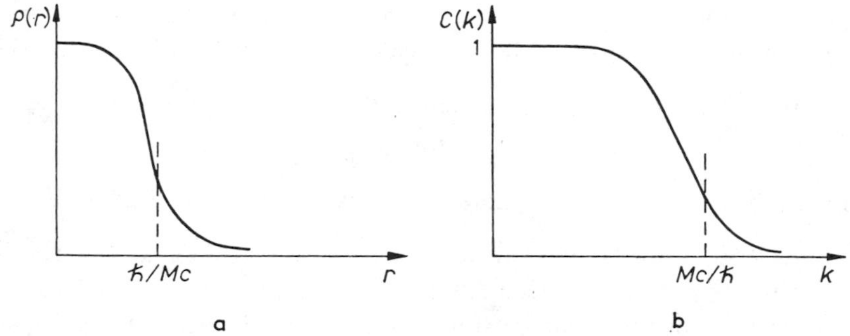

Fig. XXI.1. Form of $\varrho(r)$ and $C(k)$.

It is a real, symmetrical function, obeying the condition

$$C(0)=1,$$

and, according to well-known properties of Fourier transforms, concentrated in a domain of radius M about the point $k=0$ (cf. Fig. XXI.1*b*). Substituting expansion (XXI.46) for $\Phi(\mathbf{r})$ in the right-hand side of equation (XXI.65), one obtains, after a brief calculation:

$$H' = gL^{-3/2} \sum_{\mathbf{k}} \frac{C(k)}{\sqrt{2\omega_{\mathbf{k}}}} (a_{\mathbf{k}}\, e^{i\mathbf{k}\cdot\mathbf{R}} + a_{\mathbf{k}}{}^{\dagger}\, e^{-i\mathbf{k}\cdot\mathbf{R}}). \qquad \text{(XXI.66)}$$

This expansion differs from (XXI.64′) only by the presence of the factor $C(k)$ in each of its terms. This factor cuts off the contribution of high-frequency terms to the interaction, that is, the contribution of terms for which $k \gtrsim M$.

As will now be shown, this suppression of the high frequencies is consistent with the non-relativistic approximation. Each term of expansion (XXI.66) corresponds to a given momentum and energy transfer from the particle to the field and *vice versa*; the term $a_{\mathbf{k}} e^{i\mathbf{k}\cdot\mathbf{R}}$ absorbs a field corpuscle of momentum $\mathbf{k}$ and energy $\omega_{\mathbf{k}}$ and transfers this momentum and energy from the field to the particle; the term $a_{\mathbf{k}}{}^{\dagger} e^{-i\mathbf{k}\cdot\mathbf{R}}$ creates a field corpuscle of momentum $\mathbf{k}$ and energy $\omega_{\mathbf{k}}$, diminishing by as much the momentum and energy of the particle. When $k \gtrsim M$, the transfers are sufficiently large that the law of conservation of the number of particles of mass M can be violated and the field can absorb the particle or create a second particle of mass M. The non-relativistic approximation is therefore only justified if the contribution from the high-frequency terms is negligible, and the results that it gives, if they are correct, must not be modified by the introduction of $C(k)$. *A fortiori*, they must be insensitive to the form of $C(k)$. In the following calculations we shall suppose that

$$C(k) = \begin{cases} 1 & \text{for} \quad 0 \leqslant k \leqslant K \\ 0 & \text{for} \quad k > K \end{cases} \qquad \text{(XXI.67)}$$

and shall give to the parameter K a value of the order of M.

Finally, let us examine the invariance properties of H. Clearly H', as defined by equation (XXI.65), is invariant with respect to any displacement of the whole system (field + particle) since it may easily be shown that it commutes with the total momentum $\mathbf{P}+\mathbf{W}$ and with the total angular momentum $(\mathbf{R}\times\mathbf{P})+\mathbf{l}$ of the system. H' is also invariant under reflection if $\Phi(\mathbf{r})$ transforms into $\Phi(-\mathbf{r})$ in that operation (scalar field). H_{field} also has all of these invariance properties. If $V(R)=0$ the same is true of H_{part}, and therefore of H. If $V(R)\neq 0$, H_{part} is only invariant with respect to rotations and reflections; H is then also invariant under rotation and reflection, but not under translation.

The interest of the quantum system considered here is due to the fact that it exhibits in a simplified form the essential properties of an atom in interaction with the field of electromagnetic radiation; the particle here plays the part of the atom, the scalar field that of the electromagnetic radiation. The main difference is that the corpuscles of the electromagnetic field, the photons, have mass zero and spin 1, while the corpuscles of the field studied here have spin zero and a non-zero mass. In the rest of this section this simplified model will be used to study some of the typical properties of the atom in the presence of the electromagnetic field.

10. Weak Coupling and Perturbation Treatment

For g sufficiently small, H' may be treated as a small perturbation and the methods of Chapters XVI and XVII applied.

The unperturbed Hamiltonian is:

$$H_0 \equiv H_{\text{field}} + H_{\text{part}}.$$

In perturbation theory one employs a representation in which H_0 is diagonal. We shall adopt the representation whose basis vectors are obtained in the following way. Denote by $|\alpha\rangle, |\beta\rangle, \ldots |\lambda\rangle \ldots$ a complete orthonormal set of eigenvectors of H_{part} considered as an operator in $\mathscr{E}_{\text{part}}$, and by $E_\alpha, E_\beta, \ldots, E_\lambda, \ldots$ the corresponding eigenenergies (arranged in increasing order). By multiplying a given vector $|\lambda\rangle$ of this set by the vector $|0\rangle$ representing the corpuscular vacuum in $\mathscr{E}_{\text{field}}$, one obtains a vector of $\mathscr{E}$, which to simplify the writing will also be denoted by $|\lambda\rangle$. It is clear that:

$$H_0\,|\lambda\rangle = E_\lambda\,|\lambda\rangle.$$

A complete orthonormal set of eigenvectors of H_{field} in $\mathscr{E}_{\text{field}}$ can be obtained by repeated action of the creation operators $a_{\mathbf{k}}^\dagger$ on the vector $|0\rangle$ [cf. eq. (XXI.16)]. In the same way a complete orthonormal set of eigenvectors of H_0 in $\mathscr{E}$ can be obtained by repeated action of the creation operators $a_{\mathbf{k}}^\dagger$ on each of the vectors $|\alpha\rangle, |\beta\rangle, \ldots, |\lambda\rangle, \ldots$ defined above. This will be taken as the required basis. Denote by $|n\rangle$ a typical one of these basis vectors and by E_n the corresponding eigenenergy:

$$H_0 \, |n\rangle = E_n \, |n\rangle.$$

In the dynamical state $|n\rangle$, the particle is in a given eigenstate of H_{part} and the field contains a given number of corpuscles of well-defined momentum.

In practice, only the vectors corresponding to a very limited number of corpuscles will be involved in what follows; they can be labelled by the Greek letter indicating the dynamical state of the particle, and the wave vectors for each of the corpuscles in the field. With this notation $|\lambda\mathbf{k}\rangle$ represents the state obtained by associating a corpuscle of momentum $\mathbf{k}$ with the particle in the state λ, $|\lambda\mathbf{k}\mathbf{k}'\rangle$ the state obtained by associating the two corpuscles of momentum $\mathbf{k}$ and $\mathbf{k}'$ respectively with a particle in the state λ, etc. Note that:

$$\begin{aligned} H_0 \, |\lambda\mathbf{k}\rangle &= (E_\lambda + \omega_k) \, |\lambda\mathbf{k}\rangle \\ H_0 \, |\lambda\mathbf{k}\mathbf{k}'\rangle &= (E_\lambda + \omega_k + \omega_{k'}) \, |\lambda\mathbf{k}\mathbf{k}'\rangle. \end{aligned} \qquad \text{(XXI.68)}$$

Also

$$|\lambda\mathbf{k}\rangle = a_{\mathbf{k}}^\dagger \, |\lambda\rangle$$

and if $\mathbf{k} \neq \mathbf{k}'$,

$$|\lambda\mathbf{k}\mathbf{k}'\rangle = a_{\mathbf{k}}^\dagger a_{\mathbf{k}'}^\dagger \, |\lambda\rangle.$$

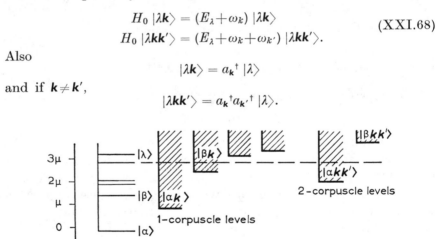

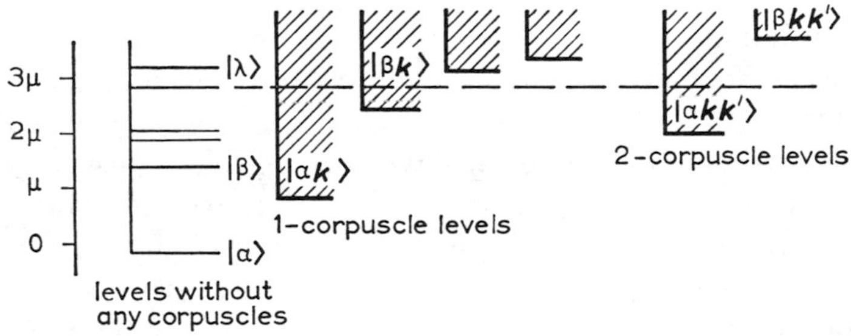

Fig. XXI.2. Typical diagram of the first levels of H_0.

A typical spectroscopic diagram giving the lowest levels of the Hamiltonian H_0 is shown in Figure XXI.2. Following the usual convention for this type of diagram (cf. Fig. XI.1, XII.1, etc.), the height of the levels above the ground state is equal to the difference between their energy and that of the ground state; levels of the same energy are consequently at the same height. The levels in the figure are classified according to the nature of the corresponding eigenstates. In the left-hand column will be found the levels of states without any corpuscle. Next come the states with a single corpuscle, in several columns each of which corresponds to a given quantum state of the particle. The first corresponds to levels $|\alpha \mathbf{k}\rangle$, where the particle is in the ground state; it is a continuous band (in the limit when $L \to \infty$), starting from a minimum corresponding to the existence of a single corpuscle of zero momentum, and consequently situated at a distance μ above the level $|\alpha\rangle$. The second column corresponds to states $|\beta \mathbf{k}\rangle$ for which the particle is in its first excited state. And so forth. After the 1-corpuscle levels we have the 2-corpuscle levels, also arranged in a series of columns corresponding each to a well-defined quantum state of the particle. And so forth.

The perturbation H' couples these various levels. In the representation defined above this coupling term is represented by a particularly simple matrix. From (XXI.66) we see that *the only non-vanishing matrix elements of H' are those between basis vectors for which the number of corpuscles differs by one.* These matrix elements may easily be calculated using the properties of the creation and annihilation operators. One finds:

$$\langle\lambda|H'|\nu\mathbf{k}\rangle = \langle\nu\mathbf{k}|H'|\lambda\rangle^* = \left(\frac{2\pi}{L}\right)^{3/2} g\,\frac{C(k)}{\sqrt{2\omega_{\mathbf{k}}}}\,\langle\lambda|U(\mathbf{k})|\nu\rangle \qquad \text{(XXI.69}a\text{)}$$

$$\langle\lambda\mathbf{k}\mathbf{k}'|H'|\nu\mathbf{k}\rangle = \langle\nu\mathbf{k}|H'|\lambda\mathbf{k}\mathbf{k}'\rangle^*$$
$$= \left(\frac{2\pi}{L}\right)^{3/2} g\,\frac{C(k)}{\sqrt{2\omega_k}}\,\langle\lambda|U^\dagger(\mathbf{k}')|\nu\rangle \quad (\mathbf{k}\neq\mathbf{k}'). \qquad \text{(XXI.69}b\text{)}$$

[If $\mathbf{k}=\mathbf{k}'$, a factor $\sqrt{2}$ must be added in the last of these expressions.] Here we have put:

$$U(\mathbf{k}) \equiv \frac{\mathrm{e}^{i\mathbf{k}\cdot\mathbf{R}}}{(2\pi)^{3/2}}. \qquad \text{(XXI.70)}$$

No matter how weak the coupling, it leads to a qualitative modification of the spectrum, since most of the bound states become unstable and can make transitions to states of lower energy with emission of one or several field-corpuscles. For example, consider the state $|\lambda\rangle$ indicated in Fig. XXI.3; it is at the same level as certain states of the continuum, namely the 1-corpuscle states of type $|\alpha\mathbf{k}\rangle$ or $|\beta\mathbf{k}\rangle$ and the 2-corpuscle states of type $|\alpha\mathbf{k}\mathbf{k}'\rangle$. The introduction of the small perturbation H' couples the discrete eigenstates to the 1-corpuscle states, the 1-corpuscle states to the 2-corpuscle states, etc., and therefore makes possible "radiative" transitions from state $|\lambda\rangle$ to states of the continuum situated at the same level; these possible decay modes of the state $|\lambda\rangle$ are schematically shown in Fig. XXI.3. The only bound states that remain stable are those for which the energy above the ground state is too small for the emission of a corpuscle

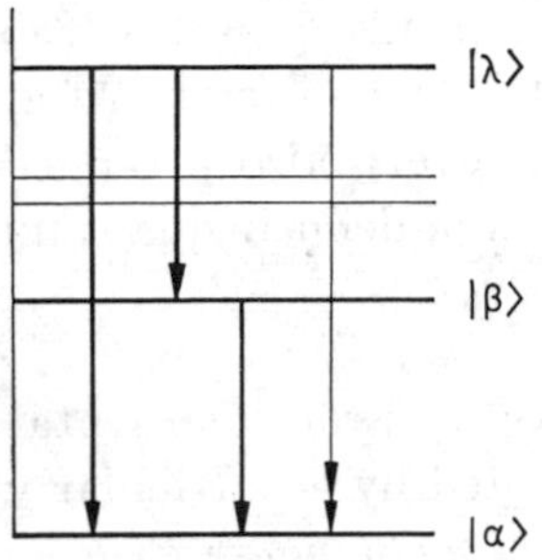

Fig. XXI.3. Radiative transitions from the level $|\lambda\rangle$. The double arrow on the right represents a transition to the ground state with emission of two corpuscles. It is a higher-order transition.

of mass μ to be energetically possible, that is, states whose energy is less than $E_\alpha+\mu$. In the example of Fig. XXI.2 the only stable state is the ground state.

The existence of the coupling term H' also leads to a certain shift of the levels of the bound states. It is, as we shall see, a second-order effect. It may nevertheless affect the stability and the decay modes of the different states of the particle since a small level shift may be enough to make certain "radiative" transitions energetically possible that previously were not, or to have the inverse effect.

11. Level Shifts

As a first application, let us calculate the level shifts mentioned at the end of the preceding paragraph. This simple perturbation calculation exhibits the main difficulties of field theory and provides some insight into the physical significance and the limitations of the theory.

We therefore consider a stable level, the ground state level for example, and we calculate the shift due to the existence of the coupling term H' by applying the method of stationary perturbations. For simplicity, we assume the level in question non-degenerate. Since H' has all the invariance properties of H_{part}, the treatment of degenerate levels is not fundamentally different. To the first order, the shift is given by formula (XVI.12). It follows from the properties of H' given above that:

$$\langle\alpha|H'|\alpha\rangle = 0.$$

The calculations must therefore be taken to the second order. Denoting the second-order correction by δE_α, one has (cf. § XVI.6):

$$\delta E_\alpha = \langle\alpha|H' \frac{1}{E_\alpha - H_0} H'|\alpha\rangle. \qquad \text{(XXI.71)}$$

We calculate this expression in the representation defined above. The only intermediate states involved are those having a single corpuscle. Taking relation (XXI.68), (XXI.69a) and (XXI.70) into account, we successively obtain:

$$\begin{aligned}\delta E_\alpha &= \sum_n \langle\alpha|H'|n\rangle \frac{1}{E_\alpha - E_n} \langle n|H'|\alpha\rangle \\ &= \sum_\nu \sum_{\mathbf{k}} \frac{|\langle\alpha|H'|\nu\mathbf{k}\rangle|^2}{E_\alpha - E_\nu - \omega_k} \\ &= g^2 \left(\frac{2\pi}{L}\right)^3 \sum_\nu \sum_{\mathbf{k}} \frac{C^2(k)}{2\omega_k} \frac{|\langle\alpha|U_{\mathbf{k}}|\nu\rangle|^2}{E_\alpha - E_\nu - \omega_k}\end{aligned}$$

whence, replacing the summation over $\mathbf{k}$ by an integration in accordance with the technique described in § 6, and adopting the cut-off function given by equation (XXI.67):

$$\delta E_\alpha = -g^2 \int_{k \leqslant K} \mathrm{d}\mathbf{k} \sum_\nu \frac{|\langle\alpha|U(\mathbf{k})|\nu\rangle|^2}{2\omega(\omega + E_\nu - E_\alpha)}. \qquad \text{(XXI.72)}$$

Since we are dealing with the ground state, the energy denominator is positive for all of the terms in the sum on the right hand side of (XXI.72). We therefore have:

$$\delta E_\alpha < 0,$$

An upper limit for $|\delta E_\alpha|$ can be obtained by replacing the quantity $(E_\nu - E_\alpha)$ in the denominator by its minimum value, that is, by 0

(E_α is the ground state); the summation over ν is then easily effected using the closure relation: $\sum_\nu |\nu\rangle\langle\nu| = 1$; since $UU^\dagger = (2\pi)^{-3}$, this sum gives $(2\pi)^{-3}/2\omega^2$. We thus obtain, after integration over the angles

$$|\delta E_\alpha| < \frac{g^2}{4\pi^2} \int_0^K \frac{k^2}{\omega^2}\, \mathrm{d}k. \tag{XXI.73}$$

The integral in (XXI.73) can be calculated exactly; since $K \gg \mu$, it is slightly smaller than K. Consequently:

$$|\delta E_\alpha| < \frac{g^2 K}{4\pi^2}. \tag{XXI.74}$$

A better estimate of the right-hand side of (XXI.72) can be obtained in the following manner. If the closure relation is directly applied, one obtains, replacing $U(\mathbf{k})$ by its definition [eq. (XXI.70)]:

$$\delta E_\alpha = -\frac{g^2}{8\pi^3} \int_{k \leqslant K} \langle\alpha|\, \mathrm{e}^{\mathrm{i}\mathbf{k}\cdot\mathbf{R}} (\omega + H_{\text{part}} - E_\alpha)^{-1}\, \mathrm{e}^{-\mathrm{i}\mathbf{k}\cdot\mathbf{R}} |\alpha\rangle \frac{\mathrm{d}\mathbf{k}}{2\omega}. \tag{XXI.75}$$

The unitary operator $\mathrm{e}^{\mathrm{i}\mathbf{k}\cdot\mathbf{R}}$ commutes with $\mathbf{R}$ and transforms $\mathbf{P}$ into $(\mathbf{P}-\mathbf{k})$. It follows that:

$$\mathrm{e}^{\mathrm{i}\mathbf{k}\cdot\mathbf{R}} H_{\text{part}}\, \mathrm{e}^{-\mathrm{i}\mathbf{k}\cdot\mathbf{R}} = \frac{(\mathbf{P}-\mathbf{k})^2}{2M} + V(R) = H_{\text{part}} + \frac{k^2}{2M} - \frac{\mathbf{P}\cdot\mathbf{k}}{M}$$

whence:

$$\mathrm{e}^{\mathrm{i}\mathbf{k}\cdot\mathbf{R}} (\omega + H_{\text{part}} - E_\alpha)^{-1}\, \mathrm{e}^{-\mathrm{i}\mathbf{k}\cdot\mathbf{R}} = \left(\omega + \frac{k^2}{2M} + H_{\text{part}} - E_\alpha - \frac{\mathbf{P}\cdot\mathbf{k}}{M}\right)^{-1}.$$

Substituting this expression into the right-hand side of (XXI.75), we find:

$$\delta E_\alpha = -\frac{g^2}{8\pi^3} \int_{k \leqslant K} \langle\alpha| \left(\omega + \frac{k^2}{2M} + H_{\text{part}} - E_\alpha - \frac{\mathbf{P}\cdot\mathbf{k}}{M}\right)^{-1} |\alpha\rangle \frac{\mathrm{d}\mathbf{k}}{2\omega}.$$

The term $\mathbf{P}\cdot\mathbf{k}/M$ in the bracket on the right-hand side can be neglected since the average value of the velocity $\mathbf{P}/M$ of the particle in the state $|\alpha\rangle$ is much smaller than 1 (non-relativistic approximation). With this approximation we obtain, after integration over the angles:

$$\delta E_\alpha \simeq -\frac{g^2}{4\pi^2} \int_0^K \frac{k^2}{\omega^2} \left(1 + \frac{k^2}{2M\omega}\right)^{-1} \mathrm{d}k, \tag{XXI.76}$$

an expression which differs from the right-hand side of (XXI.73) only by the factor $[1+(k^2/2M\omega)]^{-1}$ in the integrand. Since

$\mu \ll K \approx M$, this factor falls roughly from 1 to $\frac{2}{3}$ over the interval of integration. We may therefore write:

$$\delta E_\alpha = -\frac{sg^2 K}{4\pi^2} \qquad (s \lesssim 1). \tag{XXI.77}$$

The numerical constant s appearing in this formula has a value between $\frac{2}{3}$ and 1.

To estimate the size of the effect, we calculate its order of magnitude in the case when the various quantities in the model have numerical values of the order of those encountered in atoms [1]). M is then the mass of the electron and g^2 the fine-structure constant:

$$g^2 \simeq 10^{-1}. \tag{XXI.78}$$

Denote the distance from the level to its nearest neighbor by D/M:

$$\frac{D}{M} \simeq 10^{-4} - 10^{-5}. \tag{XXI.79}$$

With these figures,

$$|\delta E_\alpha/D| \approx g^2 M/4\pi^2 D \approx 100.$$

It is thus a very large effect, much larger than the shifts actually observed. This might lead one to question the validity of the perturbation treatment and the physical significance of its results.

However, a meaningful comparison between theory and experiment should take into account the following point. The mass M involved in a calculation of the unperturbed levels *is not* the mass that is experimentally observed. The latter is obtained by measuring the energy and the momentum of a "free" particle, that is, of a particle outside the potential $V(R)$. Such a "free" particle is nevertheless coupled to the field and therefore the measurement gives:

$$M_{\text{exp}} = M + \delta M,$$

where δM represents the contribution to the rest energy of the "free"

---

[1]) Since the forms of the couplings are not the same, the numerical results given by the scalar theory cannot be in exact agreement with those given by the Quantum Theory of Radiation. In order to compare comparable quantities, the constant g^2 is fixed so as to give a value for the dipole transition probability of the same order of magnitude as that for the dipole transitions in atoms [cf. eqs. (XXI.81) and (XXI.245)]; namely $g^2/4\pi \approx 1/137$.

particle due to the presence of the field. In the present case, a brief calculation gives

$$\delta M \approx -\frac{g^2 K}{4\pi^2}.$$

More precisely, the calculation of δM to the second order in the perturbation gives the right-hand side of equation (XXI.76) (Problem XXI.2); the shift δE_α is therefore almost entirely due to this "renormalization" of the mass [1]).

When the levels of the hydrogen atom are calculated with the Schrödinger or Dirac theories, one makes use of the experimental mass of the electron; owing to this, one accounts for the main part of the coupling of the electron with the radiation field and this explains why the calculated spectrum is so remarkably in agreement with the observed spectrum.

The "experimentally observed shift" $\delta E_\alpha'$ is the difference between the calculated shift δE_α and the shift $\delta E_\alpha^{(0)}$ obtained by merely replacing the theoretical mass by the experimental mass (also called the "renormalized" mass) in the particle Hamiltonian. In our model, this substitution of the "renormalized" mass consists in replacing H_{part} by

$$\delta M + \frac{\mathbf{P}^2}{2(M+\delta M)} + V(R)$$

and leads essentially to an overall displacement of all the levels by the quantity δM. From this we obtain:

$$\delta E_\alpha^{(0)} = \delta M \left(1 - \langle\alpha|\frac{\mathbf{P}^2}{2M^2}|\alpha\rangle\right).$$

If we stop at the second order in the perturbation method, the calculation of $\delta E_\alpha' = \delta E_\alpha - \delta E_\alpha^{(0)}$ presents no serious difficulties and gives for $|\delta E_\alpha'/D|$ a value of the order of 10^{-3}, which constitutes a reasonable order of magnitude.

The value of $\delta E_\alpha'$ thereby obtained must nevertheless be regarded with caution, since it proves to be very sensitive to the choice of the

---

[1]) Putting the cut-off at $K \approx M$, we find $\delta M/M \approx 10^{-3}$. The relative modification of the mass is therefore very small, which justifies *a posteriori* the use of the perturbation method. However, if the cut-off function is not introduced, δM is given by a divergent integral. We shall return to this difficulty later.

cut-off function. A realistic calculation must therefore start from a completely relativistic theory. In fact, we have here a difficult problem in Quantum Field Theory for which at the present time there is no completely satisfactory solution. In the Relativistic Theory, the interaction is entirely local and one obtains for δM an expression of the form: $\delta M = ZM$, where Z is a divergent integral (cf. note, p. 990). Similarly δE_α and $\delta E_\alpha^{(0)}$ are given by divergent integrals so that the expression for $\delta E_\alpha'$ is an indeterminate form of the type $\infty - \infty$.

In practice, the indetermination is removed by an *ad hoc* prescription based on considerations of relativistic invariance. One can thereby obtain results in remarkable agreement with experiment [1]). However, a rigorous justification for such calculational methods remains to be found.

Keeping in mind these limitations, we shall nevertheless continue our study of this simple model which correctly accounts for a large body of experimental facts. Effects such as the mass "renormalization" which can satisfactorily be treated only within the framework of the covariant formalism will be accounted for phenomenologically when they appear.

12. Emission of a Corpuscle

Let us turn now to the states which are unstable due to the coupling H'.

In this paragraph, we calculate the transition probabilities per unit time of the various "radiative transitions" by applying the time-dependent perturbation method (§ XVII.4).

To be definite, suppose that the spectrum of H_0 is that shown in Figure XXI.2 and consider the state $|\lambda\rangle$. The only transitions energetically possible (Fig. XXI.3) are the transitions to the ground state with emission of one or two corpuscles ($3\mu > E_\lambda - E_\alpha > 2\mu$) and transitions to the first excited state with emission of a single corpuscle ($2\mu > E_\lambda - E_\beta > \mu$). In what follows, we shall consider only transitions with emission of a single corpuscle. The emission of two corpuscles is a higher-order process and, other things being equal, g^2 times less frequent than the emission of a single corpuscle; it must therefore be left aside if we go only to the first order in the perturbation calculation.

The particle being initially in the state $|\lambda\rangle$, the probability per

---

[1]) Cf. note, p. 933.

unit time for it to make a transition to the state $|\alpha\rangle$ with emission of a corpuscle in the solid angle $(\Omega, \Omega+\mathrm{d}\Omega)$, i.e., the probability per unit time for the transition $\lambda \to \alpha\mathbf{k}$, where $\mathbf{k}$ is a vector in this solid angle, is given to the first order by the expression [cf. eq. (XVII.50)]:

$$w_{\lambda\to\alpha\mathbf{k}}\,\mathrm{d}\Omega = 2\pi\,|\langle\lambda|H'|\alpha\mathbf{k}\rangle|^2\varrho_L(\omega)\,\mathrm{d}\Omega, \qquad \text{(XXI.80)}$$

in which the energy of the corpuscle, ω, obeys the conservation law:

$$\omega = \omega_{\lambda\alpha} \equiv E_\lambda - E_\alpha.$$

Taking into account relations (XXI.49), (XXI.69*a*) and (XXI.70), formula (XXI.80) gives

$$w_{\lambda\to\alpha\mathbf{k}} = 2\pi g^2\,\frac{|\langle\lambda|\,\mathrm{e}^{i\mathbf{k}\cdot\mathbf{R}}\,|\alpha\rangle|^2}{2\omega}\,\frac{\omega k}{(2\pi)^3} = \frac{g^2k}{8\pi^2}\,|\langle\lambda|\,\mathrm{e}^{i\mathbf{k}\cdot\mathbf{R}}\,|\alpha\rangle|^2. \qquad \text{(XXI.81)}$$

By integrating over the angles, one obtains the probability of transition per unit time from λ to α, which we denote by $\Gamma_{\lambda\to\alpha}$:

$$\Gamma_{\lambda\to\alpha} \equiv \int w_{\lambda\to\alpha\mathbf{k}}\,\mathrm{d}\Omega = \frac{g^2k}{8\pi^2}\int|\langle\lambda|\,\mathrm{e}^{i\mathbf{k}\cdot\mathbf{R}}\,|\alpha\rangle|^2\,\mathrm{d}\Omega. \qquad \text{(XXI.82)}$$

Analogous expressions are found for the transitions to the state β. The total transition probability per unit time Γ_λ is:

$$\Gamma_\lambda = \Gamma_{\lambda\to\alpha} + \Gamma_{\lambda\to\beta}. \qquad \text{(XXI.83)}$$

Γ_λ is the inverse of the *lifetime* of the state $|\lambda\rangle$, as can be seen by the following semi-classical argument. Consider a statistical ensemble of particles and denote by $N_\lambda(t)$ the number of particles in the state $|\lambda\rangle$ at time t. The number of particles that effect a radiative transition in the time interval $(t, t+\mathrm{d}t)$ is $\Gamma_\lambda N_\lambda(t)\,\mathrm{d}t$. Consequently,

$$N_\lambda(t+\mathrm{d}t) = (1-\Gamma_\lambda\,\mathrm{d}t)N_\lambda(t)$$

or:

$$\frac{\mathrm{d}N_\lambda}{\mathrm{d}t} = -\Gamma_\lambda N_\lambda.$$

Consequently

$$N_\lambda(t) = N_\lambda(0)\,\mathrm{e}^{-\Gamma_\lambda t}. \qquad \text{(XXI.84)}$$

This is the well-known *law of exponential decay* with a lifetime equal to $1/\Gamma_\lambda$. In the example treated here there are essentially two possible decay modes, $\lambda \to \alpha$ and $\lambda \to \beta$ and the *branching ratio* of the first to the second is $\Gamma_{\lambda\to\alpha}/\Gamma_{\lambda\to\beta}$.

Clearly, the above semi-classical argument cannot be regarded as a proof of the exponential law, since the perturbation treatment for transition probabilities is valid only for $\Gamma_\lambda t \ll 1$ (cf. discussion at the end of § XVII.4), that is, for t small enough so that the state vector differs little from its initial value. For longer times, a more refined treatment is needed which will be given in § 13.

Let us return to the numerical values and notations of § 11 in order to determine the order of magnitude of the Γ. For not too large excitation energies we have $k \approx D$, and since the extension $\langle R\rangle$ of the wave functions of the particle is about $(2MD)^{-\frac{1}{2}}$ we have:

$$k\langle R\rangle \approx (D/2M)^{\frac{1}{2}} \simeq 5\times 10^{-3} \ll 1.$$

$\langle\lambda|e^{i\mathbf{k}\cdot\mathbf{R}}|\alpha\rangle$ can therefore be evaluated by replacing the exponential by the first term of its Taylor expansion giving a non-null contribution (long-wavelength approximation): the order of this term is essentially fixed by the angular momentum *selection rules*. In the most favourable case (dipole transitions), one finds

$$|\langle\lambda|e^{i\mathbf{k}\cdot\mathbf{R}}|\alpha\rangle| \simeq |\langle\lambda|\,\mathbf{k}\cdot\mathbf{R}\,|\alpha\rangle| \approx k\langle R\rangle$$

whence:

$$\Gamma_{\lambda\to\alpha} \approx \frac{g^2k}{2\pi}\,(k\langle R\rangle)^2 \approx 10^{-6}\,D.$$

If we take the same value for Γ_λ, we obtain a lifetime $1/\Gamma_\lambda$ very much larger (by a factor 10^6) than the characteristic period $1/D$ of the motion of the particle in its potential. It is therefore reasonable to treat, as we have done, the interaction H' responsible for the emission of the corpuscle as a small perturbation.

A formally very simple and very general expression for Γ_λ can be obtained by starting directly from formula (XXI.80) and using the definition of level densities, the conservation of energy and the closure relation. We obtain successively [1])

$$\begin{aligned}\Gamma_\lambda &= 2\pi\left(\frac{L}{2\pi}\right)^3 \sum_\nu \int \mathrm{d}\mathbf{k}\,|\langle\lambda|H'|\nu\mathbf{k}\rangle|^2\,\delta(E_\lambda - E_\nu - \omega)\\ &= 2\pi\left(\frac{L}{2\pi}\right)^3 \sum_\nu \int \mathrm{d}\mathbf{k}\,\langle\lambda|H'\delta(E_\lambda - H_0)|\nu\mathbf{k}\rangle\,\langle\nu\mathbf{k}|H'|\lambda\rangle\\ &= 2\pi\,\langle\lambda|H'\delta(E_\lambda - H_0)\,H'|\lambda\rangle.\end{aligned} \qquad \text{(XXI.85)}$$

This expression will prove useful in what follows.

---

[1]) Expression (XXI.85) appears in many problems; it is the general expression for the transition probability per unit time to the first order in the perturbation calculation. It can be deduced directly from the theory of § XVII.4 starting from formula (§ XVII.40) and using the asymptotic form (XVII.43) of the function f which appears in this formula.

13. Quantum Theory of Decaying States. Line Width

In this paragraph we shall give the exact quantum treatment of the evolution of a decaying state. It will be shown that the results given by the simplified arguments of § 12 are essentially correct, and notably that the falling-off is given to an excellent approximation by an exponential law. We shall also be led to the important concepts of level shift and line width.

Thus, we suppose that at the initial time $t=0$ the system is in a bound state of H_0 corresponding to the eigenvalue E_λ, and we consider its evolution in the course of time.

Up to the present, we have supposed that E_λ was a non-degenerate eigenvalue of H_0. This simplifying hypothesis will be invoked when we are discussing the results, but the treatment that follows is also applicable to the degenerate case. We denote by $\mathscr{E}_\lambda$ the subspace spanned by the bound states of unperturbed energy E_λ, and by P_λ and Q_λ the projectors onto $\mathscr{E}_\lambda$ and onto its complementary space respectively:

$$H_0 P_\lambda = P_\lambda H_0 = E_\lambda P_\lambda, \qquad P_\lambda + Q_\lambda = 1.$$

Let $U(t)$ be the evolution operator for the system:

$$U(t) \equiv \mathrm{e}^{-\mathrm{i}Ht}. \tag{XXI.86}$$

Our problem amounts to calculating $P_\lambda U(t) P_\lambda$ for $t>0$.

Let us introduce the resolvent:

$$G(z) \equiv \frac{1}{z-H}. \tag{XXI.87}$$

$G(z)$ is a function of the complex variable z whose singularities are the eigenvalues of H (the discrete values are simple poles, the continuous spectrum is a cut). One has [1])

$$U(t) = -\frac{1}{2\pi\mathrm{i}} \int_{-\infty}^{+\infty} \mathrm{e}^{-\mathrm{i}xt} \left[G(x^+) - G(x^-)\right] \mathrm{d}x \tag{XXI.88}$$

$$(x^\pm \equiv x \pm \mathrm{i}\varepsilon).$$

---

[1]) Relation (XXI.88) is directly obtained by using the fact that for ε infinitesimal and positive [cf. eq. (A.15e)]

$$G(x^\pm) \equiv \frac{1}{x - H \pm \mathrm{i}\varepsilon} = \mathrm{PP}\,\frac{1}{x-H} \mp \mathrm{i}\pi\delta(x-H). \tag{XXI.89}$$

Note that for $t>0$ the contribution from $G(x^-)$ to the integral on the right-hand side of (XXI.88) vanishes.

It follows that the operators $\mathscr{U}$ and $\mathscr{G}$, defined in the space $\mathscr{E}_\lambda$ by the relations:

$$\mathscr{U}(t) = P_\lambda U(t) P_\lambda, \qquad \mathscr{G}(z) = P_\lambda G(z) P_\lambda, \tag{XXI.90}$$

are related by the formula:

$$\mathscr{U}(t) = -\frac{1}{2\pi i} \int_{-\infty}^{+\infty} e^{-ixt} \left[\mathscr{G}(x^+) - \mathscr{G}(x^-)\right] dx \qquad (x^\pm \equiv x \pm i\varepsilon). \tag{XXI.91}$$

In order to obtain a workable expression for $\mathscr{G}(z)$, we put:

$$\begin{aligned} H &= H_1 + H'' \\ H_1 &\equiv P_\lambda H P_\lambda + Q_\lambda H Q_\lambda = H_0 + Q_\lambda H' Q_\lambda \\ H'' &\equiv P_\lambda H Q_\lambda + Q_\lambda H P_\lambda = P_\lambda H' Q_\lambda + Q_\lambda H' P_\lambda. \end{aligned}$$

Note that:

$$\begin{aligned} &H_1 P_\lambda = P_\lambda H_1 = E_\lambda P_\lambda \qquad [Q_\lambda, H_1] = 0 \\ &P_\lambda H'' = H'' Q_\lambda \qquad Q_\lambda H'' = H'' P_\lambda. \end{aligned}$$

From these relations, and from the operator identity:

$$(A-B)^{-1} \equiv A^{-1} + A^{-1} B (A-B)^{-1},$$

we obtain:

$$\frac{1}{z-H} = \frac{1}{z-H_1} + \frac{1}{z-H_1} H'' \frac{1}{z-H} \tag{XXI.92}$$

$$= \frac{1}{z-H_1} + \frac{1}{z-H_1} H'' \frac{1}{z-H_1} + \frac{1}{z-H_1} H'' \frac{1}{z-H_1} H'' \frac{1}{z-H} \tag{XXI.93}$$

$$P_\lambda \frac{1}{z-H} P_\lambda = \frac{P_\lambda}{z-E_\lambda} + \frac{1}{z-E_\lambda} \left(P_\lambda H'' \frac{1}{z-H_1} H'' P_\lambda \right) P_\lambda \frac{1}{z-H} P_\lambda. \tag{XXI.94}$$

Relation (XXI.94) is a relation between operators of the space $\mathscr{E}_\lambda$, namely:

$$\mathscr{G}(z) = \frac{1}{z-E_\lambda} \left[1 + \mathscr{W}(z)\, \mathscr{G}(z)\right], \tag{XXI.95}$$

where:

$$\mathscr{W}(z) \equiv P_\lambda H'' \frac{1}{z-H_1} H'' P_\lambda = P_\lambda H' Q_\lambda \frac{1}{z - Q_\lambda H Q_\lambda} Q_\lambda H' P_\lambda. \tag{XXI.96}$$

More generally, $U(t)$ and $G(z)$ are related by the transformation formulas

$$G(z) = -i \int_0^{\eta\infty} e^{izt}\, U(t)\, dt \qquad U(t) = \frac{1}{2\pi i} \int_C e^{-izt}\, G(z)\, dz$$

[η sign of $\operatorname{Im} z$; C = contour in the complex plane going from $\infty + i\varepsilon$ to $\infty - i\varepsilon$ with all the singularities of $G(z)$ i.e., all the eigenvalues of H, on its left], which are easily demonstrated in the representation where H is diagonal.

From equation (XXI.95) we obtain:

$$\mathscr{G}(z) = \frac{1}{z - E_\lambda - \mathscr{W}(z)}. \qquad \text{(XXI.97)}$$

Equations (XXI.96), (XXI.97) and (XXI.91) are exact relations which can serve as a starting point for a calculation of $\mathscr{U}(t)$.

Equations (XXI.96) and (XXI.97) define $\mathscr{W}(z)$ and $\mathscr{G}(z)$ respectively as functions of the complex variable z in the plane cut by the eigenvalues of the continuous spectrum of H. We are especially interested in the behavior of these functions in the neighborhood of the cut. Using relation (XXI.89), the Hermitean and antihermitean parts of $\mathscr{W}(x^\pm)$ can be separated. One obtains:

$$\mathscr{W}(x^\pm) = \varDelta(x) \mp \tfrac{1}{2}\mathrm{i}\varGamma(x) \qquad \text{(XXI.98)}$$

$$\varDelta(x) \equiv P_\lambda H' \,\mathrm{PP}\, \frac{1}{x - Q_\lambda H Q_\lambda} H' P_\lambda \qquad \text{(XXI.99)}$$

$$\varGamma(x) \equiv 2\pi P_\lambda H' \delta(x - Q_\lambda H Q_\lambda) H' P_\lambda. \qquad \text{(XXI.100)}$$

Note that $\varGamma(x)$ is a positive definite Hermitean operator.

We shall henceforth suppose that E_λ is a non-degenerate eigenvalue [1]) of H_0.

---

[1]) In most practical cases, the degeneracy of E_λ is due to an invariance of H_0 which remains when the coupling H' is added. For example in the radioactive decay of a nucleus of spin J, the degeneracy of order $2J + 1$ is due to invariance under rotation, which remains when the coupling responsible for the decay is added to the unperturbed Hamiltonian. Since $\mathscr{E}_\lambda$ is then an irreducible subspace, and the operators $\mathscr{W}(z)$, $\mathscr{G}(z)$ and $\mathscr{U}(t)$ are invariant, the latter are multiples of the unit operator, and they can be calculated in the same way as in the non-degenerate case. Each state of the space $\mathscr{E}_\lambda$ follows the same law of radioactive decay with the same lifetime and the same level shift.

If, on the other hand, these symmetry conditions do not hold, there can be several lifetimes and several shifts. This is what occurs for the first excited level of the hydrogen atom (cf. discussion of the Lamb shift at the end of § XX.27). Another example is that of the K^0 boson. The treatment of the general case is essentially the same as that of the non-degenerate case. With the same approximations, we obtain for $\mathscr{U}(t)$ the expression:

$$\mathscr{U}(t) \simeq \exp\left[-\mathrm{i}(E_\lambda + \mathscr{W}(E_\lambda{}^+))\, t\right]$$

which is the generalization of (XXI.109). The real and imaginary parts of the eigenvalues of the (non-Hermitean) operator $\mathscr{W}(E_\lambda^+)$ respectively give the different level shifts and corresponding lifetimes.

By hypothesis, the system is in the corresponding eigenstate $|\lambda\rangle$ at time $t=0$. We wish to determine its state vector at any later time t

$$|\Psi(t)\rangle = U(t)\,|\lambda\rangle \tag{XXI.101}$$

and in particular the component of this vector along $|\lambda\rangle$.

The operators $\mathscr{U}(t)$, $\mathscr{G}(z)$, $\mathscr{W}(z)$, $\Delta(x)$ and $\Gamma(x)$ can be replaced in the preceding work by their average value over $|\lambda\rangle$, and treated as simple functions. Equations (XXI.90), (XXI.99) and (XXI.100) are then respectively replaced by:

$$\mathscr{U}(t) \equiv \langle\lambda|U(t)|\lambda\rangle \qquad \mathscr{G}(z) \equiv \langle\lambda|G(z)|\lambda\rangle \tag{XXI.102}$$

$$\Delta(x) \equiv \langle\lambda|\, H'\,\mathrm{PP}\left(\frac{1}{x-Q_\lambda H\, Q_\lambda}\right) H'\,|\lambda\rangle \tag{XXI.103}$$

$$\Gamma(x) \equiv 2\pi\langle\lambda|H'\delta(x-Q_\lambda H Q_\lambda)H'|\lambda\rangle, \tag{XXI.104}$$

and equations (XXI.97) and (XXI.91) give respectively:

$$\mathscr{G}(x^\pm) = [x-E_\lambda-\Delta(x) \pm \tfrac{1}{2}\mathrm{i}\Gamma(x)]^{-1} \tag{XXI.105}$$

$$\mathscr{U}(t) = \frac{1}{2\pi}\int_{-\infty}^{\infty} \mathrm{e}^{-\mathrm{i}xt}\, F(x)\,\mathrm{d}x, \tag{XXI.106}$$

where:

$$F(x) \equiv \mathrm{i}(\mathscr{G}(x^+) - \mathscr{G}(x^-)) = \frac{\Gamma(x)}{(x-E_\lambda-\Delta(x))^2+\frac{1}{4}\Gamma(x)^2}. \tag{XXI.107}$$

Up to now, no approximation has been made. To evaluate $F(x)$ and $\mathscr{U}(t)$, we shall suppose the coupling weak and retain only the lowest order terms in H' in expressions (XXI.103) and (XXI.104) giving respectively $\Delta(x)$ and $\Gamma(x)$. For this we need only to replace $Q_\lambda H Q_\lambda$ by H_0 in these expressions. It is then easy to calculate $\Delta(x)$ and $\Gamma(x)$. The form of $\Gamma(x)$ is given in Fig. XXI.4. For Δ and Γ sufficiently small, $F(x)$ has a sharp maximum at about the point $x=E_\lambda$, and the main contribution to integral (XXI.106) comes from this region. This integral can therefore be evaluated by substituting for the slowly-varying functions $\Delta(x)$ and $\Gamma(x)$ their values at the point $x=E_\lambda$, namely:

$$\Delta(E_\lambda) \equiv \delta E_\lambda, \qquad \Gamma(E_\lambda) \equiv \Gamma_\lambda, \tag{XXI.108}$$

which amounts to replacing (cf. Fig. XXI.5) the function $F(x)$ by:

$$F_1(x) = \frac{\Gamma_\lambda}{(x-E_\lambda-\delta E_\lambda)^2+\frac{1}{4}\Gamma_\lambda{}^2}.$$

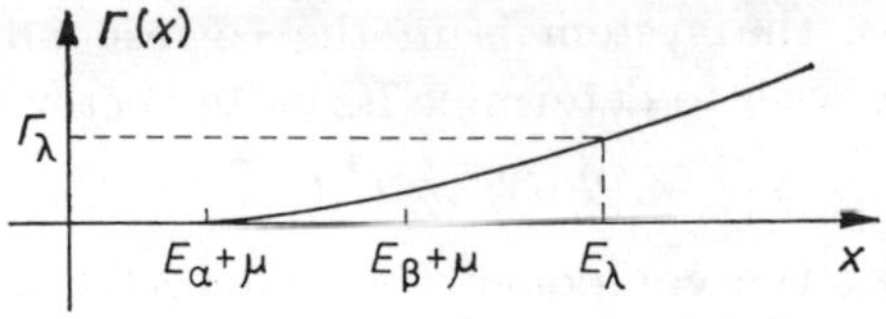

Fig. XXI.4. Form of $\Gamma(x)$. Note that $\Gamma(x) = 0$ for $x < E_\alpha + \mu$.

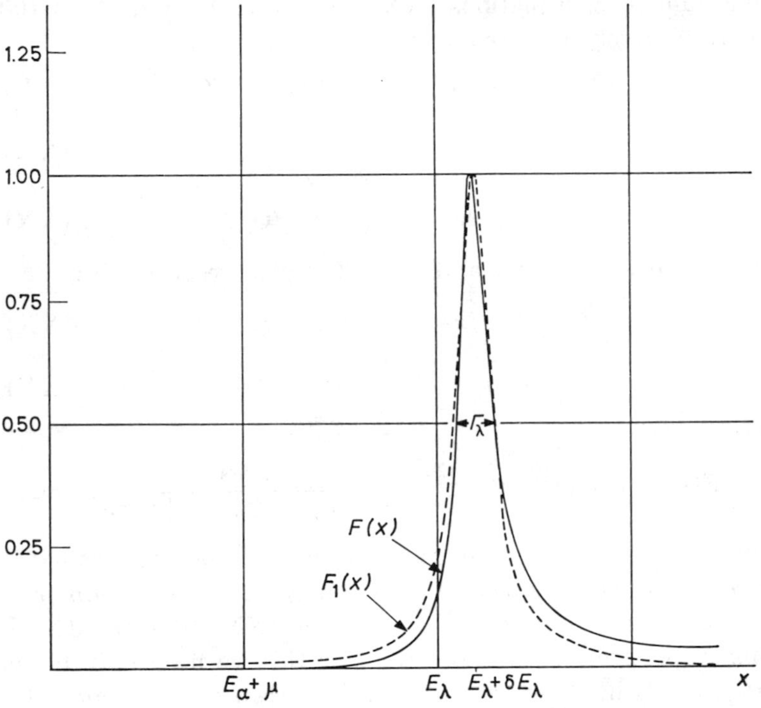

Fig. XXI.5. Typical form of $F(x)$ and $F_1(x)$.

Here the function Δ and Γ have been given an x dependence typical of the dipole transitions:

$$\Delta(x) \simeq Cst = \delta E_\lambda \qquad \frac{\Gamma(x)}{\Gamma_\lambda} \simeq \frac{(x - E_\lambda + \xi)^3}{\xi^3} \qquad (\xi = E_\lambda - E_\alpha - \mu).$$

We have taken $\delta E_\lambda / \xi = 0.2 \qquad \Gamma_\lambda / \xi = 0.1$.

The error in $U(t)$ is smaller than the absolute value of the quantity

$$\frac{1}{2\pi} \int_{-\infty}^{\infty} |F(x) - F_1(x)| \, \mathrm{d}x.$$

If Γ_λ and δE_λ are sufficiently small compared with $E_\lambda - E_\alpha - \mu$ and $E_\lambda - E_\beta - \mu$, it remains negligible in relative value except for very long times ($t \gg 1/\Gamma_\lambda$).

The integration is then easily carried out and gives:

$$\mathscr{U}(t) \simeq \mathrm{e}^{-\mathrm{i}(E_\lambda+\delta E_\lambda)t-\frac{1}{2}\Gamma_\lambda t}. \qquad \text{(XXI.109)}$$

Therefore:

$$|\mathscr{U}(t)|^2 = \mathrm{e}^{-\Gamma_\lambda t}. \qquad \text{(XXI.110)}$$

This is the expected exponential decay law.

The value of the *lifetime*, $1/\Gamma_\lambda$, is that which was calculated in § 12 [cf. eqs. (XXI.84–85), (XXI.104) and (XXI.108)].

According to formula (XXI.109), the modifications of the law of motion of the level λ due to the coupling H' consists essentially in adding to it the complex energy

$$\delta E_\lambda - \tfrac{1}{2}\mathrm{i}\Gamma_\lambda.$$

The real part, δE_λ, is the *level shift* proper; it has a form analogous to that of the shift of a stable level [cf. eqs. (XXI.71), (XXI.103) and (XXI.108)]. The imaginary part, characteristic of a decaying state, is to within a sign the half-width of the level; it is the part responsible for the existence of the exponential falling-off.

Let us now calculate the other components of $|\Psi(t)\rangle$ in the weak-coupling approximation. In this approximation the only non-vanishing components are along the vectors containing one and only one corpuscle:

$$|\Psi(t)\rangle = \mathscr{U}(t)|\lambda\rangle + \sum_{\nu\mathbf{k}} h_{\nu\mathbf{k}}(t)|\nu\mathbf{k}\rangle \qquad \text{(XXI.111)}$$

$$h_{\nu\mathbf{k}}(t) = \langle\nu\mathbf{k}|U(t)|\lambda\rangle. \qquad \text{(XXI.112)}$$

From equation (XXI.92),

$$\langle\nu\mathbf{k}|G(z)|\lambda\rangle = \langle\nu\mathbf{k}|(z-H_1)^{-1}H''|\lambda\rangle\mathscr{G}(z).$$

This equation is exact. The weak-coupling approximation consists in replacing H_1 by H_0 in the denominator on the right-hand side, which gives:

$$\langle\nu\mathbf{k}|G(z)|\lambda\rangle = \langle\nu\mathbf{k}|H'|\lambda\rangle(z-\omega-E_\nu)\mathscr{G}(z).$$

From this approximate value for the matrix element of $G(z)$ one obtains an approximate value for the corresponding element of $U(t)$ by applying formula (XXI.88), which gives an integral which may be evaluated by the residue method. For sufficiently large values of t, the only significant contribution is the one from the pole on the real axis, which gives

$$h_{\nu\mathbf{k}}(t) \simeq \langle \nu\mathbf{k}|H'|\lambda\rangle \left.\frac{\mathrm{e}^{-\mathrm{i}xt}}{x - E_\lambda - \Delta(x) + \frac{1}{2}\mathrm{i}\Gamma(x)}\right|_{x=\omega+E_\nu}.$$
$$(\Gamma t \gg 1)$$

The square of the modulus of this expression gives a probability of finding the system in the state $(\nu\mathbf{k})$ for the large values of t (large with respect to the decay lifetime). It can be put in the form:

$$|h_{\nu\mathbf{k}}(\infty)|^2 = |\langle \nu\mathbf{k}|H'|\lambda\rangle|^2 \frac{\Gamma(\omega+E_\nu)}{F(\omega+E_\nu)}, \qquad \text{(XXI.113)}$$

where $F(x)$ is the function defined by equation (XXI.107). According to the above-mentioned properties of $F(x)$ (cf. Fig. (XXI.5)), $|h_{\nu\mathbf{k}}(\infty)|^2$ takes appreciable values only for $\omega+E_\nu \simeq E_\lambda$, that is, for transitions which roughly conserve the unperturbed energy. For these – in the example treated here these are the ones for which $\nu=\alpha$ and $\nu=\beta$ – we can replace $F(x)$ by $F_1(x)$. Thus, for the transitions $\lambda \to \alpha\mathbf{k}$ we obtain the formula:

$$|h_{\nu\mathbf{k}}(\infty)|^2 = \frac{|\langle \alpha\mathbf{k}|H'|\lambda\rangle|^2}{(\omega + E_\alpha - E_\lambda - \delta E_\lambda)^2 + \frac{1}{4}\Gamma_\lambda^2}. \qquad \text{(XXI.114)}$$

According to this formula, the energy distribution of the corpuscles emitted in the transition is given by a "*Lorentz law*" *of width* Γ_λ centered about the point $E_\lambda+\delta E_\lambda-E_\alpha$, that is, centered about the Bohr frequency of the transition, corrected by the *shift* δE_λ.

The *line width* of the corpuscles emitted in the radiative transition is therefore equal, in our units where $\hbar=1$, to the inverse of the lifetime in accordance with the time-energy uncertainty relation.

Several remarks should be made regarding the significance of these results.

In the first place, to compare a distribution law such as (XXI.114) with experimental results, one should indicate how the initial state $|\lambda\rangle$ can be experimentally realized. We shall return to this point in § 15.

Apart from this, the preceding treatment has rather severe limitations. If we take the numerical results of § 11, we see that δE_λ is of the same order as δE_α, and therefore much larger than the level distance. However, if one denotes by $\delta E_\lambda{}^{(0)}$ the effect due to mass renormalization, it can be shown that the difference

$$\delta E_\lambda{}' \equiv \delta E_\lambda - \delta E_\lambda{}^{(0)}$$

is a small correction compared to the level distance. The difficulty encountered here is exactly the same as the one discussed at some length in § 11; that discussion can be repeated here point by point.

Finally – and this is obviously related to the weak-coupling approximation in the calculation of the amplitudes $h_{\nu\mathbf{k}}$ – we have not taken into account possible shifts in the levels towards which the transition is effected, nor *a fortiori* of the fact that some of these levels are themselves rendered unstable by the presence of the coupling H'.

For transitions towards stable levels or levels with a long lifetime compared with the lifetime of the initial state, formula (XXI.114) can be corrected so as to take the two last-mentioned effects into account. Denote by $E_\alpha{}^{(0)}, \ldots, E_\lambda{}^{(0)}, \ldots$ the levels obtained by substituting the experimental mass for M in the Hamiltonian H_{part}. The corrected formula is written:

$$|h_{\nu\mathbf{k}}|^2_{\text{cor}} = \frac{|\langle\alpha\mathbf{k}|H'|\lambda\rangle|^2}{(\omega + E_\alpha{}^{(0)} + \delta E_\alpha{}' - E_\lambda{}^{(0)} - \delta E_\lambda{}')^2 + \frac{1}{4}\Gamma_\lambda{}^2}. \qquad \text{(XXI.114')}$$

It is a formula of this type that is usually compared with experimental results. The agreement is excellent.

14. Elastic Scattering. Dispersion Formula

To conclude this section let us consider some simple collision problems.

As a first problem, we treat the elastic scattering of a field corpuscle by a particle in its ground state. Denote by $\mathbf{k}_i$ the wave vector of the incident corpuscle and by $\mathbf{k}_f$ a vector of the same length pointing in the direction in which the corpuscle is observed after the collision. The transition in question is therefore

$$i \to f \equiv (\alpha\mathbf{k}_i) \to (\alpha\mathbf{k}_f).$$

We put

$$k_i = k_f = k, \qquad \omega_i = \omega_f = \omega,$$

and denote the initial energy of the system by E:

$$E = \omega + E_\alpha. \qquad \text{(XXI.115)}$$

The cross section is given by the general formula:

$$\frac{\mathrm{d}\sigma_{i\to f}}{\mathrm{d}\Omega} = \frac{2\pi}{\text{incident flux}}\,|T_{i\to f}|^2\,\varrho_f(E). \qquad \text{(XXI.116)}$$

$T_{i\to f}$ is the transition amplitude:

$$T_{i\to f} \equiv \langle f|T|i\rangle \equiv \langle \alpha \boldsymbol{k}_f|T|\alpha \boldsymbol{k}_i\rangle \tag{XXI.117}$$

$$T = H' + H' \frac{1}{E - H + \mathrm{i}\varepsilon} H'. \tag{XXI.118}$$

The incident flux is equal to the product of the incident velocity, k/ω, by the density of corpuscles in the state $|\alpha \boldsymbol{k}_i\rangle$, which gives, with the normalization adopted here: $L^{-3}k/\omega$. $\varrho_f(E)$ is the density of final states at energy E [cf. eq. (XXI.49)]. One therefore has:

$$\frac{2\pi\, \varrho_f(E)}{\text{incident flux}} = \frac{L^6\, \omega^2}{4\pi^2}.$$

Whence:

$$\frac{\mathrm{d}\sigma_{i\to f}}{\mathrm{d}\Omega} = \frac{L^6\, \omega^2}{4\pi^2} |T_{i\to f}|^2. \tag{XXI.119}$$

In all of this, we have assumed that the basic formulae of collision theory are entirely valid here: equations (XXI.116) and (XXI.118) which constitute our point of departure are essentially equivalent to equations (XIX.115) and (XIX.144) respectively. The few differences are due only to notation, to the units chosen and to the normalization of the wave functions involved in the definition of the transition amplitude.

In the present case, however, these formulae are not absolutely correct. They were established under the hypothesis that the evolution of the system *before* and *after* the collision was almost entirely governed by the Hamiltonian H_0, the interaction H' being completely negligible. Such a hypothesis, entirely justified in the collision problems of Chapters X and XIX, ceases to hold here.

Let us examine, for example, the state of the system before the collision. The particle is then in its ground state and the corpuscle is represented by a wave packet moving towards it. The wave packet has not yet reached the small region about the origin in which the particle moves; the interaction corpuscle-particle is therefore negligible and the corpuscle evolves as if it were free. In this respect, the present situation does not differ from that of ordinary collision theory. But the interaction H' nevertheless cannot be neglected, since the particle, even when separated from the incident corpuscle, is always coupled with the field; to be exact, its initial state is not the eigenstate $|\alpha\rangle$ of the Hamiltonian H_0 corresponding to the energy E_α, but the eigenstate $|\bar{\alpha}\rangle$ of the Hamiltonian H which coincides with $|\alpha\rangle$ in the limit $g \to 0$, and whose eigenenergy, $E_\alpha + \delta E_\alpha$, was calculated in § 11.

To be correct, the theory must take into account the difference between the "physical state" $|\bar{\alpha}\rangle$ and the unperturbed state $|\alpha\rangle$. If the coupling is sufficiently weak, it leads essentially to an effect of renormalization of the mass, and the mechanism of the collision proper is not affected [1]).

Under these conditions, the usual formulae of collision theory are valid if we replace the mass M by the experimental mass $M+\delta M$ in the definition of the unperturbed Hamiltonian.

We shall now calculate the cross section by treating H' as a perturbation. We therefore replace T by its Born expansion (cf. eq. (XIX.143)). In the first order, the amplitude obviously vanishes:

$$\langle \alpha \mathbf{k}_f | H' | \alpha \mathbf{k}_i \rangle = 0.$$

We must therefore proceed to the second order. We denote the amplitude to the second order in H' by $T^{(\mathrm{B})}_{i\to f}$:

$$T^{(\mathrm{B})}_{i\to f} \equiv \langle \alpha \mathbf{k}_f | H' \frac{1}{E - H_0 + \mathrm{i}\varepsilon} H' | \alpha \mathbf{k}_i \rangle \tag{XXI.120}$$

$$= \sum_n \langle \alpha \mathbf{k}_f | H' | n \rangle \frac{1}{E - E_n + \mathrm{i}\varepsilon} \langle n | H' | \alpha \mathbf{k}_i \rangle. \tag{XXI.120'}$$

In the second line, the summation is extended over all of the basis vectors of the Hamiltonian H_0. Owing to the very special form of H' most of the terms in the sum vanish. The virtual states whose contribution is different to zero can be put into two categories:

(*i*) the zero-corpuscle states $|\nu\rangle$;

(*ii*) the states $|\nu \mathbf{k}_i \mathbf{k}_f\rangle$ containing two corpuscles of momentum $\mathbf{k}_i$ and $\mathbf{k}_f$ respectively.

The first correspond to the transitions:

$$(\alpha \mathbf{k}_i) \to (\nu) \to (\alpha \mathbf{k}_f)$$

in which the particle absorbs the incident corpuscle before emitting the corpuscle in the final state; the second correspond to the transitions:

$$(\alpha \mathbf{k}_i) \to (\nu \mathbf{k}_i \mathbf{k}_f) \to (\alpha \mathbf{k}_f)$$

---

[1]) In a higher approximation, one must take into account the modifications of the interaction of the incident corpuscle and the particle by the presence of virtual corpuscles surrounding the latter. This modification is essentially represented by a modification of the coupling constant ("charge renormalization").

in which the final corpuscle is emitted before the initial corpuscle is absorbed.

Let us introduce the Bohr frequencies:

$$\omega_{\nu\alpha} = E_\nu - E_\alpha \qquad (>0). \tag{XXI.121}$$

One finds

$$T^{(B)}_{i\to f} = \sum_\nu \left[\frac{\langle \alpha \mathbf{k}_f | H' | \nu \rangle \langle \nu | H' | \alpha \mathbf{k}_i \rangle}{\omega - \omega_{\nu\alpha}} - \frac{\langle \alpha \mathbf{k}_f | H' | \nu \mathbf{k}_i \mathbf{k}_f \rangle \langle \nu \mathbf{k}_i \mathbf{k}_f | H' | \alpha \mathbf{k}_i \rangle}{\omega + \omega_{\nu\alpha}} \right]. \tag{XXI.122}$$

This gives, applying equation (XXI.69) and (XXI.70) with $C(k) = 1$ (which is certainly legitimate if $k \ll M$):

$$T^{(B)}_{i\to f} = \frac{L^{-3} g^2}{2\omega} \sum_\nu \left[\frac{X_\nu}{\omega - \omega_{\nu\alpha}} - \frac{X_\nu{}'}{\omega + \omega_{\nu\alpha}} \right] \tag{XXI.123}$$

where:

$$X_\nu \equiv \langle \alpha | \, \mathrm{e}^{-\mathrm{i}\mathbf{k}_f \cdot \mathbf{R}} | \nu \rangle \langle \nu | \, \mathrm{e}^{\mathrm{i}\mathbf{k}_i \cdot \mathbf{R}} | \alpha \rangle \tag{XXI.124}$$

$$X_\nu{}' \equiv \langle \alpha | \, \mathrm{e}^{\mathrm{i}\mathbf{k}_i \cdot \mathbf{R}} | \nu \rangle \langle \nu | \, \mathrm{e}^{-\mathrm{i}\mathbf{k}_f \cdot \mathbf{R}} | \alpha \rangle. \tag{XXI.124'}$$

Substituting this expression into the right-hand side of (XXI.119), one obtains the cross section in the second-order Born approximation:

$$\frac{\mathrm{d}\sigma^{(B)}_{i\to f}}{\mathrm{d}\Omega} = \frac{g^4}{16\pi^2} \left| \sum_\nu \left(\frac{X_\nu}{\omega - \omega_{\nu\alpha}} - \frac{X_\nu{}'}{\omega + \omega_{\nu\alpha}} \right) \right|^2. \tag{XXI.125}$$

Each term in this series represents the contribution of one of the transitions described above. All things being equal, this contribution is the larger the nearer the incidence energy to the energy of the virtual state involved in that transition; when these two energies are equal, the corresponding term is infinite. There is one such critical value for ω for each transition of the first category in which the intermediate state can decay into the ground state with emission of a field-corpuscle.

When passing by one of these critical values, E_λ for example ($\omega_{\lambda\alpha} > \mu$), the denominator $\omega - \omega_{\lambda\alpha}$ vanishes and changes sign, the term $X_\lambda / (\omega - \omega_{\lambda\alpha})$ increases indefinitely and the expression for the cross section diverges. However small may be the coupling constant, the Born approximation obviously loses all validity in this domain [1]); in actual fact the cross section remains finite, but passes by a very sharp maximum. It is, as we shall see, a resonance phenomenon entirely analogous to the ones studied in Chapter X (§ 14–16).

15. Resonance Scattering. Formation of a Metastable State

To calculate the elastic scattering cross section in the neighborhood of one of these critical energies, E_λ say, we return to the exact expression for the transition amplitude. According to definitions (XXI.117) and (XXI.118),

$$\langle f|T|i\rangle = \sum_{nn'} \langle f|H'|n\rangle \langle n| \frac{1}{E - H + \mathrm{i}\varepsilon} |n'\rangle \langle n'|H'|i\rangle. \quad \text{(XXI.126)}$$

The Born approximation consists in replacing in each term of this expansion the exact Green's function $(E-H+\mathrm{i}\varepsilon)^{-1}$ by the Green's function $(E-H_0+\mathrm{i}\varepsilon)^{-1}$ of the unperturbed Hamiltonian [cf. eq. (XXI.120) and (XXI.120′)]. If the coupling constant is sufficiently small, this approximation is justified for all of the terms except the term $n=\lambda$, $n'=\lambda$, for which the factor $\langle\lambda|(E-H_0+\mathrm{i}\varepsilon)^{-1}|\lambda\rangle$ increases indefinitely when the energy passes by the value E_λ. Denote this term by $A^{(\mathrm{res})}$:

$$A^{(\mathrm{res})} \equiv \langle f|H'|\lambda\rangle \langle\lambda| \frac{1}{E - H + \mathrm{i}\varepsilon} |\lambda\rangle \langle\lambda|H'|i\rangle \quad \text{(XXI.127)}$$

and the difference by $A^{(\mathrm{pot})}$:

$$\langle f|T|i\rangle \equiv A^{(\mathrm{res})} + A^{(\mathrm{pot})}. \quad \text{(XXI.128)}$$

We shall use the Born approximation to calculate $A^{(\mathrm{pot})}$; the ex-

---

1) In the long-wavelength approximation ($k\langle R\rangle \ll 1$), one has $|X_\lambda| \simeq (k\langle R\rangle)^2$; if we put $\Delta\omega = |E - E_\lambda|$ and retain only the contribution from the dominant term, expression (XXI.125) gives:

$$\frac{\mathrm{d}\sigma}{\mathrm{d}\Omega} \simeq \frac{g^4}{16\pi^2}\left(\frac{k^2\langle R\rangle^2}{\Delta\omega}\right)^2.$$

According to a known criterion (§ XIX.7), the Born approximation ceases to be applicable when the total cross section is of the order of the geometrical cross section $4\pi\langle R\rangle^2$. This occurs here for:

$$\Delta\omega \lesssim \frac{g^2 k}{4\pi}(k\langle R\rangle).$$

With the numerical values given in § 11 this is an extremely narrow domain, of the order of $10^{-4} D$ (nevertheless much larger than the width Γ_λ).

pression obtained differs from (XXI.123) only by the absence of the term $X_\lambda/(\omega-\omega_{\lambda\alpha})$ in the summation over the states ν. It remains to calculate $A^{(\mathrm{res})}$.

By replacing the matrix elements of H' in (XXI.127) by their explicit form [cf. eq. (XXI.69) and (XXI.124)], we obtain:

$$A^{(\mathrm{res})} = L^{-3} g^2 \frac{X_\lambda}{2\omega} \mathscr{G}(E^+), \qquad \text{(XXI.129)}$$

where $\mathscr{G}(E^+)$ is the average value of the Green's function introduced in § 13:

$$\mathscr{G}(E^+) \equiv \langle\lambda| \frac{1}{E-H+\mathrm{i}\varepsilon} |\lambda\rangle. \qquad \text{(XXI.130)}$$

This function was calculated in § 13. The result is given by equation (XXI.105). Substituting the expression thus obtained in equation (XXI.129), one obtains:

$$A^{(\mathrm{res})} = \frac{L^{-3} g^2}{2\omega} \frac{X_\lambda}{E-E_\lambda-\Delta(E)+\frac{1}{2}\mathrm{i}\Gamma(E)}. \qquad \text{(XXI.131)}$$

This expression for $A^{(\mathrm{res})}$ is exact. It differs from the one given by the Born approximation only by the presence of the complex term $\Delta(E)-\frac{1}{2}\mathrm{i}\Gamma(E)$ in the denominator. This additional term removes the singularity. Its properties were examined in § 13. By replacing it by its value for $E=E_\lambda$ [cf. eqs. (XXI.103), (XXI.104) and (XXI.108)], which is certainly legitimate in the weak-coupling approximation since its energy variation is negligible in the energy band of interest, one obtains:

$$A^{(\mathrm{res})} = \frac{L^{-3} g^2}{2\omega} \frac{X_\lambda}{E-E_\lambda-\delta E_\lambda+\frac{1}{2}\mathrm{i}\Gamma_\lambda} \qquad \text{(XXI.132)}$$

This expression is characteristic of a scattering amplitude of width Γ_λ centered about the point $E_\lambda+\delta E_\lambda$.

The discussion of Chapter X on scattering resonances and their *relation to the existence of decaying states* can be repeated here. By further specifying the model, it is easy to obtain expressions practically identical to those given in § X.15 (providing $A^{(\mathrm{pot})}$ is neglected) for the scattering amplitude, the differential and total cross sections, and the "delay" in the transmission of the scattered wave (cf. Problem XXI.4). The above resonance is related to the decaying state $|\lambda\rangle$

whose properties have already been discussed in § 12 and 13.

To carry out a precise measurement of the cross section, and in particular to exhibit its characteristic variation with the energy, it is necessary that the energy uncertainty $\Delta\omega$ of the incident wave packet be sufficiently small that the scattering amplitude remains practically constant over the interval $\Delta\omega$; in the neighborhood of the resonance this requires:

$$\Delta\omega \ll \Gamma_\lambda. \tag{XXI.133}$$

The collision time, $1/\Delta\omega$, is then much larger than the lifetime $1/\Gamma_\lambda$, and the latter is unobservable.

If, instead of this, we have the complementary conditions:

$$\Delta\omega \gg \Gamma_\lambda, \tag{XXI.134}$$

it is possible to observe the time development of the phenomenon and to exhibit, after a transient period of the order of $1/\Delta\omega$, the exponentially decreasing law characteristic of the decaying state $|\lambda\rangle$. This is due to the rather special form of the scattering amplitude in the resonance region [eq. (XXI.132)], and can easily be established by repeating point by point the calculation of § X.16.

This result is a very general one, valid not only for scattering but for all collisions. Any collision resonance defined by its energy E and its width Γ is associated with a metastable state of the same energy and of lifetime $\hbar/\Gamma$, which can be observed under experimental conditions complementary to those in which one usually observes the resonance [1]).

16. Absorption of a Corpuscle (Photo-electric Effect). Radiative Capture

The problems treated thus far have involved only bound states of the particle. In this paragraph we shall treat two problems, absorp-

---

[1]) Here we have two complementary manifestations of the same property of the system, since they both follow from the same property of its resolvant $G(z)$. The latter is defined by the equation $G(z) = (z - H)^{-1}$ in the plane cut by the continuous spectrum of H: its only singularities in the cut plane are on the real axis, and are the eigenvalues of H. However its analytic continuation onto other Riemann sheets may have other singularities. Resonance and decaying state are due to the fact that $G(z)$ has a pole at point $z = E - \frac{1}{2}i\Gamma$ near the real axis on the second Riemann sheet of the lower half plane.

tion of a corpuscle and radiative capture, which deal with possible unbound states of the particle.

We shall suppose that $\lim_{R\to\infty} V(R) = 0$ and consequently that the spectrum of the particle subsystem contains a discrete set of bound states of negative energy $E_\alpha, E_\beta, \ldots, E_\lambda, \ldots$, and a continuum of unbound states of energy extending from 0 to $+\infty$. We denote by $\psi_{\boldsymbol{q}}^{(+)}$ and $\psi_{\boldsymbol{q}}^{(-)}$ the stationary waves associated with the wave vector $\boldsymbol{q}$ according to the definitions of § XIX.2. By definition, they are eigensolutions of H_{part} corresponding to the energy:

$$E = \frac{q^2}{2M}. \qquad \text{(XXI.135)}$$

They may also be regarded as eigensolutions of H_0 representing stationary collision states of the total system when the coupling term H' is neglected. We shall denote the corresponding stationary collision states when the coupling is taken into account by $\Psi_{\boldsymbol{q}}^{(+)}$ and $\Psi_{\boldsymbol{q}}^{(-)}$.

Suppose now that the particle in its ground state is bombarded by a monoergic beam of corpuscles of velocity $\boldsymbol{k}/\omega$. If the energy ω of the incident corpuscles is large enough to "ionize the atom", that is, if

$$\omega > (-E_\alpha),$$

the corpuscle may simply be absorbed, transferring the whole of its energy to the particle; the latter will then be ejected with a kinetic energy E equal to the difference between the energy received ω and the binding energy $(-E_\alpha)$:

$$E - \omega + E_\alpha.$$

This process will be recognized as the photoelectric effect (§ I.4).

Let us calculate the cross section for the absorption of a corpuscle of energy $\boldsymbol{k}$ with ejection of the particle in a given direction. We denote by $\boldsymbol{q}$ a vector pointing in this direction whose length is related to the energy E by relation (XXI.135). Thus we are concerned with the transition:

$$i \to f \equiv (\alpha\boldsymbol{k}) \to (\boldsymbol{q}).$$

As in the elastic scattering case, we suppose that the formulas of ordinary collision theory can be applied [the same qualifications apply here as in § 14]. The cross section is therefore given by formula

(XXI.116) with the same expression for the incident flux, but with $\varrho_f(E)=Mq/(2\pi)^3$ and with the transition amplitude given by [cf. eq. (XIX.122)]:

$$T_{i\to f} \equiv \langle \mathbf{q}|T|\alpha\mathbf{k}\rangle$$
$$= \langle \Psi_{\mathbf{q}}^{(-)}|H'|\alpha\mathbf{k}\rangle.$$

If one stops at the lowest order in H', $\Psi_{\mathbf{q}}^{(-)}$ may be replaced by $\psi_{\mathbf{q}}^{(-)}$ in this matrix element [cf. eq. (XIX.129–130)]; which gives

$$T_{i\to f} \simeq \langle \psi_{\mathbf{q}}^{(-)}|H'|\alpha\mathbf{k}\rangle = (L^{-3}g^2/2\omega)^{\frac{1}{2}}\langle\psi_{\mathbf{q}}^{(-)}|e^{i\mathbf{k}\cdot\mathbf{R}}|\alpha\rangle,$$

whence

$$\frac{d\sigma(\alpha\mathbf{k}\to\mathbf{q})}{d\Omega} \simeq \frac{g^2}{8\pi^2}\frac{Mq}{k}\,|\langle\psi_{\mathbf{q}}^{(-)}|\,e^{i\mathbf{k}\cdot\mathbf{R}}\,|\alpha\rangle|^2. \qquad \text{(XXI.136)}$$

In the same way we can calculate the cross section for the inverse reaction, in which the particle initially propagating with momentum $\mathbf{q}$ is captured in the state α by the potential $V(R)$, emitting a corpuscle of momentum $\mathbf{k}$:

$$\mathbf{q}\to\alpha\mathbf{k}.$$

To the first order in H', one finds:

$$\frac{d\sigma(\mathbf{q}\to\alpha\mathbf{k})}{d\Omega} \simeq \frac{g^2}{8\pi^2}\frac{Mk}{q}\,|\langle\alpha|\,e^{-i\mathbf{k}\cdot\mathbf{R}}|\psi_{\mathbf{q}}^{(+)}\rangle|^2. \qquad \text{(XXI.137)}$$

This expression can be obtained directly or can be deduced from the preceding one by applying the microreversibility relation (XIX.190) to the two reactions $\mathbf{q}\to\alpha\mathbf{k}$ and $(K\alpha)(-\mathbf{k})\to(-\mathbf{q})$, which are time reversal transforms one of the other. Indeed:

$$\langle\alpha|\,e^{-i\mathbf{k}\cdot\mathbf{R}}|\psi_{\mathbf{q}}^{(+)}\rangle = \langle\psi_{-\mathbf{q}}^{(-)}|\,e^{-i\mathbf{k}\cdot\mathbf{R}}(K|\alpha\rangle).$$

III. CLASSICAL THEORY OF ELECTROMAGNETIC RADIATION

17. The Equations of the Classical Maxwell–Lorentz Theory

The classical theory of radiation is based on Maxwell's equations [1]):

$$\operatorname{curl}\mathscr{E} + \frac{\partial\mathscr{H}}{\partial t} = 0 \qquad \text{(XXI.138}a\text{)}$$

$$\operatorname{div}\mathscr{H} = 0 \qquad \text{(XXI.138}b\text{)}$$

---

[1]) Contrary to what was done in treating the scalar field, we shall not use rationalized units here, whence the presence of factors 4π in the right-hand sides of equations (XXI.139).

$$\text{curl}\,\mathscr{H} - \frac{\partial \mathscr{E}}{\partial t} = 4\pi \mathbf{s} \qquad \text{(XXI.139a)}$$

$$\text{div}\,\mathscr{E} = 4\pi s^0. \qquad \text{(XXI.139b)}$$

These equations determine the evolution of the electric and magnetic fields $\mathscr{E}$ and $\mathscr{H}$ in the presence of a distribution of electric charge of density s^0 and a distribution of electric current of density $\mathbf{s}$. $\mathbf{s}$ and s^0 satisfy the equation of continuity

$$\text{div}\,\mathbf{s} + \frac{\partial s^0}{\partial t} = 0,$$

an evident consequence of equations (XXI.139), from which we obtain the law of conservation of electric charge.

Maxwell's equations are complemented by the Lorentz equation that determines the motion of electric charges in the presence of an electromagnetic field. According to this equation, the density of inertial force of a charge-carrying fluid is balanced at each instant by the electromagnetic force density:

$$\mathbf{f} \equiv s^0\, \mathscr{E} + (\mathbf{s} \times \mathscr{H}). \qquad \text{(XXI.140)}$$

According to the classical Lorentz theory of the electron, matter is exclusively made up of particles, each of which has a determined mass and charge. To obtain the equation of motion for each particle, we need only to take the limit of the Lorentz equation when the charge is concentrated in an infinitely small volume. Consider for example a particle of mass m and of charge e and denote by $\mathbf{R}$, $\mathbf{V}$ and $\mathbf{\Pi}$ its position, velocity and mechanical momentum respectively [$\mathbf{\Pi} = M\mathbf{V}$; M is the relativistic mass according to definition (XX.20)]. The densities s^0 and $\mathbf{s}$ – more exactly, the contributions of the particle to these quantities – are given by the relations:

$$s^0 = e\,\delta(\mathbf{r} - \mathbf{R}), \qquad \mathbf{s} = e\mathbf{V}\delta(\mathbf{r} - \mathbf{R}). \qquad \text{(XXI.141)}$$

The electromagnetic force $\mathbf{F}$ felt by the particle is obtained by taking the integral of $\mathbf{f}$ over a small domain about $\mathbf{R}$; the Lorentz equation gives [cf. eq. (XX.22)]:

$$\frac{\mathrm{d}\mathbf{\Pi}}{\mathrm{d}t} = \mathbf{F} \equiv e(\mathscr{E} + \mathbf{V} \times \mathscr{H}). \qquad \text{(XXI.142)}$$

In this equation $\mathscr{E}$ and $\mathscr{H}$ represent the values taken by the electric and magnetic fields at the point $\mathbf{R}$. Recall that

$$\mathbf{V} \equiv \frac{\mathrm{d}\mathbf{R}}{\mathrm{d}t} \equiv \frac{\mathbf{\Pi}}{M} \equiv \frac{\mathbf{\Pi}}{\sqrt{m^2 + \Pi^2}} \tag{XXI.143}$$

Equations (XXI.142) and (XXI.143) are the equations of motion of the particle in the presence of the field.

All of the preceding equations and definitions may be rewritten in covariant form. $\mathscr{E}$ and $\mathscr{H}$ form an antisymmetrical tensor $F_{\mu\nu}$ in accordance with definition (XX.9); s^0 and $\mathbf{s}$ form the current-density four-vector $s_\mu \equiv (s^0, \mathbf{s})$. The Maxwell–Lorentz equations become [1]:

$$\varepsilon^{\varkappa\lambda\mu\nu}\partial_\lambda F_{\mu\nu} = 0 \tag{XXI.138'}$$

$$\partial_\mu F^{\mu\nu} = 4\pi s^\nu \tag{XXI.139'}$$

and the equation of continuity becomes $\partial_\nu s^\nu = 0$. The force-density $\mathbf{f}$ is the space part of the four-vector:

$$f^\mu \equiv F^{\mu\nu} s_\nu . \tag{XXI.140'}$$

Similarly, $\mathbf{F}\,\mathrm{d}t$ is the space part of the four-vector $eF^{\mu\nu}\,\mathrm{d}x_\nu$; $\mathbf{\Pi}$ that of the four-vector $\Pi^\mu \equiv (M, \mathbf{\Pi})$ defined in § XX.4. Equation (XXI.142), complemented by an analogous equation for M, may be written in covariant form by introducing the proper time of the particle and its four-velocity.

18. Symmetries and Conservation Laws of the Classical Theory

The relativistic invariance of the Classical Theory leads to a certain number of symmetry properties and conservation laws. Here we shall consider in some detail the conservation of energy and of momentum, and briefly mention the conservation of angular momentum and the symmetry properties in reflection and time reversal. To simplify the discussion, we shall suppose that the system has only a single particle (an electron); the generalization to systems of several particles is obvious.

---

[1] By introducing the dual of the electromagnetic tensor: $\hat{F}^{\varkappa\lambda} \equiv \frac{1}{2}\varepsilon^{\varkappa\lambda\mu\nu}F_{\mu\nu}$ equation (XXI.138′) can be put in the simpler form:

$$\partial_\lambda \hat{F}^{\varkappa\lambda} = 0.$$

In order to obtain the energy and momentum conservation laws, we first show that f^μ, defined by equation (XXI.140′), is equal to the divergence of a certain tensor when $F^{\mu\nu}$ obeys the Maxwell–Lorentz equations.

From equation (XXI.139′),

$$\begin{aligned} f^\mu \equiv F^{\mu\nu} s_\nu &= \frac{1}{4\pi} F^{\mu\nu}(\partial^\varrho F_{\varrho\nu}) \\ &= \frac{1}{4\pi} [\partial^\varrho(F^{\mu\nu} F_{\varrho\nu}) - F_{\varrho\nu}(\partial^\varrho F^{\mu\nu})]. \end{aligned} \tag{XXI.144}$$

However, (XXI.138′) gives, taking into account that F is an antisymmetrical tensor:

$$\begin{aligned} F_{\varrho\nu}(\partial^\varrho F^{\mu\nu}) &= \tfrac{1}{2} F_{\varrho\nu}(\partial^\varrho F^{\mu\nu} + \partial^\nu F^{\varrho\mu}) = \tfrac{1}{2} F_{\varrho\nu}(\partial^\mu F^{\varrho\nu}) \\ &= \tfrac{1}{4} \partial^\mu (F_{\varrho\nu} F^{\varrho\nu}) = \tfrac{1}{4} g^{\mu\varrho} \partial_\varrho (F_{\varkappa\lambda} F^{\varkappa\lambda}). \end{aligned}$$

Substituting this expression into the right-hand side of (XXI.144) and putting:

$$T^{\mu\varrho} \equiv \frac{1}{4\pi} (F^{\mu\nu} F^\varrho{}_\nu - \tfrac{1}{4} g^{\mu\varrho} F_{\varkappa\lambda} F^{\varkappa\lambda}) \tag{XXI.145}$$

we obtain:

$$f^\mu = \partial_\varrho T^{\mu\varrho}. \tag{XXI.146}$$

This is the desired result.

$T^{\mu\varrho}$ is the "energy-momentum" tensor. Explicitly writing out the field-components in its definition, we have:

$$T^{00} = -\frac{1}{8\pi} (\mathscr{E}^2 + \mathscr{H}^2)$$

$$T^{k0} = T^{0k} = -\frac{1}{4\pi} [\mathscr{E} \times \mathscr{H}]$$

$$T^{kl} = T^{lk} = \frac{1}{4\pi} [\mathscr{E}_k \mathscr{E}_l + \mathscr{H}_k \mathscr{H}_l + \tfrac{1}{2} \delta_{kl} (\mathscr{H}^2 - \mathscr{E}^2)].$$

One defines the energy W^0 and the momentum $\mathbf{W}$ of the field by the following integrals extended over all space:

$$W^0 \equiv \frac{1}{8\pi} \int (\mathscr{E}^2 + \mathscr{H}^2) \, d\mathbf{r} \tag{XXI.147a}$$

$$\mathbf{W} \equiv \frac{1}{4\pi} \int (\mathscr{E} \times \mathscr{H}) \, d\mathbf{r} \tag{XXI.147b}$$

i.e.:

$$W^{\mu} = -\int T^{\mu 0}\, \mathrm{d}\boldsymbol{r}. \tag{XXI.148}$$

It is not *a priori* evident that W_{μ} is a four-vector. However, by using the energy and momentum conservation laws one can prove that it is.

To demonstrate the energy and momentum conservation laws, we put the equation of motion of the particle in the form

$$\frac{\mathrm{d}\Pi^{\mu}}{\mathrm{d}t} = \int f^{\mu}\, \mathrm{d}\boldsymbol{r}.$$

This equation is satisfied irrespective of the volume of integration V provided that it contains the point representing the position of the particle. Substituting for f^{μ} from (XXI.146), we obtain

$$\frac{\mathrm{d}\Pi^{\mu}}{\mathrm{d}t} = \frac{\mathrm{d}}{\mathrm{d}t}\left(\int_V T^{\mu 0}\, \mathrm{d}\boldsymbol{r}\right) + \int_V \left(\sum_k \frac{\partial T^{\mu k}}{\partial x^k}\right) \mathrm{d}\boldsymbol{r}.$$

The second integral can easily be transformed into an integral over the boundary surface of the volume V. Let us now extend the volume V to cover the whole of space. Under the hypothesis, entirely legitimate here, that the electromagnetic field vanishes sufficiently rapidly at infinity, the surface integral then tends to zero and one finds, taking definition (XXI.148) into account:

$$\frac{\mathrm{d}}{\mathrm{d}t}(\Pi^{\mu} + W^{\mu}) = 0.$$

This justifies the definition of the energy and momentum of the field adopted above, and constitutes the law of conservation of the energy and momentum of the total system (particle + field):

$$M + W^0 = Cst. \text{ in time.} \tag{XXI.149a}$$

$$\boldsymbol{\Pi} + \boldsymbol{W} = Cst. \text{ in time.} \tag{XXI.149b}$$

A similar argument leads to the following law for the conservation of the total angular momentum:

$$(\boldsymbol{R} \times \boldsymbol{\Pi}) + \boldsymbol{I} = Cst. \text{ in time} \tag{XXI.150}$$

if we take the following definition for the angular momentum of the field:

$$\boldsymbol{I} \equiv \frac{1}{4\pi} \int [\boldsymbol{r} \times (\mathscr{E} \times \mathscr{H})]\, \mathrm{d}\boldsymbol{r}. \tag{XXI.151}$$

If the system contains several particles, $\mathbf{\Pi}$ and M must be replaced by the sum of the momenta and the sum of the relativistic masses, and $(\mathbf{R}\times\mathbf{\Pi})$ by the sum of the angular momenta. With these obvious modifications, the three conservation laws (XXI.149a), (XXI.149b) and (XXI.150) remain valid.

Let us now consider the space and time reflections.

The equations of motion are invariant in a spatial reflection ($t\to t$, $\mathbf{r}\to -\mathbf{r}$) if we treat the charge e as a true scalar and the field $F^{\mu\nu}$ as a true tensor. With this convention s^0 transforms like a scalar function of three-dimensional space, $\mathbf{s}$ and $\mathscr{E}$ like polar-vector fields and $\mathscr{H}$ like an axial-vector field; in particular we have the transformation laws:

$$\mathscr{E}(t,\mathbf{r})\to -\mathscr{E}(t,-\mathbf{r}),\quad \mathscr{H}(t,\mathbf{r})\to +\mathscr{H}(t,-\mathbf{r}). \qquad \text{(XXI.152)}$$

The equations of motion are reversible in time ($t\to -t$, $\mathbf{r}\to\mathbf{r}$), if we treat the charge e as a scalar and $F^{\mu\nu}$ as a "pseudotensor". With this convention, s^0 and $\mathscr{E}$, considered as functions of $\mathbf{r}$, are invariant under time reversal, $\mathbf{s}$ and $\mathscr{H}$ change sign:

$$\mathscr{E}(t,\mathbf{r})\to +\mathscr{E}(-t,\mathbf{r}),\quad \mathscr{H}(t,\mathbf{r})\to -\mathscr{H}(-t,\mathbf{r}). \qquad \text{(XXI.153)}$$

19. Self-energy and Classical Radius of the Electron

At this point, we should mention a serious difficulty of the classical theory of radiation. In all of the preceding work, the charge of each particle is supposed to be concentrated in a very small volume, for example a small sphere whose radius a is made to tend to zero. In fact, the hypothesis of exact point-charges is not self consistent. Let us consider an isolated electron at rest at the origin of coordinates, and calculate the energy δm of the field created by this electron; this energy is commonly called the *electrostatic self-energy*. It is really a *mass renormalization* term, for in accordance with the argument of § 11, which applies here without change, the experimentally observed mass is:

$$m_{\text{exp}} = m+\delta m.$$

Since the electric field created in the external region ($r>a$) is $e\mathbf{r}/r^3$, formula (XXI.147a) gives:

$$\delta m > \frac{e^2}{8\pi}\int\frac{\mathrm{d}\mathbf{r}}{r^4} = \frac{e^2}{2a}$$

and, since $\delta m < m_{\text{exp}}$, one has: $a > e^2/2m_{\text{exp}}$. The length:

$$r_0 = \frac{e^2}{m_{\text{exp}}} \qquad (\simeq 2.82 \times 10^{-13}\ \text{cm})$$

is called the *classical radius of the electron*. The classical electron is therefore an object of finite dimensions, of the order of r_0. However, the theory is incapable of accounting for the stability of such objects, and *a fortiori*, for the details of their internal structure, i.e. the distribution of charges and currents in the region $r < r_0$. This is because the electromagnetic forces between the constitutive elements of the electron are in the main repulsive forces which tend to dissociate it; for the electron to be stable, they must be counterbalanced by cohesive forces of non-electromagnetic origin. The introduction of such forces in the case of a relativistic theory encounters serious difficulties. In practice, one contents oneself with *ad hoc* hypotheses concerning the internal structure of the electron; we must therefore expect to be able to correctly account only for phenomena which do not critically depend on the details of that structure, i.e. those involving sufficiently large wavelengths ($\lambda \gg r_0$) [1].

20. Electromagnetic Potential. Choice of the Gauge

Equations that are equivalent to equations (XXI.138) but simpler can be obtained by introducing the vector potential $\boldsymbol{A}$ and the scalar potential φ according to the definitions [cf. eq. (XX.7)]:

$$\mathscr{H} = \text{curl}\, \boldsymbol{A}, \qquad \mathscr{E} = -\frac{\partial \boldsymbol{A}}{\partial t} - \text{grad}\, \varphi. \qquad \text{(XXI.154)}$$

Equations (XXI.138) are then automatically satisfied. Equations (XXI.139) are equivalent to the equations:

$$\ddot{\boldsymbol{A}} - \triangle \boldsymbol{A} + \text{grad}\, (\dot{\varphi} + \text{div}\, \boldsymbol{A}) = 4\pi \boldsymbol{s} \qquad \text{(XXI.155}a\text{)}$$

$$\ddot{\varphi} - \triangle \varphi - \frac{\partial}{\partial t} (\dot{\varphi} + \text{div}\, \boldsymbol{A}) = 4\pi s^0. \qquad \text{(XXI.155}b\text{)}$$

Equations (XXI.154) define $\boldsymbol{A}$ and φ only to within an arbitrary

[1] The Quantum Theory also has an "ultraviolet catastrophe" of similar origin. Nevertheless, the analogy between the Classical and Quantum Theories must not be pushed too far. Effects like pair creation lead one to attribute the "quantum electron" with a radius of the order of $\hbar/mc$, that is 137 times greater than r_0.

function; if $G(t, \boldsymbol{r})$ is an arbitrary function of space and time, these equations remain satisfied if we make the substitutions:

$$\boldsymbol{A} \to \boldsymbol{A} - \operatorname{grad} G, \qquad \varphi \to \varphi + \frac{\partial G}{\partial t}. \tag{XXI.156}$$

Such a set of substitutions is called a *gauge transformation* (cf. § XX.20).

All these relations can be written in a completely covariant way. The potentials $\boldsymbol{A}$ and φ form a four-vector A^μ [cf. eq. (XX.6)]; according to equations (XXI.154), A^μ is the vector whose curl is $F^{\mu\nu}$ [cf. eq. (XX.8)], which defines it to within the gradient of an arbitrary function; the gauge transformation (XXI.156) is nothing else but the addition of a gradient:

$$A^\mu \to A^\mu + \partial^\mu G \qquad (G \text{ arbitrary}). \tag{XXI.157}$$

Equations (XXI.155) read

$$\Box A^\mu - \partial^\mu(\partial_\nu A^\nu) = 4\pi s^\mu. \tag{XXI.158}$$

The arbitrary in the gauge can be partly removed without violating the formal covariance of the theory by imposing the *Lorentz supplementary condition*

$$\partial_\nu A^\nu = 0. \tag{XXI.159}$$

The equation of motion of the potential then takes the simpler form

$$\Box A^\mu = 4\pi s^\mu. \tag{XXI.160}$$

Let χ be an arbitrary solution of the equation: $\Box \chi = 0$. The Lorentz condition fixes the gauge of the potential to within a function of this type. In other words, the definition of the field $F^{\mu\nu}$ and equations (XXI.159) and (XXI.160) are invariant in the *Lorentz gauge transformations* (sometimes called special gauge transformations):

$$A^\mu \to A^\mu + \partial^\mu \chi \qquad (\Box \chi = 0). \tag{XXI.161}$$

One can also obtain very simple equations of motion by imposing the condition

$$\operatorname{div} \boldsymbol{A} = 0. \tag{XXI.162}$$

Contrary to the Lorentz condition, (XXI.162) does not preserve the formal covariance of the theory. Nevertheless it has the advantage of completely removing the arbitrary in the gauge. The gauge thus defined is currently called the *radiation gauge*. It is the one that will be adopted in what is to follow. Before studying radiation theory in this gauge, we must recall an important property of the decomposition of vector fields.

21. Longitudinal and Transverse Parts of a Vector Field

Any real or complex vector field $\boldsymbol{B}(\boldsymbol{r})$ can be considered as a superposition of two fields:

$$\boldsymbol{B}(\boldsymbol{r}) = \boldsymbol{B}_{||}(\boldsymbol{r}) + \boldsymbol{B}_{\perp}(\boldsymbol{r}) \tag{XXI.163}$$

the one of which, $\boldsymbol{B}_{||}$, is irrotational and the other, $\boldsymbol{B}_{\perp}$, divergenceless. One has:

$$\text{curl } \boldsymbol{B}_{||} = 0, \qquad \text{div } \boldsymbol{B}_{||} = \text{div } \boldsymbol{B} \tag{XXI.164}$$

$$\text{div } \boldsymbol{B}_{\perp} = 0, \qquad \text{curl } \boldsymbol{B}_{\perp} = \text{curl } \boldsymbol{B}. \tag{XXI.165}$$

If one limits oneself to square-integrable vector fields, this decomposition is unique [1]). By definition the fields $\boldsymbol{B}_{||}$ and $\boldsymbol{B}_{\perp}$ thus defined constitute respectively the *longitudinal part and the transversal part of the field* $\boldsymbol{B}$. In addition we have

$$\boldsymbol{B}_{||} = \text{grad } U \qquad U(\boldsymbol{r}) = -\frac{1}{4\pi}\int \frac{\text{div } \boldsymbol{B}(\boldsymbol{r}')}{|\boldsymbol{r}-\boldsymbol{r}'|}\,\mathrm{d}\boldsymbol{r}' \tag{XXI.166}$$

$$\boldsymbol{B}_{\perp} = \text{curl } \boldsymbol{V} \qquad \boldsymbol{V}(\boldsymbol{r}) = \frac{1}{4\pi}\int \frac{\text{curl } \boldsymbol{B}(\boldsymbol{r}')}{|\boldsymbol{r}-\boldsymbol{r}'|}\,\mathrm{d}\boldsymbol{r}'. \tag{XXI.167}$$

This decomposition can easily be effected using the Fourier transformation. Denote the Fourier transforms of $\boldsymbol{B}$, $\boldsymbol{B}_{\perp}$ and $\boldsymbol{B}_{||}$ by $\boldsymbol{b}$, $\boldsymbol{b}_{\perp}$ and $\boldsymbol{b}_{||}$ respectively:

$$\begin{aligned} \boldsymbol{b}(\boldsymbol{k}) &= (2\pi)^{-3/2} \int \boldsymbol{B}(\boldsymbol{r})\, \mathrm{e}^{-i\boldsymbol{k}\cdot\boldsymbol{r}}\, \mathrm{d}\boldsymbol{r} \\ \boldsymbol{b}_{||}(\boldsymbol{k}) &= \ldots \qquad\qquad \text{etc.} \end{aligned} \tag{XXI.168}$$

Equations (XXI.164) and (XXI.165) are respectively equivalent to the equations

$$\boldsymbol{k}\times\boldsymbol{b}_{||} = 0 \qquad \boldsymbol{k}\cdot\boldsymbol{b}_{||} = \boldsymbol{k}\cdot\boldsymbol{b}$$

$$\boldsymbol{k}\cdot\boldsymbol{b}_{\perp} = 0 \qquad \boldsymbol{k}\times\boldsymbol{b}_{\perp} = \boldsymbol{k}\times\boldsymbol{b}.$$

---

[1]) We must also suppose $\boldsymbol{B}_{||}$ and $\boldsymbol{B}_{\perp}$ square-integrable. This decomposition will sometimes be made for fields which are not square-integrable; the longitudinal and transverse parts will then be unambiguously defined by equations (XXI.166) and (XXI.167) respectively.

$\boldsymbol{b}_{||}$ is the projection of $\boldsymbol{b}$ along the vector $\boldsymbol{k}$, whence the name of longitudinal part [1]) for $\boldsymbol{B}_{||}$; $\boldsymbol{b}_{\perp}$ is the projection of $\boldsymbol{b}$ perpendicular to the vector $\boldsymbol{k}$, whence the name of transverse part for $\boldsymbol{B}_{\perp}$. Equations (XXI.166) and (XXI.167) are respectively equivalent to the equations:

$$\boldsymbol{b}_{||} = \frac{\boldsymbol{k}(\boldsymbol{b}\cdot\boldsymbol{k})}{k^2} \qquad \boldsymbol{b}_{\perp} = \frac{\boldsymbol{k}\times(\boldsymbol{b}\times\boldsymbol{k})}{k^2}. \tag{XXI.169}$$

The Fourier transform of the function U [definition (XXI.166)] is:

$$u(\boldsymbol{k}) = -\,\mathrm{i}\,\frac{(\boldsymbol{b}\cdot\boldsymbol{k})}{k^2}.$$

[*N.B.* The Fourier transform of $1/r$ is $\sqrt{2\pi}/\pi k^2$.]

In a more general way, the square-integrable vector-field space – that is, the space of the wave function of a particle of spin 1 – is the direct sum of two orthogonal subspaces, the longitudinal-field space and the transverse-field space. The decomposition envisaged here consists in writing that $\boldsymbol{B}$ is the sum of its projections on these two complementary subspaces. These projections can automatically be obtained by choosing an appropriate basis. Denote by

$$\boldsymbol{L}^{(1)}, \boldsymbol{L}^{(2)}, \ldots, \boldsymbol{L}^{(\lambda)}, \ldots$$

a complete set of orthonormal longitudinal fields and by

$$\boldsymbol{T}^{(1)}, \boldsymbol{T}^{(2)}, \ldots, \boldsymbol{T}^{(\tau)}, \ldots$$

a complete set of orthonormal transverse fields:

$$\mathrm{curl}\,\boldsymbol{L}^{(\lambda)} = 0, \qquad \int (\boldsymbol{L}^{(\lambda)*}\cdot\boldsymbol{L}^{(\lambda')})\,\mathrm{d}\boldsymbol{r} = \delta_{\lambda\lambda'} \tag{XXI.170a}$$

$$\mathrm{div}\,\boldsymbol{T}^{(\tau)} = 0, \qquad \int (\boldsymbol{T}^{(\tau)*}\cdot\boldsymbol{T}^{(\tau')})\,\mathrm{d}\boldsymbol{r} = \delta_{\tau\tau'} \tag{XXI.170b}$$

$$\sum_\lambda L_i^{(\lambda)}(\boldsymbol{r})\,L_j^{(\lambda)*}(\boldsymbol{r}') + \sum_\tau T_i^{(\tau)}(\boldsymbol{r})\,T_j^{(\tau)*}(\boldsymbol{r}') = \delta_{ij}\,\delta(\boldsymbol{r}-\boldsymbol{r}') \tag{XXI.170c}$$

$$(i, j = x, y \text{ or } z).$$

Let us put

$$\beta_{||}^{(\lambda)} = \int (\boldsymbol{L}^{(\lambda)*}\cdot\boldsymbol{B})\,\mathrm{d}\boldsymbol{r}, \qquad \beta_{\perp}^{(\tau)} = \int (\boldsymbol{T}^{(\tau)*}\cdot\boldsymbol{B})\,\mathrm{d}\boldsymbol{r}. \tag{XXI.171}$$

---

[1]) $\boldsymbol{B}_{||}$ is not to be confused with the *radial* part of $\boldsymbol{B}$ which is the projection of $\boldsymbol{B}$ along the vector $\boldsymbol{r}$; $\boldsymbol{B}_{\mathrm{rad}} = \boldsymbol{r}(\boldsymbol{B}\cdot\boldsymbol{r})/r^2$. Note that the radial part of a purely transverse field does not, in general, vanish.

One then has:

$$\boldsymbol{B}_{\|} = \sum_{\lambda} \beta_{\|}{}^{(\lambda)} \boldsymbol{L}^{(\lambda)}, \qquad \boldsymbol{B}_{\perp} = \sum_{\tau} \beta_{\perp}{}^{(\tau)} \boldsymbol{T}^{(\tau)}. \tag{XXI.172}$$

The use of the Fourier transform amounts to choosing a particular basis, that of the fields of longitudinal and transverse plane waves. With each wave vector there is associated a longitudinal field:

$$\boldsymbol{L}^{(\boldsymbol{k})} = (2\pi)^{-3/2}\, \hat{\boldsymbol{k}}\, e^{i\boldsymbol{k}\cdot\boldsymbol{r}} \qquad (\hat{\boldsymbol{k}} \equiv \boldsymbol{k}/k) \tag{XXI.173a}$$

and two orthogonal transverse fields:

$$\boldsymbol{T}^{(\boldsymbol{k}\varpi)} = (2\pi)^{-3/2}\, \boldsymbol{\epsilon}^{(\varpi)}\, e^{i\boldsymbol{k}\cdot\boldsymbol{r}} \qquad (\varpi = 1, 2) \tag{XXI.173b}$$

$\boldsymbol{\epsilon}^{(1)}$ and $\boldsymbol{\epsilon}^{(2)}$ are two arbitrary unit vectors [1]) orthogonal to $\boldsymbol{k}$ and orthogonal to each other:

$$\boldsymbol{k}\cdot\boldsymbol{\epsilon}^{(1)} = \boldsymbol{k}\cdot\boldsymbol{\epsilon}^{(2)} = 0 \tag{XXI.174a}$$

$$\boldsymbol{\epsilon}^{(1)*}\cdot\boldsymbol{\epsilon}^{(1)} = \boldsymbol{\epsilon}^{(2)*}\cdot\boldsymbol{\epsilon}^{(2)} = 1, \qquad \boldsymbol{\epsilon}^{(1)*}\cdot\boldsymbol{\epsilon}^{(2)} = 0. \tag{XXI.174b}$$

The components of $\boldsymbol{B}$ in this basis [definitions (XXI.171)] are related to the vectors $\boldsymbol{b}_{\|}$ and $\boldsymbol{b}_{\perp}$ by the formulas [cf. eq. (XXI.169)]:

$$\boldsymbol{b}_{\|} = \beta_{\|}{}^{(\boldsymbol{k})}\, \hat{\boldsymbol{k}}, \qquad \boldsymbol{b}_{\perp} = \sum_{\varpi} \beta_{\perp}{}^{(\boldsymbol{k}\varpi)}\, \boldsymbol{\epsilon}^{(\varpi)}. \tag{XXI.175}$$

The plane waves here depend on the continuous index $\boldsymbol{k}$ and are normalized to $\delta(\boldsymbol{k}-\boldsymbol{k}')$. In order to have only discrete indices, one can, according to the usual artifice, enclose the system in a cube of side L; the constant $(2\pi)^{-3/2}$ in definitions (XXI.173*a*, *b*) must then be replaced by $L^{-3/2}$.

Among the other bases currently used are the spherical waves. We shall return to them in § 29.

22. Elimination of the Longitudinal Field

Among Maxwell's equations, equations (XXI.138*b*) and (XXI.139*b*) are not, properly speaking, equations of motion, but rather constraints imposed on the fields $\mathscr{E}$ and $\mathscr{H}$. They fix the longitudinal parts of these fields.

---

[1]) These vectors are not necessarily real. By definition a vector is real if its Cartesian components are real; the vector $\boldsymbol{k}$ is a real vector. The scalar product of two complex vectors $\boldsymbol{A}$ and $\boldsymbol{B}$ is by definition:

$$\boldsymbol{A}^*\cdot\boldsymbol{B} \equiv A_x{}^* B_x + A_y{}^* B_y + A_z{}^* B_z.$$

We see from equation (XXI.138*b*) that $\mathscr{H}_{\parallel} = 0$ and from equation (XXI.139*b*) that $\mathscr{E}_{\parallel}(t, \mathbf{r})$ *is the electrostatic field created by the charge distribution* $s_0(t, \mathbf{r})$. In order to define the dynamical state of the system, it is therefore sufficient to specify the charge distributions and currents – that is, the positions and the velocities of the particles – on the one hand, and the transverse fields $\mathscr{H}$ and $\mathscr{E}_{\perp}$ on the other. It is therefore possible to reformulate the theory eliminating completely the longitudinal part of the electromagnetic field.

Rather than proceed directly to this elimination, it is preferable to first introduce the potential $(\varphi, \mathbf{A})$ in the radiation gauge [cf. eq. (XXI.162)]. This is merely a change of variable. The field $\mathbf{A}$ is by definition purely transverse:

$$\mathbf{A}_{\parallel} = 0, \qquad \mathbf{A} = \mathbf{A}_{\perp}. \tag{XXI.176}$$

The old variables are given in terms of the new by equations (XXI.154), or:

$$\mathscr{E}_{\parallel} = -\operatorname{grad} \varphi \tag{XXI.177}$$

$$\mathscr{H} = \operatorname{curl} \mathbf{A}, \qquad \mathscr{E}_{\perp} = -\frac{\partial \mathbf{A}}{\partial t}. \tag{XXI.178}$$

φ is determined by equation (XXI.155*b*), which in this case is written:

$$\triangle \varphi = -4\pi s^0. \tag{XXI.179}$$

One finds:

$$\varphi(t, \mathbf{r}) = \int \frac{s^0(t, \mathbf{r}')}{|\mathbf{r} - \mathbf{r}'|} \, d\mathbf{r}' \tag{XXI.180}$$

from which one obtains the expression mentioned above for $\mathscr{E}_{\parallel}$ in terms of s^0. To eliminate φ from equation (XXI.155*a*) it is sufficient to separately write down the equality of the longitudinal and transverse components. The first of these equalities:

$$\operatorname{grad} \dot{\varphi} = 4\pi \mathbf{s}_{\parallel} \tag{XXI.181}$$

is identically satisfied if φ satisfies equation (XXI.180) [1]).

The second is independent of φ, and it is the equation of motion:

$$\ddot{\mathbf{A}} - \triangle \mathbf{A} = 4\pi \mathbf{s}_{\perp}. \tag{XXI.182}$$

---

[1]) For this equality to be satisfied it is sufficient that the divergence of each side be equal: $\Delta\dot{\varphi} = 4\pi \operatorname{div} \mathbf{s}$; this equation can be deduced from equation (XXI.179) by differentiating both sides of the latter with respect to the time and using the equation of continuity.

It remains to eliminate the longitudinal field from the equations of motion of the particles [eqs. (XXI.142) and (XXI.143)], that is from the expression for the Lorentz force to which each of them is subjected. The different quantities attached to each particle are denoted by the same symbols as in § 17, with an index 1, 2, ..., n, ... to distinguish between them. Thus the contribution of the nth particle to the charge density is:

$$s_n{}^0 = e_n \delta(\mathbf{r} - \mathbf{R}_n).$$

Equation (XXI.179) is therefore written:

$$\triangle \varphi = -\, 4\pi \sum_n e_n\, \delta(\mathbf{r} - \mathbf{R}_n) \qquad \text{(XXI.183)}$$

and its solution is the Coulomb potential:

$$\varphi = \sum_n \frac{e_n}{|\mathbf{r} - \mathbf{R}_n|}. \qquad \text{(XXI.184)}$$

Let $\mathbf{F}_i$ be the Lorentz force acting on the ith particle. We can write:

$$\mathbf{F}_i = \mathbf{F}_i{}^{\mathrm{tr}} + \mathbf{F}_i{}^{\mathrm{long}}$$

$$\mathbf{F}_i{}^{\mathrm{tr}} = e_i(\mathscr{E}_\perp(i) + \mathbf{V}_i \times \mathscr{H}(i)) = e_i\left(-\frac{\partial \mathbf{A}(i)}{\partial t} + \mathbf{V}_i \times \operatorname{curl} \mathbf{A}(i)\right) \qquad \text{(XXI.185)}$$

$$\mathbf{F}_i{}^{\mathrm{long}} = e_i\, \mathscr{E}_{||}(i) = -\, e_i \operatorname{grad} \varphi(i)$$

$\mathscr{E}_\perp(i)$, $\mathscr{H}(i)$, ... here denote the values taken by $\mathscr{E}_\perp$, $\mathscr{H}$, ... at the point $\mathbf{R}_i$. The desired elimination is effected by substituting expression (XXI.184) into $\mathbf{F}^{\mathrm{long}}$.

However, this substitution cannot be effected immediately, since the potential φ diverges at the point $\mathbf{R}_i$. The difficulty is due to the fact that we have assumed point charges. $\mathbf{F}_i{}^{\mathrm{long}}$ is the electrostatic force on the ith particle due to all of the charges present; we denote by $\mathbf{F}_i{}'$ the contribution to $\mathbf{F}_i{}^{\mathrm{long}}$ from the charge on the ith particle itself, and by $\mathbf{F}_i{}^{\mathrm{coul}}$ the contribution from all the other charges. So long as the particles are sufficiently well separated, the calculation of $\mathbf{F}_i{}^{\mathrm{coul}}$ may be carried through supposing point charges, giving:

$$\mathbf{F}_i{}^{\mathrm{coul}} = \sum_{n \neq i} e_i\, e_n \frac{(\mathbf{R}_i - \mathbf{R}_n)}{|\mathbf{R}_i - \mathbf{R}_n|^3}. \qquad \text{(XXI.186)}$$

But the hypothesis of point charges is obviously not justified for the calculation of $\boldsymbol{F}_i'$. In any case, whatever may be the distribution of charge inside the ith particle, one finds:

$$\boldsymbol{F}_i' = 0.$$

Thus, the force on each particle is the Lorentz force of the transverse field [eq. (XXI.185)] and the electrostatic force due to the presence of all of the *other* charges [eq. (XXI.186)]:

$$\boldsymbol{F}_i = \boldsymbol{F}_i^{\text{tr}} + \boldsymbol{F}_i^{\text{coul}}. \tag{XXI.187}$$

23. Energy, Momentum, Angular Momentum

Having eliminated the longitudinal field from the equations of motion, we now wish to eliminate it from the conservation laws for energy, momentum, and angular momentum.

By replacing $\mathscr{E}$ by $\mathscr{E}_\perp$ in the expression for the energy in the field [eq. (XXI.147*a*)], we obtain a new expression, U, depending only on the transverse components; to distinguish it from the preceding one we shall call it the *radiation energy*:

$$U \equiv \frac{1}{8\pi} \int (\mathscr{E}_\perp{}^2 + \mathscr{H}^2)\, \mathrm{d}\boldsymbol{r}. \tag{XXI.188}$$

We similarly define the *radiation momentum* $\boldsymbol{X}$ [cf. eq. (XXI.147*b*)] and the *radiation angular momentum* $\boldsymbol{G}$ [cf. eq. (XXI.151)]:

$$\boldsymbol{X} \equiv \frac{1}{4\pi} \int (\mathscr{E}_\perp \times \mathscr{H})\, \mathrm{d}\boldsymbol{r} \tag{XXI.189}$$

$$\boldsymbol{G} \equiv \frac{1}{4\pi} \int [\boldsymbol{r} \times (\mathscr{E}_\perp \times \mathscr{H})]\, \mathrm{d}\boldsymbol{r}. \tag{XXI.190}$$

U, $\boldsymbol{X}$ and $\boldsymbol{G}$ are respectively the energy, the momentum and the angular momentum of the system in the absence of charge.

They can be put in a form analogous to the one given in section I for the energy, momentum and angular momentum of the scalar field (cf. § 4, 6 and 7). By replacing $\mathscr{H}$ by curl $\boldsymbol{A}$ in expressions (XXI.188–190), by effecting a certain number of integrations by parts and by using the fact that $\mathscr{E}_\perp$ and $\boldsymbol{A}$ are transverse fields vanishing at infinity, one finds:

$$U = \frac{1}{8\pi} \int \sum_i (\mathscr{E}_{\perp i}{}^2 + (\nabla A_i)^2)\, \mathrm{d}\boldsymbol{r}, \qquad \text{(XXI.188')}$$

$$\mathscr{K} = \frac{1}{4\pi} \int \sum_i \mathscr{E}_{\perp i}(\nabla A_i)\, \mathrm{d}\boldsymbol{r}, \qquad \text{(XXI.189')}$$

and

$$\boldsymbol{G} = \boldsymbol{G}^{(0)} + \boldsymbol{G}^{(s)}, \qquad \text{(XXI.190')}$$

where:

$$\boldsymbol{G}^{(0)} \equiv \frac{1}{4\pi} \int \sum_i \mathscr{E}_{\perp i}(\boldsymbol{l} A_i)\, \mathrm{d}\boldsymbol{r}, \qquad \text{(XXI.191}a\text{)}$$

$$\boldsymbol{G}^{(s)} \equiv \frac{1}{4\pi} \int (\mathscr{E}_\perp \times \boldsymbol{A})\, \mathrm{d}\boldsymbol{r}. \qquad \text{(XXI.191}b\text{)}$$

In order to obtain these expressions it is convenient to use the techniques and notations of the tensor calculus, and in particular to use the antisymmetrical tensor of 3-dimensional Euclidean space ε_{ijk} (definition given in note, p. 510) and the identity

$$\varepsilon_{ijk}\,\varepsilon_{klm} = \delta_{il}\,\delta_{jm} - \delta_{im}\,\delta_{jl}.$$

Thus

$$\mathscr{H}^2 = (\mathrm{curl}\ \boldsymbol{A})^2 = \varepsilon_{ijk}\,\varepsilon_{klm} \frac{\partial A_j}{\partial x_i} \frac{\partial A_m}{\partial x_l} = \frac{\partial A_m}{\partial x_l} \frac{\partial A_m}{\partial x_l} - \frac{\partial A_l}{\partial x_m} \frac{\partial A_m}{\partial x_l}$$

$$= \frac{\partial A_m}{\partial x_l} \frac{\partial A_m}{\partial x_l} - \frac{\partial}{\partial x_l} \left(A_m \frac{\partial A_l}{\partial x_m} \right) + A_m \frac{\partial^2 A_l}{\partial x_m\, \partial x_l}$$

and since $\boldsymbol{A}$ is a transverse field vanishing at infinity:

$$\int \mathscr{H}^2\, \mathrm{d}\boldsymbol{r} = \int \frac{\partial A_m}{\partial x_l} \frac{\partial A_m}{\partial x_l}\, \mathrm{d}\boldsymbol{r} \equiv \int \sum_m (\nabla A_m)^2\, \mathrm{d}\boldsymbol{r}$$

from which one obtains equation (XXI.188'). Using an analogous technique, one finds:

$$(\mathscr{E}_\perp \times \mathscr{H})_i = \varepsilon_{ijk}\,\varepsilon_{klm}\, \mathscr{E}_{\perp j} \frac{\partial A_m}{\partial x_l} = \mathscr{E}_{\perp m} \frac{\partial}{\partial x_i} A_m - \frac{\partial}{\partial x_l} (\mathscr{E}_{\perp l} A_i),$$

from which one obtains equation (XXI.189'). Similarly,

$$[\boldsymbol{r} \times (\mathscr{E}_\perp \times \mathscr{H})]_i = \mathscr{E}_{\perp m} \left(\varepsilon_{ijk}\, x_j \frac{\partial A_m}{\partial x_k} \right) - \frac{\partial}{\partial x_l} (\varepsilon_{ijk}\, x_j\, \mathscr{E}_{\perp l} A_k) + \varepsilon_{ijk}\, \mathscr{E}_{\perp j} A_k$$

from which one obtains equation (XXI.190') with definitions (XXI.191a, b) of $\boldsymbol{G}^{(0)}$ and $\boldsymbol{G}^{(s)}$.

The comparison of these expressions with the corresponding expressions for the scalar field is instructive. Let us compare, for example, expressions (XXI.30) and (XXI.188′) for the energy of the field. Differences arise because: (*i*) $\mathbf{A}$ is a vector field, (*ii*) its mass is null ($\mu=0$), (*iii*) the field units adopted here differ by a factor of $\sqrt{4\pi}$ from those used in section I. Apart from this, expression (XXI.188′) appears as a simple generalization of expression (XXI.30) if we suppose, as suggested by the second of equations (XXI.178) and as will be confirmed in what follows, that the momentum canonically conjugate to the field $\mathbf{A}$ is $(-\mathscr{E}_\perp)$. The same can be said for the expressions for the momentum [eqs. (XXI.55) and (XXI.189′)] and the angular momentum [eqs. (XXI.61) and (XXI.190′)]. The vector character of the field is particularly apparent in the angular momentum; in addition to the term $\mathbf{G}^{(0)}$ obtained by a simple generalization of the expression for the angular momentum of the scalar field, there is a supplementary term $\mathbf{G}^{(s)}$; $\mathbf{G}^{(0)}$ represents the "orbital angular momentum" and $\mathbf{G}^{(s)}$ the "spin" of the field [1]).

We are now in a position to eliminate the longitudinal field from the expressions obtained in § 18 for the total energy, the total momentum and the total angular momentum of the system formed by the electromagnetic field and the charged particles interacting with this field.

Consider first the total momentum of the system. According to the definition given in § 18,

$$\begin{aligned}\mathbf{P}_{\text{tot}} &= \sum_n \mathbf{\Pi}_n + \mathbf{W} \\ &= \sum_n \mathbf{\Pi}_n + \mathbf{X} + \mathbf{X}',\end{aligned} \qquad \text{(XXI.192)}$$

where

$$\mathbf{X}' \equiv \frac{1}{4\pi} \int \mathscr{E}_{\parallel} \times \mathscr{H}) \, \mathrm{d}\mathbf{r}.$$

---

1) In the present case things are complicated by the transversality condition; among other consequences, it results from this that the amplitudes of the field $\mathbf{A}$ at each point in space do not form a set of independent dynamical variables. The particular form of the commutation relations given in Problem XXI.5 is due to these same reasons. Also for the same reasons, the vector operator $\mathbf{G}^{(0)}$ and $\mathbf{G}^{(s)}$ do not separately verify the commutation relations characteristic of angular momenta.

Replacing $\mathscr{E}_{\parallel}$ and $\mathscr{H}$ by their definitions [eqs. (XXI.177–178)], we have

$$\mathscr{E}_{\parallel} \times \mathscr{H} = -(\text{grad}\, \varphi \times \mathscr{H}) = \varphi \text{ curl } \mathscr{H} - \text{curl } (\varphi \mathscr{H})$$
$$= -\varphi(\triangle \mathbf{A}) - \text{curl } (\varphi \mathscr{H}).$$

Integrating by parts and noting that φ and $\mathbf{A}$ vanish at infinity, we obtain:

$$\mathbf{X}' = -\frac{1}{4\pi} \int \varphi(\triangle \mathbf{A})\, \mathrm{d}\mathbf{r} = -\frac{1}{4\pi} \int \mathbf{A}(\triangle \varphi)\, \mathrm{d}\mathbf{r}.$$

According to equation (XXI.183), $\Delta\varphi$ is a sum of δ-functions; the integration is easily carried out and gives:

$$\mathbf{X}' = \sum_n e_n \mathbf{A}(n)$$

where, in accordance with the convention adopted above, $\mathbf{A}(n) \equiv \mathbf{A}(\mathbf{R}_n)$. Substituting the expression found into equation (XXI.192), we are led to *define the momentum* $\mathbf{P}_n$ *of the* n^{th} *particle* by the relation [1]):

$$\mathbf{P}_n \equiv \mathbf{\Pi}_n + e_n \mathbf{A}(n). \tag{XXI.193}$$

The total momentum is then written:

$$\mathbf{P}_{\text{tot}} = \sum_n \mathbf{P}_n + \mathbf{X}. \tag{XXI.194}$$

It is the sum of the momenta of the particles and the momentum of the radiation. This sum is a constant of the motion.

One proceeds in an exactly analogous fashion in dealing with the angular momentum. One is led to define the angular momentum $\mathbf{L}_n$ of the nth particle by the relation:

$$\mathbf{L}_n \equiv \mathbf{R}_n \times \mathbf{P}_n \tag{XXI.195}$$

$\mathbf{P}_n$ being the momentum as defined above. The calculation gives the following expression for the total angular momentum of the system:

$$\mathbf{J}_{\text{tot}} = \sum_n \mathbf{L}_n + \mathbf{G}. \tag{XXI.196}$$

---

[1]) Recall that we are in radiation gauge and that the field $\mathbf{A}$ is purely transverse. More generally, we can obtain a definition *independent of gauge* by putting:

$$\mathbf{P}_n \equiv \mathbf{\Pi}_n + e_n \mathbf{A}_{\perp}(n).$$

Finally, we consider the total energy of the system. According to the definition given in § 17, it can be put in the form:

$$\sum_n M_n + U + U',$$

where

$$U' \equiv W^0 - U \equiv \frac{1}{8\pi} \int \mathscr{E}_{\|}^2 \,\mathrm{d}\mathbf{r}.$$

Replacing $\mathscr{E}_{\|}$ by its definition and effecting an integration by parts, one finds:

$$U' = \frac{1}{8\pi} \int (\operatorname{grad} \varphi)^2 \,\mathrm{d}\mathbf{r} = -\frac{1}{8\pi} \int \varphi(\triangle\varphi) \,\mathrm{d}\mathbf{r}.$$

φ is the electrostatic potential created by the electric charges present. If we assume point charges, as we have done up to the present, we find:

$$U' = \frac{1}{2} \sum_n \sum_p \frac{e_n e_p}{|\mathbf{R}_n - \mathbf{R}_p|}.$$

In this double sum, the "cross terms" $(n \neq p)$ represent the Coulomb energy of the set of particles, namely:

$$H_{\text{coul}} \equiv \sum_{n<p} \frac{e_n e_p}{|\mathbf{R}_n - \mathbf{R}_p|}. \qquad \text{(XXI.197)}$$

[The symbol $\sum_{n<p}$ denotes the sum over all pairs of particles.] The square terms are all infinite. The difficulty involved here is of the same origin as the one encountered in the calculation of $\mathbf{F}_i^{\text{long}}$ at the end of § 22. The ith square term represents the electrostatic energy of the ith particle in its own electric field; this energy, u_i', depends in a critical way on the distribution of charge inside the particle and becomes infinite in the limit when the radius of the particle tends to zero (cf. § 19); to obtain the correct value for the self-energy we must add to this term the contribution of the cohesive forces mentioned in § 19, a contribution not included in the present calculation. In the absence of a self-consistent theory of the internal structure of the particles, we shall assume that each of these "self-energy" terms can be omitted if we make an appropriate modification of the rest mass m_i in the expression for the mass energy M_i. We then obtain the following expression for the total energy of the system:

$$E_{\text{tot}} = \sum_n M_n + H_{\text{coul}} + U. \qquad \text{(XXI.198)}$$

This is the sum of the mass and Coulomb energies of the particles and of the radiation energy.

24. Hamiltonian for Free Radiation

The equations of motion obtained in § 22 can be put in canonical form. We first treat the free radiation case, that is, the case of the electromagnetic field in the absence of charge.

The dynamical state of the radiation is defined at each instant by giving the transverse field $\mathbf{A}$ and its velocity $\partial\mathbf{A}/\partial t$. The electric and magnetic fields are related to these two vector fields by equations (XXI.178). Their evolution in the course of time is determined by the equation of motion (XXI.182) which, in the absence of charge and of current, reduces to:

$$\Box \mathbf{A} \equiv \ddot{\mathbf{A}} - \triangle \mathbf{A} = 0 \qquad (\text{div } \mathbf{A} = 0). \tag{XXI.199}$$

This is the same equation as we had for the free scalar field [cf. eq. (XXI.1)]. The only difference is that here we have a field of transverse vectors rather than a scalar field, and that the mass term is null. Apart from this, the canonical formalism can be established by proceeding in exactly the same way as for the scalar field in section I. Let $\mathbf{T}^{(1)}, \mathbf{T}^{(2)}, \ldots, \mathbf{T}^{(\tau)}, \ldots$, be a complete set of orthonormal transverse fields [cf. eqs. (XXI.170)] like the set defined in § 21; we further suppose that it is a basis of *real normal coordinates*:

$$\mathbf{T}^{(\tau)*} = \mathbf{T}^{(\tau)} \qquad (\triangle + k_\tau^2)\, \mathbf{T}^{(\tau)} = 0. \tag{XXI.200}$$

The corresponding normal coordinates q_τ, are defined by [cf. eq. (XXI.6)]:

$$q_\tau = \frac{1}{\sqrt{4\pi}} \int (\mathbf{T}^{(\tau)} \cdot \mathbf{A})\, \mathrm{d}\mathbf{r}. \tag{XXI.201}$$

These are real functions of time satisfying the equation of motion:

$$\ddot{q}_\tau + k_\tau^2 q_\tau = 0, \tag{XXI.202}$$

characteristic of a harmonic oscillator of frequency k_τ. Such an oscillatory motion is given by the Hamiltonian

$$h_\tau = \tfrac{1}{2}(p_\tau^2 + k_\tau^2 q_\tau^2), \tag{XXI.203}$$

where p_τ is the momentum canonically conjugate to q_τ; p_τ is equal to $\dot{q}_\tau$ and is obtained from the "velocity" of the field, $\dot{\mathbf{A}}$, by the relation:

$$p_\tau = \frac{1}{\sqrt{4\pi}} \int (\mathbf{T}^{(\tau)} \cdot \dot{\mathbf{A}}) \, \mathrm{d}\mathbf{r}. \tag{XXI.204}$$

The total Hamiltonian of the free radiation is obtained by summing over the Hamiltonians relative to the different eigenvibrations:

$$H_{\mathrm{rad}} = \sum_\tau h_\tau . \tag{XXI.205}$$

The factor $1/\sqrt{4\pi}$ in definitions (XXI.201) and (XXI.204) is due to the units chosen here for the electromagnetic field [1]).

H_{rad} is the radiation energy in terms of the canonical variables. This can be shown as follows. One has [cf. eq. (XXI.178)]:

$$\mathbf{A} = \sqrt{4\pi} \sum_\tau q_\tau \, \mathbf{T}^{(\tau)} \tag{XXI.206}$$

$$\mathscr{E}_\perp = - \sqrt{4\pi} \sum_\tau p_\tau \, \mathbf{T}^{(\tau)} . \tag{XXI.207}$$

From the reality and orthonormalization properties of $\mathbf{T}^{(\tau)}$, we obtain:

$$\int \mathscr{E}_\perp^2 \, \mathrm{d}\mathbf{r} = 4\pi \sum_\tau p_\tau^2 . \tag{XXI.208}$$

On the other hand, since $\mathbf{T}^{(\tau)}$ is a transverse vector obeying equation (XXI.200), we have, by integrating by parts:

$$\begin{aligned} \int \sum_i (\nabla A_i)^2 \, \mathrm{d}\mathbf{r} &= - \int \sum_i A_i (\Delta A_i) \, \mathrm{d}\mathbf{r} \\ &= 4\pi \sum_\tau k_\tau^2 \, q_\tau^2 . \end{aligned} \tag{XXI.209}$$

Substituting (XXI.208) and (XXI.209) in the expression for the energy U [eq. (XXI.188′)], one finds:

$$U = \tfrac{1}{2} \sum_\tau (p_\tau^2 + k_\tau^2 \, q_\tau^2) = H_{\mathrm{rad}} .$$

25. Hamiltonian for Radiation Coupled to a Set of Particles

In the general case, we can take as canonical variables on the one hand the q_τ and p_τ introduced in the preceding paragraph to describe the dynamical state of the radiation and on the other the variables $\mathbf{R}_n$ and $\mathbf{P}_n$ giving the position and momentum of each particle. $\mathbf{P}_n$

1) Cf. note, p. 1009.

is related to the mechanical momentum of the particle by formula (XXI.193).

From the results of § 22 [eq. (XXI.182) giving the motion of $\mathbf{A}$, eqs. (XXI.185–187) giving the Lorentz force], one easily obtains the equations of motion in these new variables. In particular, equation (XXI.202) for the free oscillator is replaced by the equation:

$$\ddot{q}_\tau + k_\tau^2\, q_\tau = \sqrt{4\pi} \sum_n e_n\, \mathbf{V}_n \cdot \mathbf{T}^{(\tau)}(n)$$
$$[\mathbf{V}_n \equiv \dot{\mathbf{R}}_n;\; \mathbf{T}^{(\tau)}(n) \equiv \mathbf{T}^{(\tau)}(\mathbf{R}_n)]. \tag{XXI.210}$$

These equations of motion can be put in the canonical Hamiltonian form with the Hamiltonian:

$$H \equiv H(q_\tau, p_\tau;\; \mathbf{R}_n, \mathbf{P}_n) = H_{\text{rad}} + H_{\text{coul}} + \sum_n H_n. \tag{XXI.211}$$

H_{rad} is the free radiation Hamiltonian defined by equation (XXI.205), H_{coul} the Coulomb potential given by equation (XXI.197) and H_n the mass energy of the nth particle expressed in terms of the canonical variables, i.e.

$$H_n \equiv \sqrt{m_n^2 + (\mathbf{P}_n - e_n \mathbf{A}(n))^2}, \tag{XXI.212}$$

where:

$$\mathbf{A}(n) = \sqrt{4\pi} \sum_\tau q_\tau\, \mathbf{T}^{(\tau)}(n). \tag{XXI.213}$$

Verification of this important property is not difficult and is left to the reader.

IV. QUANTUM THEORY OF RADIATION

26. Quantization of Free Radiation. Photons

> And God said, "Let there be light": and there was light. And God saw the light, that it was good ... And the evening and the morning were the first day.

The Quantum Theory of electromagnetic radiation can be deduced from the Classical Theory by applying the correspondence principle, as was done for the scalar field.

To this effect, we take as a starting point the Hamiltonian formalism developed in § 24 and 25.

Consider first the free radiation case. To the real dynamical variables q_τ and p_τ of the Classical Theory there correspond the observables obeying the commutation relations [cf. eq. (XXI.11)]:

$$[q_\tau, q_{\tau'}] = [p_\tau, p_{\tau'}] = 0$$

$$[q_\tau, p_{\tau'}] = \mathrm{i}\delta_{\tau\tau'}.$$

The Hamiltonian governing the evolution of the system is the operator H_{rad} defined by equations (XXI.203) and (XXI.205). The radiation is therefore a superposition of quantized oscillators in accordance with Planck's law.

The entire discussion of § 3 can be applied here, in particular the part concerning the corpuscular interpretation. The radiation corpuscles are called *photons*. With each vibrational mode τ there is associated a certain type of photon characterized by the "wave function" $\boldsymbol{T}^{(\tau)}$ and whose energy is k_τ. The photons obey Bose–Einstein statistics, which is in excellent agreement with the experimental results concerning the thermodynamical properties of radiation (black body radiation etc.,). The remarks at the end of § 3 concerning the energy of the vacuum and field-fluctuations in the vacuum apply here without change.

The above quantization method is independent of the set of basis vector-fields $\boldsymbol{T}^{(\tau)}$ that is adopted; but these fields are supposed real. However, it can be reformulated so as to be valid also when the fields $\boldsymbol{T}^{(\tau)}$ are complex and the demonstration of § 5 justifying quantization with complex waves can be repeated in its entirety for the present case. The general formulas are easy to write down and will not be given here. We shall treat in some detail the plane-wave fields, and give a brief discussion of spherical-wave fields. Of all possible expansions, the plane-wave expansion is the most frequently used. The spherical-wave expansion or multipole expansion is useful in problems of emission or absorption.

27. Plane Waves. Radiation Momentum

The formulation using the plane-wave expansion is patterned on the one given in § 6 for the scalar field. We shall give the most important formulas, indicating in passing the points of difference with the scalar case.

Consider then a complete set of transverse plane-wave fields. In order to introduce discrete indices, we enclose these fields in a cube of side L, and impose the usual periodicity conditions at the edges of the cube. A field $\boldsymbol{U}^{(\boldsymbol{k}\varpi)}$ belonging to this basis is defined by giving the wave-vector $\boldsymbol{k}$ and the quantum number ϖ labeling its polarization ($\varpi = 1, 2$):

$$\boldsymbol{U}^{(\boldsymbol{k}\varpi)} = L^{-3/2}\, \boldsymbol{\epsilon}^{(\varpi)}\, \mathrm{e}^{\mathrm{i}\boldsymbol{k}\cdot\boldsymbol{r}}. \qquad \text{(XXI.214)}$$

The expression for $\boldsymbol{T}^{(\boldsymbol{k}\varpi)}$ introduced in § 21 [eq. (XXI.173*b*)] differs only in the normalization. The vectors $\boldsymbol{\epsilon}^{(1)}$ and $\boldsymbol{\epsilon}^{(2)}$ obey equations (XXI.174), which define them up to a unitary transformation.

With each plane wave $\boldsymbol{U}^{(\boldsymbol{k}\varpi)}$, we associate an annihilation operator $a_{(\boldsymbol{k}\varpi)}$ and a creation operator $a_{(\boldsymbol{k}\varpi)}{}^{\dagger}$. The field $\boldsymbol{A}$ is represented by the expansion [cf. eqs. (XXI.46) and (XXI.206)]:

$$\boldsymbol{A} = \sum_{\boldsymbol{k}} \sum_{\varpi} (2\pi/k)^{\frac{1}{2}} \left(a_{(\boldsymbol{k}\varpi)}\, \boldsymbol{U}^{(\boldsymbol{k}\varpi)} + a_{(\boldsymbol{k}\varpi)}{}^{\dagger}\, \boldsymbol{U}^{(\boldsymbol{k}\varpi)*}\right) \qquad \text{(XXI.215)}$$

and the field $\mathscr{E}_{\perp}$ by [cf. eqs. (XXI.47) and (XXI.207)]:

$$\mathscr{E}_{\perp} = \sum_{\boldsymbol{k}} \sum_{\varpi} \mathrm{i}(2\pi k)^{\frac{1}{2}} \left(a_{(\boldsymbol{k}\varpi)}\, \boldsymbol{U}^{(\boldsymbol{k}\varpi)} - a_{(\boldsymbol{k}\varpi)}{}^{\dagger}\, \boldsymbol{U}^{(\boldsymbol{k}\varpi)*}\right). \qquad \text{(XXI.216)}$$

The a and $a^{\dagger}$ obey the commutation relations characteristic of annihilation and creation operators:

$$[a_{(\boldsymbol{k}\varpi)}, a_{(\boldsymbol{k}'\varpi')}] = [a_{(\boldsymbol{k}\varpi)}{}^{\dagger}, a_{(\boldsymbol{k}'\varpi')}{}^{\dagger}] = 0 \qquad \text{(XXI.217}a\text{)}$$

$$[a_{(\boldsymbol{k}\varpi)}, a_{(\boldsymbol{k}'\varpi')}{}^{\dagger}] = \delta_{\boldsymbol{k}\boldsymbol{k}'}\, \delta_{\varpi\varpi'}. \qquad \text{(XXI.217}b\text{)}$$

The operator

$$N_{(\boldsymbol{k}\varpi)} \equiv a_{(\boldsymbol{k}\varpi)}{}^{\dagger}\, a_{(\boldsymbol{k}\varpi)} \qquad \text{(XXI.218)}$$

represents the number of photons in the state $\boldsymbol{U}^{(\boldsymbol{k}\varpi)}$.

The radiation Hamiltonian, fixed in such a way as to have the vacuum energy equal to zero, is given by

$$H_{\text{rad}} = \sum_{\boldsymbol{k}} \sum_{\varpi} N_{(\boldsymbol{k}\varpi)}\, k. \qquad \text{(XXI.219)}$$

The momentum $\boldsymbol{X}$ is defined in terms of the operators $\boldsymbol{E}_{\perp}$ and $\boldsymbol{A}$ by expression (XXI.189′). Substituting for these the expansions (XXI.216) and (XXI.215) one finds (Problem XXI.6):

$$\boldsymbol{X} = \sum_{\boldsymbol{k}} \sum_{\varpi} N_{(\boldsymbol{k}\varpi)}\, \boldsymbol{k}. \qquad \text{(XXI.220)}$$

We can conclude from expressions (XXI.219) and (XXI.220) that a photon in the state $\mathbf{U}^{(\mathbf{k}\varpi)}$ is a corpuscle of momentum $\mathbf{k}$ and energy k, that is, a corpuscle of mass null and momentum $\mathbf{k}$.

The number of states of the photon whose momentum is situated in the interval $(\mathbf{k}, \mathbf{k}+\delta\mathbf{k})$ is $2(L/2\pi)^3\delta\mathbf{k}$. The factor 2 here is due to there being two linearly independent polarization states for a given momentum ($\varpi=1$ or 2). The density of levels $\varrho_L(k)$ of energy k, of momentum in the direction Ω and *of given polarization* ϖ (definition of § 6) is:

$$\varrho_L(k) = \frac{L^3\, k^2}{(2\pi)^3} \qquad \text{(XXI.221)}$$

[cf. eq. (XXI.49)].

28. Polarization

Photons having the same momentum $\mathbf{k}$ can differ from one another by their polarization. Classically, the polarization is the direction of vibration of the transverse electric field; it is a real or complex unit vector (defined to within a phase) perpendicular to the direction of propagation $\mathbf{k}$. This definition can be extended without difficulty to the present case. To each value of $\mathbf{k}$, there correspond two linearly independent polarizations, $\boldsymbol{\epsilon}^{(1)}$ and $\boldsymbol{\epsilon}^{(2)}$, and any other possible polarization of the photon is a (unitary) linear combination of these basis polarizations [1]).

As basis polarizations, one can take two orthogonal *rectilinear polarizations*, that is two real vectors $\boldsymbol{\epsilon}^{(1)}$ and $\boldsymbol{\epsilon}^{(2)}$. They can be chosen for example such that $\boldsymbol{\epsilon}^{(1)}$, $\boldsymbol{\epsilon}^{(2)}$ and $\mathbf{k}$ form a right-handed Cartesian triad of real vectors, which fixes the basis to within a rotation about the propagation axis:

$$\boldsymbol{\epsilon}^{(\varpi)*} = \boldsymbol{\epsilon}^{(\varpi)} \qquad \boldsymbol{\epsilon}^{(1)} \times \boldsymbol{\epsilon}^{(2)} = \frac{\mathbf{k}}{k}.$$

One can also use the two *circular polarizations* $\mathbf{e}^{(+)}$ and $\mathbf{e}^{(-)}$ as a basis:

$$\begin{aligned} \mathbf{e}^{(+)} &= -\frac{\sqrt{2}}{2}\,(\boldsymbol{\epsilon}^{(1)} + \mathrm{i}\boldsymbol{\epsilon}^{(2)}) \\ \mathbf{e}^{(-)} &= \frac{\sqrt{2}}{2}\,(\boldsymbol{\epsilon}^{(1)} - \mathrm{i}\boldsymbol{\epsilon}^{(2)}). \end{aligned} \qquad \text{(XXI.222)}$$

---

[1]) Here we consider only the pure states, currently called *completely polarized*. The *partially polarized* states are statistical mixtures; they can be represented by a density operator of the (2-dimensional) space of the polarization states.

Note that:

$$\mathbf{e}^{(+)} = -\mathbf{e}^{(-)*}.$$

We shall use the symbol $\frown$ to indicate quantities defined with respect to this basis. We can thus define operators of annihilation $\hat{a}_{(\boldsymbol{k}\eta)}$ and of creation $\hat{a}_{(\boldsymbol{k}\eta)}{}^\dagger$ of circularly polarized photons: the corresponding plane wave is:

$$\hat{\mathbf{U}}^{(\boldsymbol{k}\eta)} \equiv L^{-3/2}\, \mathbf{e}^{(\eta)}\, \mathrm{e}^{i\boldsymbol{k}\cdot\boldsymbol{r}} \qquad (\eta = + \text{ or } -).$$

The interest of circular polarizations is essentially due to the following property:

A circularly polarized photon has a well-defined angular momentum along its direction of propagation; the component of the angular momentum is equal to $+1$ *or* -1 *according as the polarization is right-handed* $(\eta = +)$ *or left-handed* $(\eta = -)$.

To show this, suppose that the radiation is in one of the states $|\boldsymbol{k}\,\pm\rangle$ defined by

$$|\boldsymbol{k}\,\pm\rangle \equiv \hat{a}_{(\boldsymbol{k}\pm)}{}^\dagger\,|0\rangle.$$

This state represents a photon of momentum $\boldsymbol{k}$ and of right $(+)$ or of left $(-)$ circular polarization. It can be shown (Problem (XXI.8) that:

$$(\boldsymbol{k}\cdot\boldsymbol{G}^{(0)})\,|\boldsymbol{k}\,\pm\rangle = 0 \qquad \text{(XXI.223)}$$

$$(\boldsymbol{k}\cdot\boldsymbol{G}^{(s)})\,|\boldsymbol{k}\,\pm\rangle = (\pm\, k)\,|\boldsymbol{k}\,\pm\rangle, \qquad \text{(XXI.224)}$$

where the vector operators $\boldsymbol{G}^{(0)}$ and $\boldsymbol{G}^{(s)}$ are defined respectively by equations (XXI.191*a*) and (XXI.191*b*). According to equation (XXI.190′), the total angular momentum $\boldsymbol{G}$ is the sum of these two vector operators; denote its component along $\boldsymbol{k}$ by G_k:

$$G_k \equiv \frac{(\boldsymbol{k}\cdot\boldsymbol{G})}{k}.$$

From the two preceding equations, one obtains the desired result:

$$G_k\,|\boldsymbol{k}\,\pm\rangle = (\pm\,1)\,|\boldsymbol{k}\,\pm\rangle.$$

Q.E.D.

This property is characteristic of a particle of spin 1. More generally, if a particle of spin 1 has a well-defined momentum $\boldsymbol{k}$ the component of its orbital angular momentum along $\boldsymbol{k}$ vanishes, and the component of its spin along $\boldsymbol{k}$ can take one of the three values $+1$, 0, -1. In the particular case of a photon, however, the longitudinal plane waves, which correspond to the value 0 for the spin component, must be eliminated.

29. Multipole Expansion. Photons of Determined Angular Momentum and Parity

Rather than expanding in plane waves, we can expand in a series of spherical waves, each of which corresponds to a well-defined value of the angular momentum and parity. We shall limit ourselves here to giving the main results without the demonstrations. The latter are not difficult.

A vector field $\mathbf{B}(\mathbf{r})$ can be considered as a three-component wave function representing the dynamical state of a particle of spin 1. There exists a certain arbitrariness in the choice of the components of $\mathbf{B}$ which constitute the wave function. For example, one could take B_x, B_y and B_z but, for the needs of the present discussion, it is preferable to take the standard components:

$$B_+ = -\frac{\sqrt{2}}{2}(B_x - \mathrm{i}B_y)$$

$$B_0 = B_z$$

$$B_- = \frac{\sqrt{2}}{2}(B_x + \mathrm{i}B_y).$$

The wave function is a function of $\mathbf{r}$ and of the index μ labeling the components in question ($\mu = +,\ 0$ or $-$):

$$\Psi(\mathbf{r}, \mu) \equiv B_\mu(\mathbf{r}).$$

On this point there is a perfect parallel between particles of spin 1 and particles of spin $\frac{1}{2}$ (cf. § XIII.20–21).

The observables of this spin 1 particle are functions of its position $\mathbf{r}$, its momentum $\mathbf{p}$ and its spin $\mathbf{s}$. In the representation defined here, $\mathbf{p} = -\mathrm{i}\nabla$ and the matrices representing the components s_+, s_z, s_- of the spin are given by equations (XIII.28) taken with $j = j' = 1$. It will easily be verified that $\mathbf{s}^2 = 2$, a value characteristic of an angular momentum equal to 1.

We can define the orbital angular momentum $\boldsymbol{l}$ of the particle:

$$\boldsymbol{l} = \mathbf{r} \times \mathbf{p}$$

and its total angular momentum:

$$\boldsymbol{j} \equiv \boldsymbol{l} + \boldsymbol{s}.$$

The components of $\boldsymbol{j}$ are associated with the infinitesimal rotations of the vector field, in accordance with the usual definition of the angular momentum operator.

We similarly define the parity P; it is an operator whose action on the field $\mathbf{B}(\boldsymbol{r})$ gives its transform under reflection in the origin [1]):

$$PB_{\mu}(\boldsymbol{r}) = -B_{\mu}(-\boldsymbol{r}).$$

We now wish to construct a complete set of vector fields of well-defined angular momentum (jm) satisfying the wave equation:

$$(\triangle + k^2)\mathbf{B}(\boldsymbol{r}) = 0.$$

This amounts to finding a common set of eigenfunctions of $\boldsymbol{p}^2$, $\boldsymbol{j}^2$ and j_z. The corresponding eigenvalues are k^2, $j(j+1)$ and m respectively; k can take all values from 0 to $+\infty$ (the spectrum of k can be made discrete by enclosing the field in a sphere of finite radius R), j all integral values from 0 to $+\infty$ and m all integral values from $-j$ to $+j$.

From the properties of addition of angular momenta, one can deduce that $\boldsymbol{p}^2$, $\boldsymbol{l}^2$, $\boldsymbol{j}^2$ and j_z form a complete set of commuting observables and that to each set (kjm) there correspond:

(*i*) if $j \neq 0$, *three* linearly independent states, for which we have respectively:

$$l = j+1, \qquad j, \qquad j-1;$$

(*ii*) if $j=0$, *one and only one* state for which $l=1$.

These states have a well-defined parity, namely:

$$P = (-)^{l+1}.$$

Rather than classify the states (kjm) according to the possible values of l, as above, we can classify them according to their transverse or longitudinal character and their parity. The transverse or lon-

[1]) We suppose that $\mathbf{B}(\boldsymbol{r})$ is a field of polar vectors, whence the presence of the minus sign in the spatial reflection. To within the sign of the parity, all of the properties given below apply equally well to axial-vector fields or pseudovector fields (cf. note p. 904).

gitudinal character of a field is related to the properties of the operator $(\mathbf{s}\cdot\mathbf{p})$; in the representation adopted here we have [eq. (XIII.93)]

$$(\mathbf{s}\cdot\mathbf{p}) \equiv \text{curl}$$
$$(\mathbf{s}\cdot\mathbf{p})^2-\mathbf{p}^2 \equiv \text{grad div} \qquad (\equiv \text{curl curl} + \triangle).$$

For a longitudinal field $(\mathbf{s}\cdot\mathbf{p})^2=0$; for a transverse field, $(\mathbf{s}\cdot\mathbf{p})^2-\mathbf{p}^2=0$. It can be shown that $\mathbf{p}^2$, $(\mathbf{s}\cdot\mathbf{p})^2$, P, $\mathbf{j}^2$ and j_z form a complete set of commuting observables and that to each set (kjm) there correspond:

(*i*) if $j\neq 0$, *three* linearly independent states, for which we have respectively:

$$\begin{array}{llll} (\mathbf{s}\cdot\mathbf{p})^2= & 0 & k^2 & k^2 \\ P= & (-)^j & (-)^j & (-)^{j+1} \end{array}$$

(*ii*) if $j=0$, *one and only one* state, even and longitudinal:

$$(\mathbf{s}\cdot\mathbf{p})^2 = 0 \qquad P = +1$$

(this is the p state already mentioned above).

To construct the corresponding basis functions, we return to the functions u_{kjm} introduced in § 7 in connection with the scalar field; the constant in definition (XXI.60) is a certain function of k which we shall suppose chosen in such a way that the u_{kjm} form a complete orthonormal set of scalar functions. To each set (kjm) there corresponds one and only one longitudinal state; the corresponding basis function is:

$$\mathbf{\Lambda}_{kjm} \equiv \text{grad}\,\frac{u_{kjm}}{k}$$

(this is a vector-field of parity $(-)^j$). To each set (kjm) with the exception of the cases: $j=m=0$, there correspond two transverse states of opposite parity; the corresponding basis functions are respectively [1]):

$$\mathbf{\Theta}^{(-)}_{kjm} \equiv \frac{\boldsymbol{l}\, u_{kjm}}{\sqrt{j(j+1)}} \qquad (P=(-)^{j+1}) \qquad \text{(XXI.225}a\text{)}$$

$$\mathbf{\Theta}^{(+)}_{kjm} \equiv \frac{\nabla\times\boldsymbol{l}\, u_{kjm}}{k\sqrt{j(j+1)}} \qquad (P=(-)^{j}). \qquad \text{(XXI.225}b\text{)}$$

---

[1]) The parities indicated here are of opposite sign to those given by most authors (in particular Blatt and Weisskopf, *loc. cit.*) since the vector fields introduced here are polar-vector fields while these authors consider axial-vector fields.

Note in passing that:

$$\boldsymbol{\Theta}_{kjm}^{(\pm)} = \operatorname{curl} \frac{\boldsymbol{\Theta}_{kjm}^{(\mp)}}{k}.$$

The set of fields $\boldsymbol{\Theta}_{kjm}^{(\varpi)}$ (k varying from 0 to $+\infty$; $j=1, 2, ..., \infty$; $m=-j, ..., +j$; $\varpi=+$ or $-$) form a complete orthonormal set of transverse fields in terms of which we can expand the operators $\boldsymbol{A}$ and $\mathscr{E}_{\perp}$:

$$\boldsymbol{A} = \sum_{kjm\varpi} (2\pi/k)^{\frac{1}{2}} [a_{kjm}^{(\varpi)} \boldsymbol{\Theta}_{kjm}^{(\varpi)} + a_{kjm}^{(\varpi)\dagger} \boldsymbol{\Theta}_{kjm}^{(\varpi)*}] \qquad \text{(XXI.226)}$$

$$\mathscr{E}_{\perp} = \sum_{kjm\varpi} (2\pi k)^{\frac{1}{2}} \, \mathrm{i}[a_{kjm}^{(\varpi)} \boldsymbol{\Theta}_{kjm}^{(\varpi)} - a_{kjm}^{(\varpi)\dagger} \boldsymbol{\Theta}_{kjm}^{(\varpi)*}]. \qquad \text{(XXI.227)}$$

According to the usual terminology, the terms $\boldsymbol{\Theta}_{kjm}^{(+)}$ in these expansions represent the *electric* 2^l*-pole* contribution; the terms $\boldsymbol{\Theta}_{kjm}^{(-)}$ the *magnetic* 2^l*-pole* contribution. All of the work of § 27 in connection with the plane-wave expansion can be repeated here for the multipole expansion. The operators $a_{kjm}^{(\varpi)}$ and $a_{kjm}^{(\varpi)\dagger}$ can be respectively interpreted as annihilation and creation operators of a photon of energy k, angular momentum (jm) and parity $(-)^j\varpi$. The spectra of k, j, m and ϖ were mentioned above; it is to be observed that there is no photon with zero angular momentum.

30. Coupling with an Atomic System

> And God said, "Let there be lights in the firmament of the heaven to divide the day from the night..." and God saw that it was good. And the evening and the morning were the fourth day.

We now consider radiation coupled to a system of particles. The treatment is analogous to that of the scalar field and we shall limit ourselves here to the essential points.

The Hamiltonian of the system is, to within a few obvious modifications, the same as that of the classical theory [cf. eq. (XXI.211)]. The modifications in question depend on the dynamical properties and the spin of the particles considered. We limit ourselves here to the case of an atomic system of Z electrons and a nucleus of charge $-Ze$ (e is the charge of the electron).

We first suppose the nucleus to be absent, and form the Hamiltonian of the system of Z electrons + radiation. The total Hamiltonian is then given by equation (XXI.211), where H_{rad} represents the free radiation Hamiltonian, H_{coul} the Coulomb interaction of the electrons, and H_n the Dirac Hamiltonian of the nth electron in the presence of the field $\mathbf{A}$, i.e.:

$$H_n = \boldsymbol{\alpha}_n \cdot [\mathbf{P}_n - e\mathbf{A}(n)] + \beta_n m. \tag{XXI.228}$$

$\boldsymbol{\alpha}_n$ and β_n are the Dirac matrices relative to the nth electron.

In the non-relativistic approximation, H_n gives, after subtraction of the rest mass:

$$(H_n)_{NR} = \frac{(\mathbf{P}_n - e\mathbf{A}(n))^2}{2m} - \frac{e}{2m}(\boldsymbol{\sigma}_n \cdot \mathscr{H}(n)). \tag{XXI.229}$$

We note that the electron-radiation coupling term in H_n [eq. (XXI.228)] can be written:

$$H_n' = -e \int (\mathbf{j}_n(\mathbf{r}) \cdot \mathbf{A}(\mathbf{r}))\, \mathrm{d}\mathbf{r} \tag{XXI.230}$$

where $\mathbf{j}_n(\mathbf{r})$ represents the Dirac current density of the electron at point $\mathbf{r}$, that is [cf. eq. (XX.143)]:

$$\mathbf{j}_n(\mathbf{r}) \equiv \boldsymbol{\alpha}_n \delta(\mathbf{R}_n - \mathbf{r}). \tag{XXI.231}$$

$e\mathbf{j}_n(\mathbf{r})$ is the electric current density of the nth electron. By substituting the non-relativistic approximation for $\mathbf{j}_n$ [eq. (XX.189–190)] in (XXI.230) one obtains the coupling $(H_n')_{NR}$ in the non-relativistic approximation:

$$(H_n')_{NR} \equiv H_n^{(\mathrm{I})} + H_n^{(\mathrm{II})} + H_n'' \tag{XXI.232}$$

$$H_n^{(\mathrm{I})} = -\frac{e}{2m}(\mathbf{P}_n \cdot \mathbf{A}(n) + \mathbf{A}(n) \cdot \mathbf{P}_n) \tag{XXI.233a}$$

$$H_n^{(\mathrm{II})} = -\mathrm{i}\frac{e}{2m}[\boldsymbol{\sigma}_n \cdot ([\mathbf{P}_n \times \mathbf{A}(n)] + [\mathbf{A}(n) \times \mathbf{P}_n])] = -\frac{e}{2m}[\boldsymbol{\sigma}_n \cdot \mathscr{H}(n)] \tag{XXI.233b}$$

$$H_n'' = \frac{e^2}{2m}\mathbf{A}^2(n). \tag{XXI.233c}$$

This is just the electron-radiation coupling figuring in expression (XXI.229).

To take into account the presence of the atomic nucleus, we must add to the Hamiltonian the Coulomb interaction of the nucleus with each of the Z electrons, and also the Hamiltonian of the nucleus in the presence of the radiation, which includes a kinetic energy term and a term for the coupling with the radiation [1]). In the (essentially non-relativistic) approximation where the nucleus is treated as infinitely heavy, these last two terms are negligible; the nucleus can then be thought of as fixed at the origin and we need only to add the Z Coulomb terms $-Ze^2/R_n$. The atom is then treated simply as a set of Z electrons, each moving in the external potential $-Ze^2/R$ and coupled to the electromagnetic field. The corresponding Hamiltonian can be put in the form

$$H = H_{\text{rad}} + H_{\text{at}} + H'. \tag{XXI.234}$$

H_{rad} is still the free-radiation Hamiltonian. H_{at} is the Hamiltonian of the atom itself, that is, of the electrons in the Coulomb field of the nucleus and in Coulomb interaction with one another; it is the sum of the Coulomb interaction term H_{coul} and the kinetic energies of the Z electrons. H' is the term coupling the electrons of the atom with the radiation; it is the sum of the Z coupling terms H_n' defined by equation (XXI.230). In what follows we shall treat the motion of the electrons in the non-relativistic approximation; we therefore adopt the approximate form for H_n' given by equations (XXI.232) and (XXI.233), in other words:

$$H' = H^{(I)} + H^{(II)} + H'', \tag{XXI.235}$$

where

$$H^{(I)} = \sum_n H_n^{(I)}, \quad H^{(II)} = \sum_n H_n^{(II)}, \quad H'' = \sum_n H_n''. \tag{XXI.235'}$$

Two approximation methods are generally used to study such a system.

The first of these consists in *treating the electromagnetic radiation classically*. It is justified in all cases when the energy transfer between the atom and the radiation field is so large compared with the energy of the emitted or absorbed photons that the discontinuous character of this transfer can be neglected. It is therefore a good approximation for strong intensities and low frequencies (many photons present).

---

[1]) Here we suppose that the nucleus can be treated as a point charge. This approximation is legitimate provided that the frequencies which come into play are small compared with the excitation energies of the nucleus.

It is particularly suited to the study of an atom in a static electromagnetic field or in a radioelectric field. The electromagnetic field is then considered as a given, possibly time-dependent, external field, and the problem reduces to the study of an atom in an external field.

The second method consists in *treating the coupling term H' as a small perturbation* as has already been done in the case of the scalar field.

The discussion of § 10 can be repeated here with very little change. The unperturbed Hamiltonian is:

$$H_0 \equiv H_{\text{rad}} + H_{\text{at}}.$$

In order to apply the perturbation method we must use a representation in which H_0 is diagonal. Taking the plane wave represention defined in § 27 for the radiation field, we define the basis vectors of H_0 as the simultaneous eigenvectors of H_{at} and of the operators $N_{(\boldsymbol{k}\varpi)}$ representing the number of photons of given momentum and polarization.

The matrix elements of H' in this representation are easily obtained by using its expression in terms of the $a_{(\boldsymbol{k}\varpi)}$ and the $a_{(\boldsymbol{k}\varpi)}{}^{\dagger}$. Substituting expansion (XXI.215) for $\boldsymbol{A}$ in expression (XXI.233) one finds

$$H_n{}^{(\mathrm{I})} = -\frac{e}{m}\sum_s \left(\frac{2\pi}{kL^3}\right)^{\frac{1}{2}} (a_s(\boldsymbol{P}\cdot\boldsymbol{\epsilon})\,\mathrm{e}^{\mathrm{i}\boldsymbol{k}\cdot\boldsymbol{R}} + \text{Herm. conj.}) \qquad (\text{XXI}.236a)$$

$$H_n{}^{(\mathrm{II})} = -\frac{e}{2m}\sum_s \left(\frac{2\pi}{kL^3}\right)^{\frac{1}{2}} (\mathrm{i}\,a_s(\boldsymbol{\sigma}\cdot\boldsymbol{k}\times\boldsymbol{\epsilon})\,\mathrm{e}^{\mathrm{i}\boldsymbol{k}\cdot\boldsymbol{R}} + \text{Herm. conj.}) \quad (\text{XXI}.236b)$$

$$\begin{aligned} H_n'' = \frac{e^2}{2m}\sum_s\sum_{s'} \frac{\pi}{\sqrt{kk'}\,L^3} \big([a_s a_{s'}(\boldsymbol{\epsilon}\cdot\boldsymbol{\epsilon}')\,\mathrm{e}^{\mathrm{i}(\boldsymbol{k}+\boldsymbol{k}')\cdot\boldsymbol{R}} + \text{Herm. conj.}] \\ + [a_s{}^{\dagger} a_{s'}(\boldsymbol{\epsilon}^*\cdot\boldsymbol{\epsilon}')\,\mathrm{e}^{\mathrm{i}(\boldsymbol{k}'-\boldsymbol{k})\cdot\boldsymbol{R}} + \text{Herm. conj.}]\big). \end{aligned} \qquad (\text{XXI}.237)$$

[To simplify the writing we have put $s \equiv (\boldsymbol{k}\,\varpi)$ and $s' \equiv (\boldsymbol{k}'\varpi')$, and have represented the vectors $\boldsymbol{R}_n$, $\boldsymbol{P}_n$, $\boldsymbol{\sigma}_n$, $\boldsymbol{\epsilon}^{(\varpi)}$ and $\boldsymbol{\epsilon}^{(\varpi')}$ by $\boldsymbol{R}$, $\boldsymbol{P}$, $\boldsymbol{\sigma}$, $\boldsymbol{\epsilon}$ and $\boldsymbol{\epsilon}'$ respectively.] The desired expression for H' is obtained by substituting these expansions in (XXI.235) and (XXI.235′).

The presence of the coupling term H' has the effect of displacing all of the atomic levels, and of rendering them all unstable with the exception of the ground state (recall that the photon mass is null). This effect can be treated entirely within the framework of the perturbation method. One obviously encounters the same difficulties as in the scalar case, and this in spite of the fact that the coupling constant c is small ($e^2 = 1/137$). In particular, there is an "ultraviolet catastrophe" related to the fact that H' is a local interaction [cf. eq. (XXI.230) and (XXI.231)]. This catastrophe can be avoided by introducing a suitable cut-off. For the same reasons as given before, one usually places this cut-off at a frequency of the order of m. The qualifications that must be made with regard to this cut-off procedure and the difficulties relating to the necessity of renormalizing the mass and the charge of the particles have already been discussed. All of the considerations of section II concerning level shifts and properties of metastable states (lifetime, line width, formation and decay modes) can be extended without any essential change to the radiation case [1]). Similarly, the few collision problems treated in section II can be treated in the radiation case by the same methods. In concluding this chapter we shall describe two simple applications of the Quantum Theory of Radiation; the calculation of probabilities for the emission of radiation by an atom and the calculation of the cross section for Compton scattering in the low frequency limit.

31. Emission of a Photon by an Atom. Dipole Emission

Consider an atom in one of its excited states $|\lambda\rangle$ of energy E_λ. Such an atom is capable of making transitions to any one of the states $|\alpha\rangle$, $|\beta\rangle$, ... whose energy E_α, E_β, ... is lower than E_λ, with emission of a photon whose energy is equal to the difference between the energies of the initial and final states.

Let us therefore consider the transition:

$$\lambda \to \mu \mathbf{k} \boldsymbol{\epsilon}.$$

μ is the final state of the atom, $\mathbf{k}$ and $\boldsymbol{\epsilon}$ the momentum and polarization of the photon emitted, and

$$k = E_\lambda - E_\mu. \tag{XXI.238}$$

[1]) The radiation case is complicated by the fact that photons are corpuscles of zero mass and spin 1. The zero mass results, in addition to the "ultraviolet catastrophe", in an "infrared catastrophe", that is, in the existence of low-frequency divergences in certain terms in the perturbation expansion. The "infrared catastrophe" is a difficulty of the method itself and can be avoided by improving the method. The "ultraviolet catastrophe", on the other hand, is a difficulty in the theory proper, for which at the present time there is no fully satisfactory solution.

The transition probability per unit time $w_{\lambda\to\mu\mathbf{k}\boldsymbol{\epsilon}}$ is given to the first order in the perturbation calculation by the formula (cf. § 12):

$$w_{\lambda\to\mu\mathbf{k}\boldsymbol{\epsilon}} = 2\pi|\langle\lambda|H'|\mu\mathbf{k}\boldsymbol{\epsilon}\rangle|^2 \left(\frac{L^3k^2}{(2\pi)^3}\right). \qquad \text{(XXI.239)}$$

It will be seen from equation (XXI.235) that, H' is composed of three terms. The contribution from the third term, H'', to the matrix element in the above formula vanishes [1]). The contributions from the first two terms are easily obtained with the aid of expansions (XXI.236), giving

$$\langle\lambda|H^{(\mathrm{I})}|\mu\mathbf{k}\boldsymbol{\epsilon}\rangle = -\frac{e}{m}\left(\frac{2\pi}{kL^3}\right)^{\frac{1}{2}} F^{(\mathrm{I})} \qquad \text{(XXI.240}a\text{)}$$

$$\langle\lambda|H^{(\mathrm{II})}|\mu\mathbf{k}\boldsymbol{\epsilon}\rangle = \frac{\mathrm{i}e}{m}\left(\frac{2\pi}{kL^3}\right)^{\frac{1}{2}} F^{(\mathrm{II})}, \qquad \text{(XXI.240}b\text{)}$$

where

$$F^{(\mathrm{I})} \equiv \langle\lambda|\sum_n (\boldsymbol{\epsilon}\cdot\mathbf{P}_n)\,\mathrm{e}^{\mathrm{i}\mathbf{k}\cdot\mathbf{R}_n}|\mu\rangle \qquad \text{(XXI.241}a\text{)}$$

$$F^{(\mathrm{II})} \equiv \langle\lambda|\,\tfrac{1}{2}\sum_n (\boldsymbol{\epsilon}\cdot\mathbf{k}\times\boldsymbol{\sigma}_n)\,\mathrm{e}^{\mathrm{i}\mathbf{k}\cdot\mathbf{R}_n}|\mu\rangle. \qquad \text{(XXI.241}b\text{)}$$

Substituting these expressions in (XXI.239), we finally obtain the formula:

$$w_{\lambda\to\mu\mathbf{k}\boldsymbol{\epsilon}} = \frac{e^2k}{2\pi m^2}\,|F^{(\mathrm{I})} - \mathrm{i}F^{(\mathrm{II})}|^2, \qquad \text{(XXI.242)}$$

where $F^{(I)}$ and $F^{(II)}$ denote the matrix elements defined by relations (XXI.241).

In ordinary atomic transitions, the order of magnitude of the transition probability depends critically on the angular momenta j_λ and j_μ and the parities Π_λ and Π_μ of states $|\lambda\rangle$ and $|\mu\rangle$ respectively.

If $j_\lambda = j_\mu = 0$ the transition probability vanishes since the matrix elements $F^{(I)}$ and $F^{(II)}$ are identically null (Problem XXI.10). *This*

---

[1]) The action of H'' either conserves the number of photons present, or increases or diminishes this number by 2 units. Note that H'' is of the second order in e and can therefore be omitted in a perturbation calculation to the first order in e. In calculating the level shift, which is of the second order (cf. § 11), the contribution from H'' ceases to be negligible. It is also important in photon scattering (cf. § 32).

is the well known $0 \to 0$ *selection rule.* It is related to the fact that there is no photon of zero angular momentum (cf. § 29).

If j_λ or j_μ is different to zero, the transition probability can be evaluated by making the long wavelength approximation. Let R be a length of the order of atomic dimensions; in ordinary atomic transitions,

$$k \lesssim \frac{e^2}{R} \simeq me^4,$$

so that

$$kR \lesssim e^2 \ll 1.$$

Expressions (XXI.241) can therefore be evaluated by replacing the exponentials by the first term in their Taylor expansion having a non-vanishing contribution. The order of this term is mainly determined by the selection rules for angular momentum and parity, a subject that will not be gone into here [1]). All things being equal, the transition probability is greatest in the case of the so-called *electric dipole* transitions, in which case

$$\Delta j \equiv |j_\lambda - j_\mu| \leqslant 1 \qquad \Delta\Pi \equiv \Pi_\lambda \Pi_\mu = -1 \qquad \text{(XXI.243)}$$
$$(j_\lambda + j_\mu = 0 \ \text{excepted}).$$

Next come the magnetic dipole ($\Delta j \leqslant 1, \Delta\Pi = 1, j_\lambda + j_\mu \neq 0$) and the electric quadrupole ($\Delta j \leqslant 2, \Delta\Pi = +1, j_\lambda + j_\mu \neq 0$ or 1) transitions which are $(kR)^{-2}$ times slower than the electric dipole transitions.

If the conditions for electric dipole emission, (XXI.243), are fulfilled, we may write:

$$F^{(\mathrm{I})} \simeq \langle\lambda| \sum_n (\boldsymbol{\epsilon} \cdot \mathbf{P}_n) |\mu\rangle$$

$$F^{(\mathrm{II})} \simeq \tfrac{1}{2} \mathrm{i} \langle\lambda| \sum_n (\boldsymbol{\epsilon} \cdot \mathbf{k} \times \boldsymbol{\sigma}_n)(\mathbf{k} \cdot \mathbf{R}_n) |\mu\rangle.$$

---

[1]) The results appear in a more natural way if we use a multipole expansion rather than the expansion in plane waves; due to the selection rules most of the contributions vanish, the others can be evaluated by replacing the multipole fields $\boldsymbol{\Theta}$ by the first term in their expansion in powers of kr. Note [cf. eq. (XXI.225)] that when $kr \ll 1$:

$$\boldsymbol{\Theta}^{(+)}_{kjm} \propto (kr)^{j-1} \qquad \boldsymbol{\Theta}^{(-)}_{kjm} \propto (kr)^j.$$

A complete discussion of this method, with reference to radiative transitions in nuclei, can be found in J. Blatt and V. Weisskopf, Ch. XII, *loc. cit.*, note 2, p. 576.

We therefore have roughly: $F^{(I)} \approx 1/R$, $F^{(II)} \approx k^2R$ i.e.:

$$|F^{(II)}/F^{(I)}| \approx (kR)^2 \ll 1.$$

The contribution of $F^{(II)}$ is negligible compared with that of $F^{(I)}$. In order to calculate $F^{(I)}$, it is convenient to introduce the electric dipole moment of the electrons:

$$\mathbf{D} \equiv e \sum_n \mathbf{R}_n. \qquad \text{(XXI.244)}$$

[This is the vector operator denoted by $\mathbf{Q}^{(l)}$ in § XIII.33 and XVII.3; cf. eq. (XVII.35).]

$\mathbf{D}$ satisfies the relation:

$$[\mathbf{D}, H_{\text{at}}] = \text{i}e \sum_n \frac{\mathbf{P}_n}{m}.$$

Therefore:

$$\frac{\text{i}e}{m} \langle\lambda| \sum_n \mathbf{P}_n |\mu\rangle = \langle\lambda| (\mathbf{D} H_{\text{at}} - H_{\text{at}} \mathbf{D}) |\mu\rangle$$

$$= (E_\mu - E_\lambda) \langle\lambda|\mathbf{D}|\mu\rangle = -k\langle\lambda|\mathbf{D}|\mu\rangle,$$

whence

$$F^{(\text{I})} = \frac{\text{i}mk}{e} \langle\lambda| (\mathbf{D}\cdot\boldsymbol{\epsilon}) |\mu\rangle$$

and

$$w_{\lambda\to\mu\mathbf{k}\boldsymbol{\epsilon}} = \frac{k^3}{2\pi} |\langle\lambda| (\mathbf{D}\cdot\boldsymbol{\epsilon}) |\mu\rangle|^2. \qquad \text{(XXI.245)}$$

It is convenient at this point to specify the "magnetic quantum numbers" m_λ and m_μ of the initial and final states, and to introduce the reduced matrix element $\langle\lambda\|\mathbf{D}\|\mu\rangle$ in accordance with definition (XIII.125). If D_q denotes the qth standard component of the vector operator $\mathbf{D}$, the Wigner–Eckart theorem gives:

$$\langle\lambda j_\lambda m_\lambda|D_q|\mu j_\mu m_\mu\rangle = (2j_\lambda + 1)^{-\frac{1}{2}} \langle j_\mu 1 m_\mu q | j_\lambda m_\lambda\rangle \langle\lambda\|\mathbf{D}\|\mu\rangle.$$

Since $\boldsymbol{\epsilon}\cdot\mathbf{D} = \sum_q \varepsilon_q D_q$, where ε_q ($q = +, 0, -$) denotes the standard components of the polarization vector [definition (XIII.94)], we finally obtain:

$$w_{\lambda\to\mu\mathbf{k}\boldsymbol{\epsilon}} = \left[\frac{k^3|\langle\lambda\|\mathbf{D}\|\mu\rangle|^2}{2\pi}\right] \times \left[\frac{|\sum_q \varepsilon_q \langle j_\mu 1 m_\mu q|j_\lambda m_\lambda\rangle|^2}{(2j_\lambda + 1)}\right]. \qquad \text{(XXI.246)}$$

If the atom is unpolarized in its initial state and if the polarization in the final state is not observed, we must sum over m_μ and average over m_λ, i.e.:

$$\langle w_{\lambda\to\mu\mathbf{k}\boldsymbol{\epsilon}}\rangle = \frac{1}{2j_\lambda+1}\sum_{m_\lambda m_\mu} w_{\lambda\to\mu\mathbf{k}\boldsymbol{\epsilon}}.$$

This is easily done using the symmetry and orthogonality properties of the C.–G. coefficients [cf. eq. (C.13c) and (C.14a)], and gives:

$$\langle w_{\lambda\to\mu\mathbf{k}\boldsymbol{\epsilon}}\rangle = \frac{k^3|\langle\lambda\|\mathbf{D}\|\mu\rangle|^2}{6\pi(2j_\lambda+1)}.$$

As might have been expected, the expression obtained depends neither on the direction of emission nor on the polarization of the photon emitted. The total transition probability $\lambda\to\mu$ per unit time is obtained by summing over the two polarization states and integrating over the angles of emission, i.e. by multiplying the expression by 8π:

$$w^{(\mathrm{tot})}_{\lambda\to\mu} = \frac{4k^3}{3(2j_\lambda+1)}|\langle\lambda\|\mathbf{D}\|\mu\rangle|^2. \qquad \text{(XXI.247)}$$

32. Low Energy Compton Scattering. The Thomson Formula

As an example of a collision problem, rather than consider those treated in section II – and which can be solved by the same methods – we shall consider the simpler problem of Compton scattering (the scattering of photons by free electrons) [1]).

The state of the system before collision consists of an electron of given momentum $\mathbf{P}_\mathrm{i}$ and a photon whose momentum and polarization are denoted by $\mathbf{k}_\mathrm{i}$ and $\boldsymbol{\epsilon}_\mathrm{i}$ respectively. It is represented by a certain ket vector $|i\rangle$

$$|i\rangle \equiv |\mathbf{P}_\mathrm{i}\mathbf{k}_\mathrm{i}\boldsymbol{\epsilon}_\mathrm{i}\rangle.$$

We wish to calculate the cross section for scattering from this initial state to a certain final state in which the momentum of the electron, the momentum of the photon and its polarization are $\mathbf{P}_\mathrm{f}$, $\mathbf{k}_\mathrm{f}$ and $\boldsymbol{\epsilon}_\mathrm{f}$ respectively and which we denote by $|f\rangle$:

$$|f\rangle \equiv |\mathbf{P}_\mathrm{f}\mathbf{k}_\mathrm{f}\boldsymbol{\epsilon}_\mathrm{f}\rangle.$$

Energy and momentum are conserved in the collision.

---

[1]) In the case of a scalar field, the scattering cross section for a field corpuscle by a free particle vanishes.

In order to calculate the cross section for all energies, the electron must be treated as a Dirac particle coupled to the radiation field by the interaction $-e\boldsymbol{\alpha}\cdot\mathbf{A}(\mathbf{R})$. In this paragraph, we shall limit ourselves to treating the problem in the low-frequency limit [1]).

The electron is supposed initially at rest ($\mathbf{P}_{\mathrm{i}}=0$), and the incident photon sufficiently soft for the energy transferred to the electron to be small compared with its rest mass:

$$k_{\mathrm{f}} \ll m$$

(whence: $k_{\mathrm{f}} \simeq k_{\mathrm{i}}$, $P_{\mathrm{f}} \approx k_{\mathrm{f}}$). One may then treat the electron in the non-relativistic approximation, and take as the Hamiltonian for the system:

$$H = H_0 + H',$$

where

$$H_0 = H_{\mathrm{rad}} + \frac{\mathbf{P}^2}{2m}.$$

In accordance with equation (XXI.235) H' is the sum of three terms $H^{(\mathrm{I})}$, $H^{(\mathrm{II})}$ and H'', defined by equations (XXI.236a), (XXI.236b) and (XXI.237) respectively.

To calculate the collision cross section we apply the formulas of collision theory. It is clear that the reservations made regarding this point in § 14 must also be made here. We shall not return to this question but will suppose, as in § 14, that the formulas given by collision theory are correct providing the electron mass m appearing in them is the mass that is experimentally measured.

However, the straightforward application of the collision theory formalism encounters another difficulty, namely the impossibility of defining and separating out the center-of-mass variables. This difficulty is only an apparent one. In reality, the elimination of the motion of the center of mass plays only an accessory role in non-relativistic collision theory; the resulting simplifications are due to the fact that the total momentum of the system is conserved in the collision. It is possible to reformulate Collision Theory without making this elimination and the conservation of momentum then appears explicitly.

---

[1]) The general case can be treated by the same method (cf. Heitler, *loc. cit.*) and leads to the Klein–Nishina formula. The calculations are long but not difficult. In fact, they can be considerably shortened by using the covariant formulation of the Quantum Theory of Radiation (cf. Jauch and Röhrlich, *loc. cit.*).

This new formulation will be used here. The only modification concerns the definition of the transition amplitude $T_{i \to f}$. We shall adopt for T the same formal definition:

$$T \equiv H' + H' \frac{1}{E - H + i\varepsilon} H'.$$

Since T is invariant under translation, the matrix element $\langle f|T|i\rangle$ has a δ-function factor assuring the conservation of the total momentum. $T_{i\to f}$ is defined by the relation:

$$\langle f|T|i\rangle = (2\pi)^3\, \delta(\mathbf{P}_f + \mathbf{k}_f - \mathbf{P}_i - \mathbf{k}_i)\, T_{i\to f}. \qquad \text{(XXI.248)}$$

The factor $(2\pi)^3$ is introduced here to take into account the normalization adopted for the electron plane wave:

$$\langle \mathbf{P}|\mathbf{P}'\rangle = (2\pi)^3\, \delta(\mathbf{P} - \mathbf{P}').$$

The collision cross section is now still given by the general formula (XXI.116).

In order to calculate $\langle f|T|i\rangle$, we expand T into a power series in e and retain only the terms of lowest order, namely the terms in e^2:

$$\langle f|T|i\rangle = \langle f|H''|i\rangle + \langle f|(H^{(\mathrm{I})} + H^{(\mathrm{II})}) \frac{1}{E - H_0 + i\varepsilon} (H^{(\mathrm{I})} + H^{(\mathrm{II})})|i\rangle + O(e^4). \qquad \text{(XXI.249)}$$

It is clear from expressions (XXI.236*a*, *b*) and (XXI.237), that each of the two terms on the right-hand side contains the factor:

$$\int e^{i(\mathbf{P}_i + \mathbf{k}_i - \mathbf{P}_f - \mathbf{k}_f)\cdot \mathbf{R}}\, d\mathbf{R} \equiv (2\pi)^3\, \delta(\mathbf{P}_f + \mathbf{k}_f - \mathbf{P}_i - \mathbf{k}_i).$$

This is the above-mentioned conservation-of-momentum factor. From expression (XXI.237),

$$\langle f|H''|i\rangle = \frac{2\pi e^2}{mkL^3} (\boldsymbol{\epsilon}_f{}^* \cdot \boldsymbol{\epsilon}_i) \int e^{i(\mathbf{k}_i + \mathbf{P}_i - \mathbf{k}_f - \mathbf{P}_f)\cdot \mathbf{R}}\, d\mathbf{R} \qquad \text{(XXI.250)}$$

putting: $k = (k_i k_f)^{\frac{1}{2}}$. Since we are considering only the low-frequency limit, we neglect terms of the order of k/m beside unity and write simply:

$$k_i \simeq k_f \simeq k.$$

It is easily shown that the contribution from the second term on the right-hand side of equation (XXI.249) is an order of k/m higher than that of the first term. It will therefore be ignored. Thus, in the present approximation ($e^2 \ll 1$, $k \ll m$):

$$T_{\mathrm{i}\to\mathrm{f}} = \frac{2\pi e^2}{mkL^3}\,(\boldsymbol{\epsilon}_{\mathrm{f}}{}^* \cdot \boldsymbol{\epsilon}_{\mathrm{i}}) \tag{XXI.251}$$

whence the scattering cross section [cf. eq. (XXI.116)]:

$$\begin{aligned}\frac{\mathrm{d}\sigma_{\mathrm{i}\to\mathrm{f}}}{\mathrm{d}\Omega} &= 2\pi L^3 |T_{\mathrm{i}\to\mathrm{f}}|^2 \left(\frac{L^3k^2}{(2\pi)^3}\right)\\ &= \frac{e^4}{m^2}\,|\boldsymbol{\epsilon}_{\mathrm{f}}{}^* \cdot \boldsymbol{\epsilon}_{\mathrm{i}}|^2.\end{aligned} \tag{XXI.252}$$

To obtain the scattering cross section for non-polarized photons in the direction $\boldsymbol{k}_{\mathrm{f}}$ we must average over the two possible initial polarization states and sum over the two possible final polarization states. Denoting the scattering angle of the photons by θ ($\cos\theta = \boldsymbol{k}_{\mathrm{i}}\cdot\boldsymbol{k}_{\mathrm{f}}/k^2$), we then obtain:

$$\begin{aligned}\left.\frac{\mathrm{d}\sigma_{\mathrm{i}\to\mathrm{f}}}{\mathrm{d}\Omega}\right|_{\text{non pol}} &= \frac{1}{2}\sum_{\boldsymbol{\epsilon}_{\mathrm{i}}\boldsymbol{\epsilon}_{\mathrm{f}}} \frac{\mathrm{d}\sigma_{\mathrm{i}\to\mathrm{f}}}{\mathrm{d}\Omega}\\ &= \frac{1}{2}\,\frac{e^4}{m^2}\,(1+\cos^2\theta).\end{aligned} \tag{XXI.253}$$

The total scattering cross section for the photons, σ_{tot} is obtained by integrating over the angles of emission. One finds:

$$\sigma_{\mathrm{tot}} = \frac{8\pi}{3}\,\frac{e^4}{m^2}. \tag{XXI.254}$$

These results are all in good agreement with experiment.

Expressions (XXI.252–254) will be found to be identical with those given by Classical Radiation Theory [1]). In particular, we obtain the *classical Thomson formula* for the total cross section. This identity of the results of the two theories confirms what was said in § I.5 concerning the significance and the limitations of the classical Theory of the Compton effect. The Classical Theory obviously cannot account for the corpuscular character of radiation, nor for the fact that the transfers of momentum and energy between the radiation and the

---

[1]) The constant $\hbar$ does not appear in these expressions. Each of them is proportional to the square of the classical radius of the electron: $r_0 = e^2/mc^2$. Expression (XXI.252), for example, can also be written $r_0{}^2 \cos^2\alpha$, where α denotes the angle between the initial and final polarizations (supposed rectilinear).

electron take place by discrete quanta; but it correctly predicts the average value of the momentum transferred to the electron per unit time and per unit incident flux [eq. (XXI.254)], and the angular distribution and the polarization of the scattered radiation [eq. (XXI.252)] and also, when the Doppler effect is taken into account, the shift in the wavelength of the scattered radiation [eqs. (I.5) and (I.6)].

The agreement of the two theories is fully realized only in the low-frequency limit where the radiation wavelength, $1/k$, is so large that the scattering process is practically independent of the internal structure of the electron. Since the electron is a quantum object, its dimensions are of the order of $1/m$ and the effects of its structure [1]) are of the order of k/m. In the non-relativistic limit, they are given by the second term in expression (XXI.249). When the incident energy is increased, the quantum nature of the electron becomes more and more evident and one observes increasingly pronounced deviations from the predictions of the Classical Theory.

EXERCISES AND PROBLEMS

1. $\Phi(\mathbf{r})$ denoting the real scalar field of section I, we wish to measure the integral of this observable over a finite domain; more generally, we consider the integral:

$$\hat{\Phi} \equiv \int \Phi(\mathbf{r})\, P(\mathbf{r})\, \mathrm{d}\mathbf{r},$$

where $P(\mathbf{r})$ is a given real non-negative function whose integral over all space is equal to 1. We put:

$$\chi(\boldsymbol{\varkappa}) \equiv \int \exp\,(\mathrm{i}\boldsymbol{\varkappa}\cdot\mathbf{r})\, P(\mathbf{r})\, \mathrm{d}\mathbf{r} \qquad (\chi(0) = 1).$$

Show that the statistical distribution of $\hat{\Phi}$ in the vacuum state is a Gaussian and that:

$$(\triangle\hat{\Phi})^2 = \int \frac{|\chi(\boldsymbol{\varkappa})|^2}{16\pi^3(\mu^2+\varkappa^2)^{\frac{1}{2}}}\, \mathrm{d}\boldsymbol{\varkappa}.$$

In particular, if the weight function $P(\mathbf{r})$ has appreciable values only in a domain of linear dimensions a, and $\mu a \ll 1$, one has: $\triangle\hat{\Phi} \approx 1/a$.

Treat the same problem with the electromagnetic field and show that in the vacuum state: $\triangle\mathscr{E}_\perp \approx \triangle\mathscr{H} \approx 1/a^2$.

---

[1]) In the classical theory, structural effects are of the order of ke^2/m, the ratio of the classical radius to the wavelength of the radiation.

2. Show that the correction δM defined in § 11 is given to the second order by the expression on the right-hand side of eq. (XXI.76).

3. Consider the elastic scattering problem defined in § 14; suppose the target non-polarized and denote the scattering angle by θ: $\cos\theta = \mathbf{k}_i \cdot \mathbf{k}_f / k^2$. Show that, in the second-order Born approximation and in the long-wave-length limit ($k\langle R\rangle \ll 1$), the angular distribution of elastically scattered corpuscles is in $\cos^2\theta$ and that the cross section tends to zero in the limit when $k \to 0$ (this property is characteristic of scalar coupling).

4. We consider the resonant scattering problem of § 15 and follow the notation employed there. Suppose that the initial state $|\alpha\rangle$ of the atomic system has a zero angular momentum, and that the resonant state $|\lambda\rangle$ has an angular momentum equal to $\boldsymbol{l}$. Show that, if we neglect the contribution $A^{(\text{pot})}$, the transition amplitude T for the elastic scattering process $\mathbf{k}_i \to \mathbf{k}_f$ is given by the formula:

$$T = \frac{\Pi}{\omega L^3} \frac{2l+1}{k} P_l(\cos\theta) \frac{\Gamma_{\lambda\to\alpha}}{(E - E_\lambda - \delta E_\lambda) + \frac{1}{2}\mathrm{i}\Gamma_\lambda}$$

in which θ denotes the scattering angle and $\Gamma_{\lambda\to\alpha}$ the probability of the radiative transition $\lambda \to \alpha$ [cf. eq. (XXI.82)] and that consequently the elastic scattering cross section $\mathrm{d}\sigma_{\text{el}}/\mathrm{d}\Omega$ is given by the formula:

$$\frac{\mathrm{d}\sigma_{\text{el}}}{\mathrm{d}\Omega} = \frac{(2l+1)^2}{k^2} P_l^2(\cos\theta) \frac{\Gamma^2_{\lambda\to\alpha}}{4(E - E_\lambda - \delta E_\lambda)^2 + \Gamma_\lambda^2}.$$

Show that these two expressions are a simple generalization of those obtained in the resonance scattering of a particle in a central potential [eqs. (X.64) and (X.65)] and that the discussion and the calculations of § X.15 and X.16 concerning the notion of resonance and of a metastable state apply in the present case.

5. $A_j(\mathbf{r})$ and $\mathscr{E}_i(\mathbf{r}')$ denoting respectively the jth and the ith components of the potential $\mathbf{A}$ (in radiation gauge) and of the transverse electric field $\mathscr{E}_\perp$ prove the commutation relation:

$$[\mathscr{E}_i(\mathbf{r}), A_j(\mathbf{r}')] = 4\pi\mathrm{i}\theta_{ij}(\mathbf{r}-\mathbf{r}'),$$

where

$$\theta_{ij}(\mathbf{r}-\mathbf{r}') \equiv \delta_{ij}\,\delta(\mathbf{r}-\mathbf{r}') - \frac{\partial^2}{\partial x_i \partial x_j'}\left(\frac{1}{4\pi|\mathbf{r}-\mathbf{r}'|}\right)$$

[$\theta_{ij}(\mathbf{r}-\mathbf{r}')$ is the projector onto the subspace of transverse vector fields].

6. Prove formula (XXI.220) giving the total momentum of the free radiation field.

7. Show that the intrinsic part $\mathbf{G}^{(s)}$ of the angular momentum of the radiation satisfies the formula:

$$\mathbf{G}^{(s)} = -\mathrm{i} \sum_{\mathbf{k}\varpi\varpi'} a_{(\mathbf{k}\varpi)}{}^\dagger\, a_{(\mathbf{k}\varpi')}\, (\boldsymbol{\epsilon}^{(\varpi)*} \times \boldsymbol{\epsilon}^{(\varpi')})$$

(notations of § 27); in particular, if $N_{\mathbf{k}+}$ and $N_{\mathbf{k}-}$ denote the respective number of right-handed and left-handed photons of momentum $\mathbf{k}$ [definition (XXI.222)], we have:

$$\mathbf{G}^{(s)} = \sum_{\mathbf{k}} (N_{\mathbf{k}+} - N_{\mathbf{k}-})\, \mathbf{k}/k.$$

8. Prove relations (XXI.223) and (XXI.224).

9. 1) Let $u^{LM}(\mathbf{r})$ be a scalar field transforming under rotation like the spherical harmonic $Y_L{}^M(\theta, \varphi)$, and $\mathbf{V}(\mathbf{r}, \mathbf{p})$ a vector (polar or axial) formed from the vectors $\mathbf{r}$ and $\mathbf{p}$. Show that the vector fields $\mathbf{U}^{LM}(\mathbf{r})$ defined by

$$\mathbf{U}^{LM} \equiv \mathbf{V}(\mathbf{r}, -\mathrm{i}\nabla)\, u^{LM}(\mathbf{r}),$$

where $\mathbf{V}$ is an operator acting on the function u^{LM}, represent a state of angular momentum (LM).

[In virtue of this theorem, the vector fields $\mathbf{\Lambda}_{kjm}$ and $\mathbf{\Theta}_{kjm}$ defined in § XXI.29 represent states of angular momentum $(j\ m)$.]

2) In the same way as a particle of spin 1 has a 3-component wave function forming a vector field, a particle of integer spin s has a $(2s+1)$ component wave function forming an irreducible tensor field of order s. Let $X_\mu{}^{(s)}(\mathbf{r}, \mathbf{p})$ be the μth component of an irreducible tensor of order s formed with the vectors $\mathbf{r}$ and $\mathbf{p}$. Show that the tensor field $\mathbf{U}^{LM}(\mathbf{r})$ whose μth component is given by

$$U^{LM}(\mathbf{r}) = X_\mu{}^{(s)}(\mathbf{r}, -\mathrm{i}\nabla)\, U^{LM}(\mathbf{r}) \qquad (\mu = -s, \ldots, +s)$$

represents a state of angular momentum (LM) of this particle of spin s.

10. Using the explicit formulas for the matrix elements eqs. (241a, b), show that the probability of emission of a photon vanishes if the spins of the initial and final states are both null (0 → 0 *selection rule*).
[N.B. This property is obvious if the multipole expansion is used instead of the plane-wave expansion.]

11. Calculate the probability per unit time for the radiative transition $2p \to 1s$ in the hydrogen atom (one finds: $w_{2p\to 1s} = 6.25 \times 10^8\ \mathrm{sec}^{-1}$).

12. Show that in the long-wavelength approximation, the probability of a *magnetic dipole* radiative transition $\lambda \to \mu\mathbf{k}\boldsymbol{\epsilon}$ (notation of § 30) is given by the formula [cf. eq. (XXI.245)]

$$w_{\lambda\to\mu\mathbf{k}\boldsymbol{\epsilon}} = \frac{k}{2\pi} |\langle\lambda|[\mathbf{M}\cdot(\boldsymbol{\epsilon}\times\mathbf{k})]|\mu\rangle|^2,$$

where $\boldsymbol{M}$ is the total magnetic moment of the atomic system namely:

$$\boldsymbol{M} = \frac{e}{2m} \sum_i (\boldsymbol{l}_i + 2\boldsymbol{s}_i).$$

[N.B. This formula correctly gives the radiative transition probability when $\Delta\Pi = +1$ and $j_\lambda + j_\mu \leqslant 1$; if $j_\lambda + j_\mu \geqslant 2$, the electric quadrupole contribution is not null and in general cannot be neglected.]

From this deduce that the total magnetic dipole transition probability is given by the formula [cf. eq. (XXI.247)]:

$$w^{(\mathrm{tot})}_{\lambda\to\mu} = \frac{4k^3}{3(2j_\lambda + 1)} |\langle\lambda||\boldsymbol{M}||\mu\rangle|^2.$$

Show that in the case of the transition $2s \to 1s$ of the hydrogen atom, this quantity vanishes in the non-relativistic approximation (i.e. if one uses the wave function of the Schrödinger theory).

13. Calculate the cross section for the photoelectric effect for the ground state of the hydrogen atom. Suppose that: $me^4 \ll k \ll m$ ($m \equiv$ mass of the electron, $k \equiv$ momentum of the incident photon, $\hbar = c = 1$); consequently, the energy transferred to the photoelectron is large enough for its final state to be treated as a plane wave, but its velocity v is small enough for it to be treated as a non-relativistic particle. Since the magnetic interaction (the term $H^{(II)}$), gives a negligible contribution, one finds:

$$\frac{\mathrm{d}\sigma}{\mathrm{d}\Omega} = 4\sqrt{2}\, e^8 \left(\frac{m}{k}\right)^{7/2} \times \frac{e^4}{m^2} \frac{\cos^2\varphi}{(1 - v\cos\theta)^4}$$

φ and θ denoting respectively the angles made by the direction of emission with those of the polarization (supposed rectilinear) and the momentum of the incident photon. One obtains the results of the semi-classical theory of the effect (cf. Problem XVII.2) by putting $v = 0$ in this formula.

APPENDIX C[1])

VECTOR ADDITION COEFFICIENTS AND ROTATION MATRICES

PLAN OF THE APPENDIX

---

[1]) This Appendix was prepared in collaboration with J. Horowitz. For a more complete treatment of these questions, see notably A. E. Edmonds, *Angular Momentum in Quantum Mechanics* (Princeton University Press, 1957), which, in addition, gives a list of the principal tables now published. See also U. Fano and G. Racah, *Irreducible Tensorial Sets* (Academic Press Inc., New York, 1959).

1. Angular Momentum. Notations and Conventions

The following notations and conventions concerning the angular momentum will be adopted throughout the Appendix.

Units: $\hbar = 1$.

Angular momentum components: $\mathbf{J}$, angular momentum operator, having cartesian coordinates J_x, J_y and J_z.

$$J_{\pm} = J_x \pm \mathrm{i} J_y. \tag{C.1}$$

Commutation relations

$$[J_x, J_y] = \mathrm{i} J_z \qquad [J_y, J_z] = \mathrm{i} J_x \qquad [J_z, J_x] = \mathrm{i} J_y \tag{C.2}$$

$$[J_z, J_{\pm}] = \pm J_{\pm} \qquad [J_+, J_-] = 2J_z. \tag{C.3}$$

Basis vectors of a standard representation $\{\mathbf{J}^2 J_z\}$: $|\tau JM\rangle$

$$\mathbf{J}^2 |\tau JM\rangle = J(J+1)\, |\tau JM\rangle \tag{C.4}$$

$$J_z |\tau JM\rangle = M |\tau JM\rangle \tag{C.5}$$

$$J_{\pm} |\tau JM\rangle = \sqrt{J(J+1) - M(M \pm 1)}\, |\tau J\, M \pm 1\rangle \tag{C.6}$$

$$\langle \tau JM | \tau' J' M' \rangle = \delta_{\tau\tau'}\, \delta_{JJ'}\, \delta_{MM'} \tag{C.7}$$

(J integral or half-integral $\geqslant 0$, $M = -J, -J+1, \ldots, +J$).

τ denotes the quantum numbers that must be added to J and M to form a complete set; in the rest of the Appendix it will be omitted when not needed.

I. CLEBSCH–GORDON (C.–G.) COEFFICIENTS AND "3j" SYMBOLS

2. Definition and Notations

$\mathbf{j}_1$, $\mathbf{j}_2$ angular momenta of quantum systems 1 and 2 respectively.

$\mathbf{J}$, angular momentum of the total system of 1 and 2 taken together:

$$\mathbf{J} = \mathbf{j}_1 + \mathbf{j}_2. \tag{C.8}$$

The tensor product of the $(2j_1+1)$ vectors of system 1

$$|j_1 m_1\rangle \qquad (j_1 \text{ fixed, } m_1 = -j_1, \ldots, +j_1)$$

by the $(2j_2+1)$ vectors of system 2

$$|j_2 m_2\rangle \qquad (j_2 \text{ fixed, } m_2 = -j_2, \ldots, +j_2)$$

gives the $(2j_1+1)(2j_2+1)$ simultaneous eigenvectors of $\mathbf{j}_1^2$, $\mathbf{j}_2^2$, j_{1z}, j_{2z}, the vectors

$$|j_1 j_2 m_1 m_2\rangle \equiv |j_1 m_1\rangle |j_2 m_2\rangle \tag{C.9}$$

from which we can obtain, by a unitary transformation, the $(2j_1+1)$ $(2j_2+1)$ simultaneous eigenvectors of $\mathbf{j}_1^2$, $\mathbf{j}_2^2$, $\mathbf{J}^2$, J_z, the vectors

$$|j_1 j_2 J M\rangle \tag{C.10}$$
$$(J = |j_1 - j_2|, \ldots, j_1+j_2;\ M = -J, \ldots, +J).$$

Definition

The Clebsch–Gordon [1]), or vector addition, coefficients

$$\langle j_1 j_2 m_1 m_2 | J M\rangle$$

are the coefficients of that unitary transformation:

$$|j_1 j_2 J M\rangle = \sum_{m_1 m_2} |j_1 j_2 m_1 m_2\rangle \langle j_1 j_2 m_1 m_2 | J M\rangle. \tag{C.11}$$

Phase convention [2])

We complete the definition of the vectors in (C.9) and (C.10) by fixing their relative phases as follows:

(*i*) the $|j_1 m_1\rangle$, the $|j_2 m_2\rangle$ and the $|j_1 j_2 J M\rangle$ obey relations (C.6);

(*ii*) $\langle j_1 j_2 j_1 (j_1 - J)\, | J J\rangle$ real > 0.

---

[1]) There are many symbols employed in the literature to denote the Clebsch–Gordon coefficients. We note in particular:

$\langle j_1 j_2 m_1 m_2 | j_1 j_2 J M\rangle$ [Condon and Shortly, *Theory of Atomic Spectra* (University Press, Cambridge, 4th ed., 1957)].

$C_{j_1 j_2}(JM; m_1 m_2)$ [Blatt and Weisskopf, *Theoretical Nuclear Physics* (Wiley, New York, 1952)].

$S^{j_1 j_2}_{J m_1 m_2}$ [E. P. Wigner, *Group Theory and its Application to the Quantum Mechanics of Atomic Spectra* (English translation; Academic Press, New York, 1958)].

[2]) This convention is adopted by most authors, in particular by Wigner, Condon and Shortly, Blatt and Weisskopf, *op. cit.* note 1 of this page, and by Racah, Phys. Rev. 62 (1942) 437.

"3j" *symbol* (Wigner) [1]):

$$\begin{pmatrix} j_1 & j_2 & J \\ m_1 & m_2 & -M \end{pmatrix} \equiv \frac{(-)^{j_1-j_2+M}}{\sqrt{2J+1}} \langle j_1 j_2 m_1 m_2 | JM \rangle. \tag{C.12}$$

3. Principal Properties

Reality. They are all real:

$$\langle j_1 j_2 m_1 m_2 | JM \rangle^* = \langle j_1 j_2 m_1 m_2 | JM \rangle.$$

Selection rules

(*i*) $m_1 + m_2 = M$;

(*ii*) $|j_1 - j_2| \leqslant J \leqslant j_1 + j_2$ ("triangular inequalities").

If these two conditions are not met, $\langle j_1 j_2 m_1 m_2 | JM \rangle = 0$.

Symmetries:

$$\begin{pmatrix} j_1 & j_2 & j_3 \\ m_1 & m_2 & m_3 \end{pmatrix} \text{ is:}$$

(*i*) invariant in a circular permutation of the three columns;

(*ii*) multiplied by $(-)^{j_1+j_2+j_3}$ in a permutation of two columns;

(*iii*) multiplied by $(-)^{j_1+j_2+j_3}$ when we simultaneously change the signs of m_1, m_2, and m_3.

Consequences:

$$\langle j_1 j_2 m_1 m_2 | JM \rangle = (-)^{j_1+j_2-J} \langle j_2 j_1 m_2 m_1 | JM \rangle \tag{C.13a}$$

$$= (-)^{j_1-J+m_2} \sqrt{\frac{2J+1}{2j_1+1}} \langle J j_2 M -m_2 | j_1 m_1 \rangle \tag{C.13b}$$

$$= (-)^{j_2-J-m_1} \sqrt{\frac{2J+1}{2j_2+1}} \langle j_1 J -m_1 M | j_2 m_2 \rangle \tag{C.13c}$$

$$= (-)^{j_1+j_2-J} \langle j_1 j_2 -m_1 -m_2 | J -M \rangle. \tag{C.13d}$$

---

[1]) Racah, *op. cit.*, note 2, p. 1055, employs the symbol:

$$V(abc, \alpha\beta\gamma) \equiv (-)^{a-b-c} \begin{pmatrix} abc \\ \alpha\beta\gamma \end{pmatrix} \equiv \frac{(-)^{c-\gamma}}{\sqrt{2c+1}} \langle ab\alpha\beta | c -\gamma \rangle.$$

Orthogonality relations

$$\sum_{m_1=-j_1}^{+j_1} \sum_{m_2=-j_2}^{+j_2} \langle j_1 j_2 m_1 m_2 | JM \rangle \langle j_1 j_2 m_1 m_2 | J'M' \rangle = \delta_{JJ'} \delta_{MM'} \tag{C.14a}$$
$$(|j_1 - j_2| \leqslant J \leqslant j_1 + j_2; \quad -J \leqslant M \leqslant J)$$

$$\sum_{J=|j_1-j_2|}^{j_1+j_2} \sum_{M=-J}^{+J} \langle j_1 j_2 m_1 m_2 | JM \rangle \langle j_1 j_2 m_1' m_2' | JM \rangle = \delta_{m_1 m_1'} \delta_{m_2 m_2'} \tag{C.14b}$$
$$(-j_1 \leqslant m_1 \leqslant +j_1; \quad -j_2 \leqslant m_2 \leqslant +j_2)$$

$$\sum_{m_1=-j_1}^{+j_1} \sum_{m_2=-j_2}^{+j_2} \begin{pmatrix} j_1 & j_2 & j_3 \\ m_1 & m_2 & m_3 \end{pmatrix} \begin{pmatrix} j_1 & j_2 & j_3' \\ m_1 & m_2 & m_3' \end{pmatrix} = \frac{1}{2j_3+1} \delta_{j_3 j_3'} \delta_{m_3 m_3'} \tag{C.15a}$$

$$\sum_{j_3=|j_1-j_2|}^{j_1+j_2} \sum_{m_3=-j_3}^{+j_3} (2j_3+1) \begin{pmatrix} j_1 & j_2 & j_3 \\ m_1 & m_2 & m_3 \end{pmatrix} \begin{pmatrix} j_1 & j_2 & j_3 \\ m_1' & m_2' & m_3 \end{pmatrix} = \delta_{m_1 m_1'} \delta_{m_2 m_2'}. \tag{C.15b}$$

Composition relation for the spherical harmonics

$$\ldots{}^{m_1}_{l_1}(\Omega)\, Y^{m_2}_{l_2}(\Omega)\, Y^{m_3}_{l_3}(\Omega)\, \mathrm{d}\Omega = \left[\frac{(2l_1+1)(2l_2+1)(2l_3+1)}{4\pi}\right]^{\frac{1}{2}} \begin{pmatrix} l_1 & l_2 & l_3 \\ 0 & 0 & 0 \end{pmatrix} \begin{pmatrix} l_1 & l_2 & l_3 \\ m_1 & m_2 & m_3 \end{pmatrix} \tag{C.16}$$

whence:

$$\ldots{}^{1}(\Omega)\, Y^{m_2}_{l_2}(\Omega)$$

$$\sum_{\ldots=|l_1-l_2|}^{l_1+l_2} \sum_{M=-L}^{L} \left[\frac{(2l_1+1)(2l_2+1)}{4\pi(2L+1)}\right]^{\frac{1}{2}} \langle l_1 l_2 0 0 | L0 \rangle \langle l_1 l_2 m_1 m_2 | LM \rangle\, Y^M_L(\Omega) \tag{C.17a}$$

$$\sum_{\ldots=|l_1-l_2|}^{l_1+l_2} \sum_{M=-L}^{L} (-)^M \left[\frac{(2l_1+1)(2l_2+1)(2L+1)}{4\pi}\right]^{\frac{1}{2}} \begin{pmatrix} l_1 & l_2 & L \\ 0 & 0 & 0 \end{pmatrix} \begin{pmatrix} l_1 & l_2 & L \\ m_1 & m_2 & M \end{pmatrix} Y_L^{-M}(\Omega). \tag{C.17b}$$

4. Methods of Calculation

Recursion relations

Relating the C.–G. whose arguments differ at most by:

(*i*) $\Delta J - 0 \qquad \Delta M = +1$

$$\sqrt{J(J+1)-M(M+1)}\, \langle j_1 j_2 m_1 m_2 | JM \rangle$$
$$= \sqrt{j_1(j_1+1)-m_1(m_1+1)}\, \langle j_1 j_2\, m_1+1\, m_2 | J\, M+1 \rangle \tag{C.18}$$
$$+ \sqrt{j_2(j_2+1)-m_2(m_2+1)}\, \langle j_1 j_2 m_1\, m_2+1 | J\, M+1 \rangle$$

(*ii*) $\Delta J = 0 \qquad \Delta M = -1$

$$\sqrt{J(J+1)-M(M-1)}\, \langle j_1 j_2 m_1 m_2 | JM \rangle$$
$$= \sqrt{j_1(j_1+1)-m_1(m_1-1)}\, \langle j_1 j_2\, m_1-1\, m_2 | J\, M-1 \rangle \tag{C.19}$$
$$+ \sqrt{j_2(j_2+1)-m_2(m_2-1)}\, \langle j_1 j_2 m_1\, m_2-1 | J\, M-1 \rangle$$

(*iii*) $\Delta J = \pm 1 \qquad \Delta M = 0$

$$A_0 \langle j_1 j_2 m_1 m_2 | J M \rangle = A_+ \langle j_1 j_2 m_1 m_2 | J+1\ M \rangle + A_- \langle j_1 j_2 m_1 m_2 | J-1\ M \rangle \tag{C.20}$$

with

$$A_0 = m_1 - m_2 + M \frac{j_2(j_2+1) - j_1(j_1+1)}{J(J+1)} \qquad (M = m_1 + m_2)$$

$$A_+ = f(J+1)$$

$$A_- = f(J)$$

$$f(x) = \sqrt{x^2 - M^2} \left[\frac{[(j_1+j_2+1)^2 - x^2][x^2 - (j_1-j_2)^2]}{4x^2(2x-1)(2x+1)} \right]^{\frac{1}{2}}$$

The Racah formula

$$\begin{pmatrix} a\, b\, c \\ \alpha \beta \gamma \end{pmatrix} = (-)^{a-b-\gamma} \sqrt{\Delta(abc)} \sqrt{(a+\alpha)!\,(a-\alpha)!\,(b+\beta)!\,(b-\beta)!\,(c+\gamma)!\,(c-\gamma)!} \qquad \text{C.}$$

$$\times \sum_t (-)^t [t!(c-b+t+\alpha)!\,(c-a+t-\beta)!\,(a+b-c-t)!\,(a-t-\alpha)!\,(b-t+\beta)!]^{-1}$$

$$(\alpha+\beta+\gamma=0, \qquad |a-b| \leqslant c \leqslant a+b)$$

with

$$\Delta(abc) \equiv \frac{(a+b-c)!\,(b+c-a)!\,(c+a-b)!}{(a+b+c+1)!} \tag{C.22}$$

$\sum_t$ extends over all integral values of t for which the factorials have a meaning, i.e. for which the arguments of the factorials are positive or null ($0! = 1$). The number of terms in this sum is $\nu + 1$, where ν is the smallest of the nine numbers:

$$\begin{array}{lll} a \pm \alpha & b \pm \beta & c \pm \gamma \\ a+b-c & b+c-a & c+a-b. \end{array}$$

5. Special Values and Tables

Special values

(*i*) J and M taking their maximum value:

$$\langle j_1 j_2 j_1 j_2 | j_1+j_2\ j_1+j_2 \rangle = 1;$$

(*ii*) one of the j null: $\langle j 0 m 0 | j m \rangle = 1$ or

$$\begin{pmatrix} j & j & 0 \\ m & -m & 0 \end{pmatrix} = \frac{(-)^{j-m}}{\sqrt{2j+1}};$$

(*iii*) $m_1 = m_2 = m_3 = 0$:

if $l_1+l_2+l_3$ is odd,

$$\begin{pmatrix} l_1 & l_2 & l_3 \\ 0 & 0 & 0 \end{pmatrix} = 0; \tag{C.23a}$$

if $2p \equiv l_1+l_2+l_3$ is even

$$\begin{pmatrix} l_1 & l_2 & l_3 \\ 0 & 0 & 0 \end{pmatrix} = (-)^p \sqrt{\Delta(l_1\, l_2\, l_3)}\, \frac{p!}{(p-l_1)!\,(p-l_2)!\,(p-l_3)!} \tag{C.23b}$$

(l_1, l_2, l_3 integers $\geqslant 0$ verifying the "triangular inequalities").

Special cases of the Racah formula

The formulae below, or those obtained from them by use of the symmetry relations, give the C.–G. in the following special cases:

(*i*) $m_1 = \pm j_1$ or $m_2 = \pm j_2$ or $M = \pm J$:

$$j_2 m_1 m_2|JJ\rangle = \langle j_2 j_1 \; -m_2 \; -m_1|J \; -J\rangle$$

$$(-)^{j_1-m_1} \sqrt{\frac{(2J+1)!\,(j_1+j_2-J)!}{(j_1+j_2+J+1)!\,(J+j_1-j_2)!\,(J+j_2-j_1)!}} \sqrt{\frac{(j_1+m_1)!\,(j_2+m_2)!}{(j_1-m_1)!\,(j_2-m_2)!}} \tag{C.24}$$

$$(m_1+m_2=J);$$

(*ii*) one of the j is the sum of the two others:

if $J=j_1+j_2$

$$\langle j_1 j_2 m_1 m_2|JM\rangle = \sqrt{\frac{(2j_1)!\,(2j_2)!}{(2J)!}} \sqrt{\frac{(J+M)!\,(J-M)!}{(j_1+m_1)!\,(j_1-m_1)!\,(j_2+m_2)!\,(j_2-m_2)!}} \tag{C.25}$$

$$\langle J\, j_2\, M-m_2|j_1 m_1\rangle = (-)^{j_2-m_2} \sqrt{\frac{2j_1+1}{2J+1}}\, \langle j_1 j_2 m_1 m_2|JM\rangle. \tag{C.26}$$

Tables of the "3j" symbols

The following tables give expressions for the symbol

$$\begin{pmatrix} j & s & (j+e) \\ m & \mu & (-m-\mu) \end{pmatrix}$$

as a function of j and m for

$$s = 0, \tfrac{1}{2}, 1, \tfrac{3}{2}, 2$$
$$0 \leqslant e \leqslant s \qquad 0 \leqslant \mu \leqslant s.$$

With these, and with the aid of the symmetry relations, we can easily calculate any of the C.–G. for which one of the j is equal to 0, $\frac{1}{2}$, 1, $\frac{3}{2}$ or 2.

The tabulated function is the function $\Phi^s_{\mu e}(jm)$ defined by

$$\begin{pmatrix} j & s & (j+e) \\ m & \mu & (-m-\mu) \end{pmatrix} = (-)^{j+m}\sqrt{\frac{(2j+e-s)!}{(2j+e+s+1)!}\,\frac{(j+m+\mu+e)!}{(j+m)!}}\,\Phi^s_{\mu e} \quad (C.27)$$

$s = 0$ $\Phi^0_{00} = 1$

$s = \frac{1}{2}$ $\Phi^{\frac{1}{2}}_{\frac{1}{2}\frac{1}{2}} = 1$

$s = 1$

Table of $\Phi^1_{\mu e}$

	$e = 0$	$e = 1$
$\mu = 0$	$-2m$	$-\sqrt{2(j-m+1)}$
$\mu = 1$	$-\sqrt{2(j-m)}$	1

$s = {}^3/_2$

Table of $\Phi^{3/2}_{\mu e}$

	$e = \frac{1}{2}$	$e = {}^3/_2$
$\mu = \frac{1}{2}$	$j-3m$	$-\sqrt{3(j-m+1)}$
$\mu = {}^3/_2$	$-\sqrt{3(j-m)}$	1

$s = 2$

Table of $\Phi^2_{\mu e}$

	$e = 0$	$e = 1$	$e = 2$
$\mu = 0$	$2[3m^2 - j(j+1)]$	$2m\sqrt{6(j-m+1)}$	$\sqrt{6(j-m+2)(j-m+1)}$
$\mu = 1$	$(2m+1)\sqrt{6(j-m)}$	$2(j-2m)$	$-2\sqrt{j-m+1}$
$\mu = 2$	$\sqrt{6(j-m)(j-m-1)}$	$-2\sqrt{(j-m)}$	1

II. RACAH COEFFICIENTS AND "6j" SYMBOLS

6. Definition and Notations

Coupling of three angular momenta

$\mathbf{J}$, total angular momentum of a system formed of three separate component systems, of angular momenta $\mathbf{j}$, $\mathbf{j}'$, $\mathbf{j}''$ respectively:

$$\mathbf{J} = \mathbf{j}+\mathbf{j}'+\mathbf{j}''.$$

In the $(2j+1)(2j'+1)(2j''+1)$-dimensional space spanned by the vectors $|mm'm''\rangle \equiv |jm\rangle|j'm'\rangle|j''m''\rangle$ (j, j', j'' given; m, m', m'' variable), the subspace of angular momentum (JM) is usually of more than one dimension [$2J$ and $2M$, integral numbers even or odd like $2(j+j'+j'')$; $\min|j \pm j' \pm j''| \leqslant J \leqslant j+j'+j''$; $-J \leqslant M \leqslant +J$].

The following two coupling schemes permit the construction of two (in general different) systems of basis vectors for this subspace [1]:

a) $\mathbf{j}'+\mathbf{j}=\mathbf{g}'$, $\mathbf{g}'+\mathbf{j}''=\mathbf{J}$ (Fig. C.1*a*) vectors $|(j'j)g', j''; JM\rangle$

$$|(j'j)g',j''; JM\rangle = \sum_{\substack{mm'm'' \\ \mu'}} |mm'm''\rangle \langle j'jm'm|g'\mu'\rangle \langle g'j''\mu'm''|JM\rangle$$

b) $\mathbf{j}+\mathbf{j}''=\mathbf{g}''$, $\mathbf{j}'+\mathbf{g}''=\mathbf{J}$ (Fig. C.1*b*) vectors $|j', (jj'')\,g''; JM\rangle$

$$|j',(jj'')g''; JM\rangle = \sum_{\substack{mm'm'' \\ \mu''}} |mm'm''\rangle \langle jj''mm''|g''\mu''\rangle \langle j'g''m'\mu''|JM\rangle.$$

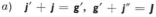

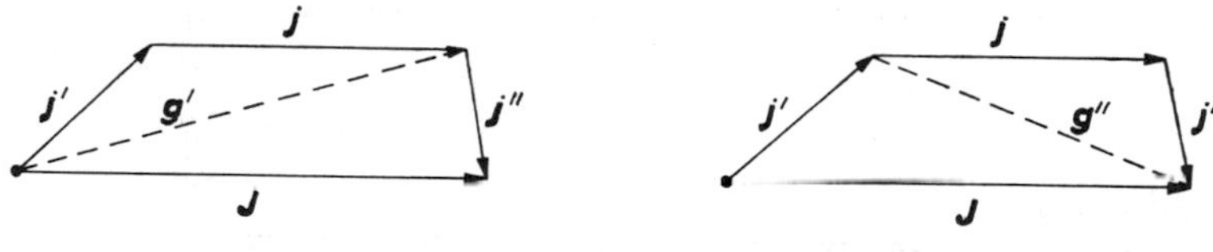

a) $\mathbf{j}' + \mathbf{j} = \mathbf{g}'$, $\mathbf{g}' + \mathbf{j}'' = \mathbf{J}$ *b*) $\mathbf{j} + \mathbf{j}'' = \mathbf{g}''$, $\mathbf{j}' + \mathbf{g}'' = \mathbf{J}$

Fig. C.1. $\mathbf{J} = \mathbf{j} + \mathbf{j}' + \mathbf{j}''$. Different coupling schemes.

We can pass from one system to the other by a certain unitary transformation.

---

[1] The order in which the different vectors are coupled is important. By changing that order, for example by interchanging the order of j and j'' in the coupling scheme (a), we may modify the sign of the resulting vector.

Definition of the Wigner "6j" symbols $\begin{Bmatrix} j_1 & j_2 & j_3 \\ J_1 & J_2 & J_3 \end{Bmatrix}$

They are related to the coefficients of this unitary transformation by the defining relation

$$\langle j', (j j'') g''; JM | (j' j) g', j''; J' M' \rangle = \delta_{JJ'} \delta_{MM'} \sqrt{(2g'+1)(2g''+1)} \, (-)^{j+j'+j''+J} \begin{Bmatrix} j' & j & g' \\ j'' & J & g'' \end{Bmatrix} \tag{C.28}$$

i.e.

$$|(j' j) g', j''; JM\rangle = \sum_{g''} |j', (j j'') g''; JM\rangle \sqrt{(2g'+1)(2g''+1)} \, (-)^{j+j'+j''+J} \begin{Bmatrix} j' & j & g' \\ j'' & J & g'' \end{Bmatrix} \tag{C.29}$$

The Racah W coefficients [1)]

Racah uses certain W coefficients equal to the "6j" to within a sign:

$$\begin{Bmatrix} j_1 & j_2 & j_3 \\ J_1 & J_2 & J_3 \end{Bmatrix} = (-)^{j_1+j_2+J_1+J_2} W(j_1 j_2 J_2 J_1; j_3 J_3). \tag{C.30}$$

Associated coefficients

In expressions for angular distributions one sometimes encounters the coefficients $Z(LJL'J'; j\lambda)$ and $F_\lambda(LL'J_1J_2)$, for which there are detailed tables, and which are defined respectively by

$$Z(L J L' J'; j \lambda) = (-)^{J+J'+\frac{1}{2}(L'-L+\lambda)} \sqrt{(2L+1)(2L'+1)(2J+1)(2J'+1)(2\lambda+1)} \times \begin{pmatrix} L & L' & \lambda \\ 0 & 0 & 0 \end{pmatrix} \begin{Bmatrix} L & L' & \lambda \\ J' & J & j \end{Bmatrix}. \tag{C.31a}$$

$$F_\lambda(L L' J_1 J_2) = (-)^{J_1+J_2-1} \sqrt{(2L+1)(2L'+1)(2J_2+1)(2\lambda+1)} \times \begin{pmatrix} L & L' & \lambda \\ 1 & -1 & 0 \end{pmatrix} \begin{Bmatrix} L & L' & \lambda \\ J_2 & J_2 & J_1 \end{Bmatrix}. \tag{C.31b}$$

The $F_\lambda(LL'J_1J_2)$ are involved notably when the reaction products include particles of spin 1, and the polarization is not observed.

---

1) Racah, *op. cit.* The sign factors disappear from the two preceding relations when we substitute the W for the "6j". However, the "6j" have simpler symmetry relations (cf. § 7).

Associated tetrahedron for the "6j"

In order to avoid certain confusions in the manipulation of the W coefficients and the "6j" symbols, it is useful to associate with each

$$\begin{Bmatrix} j' & j & g' \\ j'' & J & g'' \end{Bmatrix}$$

a certain tetrahedron in which each edge represents one of the six angular momenta of the symbol (Fig. C.2). In this representation,

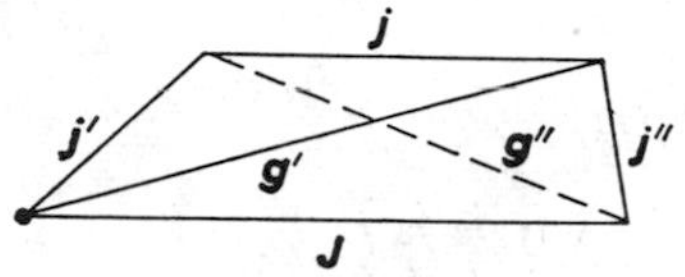

Fig. C.2. Tetrahedron associated with the symbol $\begin{Bmatrix} j' & j & g' \\ j'' & J & g'' \end{Bmatrix}$.

each pair of opposite edges is associated with the two angular momenta from a given column, and also the three angular momenta of the first line correspond to the edges of one of the faces of the tetrahedron. In addition, to each face correspond three angular momenta, of which the one is obtained by vector addition of the other two, as follows from the definition of the "6j".

7. Principal Properties

Reality: the "6j" are all real.

Selection rules

In order to have $\begin{Bmatrix} j_1 & j_2 & j_3 \\ J_1 & J_2 & J_3 \end{Bmatrix} \neq 0,$

the three angular momenta represented by each face of the tetrahedron must be such that it is possible for one of them to be the sum of the two others. In other words, it is necessary that the elements of each of the triads

$$(j_1 j_2 j_3) \quad (j_1 J_2 J_3) \quad (J_1 j_2 J_3) \quad (J_1 J_2 j_3)$$

(*i*) satisfy the triangular inequalities;

(*ii*) have an integral sum.

(*N.B.* either the six j are integral, or the three j of a same face are integral, or two j corresponding to opposite edges are integral.)

Symmetry relations. The "6j" symbol is invariant

(*i*) in a permutation of its columns,

e.g.: $$\begin{Bmatrix} j_1 & j_2 & j_3 \\ J_1 & J_2 & J_3 \end{Bmatrix} = \begin{Bmatrix} j_2 & j_1 & j_3 \\ J_2 & J_1 & J_3 \end{Bmatrix};$$

(*ii*) in an exchange of two elements of the first line with the corresponding elements in the second line,

e.g.:
$$\begin{Bmatrix} j_1 & j_2 & j_3 \\ J_1 & J_2 & J_3 \end{Bmatrix} = \begin{Bmatrix} J_1 & J_2 & j_3 \\ j_1 & j_2 & J_3 \end{Bmatrix}.$$

In other words, to define a "$6j$" symbol it is sufficient to give the six angular momenta and their relative positions on the associated tetrahedron.

Fundamental relations in terms of the C.–G.

The following relations relate the symbol $\begin{Bmatrix} j_1 & j_2 & j_3 \\ J_1 & J_2 & J_3 \end{Bmatrix}$ to the C.–G. coefficients formed with the triads $(j_1 j_2 j_3)$, $(j_1 J_2 J_3)$, $(J_1 j_2 J_3)$, $(J_1 J_2 j_3)$ relative to each of the four faces of the associated tetrahedron:

$$\begin{aligned} &\sum_{\substack{M_1 M_2 M_3 \\ m_1 m_2}} (-)^{J_1+J_2+J_3+M_1+M_2+M_3} \\ &\times \begin{pmatrix} J_1 & J_2 & j_3 \\ M_1 & -M_2 & m_3 \end{pmatrix} \begin{pmatrix} J_2 & J_3 & j_1 \\ M_2 & -M_3 & m_1 \end{pmatrix} \begin{pmatrix} J_3 & J_1 & j_2 \\ M_3 & -M_1 & m_2 \end{pmatrix} \begin{pmatrix} j_1 & j_2 & j_3' \\ m_1 & m_2 & m_3' \end{pmatrix} \\ &= \delta_{j_3 j_3'} \delta_{m_3 m_3'} \frac{1}{2j_3+1} \begin{Bmatrix} j_1 & j_2 & j_3 \\ J_1 & J_2 & J_3 \end{Bmatrix}. \end{aligned} \quad \text{(C.32)}$$

(*N.B.* This sum is actually only over two indices, the M and the m being related.)

$$\begin{aligned} &\sum_{M_1 M_2 M_3} (-)^{J_1+J_2+J_3+M_1+M_2+M_3} \begin{pmatrix} J_1 & J_2 & j_3 \\ M_1 & -M_2 & m_3 \end{pmatrix} \begin{pmatrix} J_2 & J_3 & j_1 \\ M_2 & -M_3 & m_1 \end{pmatrix} \begin{pmatrix} J_3 & J_1 & j_2 \\ M_3 & -M_1 & m_2 \end{pmatrix} \\ &= \begin{pmatrix} j_1 & j_2 & j_3 \\ m_1 & m_2 & m_3 \end{pmatrix} \begin{Bmatrix} j_1 & j_2 & j_3 \\ J_1 & J_2 & J_3 \end{Bmatrix}. \end{aligned} \quad \text{(C}$$

(*N.B.* This sum is actually only over one index.)

$$\begin{aligned} &\sum_{g m_g} (-)^{g+m_g}(2g+1) \begin{Bmatrix} j_1 & J_1 & g \\ J_2 & j_2 & f \end{Bmatrix} \begin{pmatrix} j_1 & J_1 & g \\ m_1 & M_1 & -m_g \end{pmatrix} \begin{pmatrix} j_2 & J_2 & g \\ m_2 & M_2 & m_g \end{pmatrix} \\ &= (-)^{j_2+J_1+f+g} \sum_{m_f} (-)^{f+m_f} \begin{pmatrix} j_1 & j_2 & f \\ m_1 & m_2 & -M_f \end{pmatrix} \begin{pmatrix} J_1 & J_2 & f \\ M_1 & M_2 & m_f \end{pmatrix}. \end{aligned} \quad \text{(C.34)}$$

(*N.B.* The sums over m_g and m_f have each just one term.)

The Racah–Elliot relations and the orthogonality relation

$$\sum_x (-)^{2x}(2x+1)\begin{Bmatrix} a & b & x \\ a & b & f \end{Bmatrix} = 1. \tag{C.35a}$$

$$\sum_x (-)^{a+b+x}(2x+1)\begin{Bmatrix} a & b & x \\ b & a & f \end{Bmatrix} = \delta_{f0}\sqrt{(2a+1)(2b+1)}. \tag{C.35b}$$

$$\sum_x (2x+1)\begin{Bmatrix} a & b & x \\ c & d & f \end{Bmatrix}\begin{Bmatrix} c & d & x \\ a & b & g \end{Bmatrix} = \delta_{fg}\frac{1}{2f+1}. \tag{C.35c}$$

$$\sum_x (-)^{f+g+x}(2x+1)\begin{Bmatrix} a & b & x \\ c & d & f \end{Bmatrix}\begin{Bmatrix} c & d & x \\ b & a & g \end{Bmatrix} = \begin{Bmatrix} a & d & f \\ b & c & g \end{Bmatrix}. \tag{C.35d}$$

$$\sum_x (-)^{a+b+c+d+e+f+g+h+x+j}(2x+1)\begin{Bmatrix} a & b & x \\ c & d & g \end{Bmatrix}\begin{Bmatrix} c & d & x \\ e & f & h \end{Bmatrix}\begin{Bmatrix} e & f & x \\ b & a & j \end{Bmatrix} = \begin{Bmatrix} g & h & j \\ e & a & d \end{Bmatrix}\begin{Bmatrix} g & h & j \\ f & b & c \end{Bmatrix}. \tag{C.35e}$$

8. Racah Formula and Tables

The Racah formula

$$\begin{Bmatrix} j_1 & j_2 & j_3 \\ J_1 & J_2 & J_3 \end{Bmatrix} = [\Delta(j_1j_2j_3)\,\Delta(j_1J_2J_3)\,\Delta(J_1j_2J_3)\,\Delta(J_1J_2j_3)]^{\frac{1}{2}}$$
$$\times \sum_t \frac{(-)^t(t+1)!}{(t-j_1-j_2-j_3)!\,(t-j_1-J_2-J_3)!\,(t-J_1-j_2-J_3)!\,(t-J_1-J_2-j_3)! \times (j_1+j_2+J_1+J_2-t)!\,(j_2+j_3+J_2+J_3-t)!\,(j_3+j_1+J_3+J_1-t)!} \tag{C.36}$$

Same definition of $\Delta(abc)$ and same summation convention as for (C.22). The number of terms in $\sum_t$ is equal to $1+\sigma$ where σ is the smallest of the twelve numbers

$$\begin{matrix} j_1+j_2-j_3 & j_1+J_2-J_3 & J_1+j_2-J_3 & J_1+J_2-j_3 \\ j_2+j_3-j_1 & J_2+J_3-j_1 & j_2+J_3-J_1 & J_2+j_3-J_1 \\ j_3+j_1-j_2 & J_3+j_1-J_2 & J_3+J_1-j_2 & j_3+J_1-J_2 \end{matrix}$$

Special cases

(*i*) one of the j is null

$$\begin{Bmatrix} j & j' & 0 \\ J & J' & g \end{Bmatrix} = (-)^{j+J+g}\frac{\delta_{jj'}\,\delta_{JJ'}}{\sqrt{(2j+1)(2J+1)}} \qquad (|j-J| \leqslant g \leqslant j+J) \tag{C.37}$$

(ii) one of the j is equal to $\boxed{\tfrac{1}{2}}$

$$\begin{Bmatrix} j & j+\frac{1}{2} & \frac{1}{2} \\ J & J+\frac{1}{2} & g+\frac{1}{2} \end{Bmatrix} = (-)^{1+g+j+J}\left[\frac{(1+g+j-J)(1+g-j+J)}{(2j+1)(2j+2)(2J+1)(2J+2)}\right]^{\frac{1}{2}} \quad \text{(C.38)}$$
$$(|j-J| \leqslant g \leqslant j+J).$$

$$\begin{Bmatrix} j & j+\frac{1}{2} & \frac{1}{2} \\ J+\frac{1}{2} & J & g \end{Bmatrix} = (-)^{1+g+j+J}\left[\frac{(1-g+j+J)(2+g+j+J)}{(2j+1)(2j+2)(2J+1)(2J+2)}\right]^{\frac{1}{2}} \quad \text{(C.39)}$$
$$(|j-J| \leqslant g \leqslant j+J).$$

III. "9j" SYMBOLS

9. Definition and Principal Properties

Coupling of four angular momenta and definition of the "9j":

$\mathbf{J}$, total angular momentum of a system formed of four separate component systems with respective angular momenta $\mathbf{j}_1$, $\mathbf{j}_2$, $\mathbf{j}_3$, $\mathbf{j}_4$:

$$\mathbf{J} = \mathbf{j}_1 + \mathbf{j}_2 + \mathbf{j}_3 + \mathbf{j}_4.$$

In the $\prod_{i=1}^{4}(2j_i+1)$ dimensional space spanned by the vectors

$$|m_1 m_2 m_3 m_4\rangle \equiv \prod_{i=1}^{4} |j_i m_i\rangle \qquad (j_i \text{ given, } m_i \text{ variable}),$$

the following two coupling schemes lead to two distinct systems of basis vectors for the subspace of angular momentum (JM):

a) $\mathbf{j}_1 + \mathbf{j}_2 = \mathbf{J}_{12} \quad \mathbf{j}_3 + \mathbf{j}_4 = \mathbf{J}_{34} \quad \mathbf{J}_{12} + \mathbf{J}_{34} = \mathbf{J}$
vectors $|(j_1 j_2)J_{12}, j_3 j_4(J_{34}); JM\rangle$;

b) $\mathbf{j}_1 + \mathbf{j}_3 = \mathbf{J}_{13} \quad \mathbf{j}_2 + \mathbf{j}_4 = \mathbf{J}_{24} \quad \mathbf{J}_{13} + \mathbf{J}_{24} = \mathbf{J}$
vectors $|(j_1 j_3)J_{13}, (j_2 j_4)J_{24}; JM\rangle$.

The Wigner "9j" symbols are to within a constant the coefficients of the unitary transformation that takes us from one basis to the other. By definition

$$\langle (j_1 j_2) J_{12}, (j_3 j_4) J_{34}; JM | (j_1 j_3) J_{13}, (j_2 j_4) J_{24}; J'M'\rangle$$
$$= \delta_{JJ'}\,\delta_{MM'} \sqrt{(2J_{12}+1)(2J_{34}+1)(2J_{13}+1)(2J_{24}+1)} \begin{Bmatrix} j_1 & j_2 & J_{12} \\ j_3 & j_4 & J_{34} \\ J_{13} & J_{24} & J \end{Bmatrix}. \quad \text{(C.4}$$

One can also define the "9j" by

$$j_1 j_2) J_{12}, j_3] J_{123} j_4; JM | [(j_4 j_2) J_{42}, j_3] J_{423} j_1; J'M' \rangle \tag{C.40b}$$

$$(-)^{J_{423}+j_1-J_{123}-j_4} \delta_{JJ'} \delta_{MM'} \sqrt{(2J_{12}+1)(2J_{123}+1)(2J_{42}+1)(2J_{423}+1)} \begin{Bmatrix} j_2 & J_{12} & j_1 \\ J_{42} & j_3 & J_{423} \\ j_4 & J_{123} & J \end{Bmatrix}.$$

The following notation is also employed

$$\times \begin{pmatrix} j_1 & j_2 & J_{12} \\ j_3 & j_4 & J_{34} \\ J_{13} & J_{24} & J \end{pmatrix} = \begin{Bmatrix} j_1 & j_2 & J_{12} \\ j_3 & j_4 & J_{34} \\ J_{13} & J_{24} & J \end{Bmatrix}.$$

A relation in terms of the "3j" symbols

$$\begin{pmatrix} J_{13} & J_{24} & J \\ M_{13} & M_{24} & M \end{pmatrix} \begin{Bmatrix} j_1 & j_2 & J_{12} \\ j_3 & j_4 & J_{34} \\ J_{13} & J_{24} & J \end{Bmatrix} = \sum_{\substack{m_1 m_2 m_3 m_4 \\ M_{12} M_{34}}} \begin{pmatrix} j_1 & j_2 & J_{12} \\ m_1 & m_2 & M_{12} \end{pmatrix}$$
$$\times \begin{pmatrix} j_3 & j_4 & J_{34} \\ m_3 & m_4 & M_{34} \end{pmatrix} \begin{pmatrix} j_1 & j_3 & J_{13} \\ m_1 & m_3 & M_{13} \end{pmatrix} \begin{pmatrix} j_2 & j_4 & J_{24} \\ m_2 & m_4 & M_{24} \end{pmatrix} \begin{pmatrix} J_{12} & J_{34} & J \\ M_{12} & M_{34} & M \end{pmatrix}. \tag{C.40c}$$

Symmetry relations

$$\begin{Bmatrix} J_1 & J_2 & J_3 \\ J_4 & J_5 & J_6 \\ J_7 & J_8 & J_9 \end{Bmatrix}$$ is

(*i*) multiplied by $(-)^R$, where $R = \sum_{i=1}^{9} J_i$, in the exchange of two lines or two columns;

(*ii*) invariant in a reflection through one of the diagonals.

Orthogonality relation

$$\sum_{J_{13} J_{24}} (2J_{13}+1)(2J_{24}+1) \begin{Bmatrix} j_1 & j_2 & J_{12} \\ j_3 & j_4 & J_{34} \\ J_{13} & J_{24} & J \end{Bmatrix} \begin{Bmatrix} j_1 & j_2 & J_{12}' \\ j_3 & j_4 & J_{34}' \\ J_{13} & J_{24} & J \end{Bmatrix} = \frac{\delta_{J_{12} J_{12}'} \delta_{J_{34} J_{34}'}}{(2J_{12}+1)(2J_{34}+1)}.$$

A relation in terms of the "6j" symbols

$$\begin{Bmatrix} j_1 & j_2 & J_{12} \\ j_3 & j_4 & J_{34} \\ J_{13} & J_{24} & J \end{Bmatrix} = \sum_g (-)^{2g} (2g+1) \begin{Bmatrix} j_1 & j_2 & J_{12} \\ J_{34} & J & g \end{Bmatrix} \begin{Bmatrix} j_3 & j_4 & J_{34} \\ j_2 & g & J_{24} \end{Bmatrix} \begin{Bmatrix} J_{13} & J_{24} & J \\ g & j_1 & j_3 \end{Bmatrix}. \tag{C.41}$$

Case when one of the j is null

$$\begin{Bmatrix} j_1 & j_2 & f \\ j_3 & j_4 & f' \\ g & g' & 0 \end{Bmatrix} = \delta_{ff'}\,\delta_{gg'}\,\frac{(-)^{j_2+j_3+f+g}}{\sqrt{(2f+1)(2g+1)}} \begin{Bmatrix} j_1 & j_2 & f \\ j_4 & j_3 & g \end{Bmatrix}. \tag{C.42}$$

IV. ROTATION MATRICES

10. Rotations. Rotation Operators. $R^{(J)}$ Matrices

$$\mathscr{R}_{\boldsymbol{u}}(\varphi) \equiv \text{Rotation through an angle } \varphi \text{ about the axis } \boldsymbol{u}$$

$$\begin{aligned} \mathscr{R}(\alpha\beta\gamma) &\equiv \text{Rotation with Euler angles } (\alpha, \beta, \gamma) \\ &\equiv \mathscr{R}_Z(\gamma)\,\mathscr{R}_u(\beta)\,\mathscr{R}_z(\alpha) \end{aligned} \tag{C.43}$$

The operations on the right-hand side are to be performed in the order from *right to left* (cf. Fig. C.3).

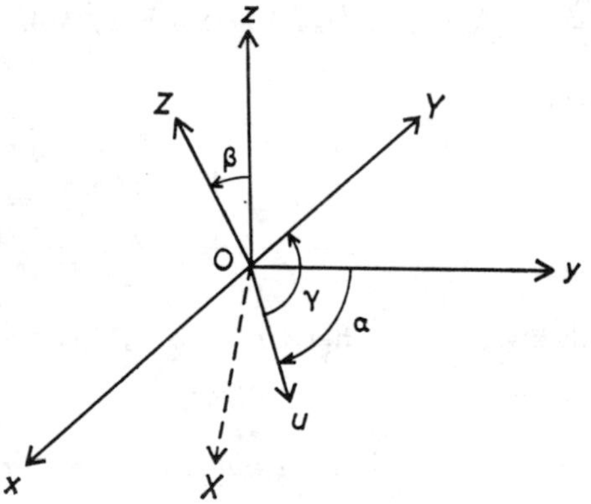

Fig. C.3. The Euler angles

$\alpha = (Oy, Ou)$, $\beta = (Oz, OZ)$, $\gamma = (Ou, OY)$.

Associated matrix: matrix for the transformation of the coordinates of vectors (denoted by the same letter $\mathscr{R}$ as the rotation itself).

If $\boldsymbol{V}(V_1, V_2, V_3)$ is any vector, and $\boldsymbol{V}'(V_1', V_2', V_3')$ its transform in the rotation $\mathscr{R}$, we have:

$$V_i' = \mathscr{R}_{ij} V_j, \quad \mathscr{R}_{ij} \text{ elements of the associated matrix.}$$

[*Consequence.* $\boldsymbol{A}_j$ being the transform of the unit vector $\boldsymbol{a}_j$ along the jth axis ($j=1$, 2 or 3) we have: $\boldsymbol{A}_j \equiv \mathscr{R}[\boldsymbol{a}_j] = \boldsymbol{a}_i \mathscr{R}_{ij}$, $\mathscr{R}_{ij} = \boldsymbol{a}_i \cdot \boldsymbol{A}_j$]

$$\mathscr{R}^* = \mathscr{R} \qquad \widetilde{\mathscr{R}} = \mathscr{R}^{-1} \qquad \det \mathscr{R} = 1 \tag{C.44}$$

$$(\alpha\beta\gamma) \equiv \begin{pmatrix} \cos\gamma\cos\beta\cos\alpha - \sin\gamma\sin\alpha & -\sin\gamma\cos\beta\cos\alpha - \cos\gamma\sin\alpha & \sin\beta\cos\alpha \\ \cos\gamma\cos\beta\sin\alpha + \sin\gamma\cos\alpha & -\sin\gamma\cos\beta\sin\alpha + \cos\gamma\cos\alpha & \sin\beta\sin\alpha \\ -\cos\gamma\sin\beta & \sin\gamma\sin\beta & \cos\beta \end{pmatrix}. \tag{C.45}$$

Rotation operator

Unitary operator R, which applied to a ket $|\rangle$ gives its transform in the rotation $\mathscr{R}$:

$$\mathscr{R}[|\rangle] \equiv R|\rangle \qquad R^\dagger R = RR^\dagger = 1. \tag{C.46}$$

If Q is an observable of the quantum system:

$$\mathscr{R}[Q] \equiv RQR^{-1}. \tag{C.47}$$

If $\boldsymbol{B} \equiv (B_x, B_y, B_z)$ is a vector operator attached to the system ($B_i \equiv \boldsymbol{B}\cdot\boldsymbol{a}_i$)

$$\mathscr{R}[B_i] \equiv RB_iR^{-1} = (\boldsymbol{B}\cdot\boldsymbol{A}_i) = \widetilde{\mathscr{R}}_{ij}B_j. \tag{C.48}$$

N.B. It is the inverse of $\mathscr{R}$ and not $\mathscr{R}$ itself that occurs here.

The application of (C.48) to the transformation of the components of the angular momentum $\boldsymbol{J}$ in the rotation $\mathscr{R}(\alpha\beta\gamma)$ gives

$$RJ_\pm R^{-1} = e^{\mp i\gamma}\left[\frac{1+\cos\beta}{2}e^{\mp i\alpha}J_\pm - \frac{1-\cos\beta}{2}e^{\pm i\alpha}J_\mp - \sin\beta\, J_z\right] \tag{C.49a}$$

$$RJ_zR^{-1} = \tfrac{1}{2}\sin\beta\,(e^{-i\alpha}J_+ + e^{i\alpha}J_-) + \cos\beta\, J_z. \tag{C.49b}$$

Expression in terms of the total angular momentum $\boldsymbol{J}$

Infinitesimal rotation:

$$R_{\boldsymbol{u}}(\varepsilon) = 1 - i\varepsilon(\boldsymbol{J}\cdot\boldsymbol{u}) \qquad (\varepsilon \ll 1). \tag{C.50}$$

Finite rotations:

$$R_{\boldsymbol{u}}(\varphi) = e^{-i\varphi(\boldsymbol{J}\cdot\boldsymbol{u})} \tag{C.51}$$

$$R(\alpha\beta\gamma) = e^{-i\alpha J_z}\, e^{-i\beta J_y}\, e^{-i\gamma J_z}. \tag{C.52}$$

Correspondence between rotations and rotation operators

There is a one-to-one correspondence between infinitesimal rotations and R operators infinitely close to 1, but the same is not necessarily true for the finite rotations.

To any finite rotation $\mathscr{R}$, there correspond in general two rotations, R' and R'', related by the equation

$$R'' = DR'$$

where D is the operator defined by:

$$D = \begin{cases} +1 & \text{if } J \text{ is integral} \\ -1 & \text{if } J \text{ is half-integral.} \end{cases}$$

In order to have $R' = R''$, it is necessary that the space of state vectors be made up exclusively of states of integral J.

$$R_{\mathbf{u}}(2\pi) = D$$
$$R_{\mathbf{u}}(4\pi) = 1.$$

Let $(\alpha\beta\gamma)$ and $(\alpha_1\beta_1\gamma_1)$ be two sets of Euler angles defining the same rotation [eq. (XIII.42)]:

$$R(\alpha_1\beta_1\gamma_1) = D^{n_\alpha+n_\beta+n_\gamma} R(\alpha\beta\gamma). \tag{C.53}$$

Rotation matrices $R^{(J)}(\alpha\beta\gamma)$

Matrix of $(2J+1)$ dimensions with elements:

$$\begin{aligned} R^{(J)}_{MM'}(\alpha\beta\gamma) &\equiv \langle JM|R(\alpha\beta\gamma)|JM'\rangle \\ &\equiv \langle JM|\, e^{-i\alpha J_z}\, e^{-i\beta J_y}\, e^{-i\gamma J_z}\,|JM'\rangle. \end{aligned} \tag{C.54}$$

The vectors $|JM\rangle$ (J fixed, $M = -J, \ldots, +J$) are $(2J+1)$ eigenvectors of $\mathbf{J}^2$ and J_z, obtained one from another by relations (C.6).

Matrix $r^{(J)}(\beta)$

$$\begin{aligned} r^{(J)}(\beta) &\equiv R^{(J)}(0, \beta, 0) \\ r^{(J)}_{MM'}(\beta) &\equiv \langle JM|\, e^{-i\beta J_y}\,|JM'\rangle \end{aligned} \tag{C.55}$$

$$R^{(J)}_{MM'}(\alpha\beta\gamma) = e^{-i\alpha M}\, r^{(J)}_{MM'}(\beta)\, e^{-i\gamma M'}. \tag{C.56}$$

11. General Properties of the $R^{(J)}$ Matrices

Inverse:

$$[R^{(J)}(\alpha\beta\gamma)]^{-1} = R^{(J)}(-\gamma, -\beta, -\alpha). \tag{C.57}$$

Determinant:

$$\det R^{(J)} = 1. \tag{C.58}$$

Uniformity:

$$R_{\mathbf{u}}{}^{(J)}(2\pi) = (-)^{2J}. \tag{C.59}$$

To each set of Euler angles there corresponds a single $R^{(J)}$ matrix.

To each rotation $\mathscr{R}$ there corresponds a single $R^{(J)}$ matrix if J is integral, and two matrices of which one is the negative of the other if J is half-integral.

Reality: $r^{(J)}(\beta)$ is a real matrix.

Rotations through an angle π about the axes

Notation: $X, Y, Z \equiv$ Rotation operators for rotations through $+\pi$ about Ox, Oy, Oz respectively.

$$X^2 = Y^2 = Z^2 = XYZ = (-)^{2J}. \tag{C.60}$$

$$X|JM\rangle = \mathrm{e}^{-\mathrm{i}\pi J}|J\ -M\rangle, \qquad \text{whence } X^{(J)}_{MM'} = \mathrm{e}^{-\mathrm{i}\pi J}\,\delta_{M\ -M'}. \tag{C.61}$$

$$Y|JM\rangle = (-)^{J-M}|J\ -M\rangle, \qquad \text{whence } Y^{(J)}_{MM'} = (-)^{J+M}\,\delta_{M\ -M'}. \tag{C.62}$$

$$Z|JM\rangle = \mathrm{e}^{-\mathrm{i}\pi M}|JM\rangle, \qquad \text{whence } Z^{(J)}_{MM'} = \mathrm{e}^{-\mathrm{i}\pi M}\,\delta_{MM'}. \tag{C.63}$$

Transformation of the angular momentum operator in the rotation Y:

$$YJ_xY^\dagger = -J_x \quad YJ_yY^\dagger = J_y \quad YJ_zY^\dagger = -J_z \quad YJ_\pm Y^\dagger = -J_\mp$$

whence:

$$YR^{(J)}Y^\dagger = R^{(J)*}. \tag{C.64}$$

Symmetry relations [deduced from (C.62) and (C.64)]

$$r^{(J)}_{MM'} = (-)^{M-M'}\,r^{(J)}_{-M,\,-M'}. \tag{C.65}$$

$$R^{(J)*}_{MM'} = (-)^{M-M'}\,R^{(J)}_{-M,\,-M'}. \tag{C.66}$$

Unitarity and orthogonality relations

$R^{(J)\dagger} = R^{(J)-1}$ whence the unitarity relations

$$\sum_M R^{(J)}_{MM'}\,R^{(J)*}_{MM''} = \delta_{M'M''} \qquad \sum_M R^{(J)}_{M'M}\,R^{(J)*}_{M''M} = \delta_{M'M''} \tag{C.67}$$

and, taking into account the symmetry relations, the orthogonality relations

$$\begin{aligned}\sum_M (-)^{J+M}\,R^{(J)}_{MM'}\,R^{(J)}_{-M\ -M''} &= (-)^{J+M'}\,\delta_{M'M''}\\ \sum_M (-)^{J+M}\,R^{(J)}_{M'M}\,R^{(J)}_{-M''\ -M} &= (-)^{J+M'}\,\delta_{M'M''}.\end{aligned} \tag{C.68}$$

Composition and reduction formulae

In the following formulae the matrices $R^{(j_1)}$, $R^{(j_2)}$, $R^{(J)}$ are relative to the same Euler angles.

Reduction of the tensor product $R^{(j_1)} \otimes R^{(j_2)}$:

$$R^{(j_1)}_{m_1 m_1'} R^{(j_2)}_{m_2 m_2'} = \sum_{J=|j_1-j_2|}^{j_1+j_2} \sum_{M,\, M'=-J}^{+J} \langle j_1 j_2 m_1 m_2 | JM \rangle\, R^{(J)}_{MM'}\, \langle j_1 j_2 m_1' m_2' | JM' \rangle. \quad \text{(C.69)}$$

Composition formula:

$$R^{(J)}_{MM'} = \sum_{m_1,\, m_1'=-j_1}^{+j_1} \sum_{m_2,\, m_2'=-j_2}^{+j_2} \langle j_1 j_2 m_1 m_2 | JM \rangle\, R^{(j_1)}_{m_1 m_1'} R^{(j_2)}_{m_2 m_2'}\, \langle j_1 j_2 m_1' m_2' | JM' \rangle. \quad \text{(C.70)}$$

In particular, if $J = j_1 + j_2$

$$\begin{aligned} R^{(J)}_{JJ} &= R^{(j_1)}_{j_1 j_1} R^{(j_2)}_{j_2 j_2} \\ R^{(J)}_{J,\, -J} &= R^{(j_1)}_{j_1,\, -j_1} R^{(j_2)}_{j_2,\, -j_2}. \end{aligned} \quad \text{(C.71)}$$

12. Calculation of the Matrix Elements $R^{(J)}_{MM'}$

Principal methods of calculation

When the matrix $r^{(J)}(\beta)$ is known, we can easily deduce the matrix $R^{(J)}(\alpha\beta\gamma)$ from (C.56).

$r^{(J)}$ is real, unitary, and has the symmetry property (C.65):

$$r^{(J)}_{MM'}(\beta) = r^{(J)}_{M'M}(-\beta) = (-)^{M-M'}\, r^{(J)}_{-M\, -M'}(\beta).$$

Thus we need only to know the matrix elements corresponding to $M \geqslant 0$ and $M \geqslant M'$ to deduce all of them.

As for these we may:

a) calculate them directly by the Wigner formula given below;

b) obtain them by application of formula (C.70) for the composition of matrix elements $r^{(j_1)}$, $r^{(j_2)}$ for smaller angular momenta; in particular all of the $r^{(J)}$ can be obtained one after the other from $r^{(\frac{1}{2})}$;

c) obtain them one from another using the recursion relations that follow from equations (C.49).

The Wigner formula

Put:

$$\xi \equiv \cos \tfrac{1}{2}\beta, \qquad \eta \equiv \sin \tfrac{1}{2}\beta.$$

We have:

$$r^{(J)}_{MM'} = \sum_t (-)^t \frac{\sqrt{(J+M)!\,(J-M)!\,(J+M')!\,(J-M')!}}{(J+M-t)!\,(J-M'-t)!\,t!\,(t-M+M')!} \times \xi^{2J+M-M'-2t}\, \eta^{2t-M+M'}. \quad \text{(C.72)}$$

Same summation convention as for (C.21). The number of terms in $\sum_t$ is equal to $1+\tau$ where τ is the smallest of the four numbers $J \pm M$, $J \pm M'$.

With respect to the variables ξ and η, $r^{(J)}_{MM'}$ is a homogeneous polynomial of degree $2J$.

Special cases of the Wigner formula

$$\begin{aligned} r^{(J)}_{MJ} &= (-)^{J-M}\, r^{(J)}_{JM} = r^{(J)}_{-J-M} = (-)^{J-M}\, r^{(J)}_{-M-J} \\ &= \sqrt{\frac{(2J)!}{(J+M)!\,(J-M)!}}\; \xi^{J+M}\, \eta^{J-M} \end{aligned} \tag{C.73}$$

$$r^{(J)}_{JJ} = r^{(J)}_{-J-J} = \xi^{2J} \qquad r^{(J)}_{J-J} = (-)^{2J}\, r^{(J)}_{J-J} = \eta^{2J}.$$

Case $J=\frac{1}{2}$

$$R^{\frac{1}{2}}(\alpha\,\beta\,\gamma) = \begin{pmatrix} e^{-\frac{1}{2}i\alpha}\cos\frac{1}{2}\beta\; e^{-\frac{1}{2}i\gamma} & -e^{-\frac{1}{2}i\alpha}\sin\frac{1}{2}\beta\; e^{+\frac{1}{2}i\gamma} \\ e^{+\frac{1}{2}i\alpha}\sin\frac{1}{2}\beta\; e^{-\frac{1}{2}i\gamma} & e^{+\frac{1}{2}i\alpha}\cos\frac{1}{2}\beta\; e^{+\frac{1}{2}i\gamma} \end{pmatrix} \tag{C.74}$$

(in this expression, the successive lines correspond to $M=\frac{1}{2}, -\frac{1}{2}$; the columns are arranged in the same order from left to right).

13. Integral Values of J ($J=l$) and Rotation of the Spherical Harmonics

Case $l=1$

$$r^{(1)}(\beta) = \begin{pmatrix} \frac{1}{2}(1+\cos\beta) & -\frac{1}{2}\sqrt{2}\sin\beta & \frac{1}{2}(1-\cos\beta) \\ \frac{1}{2}\sqrt{2}\sin\beta & \cos\beta & -\frac{1}{2}\sqrt{2}\sin\beta \\ \frac{1}{2}(1-\cos\beta) & \frac{1}{2}\sqrt{2}\sin\beta & \frac{1}{2}(1+\cos\beta) \end{pmatrix}. \tag{C.75}$$

(In this expression, the successive lines correspond to $M=+1, 0, -1$; the columns are arranged in the same order from left to right.)

Rotation of the spherical harmonics

$\omega \equiv (\theta, \varphi)$ polar angles of a unit vector $\mathbf{v}$ with respect to the coordinate system Oxyz ($v_1 = \sin\theta\cos\varphi$, $v_2 = \sin\theta\sin\varphi$, $v_3 = \cos\theta$).

$\Omega \equiv (\Theta, \Phi)$ polar angles of the same vector $\mathbf{v}$ with respect to the system OXYZ.

$(\alpha\beta\gamma)$ Euler angles of the rotation taking Oxyz into OXYZ [1]).

[1]) To remove the arbitrariness in the choice of the Euler angles, we add the supplementary conditions

$$0 \leqslant \alpha \leqslant 2\pi \qquad 0 \leqslant \beta \leqslant \pi \qquad -\pi \leqslant \gamma \leqslant +\pi$$

(with this choice, OuzZ is a right-handed system). Then:

(*i*) the polar coordinates of OZ with respect to Oxyz are (β, α);
(*ii*) the polar coordinates of Oz with respect to OXYZ are $(\beta, \pi-\gamma)$.

Θ and Φ are well-defined functions of θ and φ in which α, β, γ appear as parameters.

$\omega_1 \equiv (\theta_1, \varphi_1)$ polar angles with respect to $Oxyz$ of the vector $\mathbf{v}_1 \equiv \mathscr{R}^{-1}\mathbf{v}$, which the rotation $\mathscr{R}(\alpha\beta\gamma)$ transforms into $\mathbf{v}$. We have: $\omega_1 = \Omega$.

The spherical harmonic $Y_l^m(\omega)$ represents a certain ket vector, $|lm\rangle$, in the representation $\{\omega\}$:

$$Y_l^m(\omega) = \langle\omega|lm\rangle.$$

The rotation $\mathscr{R}(\alpha\beta\gamma)$ transforms this ket into a ket $R(\alpha\beta\gamma)|lm\rangle$ whose component in the direction $\mathbf{v}$ is equal to the component of $|lm\rangle$ in the direction $\mathbf{v}_1$:

$$Y_l^m(\Omega) \equiv \langle\omega_1|lm\rangle = \langle\omega|R|lm\rangle$$

whence the formula for the *rotation of spherical harmonics*:

$$Y_l^m(\Omega) = \sum_{m'=-l}^{+l} Y_l^{m'}(\omega)\, R^{(l)}_{m'\,m}(\alpha\,\beta\,\gamma). \tag{C.76}$$

Scalar product and addition theorem

Let $\mathbf{v}$, $\mathbf{v}'$ be two unit vectors, ω, ω' their respective polar angles with respect to $Oxyz$ and Ω, Ω' the polar angles of the same two vectors with respect to $OXYZ$. Relation (C.76) and the unitarity relation for $R^{(l)}$ give

$$\sum_m Y_l^m(\Omega)\, Y_l^{m*}(\Omega') = \sum_m Y_l^m(\omega)\, Y_l^{m*}(\omega'). \tag{C.77}$$

In particular, if $\mathbf{v}'$ is directed along OZ, we have the addition theorem

$$\sqrt{\frac{2l+1}{4\pi}}\, Y_l^0(\Omega) \equiv \frac{2l+1}{4\pi}\, P_l(\cos\Theta) = \sum_{m=-l}^{+l} Y_l^m(\theta, \varphi)\, Y_l^{m*}(\beta, \alpha). \tag{C.78}$$

$r^{(l)}_{mm'}$ *in terms of* $\cos\beta$ *and* $\sin\beta$

For integral l

(*i*) if $(-)^{m+m'} = +1$, $r^{(l)}_{mm'} =$ polynomial of degree l in $\cos\beta$;

(*ii*) if $(-)^{m+m'} = -1$, $r^{(l)}_{mm'} = \sin\beta \times$ (polynomial of degree $(l-1)$ in $\cos\beta$).

In particular

$$r^{(l)}_{ml}(\beta) = \sqrt{\frac{(2l)!}{(l+m)!\,(l-m)!}}\, \frac{1}{2^l}\, (1+\cos\beta)^m \sin^{l-m}\beta. \tag{C.79}$$

$R^{(l)}_{mm'}$ *when* m *or* $m'=0$

$$R^{(l)}_{m0}(\alpha\beta\gamma) = \sqrt{\frac{4\pi}{2l+1}}\, Y_l^{m*}(\beta\alpha). \tag{C.80a}$$

$$R^{(l)}_{0m}(\alpha\beta\gamma) = (-)^m \sqrt{\frac{4\pi}{2l+1}}\, Y_l^{m*}(\beta\gamma). \tag{C.80b}$$

$$R^{(l)}_{00}(\alpha\beta\gamma) = P_l(\cos\beta). \tag{C.80c}$$

V. IRREDUCIBLE TENSOR OPERATORS

14. Definition and Principal Properties

Definition

Tensor operator $\equiv$ set of operators that transform linearly one into another under rotation.

Irreducible tensor operator:

The $(2k+1)$ operators $T_q{}^{(k)}$ $(q=-k, \ldots, +k)$ are by definition the *standard components of an irreducible tensor operator* of order k, $\mathbf{T}^{(k)}$, if they transform under rotation according to the formula

$$R T^{(k)}_q R^{-1} = \sum_{q'=-k}^{+k} T^{(k)}_{q'} R^{(k)}_{q'q}. \tag{C.81}$$

Vector operator $\equiv$ irreducible tensor operator of order 1. If V_x, V_y, V_z are its components along $Oxyz$, its standard components are

$$V_+ = -\tfrac{1}{2}\sqrt{2}(V_x + \mathrm{i}V_y), \quad V_0 = V_z, \quad V_- = \tfrac{1}{2}\sqrt{2}(V_x - \mathrm{i}V_y).$$

Scalar operator $\equiv$ irreducible tensor operator of order 0.

Commutation relations with $\boldsymbol{J}$

$$[J_\pm, T^{(k)}_q] = \sqrt{k(k+1) - q(q\pm 1)}\; T^{(k)}_{q\pm 1}. \tag{C.82a}$$

$$[J_z, T^{(k)}_q] = q T^{(k)}_q. \tag{C.82b}$$

Hermitean conjugate [1]:

$$\mathbf{S}^{(k)} = \mathbf{T}^{(k)\dagger} \quad \text{if} \quad S^{(k)}_q = (-)^q\, T^{(k)\dagger}_{-q}. \tag{C.83}$$

[1] We adopt here the definition of Racah (*loc. cit.*). With this definition the spherical harmonics $Y_l{}^m$ of a given order l form a Hermitean tensor operator. Note that the tensor product (defined below) of commuting, irreducible, Hermitean, tensor operators is not always Hermitean. In order for it to be so, we must modify the definition of Hermitean conjugation by replacing $(-)^q$ by $(-)^{k+q}$. With this new definition, the spherical harmonics of odd order are anti-Hermitean.

N.B. Our definition of Hermitean conjugation also applies to tensor operators of half-integral order if we let $(-)^q$ signify $\mathrm{e}^{\mathrm{i}\pi q}$.

Fundamental property (Wigner–Eckart)

$$\langle \tau J M | T_q^{(k)} | \tau' J' M' \rangle = \frac{(-)^{2k}}{\sqrt{2J+1}} \langle \tau J \| \mathbf{T}^{(k)} \| \tau' J' \rangle \langle J' k M' q | J M \rangle$$
$$= (-)^{J-M} \langle \tau J \| \mathbf{T}^{(k)} \| \tau' J' \rangle \begin{pmatrix} J & k & J' \\ -M & q & M' \end{pmatrix}. \qquad \text{(C.84)}$$

$\langle \tau J \| \mathbf{T}^{(k)} \| \tau' J' \rangle$ is by definition the *reduced matrix element* [1]).

We have the conjugation relation (k integral):

$$\langle \tau J \| \mathbf{T}^{(k)} \| \tau' J' \rangle^* = (-)^{J'-J} \langle \tau' J' \| \mathbf{T}^{(k)\dagger} \| \tau J \rangle. \qquad \text{(C.85)}$$

Special tensor operators

identity operator:

$$\langle \alpha J \| \alpha' J' \rangle = \delta_{\alpha\alpha'} \delta_{JJ'} \sqrt{2J+1}$$

total angular momentum:

$$\langle \alpha J \| \mathbf{J} \| \alpha' J' \rangle = \delta_{\alpha\alpha'} \delta_{JJ'} \sqrt{J(J+1)(2J+1)}.$$

15. Tensor Products of Irreducible Tensor Operators [2])

Definitions

Let $\mathbf{T}^{(k_1)}$, $\mathbf{U}^{(k_2)}$, be two irreducible tensor operators of order k_1, k_2 respectively. By definition:

$\mathbf{T}^{(k_1)} \otimes \mathbf{U}^{(k_2)} \equiv$ set of the $(2k_1+1)(2k_2+1)$ operators $T_{q_1}^{(k_1)} U_{q_2}^{(k_2)}$ (not necessarily linearly independent). It is a (reducible) tensor operator.

$\mathbf{V}^{(K)} \equiv [\mathbf{T}^{(k_1)} \otimes \mathbf{U}^{(k_2)}]_K$, *tensor product of order* K, is the irreducible tensor operator of order K, of components

$$V_Q^{(K)} = \sum_{q_1 q_2} \langle k_1 k_2 q_1 q_2 | K Q \rangle T_{q_1}^{(k_1)} U_{q_2}^{(k_2)} \qquad \text{(C.86)}$$

(one necessarily has $|k_1 - k_2| \leqslant K \leqslant k_1 + k_2$).

If $k_1 = k_2 = k$, we define the scalar product [3]):

$$S \equiv (\mathbf{T}^{(k)} \cdot \mathbf{U}^{(k)}) = \sum_q (-)^q T_q^{(k)} U_{-q}^{(k)}. \qquad \text{(C.87)}$$

N.B. $S = (-)^k \sqrt{2k+1}\, V_0^{(0)}$.

---

[1]) The definition adopted here is that of Racah (*loc. cit.*).

[2]) In all of the following formulas we limit ourselves to tensor operators of integral order.

[3]) With this definition, the scalar product of two vector operators $(\mathbf{V} \cdot \mathbf{W})$ is given, in agreement with the usual definition, by $V_x W_x + V_y W_y + V_z W_z$.

Expressions for the reduced matrix elements

Suppose we have a quantum system made up of two component systems, 1 and 2, of angular momentum $\mathbf{J}_1$ and $\mathbf{J}_2$ respectively ($\mathbf{J}=\mathbf{J}_1+\mathbf{J}_2$).

$|\tau_1 J_1 M_1\rangle$ basis vectors of system 1.

$|\tau_2 J_2 M_2\rangle$ basis vectors of system 2.

$\mathbf{T}^{(k_1)}$, $\mathbf{U}^{(k_2)}$ irreducible tensor operators, acting exclusively on the variables of systems 1 and 2 respectively.

$\mathbf{V}^{(K)}$ tensor product of order K according to definition (C.86).

In the standard representation $\{\tau_1\tau_2\mathbf{J}_1^2\mathbf{J}_2^2\mathbf{J}^2 J_z\}$ the reduced matrix elements of $\mathbf{V}^{(K)}$ are given by the composition formula

$$\langle\tau_1\tau_2 J_1 J_2 J\|\mathbf{V}^{(K)}\|\tau_1'\tau_2' J_1' J_2' J'\rangle = \sqrt{(2J+1)(2K+1)(2J'+1)} \times \begin{Bmatrix} J_1' & J_2' & J' \\ k_1 & k_2 & K \\ J_1 & J_2 & J \end{Bmatrix} \langle\tau_1 J_1\|T^{(k_1)}\|\tau_1' J_1'\rangle \langle\tau_2 J_2\|U^{(k_2)}\|\tau_2' J_2'\rangle. \tag{C.88}$$

Particular cases where the "9J" symbol reduces to a "6J" symbol

$\mathbf{U}=1 \qquad K=k_1=k.$

$$\langle\tau_1\tau_2 J_1 J_2 J\|\mathbf{T}^{(k)}\|\tau_1'\tau_2' J_1' J_2' J'\rangle = \delta_{\tau_2\tau_2'}\,\delta_{J_2 J_2'}\langle\tau_1 J_1\|\mathbf{T}^{(k)}\|\tau_1' J_1'\rangle \times(-)^{J'+J_1+J_2+k}\sqrt{(2J+1)(2J'+1)}\begin{Bmatrix} J_1 & k & J_1' \\ J' & J_2 & J \end{Bmatrix} \tag{C.89}$$

$\mathbf{T}=1 \qquad K=k_2=k.$

$$\langle\tau_1\tau_2 J_1 J_2 J\|\mathbf{U}^{(k)}\|\tau_1'\tau_2' J_1' J_2' J'\rangle = \delta_{\tau_1\tau_1'}\,\delta_{J_1 J_1'}\langle\tau_2 J_2\|\mathbf{U}^{(k)}\|\tau_2' J_2'\rangle \times(-)^{J+J_1+J_2'+k}\sqrt{(2J+1)(2J'+1)}\begin{Bmatrix} J_2 & k & J_2' \\ J' & J_1 & J \end{Bmatrix} \tag{C.90}$$

$K=0 \qquad k_1=k_2=k.$

$$\langle\tau_1\tau_2 J_1 J_2 J M|(\mathbf{T}^{(k)}\cdot\mathbf{U}^{(k)})|\tau_1'\tau_2' J_1' J_2' J' M'\rangle = \delta_{JJ'}\,\delta_{MM'}\,(-)^{J+J_2+J_1'}\begin{Bmatrix} J_1 & k & J_1' \\ J_2' & J & J_2 \end{Bmatrix}\langle\tau_1 J_1\|\mathbf{T}^{(k)}\|\tau_1' J_1'\rangle\langle\tau_2 J_2\|\mathbf{U}^{(k)}\|\tau_2' J_2'\rangle. \tag{C.91}$$

In particular, when $\mathbf{T}^{(k)}=\mathbf{J}_1$, eq. (C.89) gives:

$$\langle J_1 J_2\, J+1\|\mathbf{J}_1\|J_1 J_2 J\rangle = \frac{1}{2}\sqrt{\frac{[(S+1)^2-(J+1)^2]\,[(J+1)^2-d^2]}{J+1}} \tag{C.92}$$

$$\langle J_1 J_2 J \| \boldsymbol{J}_1 \| J_1 J_2 J \rangle$$
$$= \tfrac{1}{2}[d(S+1)+J(J+1)] \sqrt{\frac{2J+1}{J(J+1)}} \tag{C.93}$$
$$= \tfrac{1}{2}[J_1(J_1+1)+J(J+1)-J_2(J_2+1)] \sqrt{\frac{2J+1}{J(J+1)}}$$

$$\langle J_1 J_2\, J-1 \| \boldsymbol{J}_1 \| J_1 J_2 J \rangle = -\frac{1}{2}\sqrt{\frac{[(S+1)^2-J^2]\,[J^2-d^2]}{J+1}} \tag{C.94}$$

with

$$S = J_1+J_2 \qquad d = J_1-J_2 \qquad (|d| \leqslant J \leqslant S).$$

APPENDIX D

ELEMENTS OF GROUP THEORY

PLAN OF THE APPENDIX

1. Introduction

It frequently occurs that the equations of motion for systems studied in Quantum Mechanics are invariant with respect to certain groups of transformations or, more generally, that the observables dealt with have particularly simple transformation properties with respect to these groups. The methods of Group Theory allow one to sort out the consequences and simplifications that result from the existence of these symmetries.

In actual fact, with a strong dose of intuition and a certain address in the manipulation of operators, one can often exploit these symmetry properties without explicit recourse to the Theory of Groups. A good many excellent physicists prefer to leave the matter there, even if it means having to rediscover from time to time for each particular problem "well-known" results from Group Theory of which they have need. However, in some fields of Physics, like the study of polyatomic molecules or crystals, the required dose of intuition and address is too strong, and the conscientious and avowed use of Group Theory cannot be avoided. When less complicated symmetries are involved, the recourse to Group Theory, while not indispensible, often permits one better to state the problems and automatically provides certain elements of their solution.

The object of this appendix is to familiarize the reader with the Theory of Groups and to provide an introduction to more complete works on the subject [1]).

It consists of a discussion of the principal concepts and the properties most often used in Quantum Mechanics. The demonstrations have nearly all been omitted. Most of them, and in particular all those of sections I and II, are very simple.

I. GENERALITIES CONCERNING GROUPS

2. Definitions

GROUP

A set $\mathscr{G}$ of operations $a, b, c, \ldots$, forms a group if:

---

[1]) The reader is referred in particular to E. P. Wigner, *loc. cit.* note, p. 1055 and (in German) B. L. van de Waerden, *Die Gruppentheoretische Methode in der Quantenmechanik* (Edwards, Ann Arbor, Michigan, 1944). On continuous groups, see G. Racah, *Princeton Lecture Notes on Group Theory and Spectroscopy* (1951).

(*i*) the *product* of any two of them also belongs to the set [1] [2]:

$$\text{if } a \in \mathscr{G} \text{ and } b \in \mathscr{G}, \text{ then } ab \in \mathscr{G};$$

(*ii*) one of them, I, is the *unit element*:

$$I \in \mathscr{G} \text{ such that, for any } a \in \mathscr{G},\ Ia = aI = a;$$

(*iii*) each of them, a, has a *reciprocal* (or inverse), a^{-1}, belonging to the set:

$$\text{if } a \in \mathscr{G}, \text{ then } a^{-1} \in \mathscr{G} \text{ such that } a^{-1}a = aa^{-1} = I;$$

(*iv*) the product is *associative*:

$$(ab)c = a(bc).$$

Finite group

Group having a finite number N of elements. N is the *order* of the group.

Examples. The group of spatial reflections is a finite group of order 2; its two elements are the identity I and the reflection through the origin s; $s^2 = I$. The group of permutations of n objects, $\mathscr{S}_n$, is a finite group of order $n!$.

Continuous group

Group having an infinite number of elements depending on one or several continuous parameters.

Examples. Group of rotations in ordinary space $\mathscr{R}_3$; group of translations in ordinary space.

Abelian group

Group whose elements all *commute*:

$$ab = ba \text{ for any } a \text{ and } b \in \mathscr{G}$$

Examples. Spatial reflections; spatial translations; rotations about Oz.

3. Classes of a Group

Conjugate elements

Two elements a and b of the group $\mathscr{G}$ are conjugate to one another

---

1) By convention, $a \in \mathscr{G}$ means: the element a belongs to the set $\mathscr{G}$.

2) The operation denoted by ab consists in first applying b, and then applying a to the result obtained. ab and ba may be different.

if there exists an element x of $\mathscr{G}$ such that

$$b = x\,a\,x^{-1}.$$

(*N.B.* x is not unique.)

If b is conjugate to a, a is conjugate to b: conjugation is a reciprocal correspondence. Moreover, if two elements b and c are conjugate to a third element a, they are conjugate to each other.

CLASS

The set of conjugates of a given element a of the group $\mathscr{G}$ is by definition a class of $\mathscr{G}$. The element a itself belongs to the set.

The class of elements conjugate to b and the class of elements conjugate to a are identical if b is conjugate to a, and otherwise have no common element. Each element of $\mathscr{G}$ belongs to a well-defined class: the entire group can be subdivided into classes.

If a given element of $\mathscr{G}$ commutes with all the others, it forms a class by itself. In particular, the identity I forms a class by itself.

Example. The set $\mathscr{R}(\varphi)$ of rotations having the same angle φ and differing only in the direction of the axis of rotation constitutes a class of the group $\mathscr{R}_3$; to each angle $\varphi(0 \leqslant \varphi' < \pi)$ there corresponds a class of this group.

4. Subgroups of a Group

DEFINITION

$\mathscr{H}$ is a subgroup of $\mathscr{G}$ if it is a group whose elements all belong to the group $\mathscr{G}$.

Example. The rotations about Oz form a subgroup of $\mathscr{R}_3$; the translations parallel to Oz form a subgroup of the spatial-translation group.

COSETS

If x is an element of $\mathscr{G}$ we can form from each element h of the subgroup $\mathscr{H}$ the element xh. We shall denote the set of these elements by $x\mathscr{H}$. There is a one-to-one correspondence between the elements of $\mathscr{H}$ and the elements of $x\mathscr{H}$.

There are two cases to consider:

(*a*) if $x \in \mathscr{H}$, $x\mathscr{H}$ is the subgroup $\mathscr{H}$ itself;

(*b*) if $x \notin \mathscr{H}$, $x\mathscr{H}$ is not a group, and is called the left coset of the subgroup $\mathscr{H}$.

The right coset $\mathscr{H}x$ is similarly defined. In what follows we shall consider only left cosets; right cosets obviously have the same properties.

Two cosets $x_1\mathscr{H}$, $x_2\mathscr{H}$ *either* contain the same elements *or* have no element in common, according as $x_2^{-1}x_1$ does or does not belong to $\mathscr{H}$.

Any element of $\mathscr{G}$ belongs either to $\mathscr{H}$ or to one of its cosets. The subgroup $\mathscr{H}$ and its various cosets constitute the whole group $\mathscr{G}$.

Conjugate subgroups of $\mathscr{H}$

If $\mathscr{H}$ is a subgroup of $\mathscr{G}$, and x an element of $\mathscr{G}$ but not of $\mathscr{H}$, then $x\mathscr{H}x^{-1}$ is also a subgroup of $\mathscr{G}$, called *conjugate* to $\mathscr{H}$.

(*N.B.* If $x \in \mathscr{H}$, $x\mathscr{H}x^{-1}$ is the group $\mathscr{H}$ itself.)

The conjugate subgroups of $\mathscr{H}$ are not necessarily different from $\mathscr{H}$ nor necessarily different from one another.

Invariant subgroup, factor (or quotient) group

$\mathscr{H}$ is an invariant subgroup of $\mathscr{G}$ if it is identical with all its conjugates:

$$\mathscr{H} = x\mathscr{H}x^{-1} \text{ for any } x \in \mathscr{G}.$$

Equivalent definition. A subgroup of $\mathscr{G}$ is invariant if its elements are all those of one or several classes of $\mathscr{G}$.

N.B. This second definition is very useful when we wish to find all the invariant subgroups of a given group.

If $\mathscr{H}$ is an invariant subgroup, $x\mathscr{H}$ and $y\mathscr{H}$ two of its cosets, the product of an element of $x\mathscr{H}$ by an element of $y\mathscr{H}$ belongs to the coset $yx\mathscr{H}$:

$$(y\mathscr{H})(x\mathscr{H}) = (yx\mathscr{H}).$$

(*N.B.* If $\mathscr{H}$ is an invariant subgroup, $x\mathscr{H} = \mathscr{H}x$.)

The set formed by the invariant subgroup and its cosets form a group having $\mathscr{H}$ for unit element: the *factor* (or quotient) *group* $\mathscr{G}/\mathscr{H}$.

Example. The group $\mathscr{A}_n$ of even permutations of n objects is an invariant subgroup of $\mathscr{S}_n$. It has one, and only one, coset, the set of odd permutations: the quotient group therefore has two elements.

Simple, semi-simple group

A group is simple if its only invariant subgroup is the identity element.

Example. Group of spatial rotations.

A group is semi-simple if its only invariant Abelian subgroup is the identity element.

Example. The group $\mathscr{S}_n$.

5. Isomorphism, Homomorphism

ISOMORPHISM

Two groups $\mathscr{G}$ *and* $\hat{\mathscr{G}}$ *are isomorphic when there exists a one-to-one correspondence between their elements that conserves the law of multiplication*, i.e.:

(*i*) to each element g_i of $\mathscr{G}$ there corresponds one, and only one, element $\hat{g}_i$ of $\hat{\mathscr{G}}$, and conversely;

(*ii*) if $g_i g_j = g_k$, then $\hat{g}_i \hat{g}_j = \hat{g}_k$.

Examples. The symmetries of the equilateral triangle form a group isomorphic to $\mathscr{S}_3$; the symmetries of the regular tetrahedron form a group isomorphic to $\mathscr{S}_4$.

HOMOMORPHISM

If the correspondence between the elements of $\mathscr{G}$ and $\hat{\mathscr{G}}$ is not one-to-one then these two groups are homomorphic.

More precisely, $\mathscr{G}$ is homomorphic to $\hat{\mathscr{G}}$ if:

(*i*) to each element g_i of $\mathscr{G}$ there corresponds one, and only one, element $\hat{g}_i$ of $\hat{\mathscr{G}}$, and to each element of $\hat{\mathscr{G}}$ at least one (and perhaps more than one) element of $\mathscr{G}$;

(*ii*) $g_i g_j = g_k$ implies $\hat{g}_i \hat{g}_j = \hat{g}_k$.

If $\mathscr{G}$ has an invariant subgroup $\mathscr{H}$, it is homomorphic to the factor group $\mathscr{G}/\mathscr{H}$.

If $\mathscr{G}$ is homomorphic to $\hat{\mathscr{G}}$, the set $\mathscr{H}$ of elements of $\mathscr{G}$ homomorphic to the identity $\hat{I}$ form an invariant subgroup of $\mathscr{G}$, the set of elements of $\mathscr{G}$ homomorphic to a given element of $\hat{\mathscr{G}}$ different to $\hat{I}$ form a coset of this subgroup; the quotient group $\mathscr{G}/\mathscr{H}$ is isomorphic to $\hat{\mathscr{G}}$.

II. LINEAR REPRESENTATIONS OF A GROUP

6. Definitions

GROUPS OF LINEAR SUBSTITUTIONS

The product of square matrices is an associative operation. If a set of $n \times n$ matrices satisfy the axioms (*i*), (*ii*) and (*iii*) defining a group, then they form a certain group **G**.

Each matrix represents a certain linear operator G of an n-dimensional vector space $\mathscr{E}_n$, and therefore defines a linear transformation of the vectors of that space: if $|1\rangle, |2\rangle, \ldots, |n\rangle$ are the n basis vectors of $\mathscr{E}_n$ (this basis is not necessarily orthonormal), the transformation of each of them is given by the equation:

$$G|k\rangle = \sum_j |j\rangle\, G_{jk}.$$

The type of group just defined – which will be denoted in boldface roman letters – is called a *group of* (n-dimensional) *linear substitutions.*

Representation of a group

By definition, *a* (linear) *representation of a group $\mathscr{G}$ is a group of linear substitutions to which $\mathscr{G}$ is homomorphic.*

Let **G** be such a group and $\mathscr{E}$ the vector space in which its matrices operate. By definition, $\mathscr{E}$ is the *representation space,* and the number n of its dimensions *the degree* (or dimension) *of the representation.* If $\mathscr{G}$ is isomorphic to **G**, the representation is said to be *faithful.* If not, the elements of $\mathscr{G}$ homomorphic to the matrix 1 form an invariant subgroup $\mathscr{H}$ and **G** is a faithful representation of the quotient group $\mathscr{G}/\mathscr{H}$.

Representations of degree 1

Any group has at least one representation of the first degree, *its identical representation,* in which each element of the group is represented by thc number 1.

For there to be any more of them, it must have invariant subgroups whose quotient groups are Abelian; all other first degree representations of the group are the representations of these Abelian quotient groups (cf. the case of $\mathscr{S}_n$, § 17).

Unitary representation

A representation **G** is unitary if all of its matrices are unitary.

Equivalent representations

Two representations **G**, **G**′ are equivalent if they have the same number of dimensions and if each matrix $G'(g)$ of the one results from a certain linear transformation T of the matrix $G(g)$ of the other representing the same operation of the group $\mathscr{G}$:

$$G'(g) = T\,G(g)\,T^{-1} \text{ for any } g \in \mathscr{G},$$

or again

$$\mathbf{G}' = T\,\mathbf{G}\,T^{-1}.$$

We write symbolically

$$\mathbf{G}' \simeq \mathbf{G}.$$

If we identify the representation spaces $\mathscr{E}$ and $\mathscr{E}'$, the passage from $\mathbf{G}$ to the equivalent representation $\mathbf{G}'$ corresponds to taking a new set of basis vectors in that space.

Conjugate representations

Two representations $\mathbf{G}$, $\mathbf{G}^*$, whose matrices $G(g)$, $G^*(g)$ are complex conjugates one of the other, are by definition conjugate representations.

A representation $\mathbf{G}$ is self-conjugate if it is equivalent to its conjugate: $\mathbf{G} \simeq \mathbf{G}^*$.

Characters

By definition, the trace of the matrix $G(g)$ representing the operation g in the representation $\mathbf{G}$ of $\mathscr{G}$ is the character χ of g in that representation

$$\chi(g) \equiv \operatorname{Tr} G(g).$$

It follows from the properties of the trace that two operations belonging to the same class have the same character: *character is a function of class.*

For the same reason, *two equivalent representations have the same set of characters*:

$$\chi'(g) = \chi(g) \quad \text{if} \quad G'(g) = T\,G(g)\,T^{-1}.$$

We write symbolically:

$$\boldsymbol{\chi}' = \boldsymbol{\chi} \qquad \text{if} \qquad \mathbf{G}' \simeq \mathbf{G}.$$

N.B. If G is self-conjugate, its characters are real.

7. Operations on Representation Spaces. Reducibility [1]

DIRECT SUM

Let $\mathbf{G}^a$, $\mathbf{G}^b$ be two representations of the same group $\mathscr{G}$; n_a, n_b their respective degrees; and $\mathscr{E}_a$, $\mathscr{E}_b$ their respective representation spaces.

If $|a1\rangle, |a2\rangle, \ldots, |an_a\rangle$ are the basis vectors of $\mathscr{E}_a$, $|b1\rangle, \ldots, |bn_b\rangle$, those of $\mathscr{E}_b$, the linear substitutions representing the operation g in these two representations are then defined by the laws of transformation of the basis vectors:

$$g[|a\varkappa\rangle] = \sum_\lambda |a\lambda\rangle\, G^a_{\lambda\varkappa}(g) \qquad g[|b\mu\rangle] = \sum_\nu |b\nu\rangle\, G^b_{\nu\mu}(g). \tag{D.1}$$

By definition, the direct sum $\mathscr{E}_a \dotplus \mathscr{E}_b$ of the spaces $\mathscr{E}_a$ and $\mathscr{E}_b$ is the space spanned by the $n_a + n_b$ vectors $|a1\rangle, \ldots, |an_a\rangle, \ldots, |bn_b\rangle$.

The matrices of this new space can be put into the form

$$M \equiv \begin{pmatrix} M_{aa} & M_{ab} \\ M_{ba} & M_{bb} \end{pmatrix}.$$

M_{aa} is an $n_a \times n_a$ matrix transforming the vectors of the space $\mathscr{E}_a$ into vectors of $\mathscr{E}_a$; M_{bb} an $n_b \times n_b$ matrix transforming the vectors of $\mathscr{E}_b$ into vectors of $\mathscr{E}_b$, M_{ab} an $n_a \times n_b$ matrix transforming the vectors of $\mathscr{E}_b$ into vectors of $\mathscr{E}_a$, and M_{ba} an $n_b \times n_a$ matrix having the inverse property. In particular, if A is a matrix of $\mathscr{E}_a$, B a matrix of $\mathscr{E}_b$, we can form by direct addition the matrix $A \dotplus B$ of the form (blockdiagonal form)

$$A \dotplus B = \begin{pmatrix} A & 0 \\ 0 & B \end{pmatrix}.$$

Note that:

$$\operatorname{Tr}(A \dotplus B) = \operatorname{Tr} A + \operatorname{Tr} B, \qquad \det(A \dotplus B) = \det A \det B. \tag{D.2}$$

The operation of direct addition of matrices conserves the identity and the law of matrix multiplication:

$$1_{(a+b)} = 1_{(a)} \dotplus 1_{(b)} \quad (A_1 \dotplus B_1)(A_2 \dotplus B_2) = A_1 A_2 \dotplus B_1 B_2.$$

---

[1] The properties set forth in this paragraph are general properties of sets of matrices in one-to-one correspondence. They remain valid even if these sets of matrices do not form a group.

It follows that the set $\mathbf{G}^{a+b}$ of the matrices $G^a(g) \dotplus G^b(g)$ constitutes a representation of the group $\mathscr{G}$. The operation g is there represented by a linear substitution that is defined by the laws of transformation (D.1) of the $n_a + n_b$ basis vectors of $\mathscr{E}_a \dotplus \mathscr{E}_b$. For the characters of that representation we have: $\chi^{a+b}(g) = \chi^a(g) + \chi^b(g)$; in other words

$$\boldsymbol{\chi}^{a+b} = \boldsymbol{\chi}^a + \boldsymbol{\chi}^b. \tag{D.3}$$

TENSOR PRODUCT (OR KRONECKER PRODUCT OR DIRECT PRODUCT)

The operation of taking the tensor product of spaces or of matrices has already been defined (Ch. VII).

In taking the tensor product of $\mathscr{E}_a$ by $\mathscr{E}_b$, we form the $n_a n_b$-dimensional space $\mathscr{E}_a \otimes \mathscr{E}_b$ whose basis vectors are $|ab\varkappa\mu\rangle \equiv |a\varkappa\rangle |b\mu\rangle$ ($\varkappa = 1, 2, \ldots, n_a$; $\mu = 1, 2, \ldots, n_b$). The matrices $G^a(g) \otimes G^b(g)$ formed by tensor multiplication of the matrices representing g in $\mathbf{G}^a$ and $\mathbf{G}^b$ form a representation $\mathbf{G}^{ab} \equiv \mathbf{G}^a \otimes \mathbf{G}^b$ of degree $n_a n_b$ of the group $\mathscr{G}$ in which a given operation of the group is defined by the law:

$$g[|ab\, \varkappa\mu\rangle] = \sum_{\lambda\nu} |ab\, \lambda\nu\rangle\, G^a_{\lambda\varkappa}(g)\, G^b_{\nu\mu}(g). \tag{D.4}$$

The characters of this representation are given by the relations:

$$\chi^{ab}(g) = \chi^a(g)\, \chi^b(g). \tag{D.5}$$

REDUCIBILITY

An *invariant subspace* of the space $\mathscr{E}$ of a representation $\mathbf{G}$ is a subspace of $\mathscr{E}$ whose vectors are transformed linearly one into another by the matrices of $\mathbf{G}$.

The representation $\mathbf{G}$ is said to be:

(*i*) *irreducible* if $\mathscr{E}$ contains no invariant subspace (other than itself or the null space);

(*ii*) *reducible* if it is not irreducible:

$$\mathscr{E} = \mathscr{E}_1 \dotplus \mathscr{E}_2 \quad (\mathscr{E}_1, \mathscr{E}_2 \neq 0), \quad \mathscr{E}_1 \text{ invariant subspace.}$$

In the second case, if $\mathscr{E}_2$ is also invariant, $\mathbf{G}$ is said to be *decomposable*. One can then, with a suitable linear transformation, transform the basis vectors of $\mathscr{E}$ into vectors situated either in $\mathscr{E}_1$ or in $\mathscr{E}_2$. The equivalent representation obtained is the direct sum of a representation $\mathbf{G}_1$ in $\mathscr{E}_1$ and a representation $\mathbf{G}_2$ in $\mathscr{E}_2$:

$$\mathbf{G} \simeq \mathbf{G}_1 \dotplus \mathbf{G}_2.$$

$\mathbf{G}_1$ and $\mathbf{G}_2$ are called the *components* of $\mathbf{G}$.

A representation $\mathbf{G}$ is *completely reducible* if it can be put into the form of a (direct) sum of irreducible components:

$$\mathbf{G} \simeq \mathbf{G}^{(1)} + \mathbf{G}^{(2)} + \dots \quad (\mathbf{G}^{(1)}, \mathbf{G}^{(2)}, \dots \text{ irreducible}).$$

Any unitary representation is either irreducible or completely reducible.

The rotation matrices $R^{(j)}$ (Appendix C, section 4) relative to a given value of j form an irreducible unitary representation $\mathbf{D}^{(j)}$ of a group. Strictly speaking, $\mathbf{D}^{(j)}$ represents the rotation group $\mathscr{R}_3$ only if j is an integer.

For any j, the $\mathbf{D}^{(j)}$ are the irreducible representations of a group whose infinitesimal transformations are the same as those of $\mathscr{R}_3$ ("covering group" of $\mathscr{R}_3$), the group $\mathscr{U}_2$ of two-dimensional, unimodular, unitary, linear substitutions, group of which $\mathscr{R}_3$ is a factor group. When j is half-integral, $\mathbf{D}^{(j)}$ is a faithful representation of $\mathscr{U}_2$ and there corresponds to each element of $\mathscr{R}_3$ two matrices of $\mathbf{D}^{(j)}$ of opposite sign.

All the irreducible representations of an Abelian group are of degree 1.

Homomorphic mapping of one representation space onto another

A *linear mapping of* $\mathscr{E}_a$ *into* $\mathscr{E}_b$ is a linear correspondence in which each vector $|a\rangle$ of $\mathscr{E}_a$ corresponds to one, and only one vector $|b\rangle$ of $\mathscr{E}_b$. The correspondence is *homomorphic* if it conserves the transformation properties of the vectors in the various operations of the group, that is, if the correspondence

$$|a\rangle \rightarrow |b\rangle$$

implies that

$$g[|a\rangle] \rightarrow g[|b\rangle] \quad \text{for any } g \in \mathscr{G}$$

A mapping of $\mathscr{E}_a$ into $\mathscr{E}_b$ is completely determined if we know the $n_b \times n_a$ matrix defining the vector of $\mathscr{E}_b$ corresponding to each basis vector of $\mathscr{E}_a$:

$$|a\varkappa\rangle \rightarrow \sum_\mu |b\mu\rangle\, S_{\mu\varkappa}. \tag{D.6}$$

If the mapping is homomorphic, we have the matrix equation

$$S\, G^a(g) = G^b(g)\, S \quad \text{for any } g \in \mathscr{G},$$

i.e.

$$S\, \mathbf{G}^a = \mathbf{G}^b S. \tag{D.7}$$

When the ensemble of vectors $|b\rangle$ corresponding to the vectors of $\mathscr{E}_a$ span the whole of $\mathscr{E}_b$ (this supposes $n_a \geqslant n_b$), we have *a mapping of* $\mathscr{E}_a$ *onto* $\mathscr{E}_b$ (the *whole* of E_b understood). In this case, all of the $n_b \times n_b$ determinants contained in S are different to zero.

When the correspondence is also one-to-one ($n_a = n_b$), the matrix S is non-singular: $\det S \neq 0$. In this case, the homomorphic mapping of $\mathscr{E}_a$ onto $\mathscr{E}_b$ is called an *isomorphic correspondence* and we obviously have:

$$\mathbf{G}^a \simeq \mathbf{G}^b.$$

8. Fundamental Theorems

The applications of Group Theory in quantum mechanics are based essentially on the following theorems:

Schur's lemma

If $\mathbf{G}^a$ *and* $\mathbf{G}^b$ *are two irreducible representations of the same group, and if there exists a homomorphic mapping of the space of one into the space of the other, then the matrix* S *that defines that mapping* [S satisfies equations (D.6) and (D.7)] *has the following properties*:

a) *if* $\mathbf{G}^a$ *and* $\mathbf{G}^b$ *are inequivalent, necessarily* $S = 0$;

b) *if* $\mathbf{G}^a \simeq \mathbf{G}^b$ *either* $S = 0$, *or* $\det S \neq 0$;

c) *if* $\mathbf{G}^a \equiv \mathbf{G}^b$, *S is a multiple of the unit matrix*: $S = c\mathbf{1}$ (c, constant).

Corollary

If a (square) matrix S commutes with all the matrices of an *irreducible* representation $\mathbf{G}$ of a group, then it is a multiple of the unit matrix:

$$\text{if } [S, \mathbf{G}] = 0, \textit{ necessarily } S = c\mathbf{1}$$

Completely reducible representations. Uniqueness theorems

Suppose that we have two decompositions into *irreducible* parts of a completely reducible representation $\mathbf{G}$:

$$\mathbf{G} \simeq \mathbf{G}_1 + \mathbf{G}_2 + \ldots + \mathbf{G}_p \qquad \mathbf{G} \simeq \mathbf{G}_1' + \mathbf{G}_2' + \ldots + \mathbf{G}_{p'}'.$$

It can be shown that $p = p'$, and that there is a one-to-one correspondence between each term of the first decomposition and a term in the second which is equivalent to it. In other words:

Uniqueness theorem. *If* $\mathbf{G}$ *is completely reducible, its decomposition into irreducible parts is unique to within an equivalence.*

Henceforth, unless otherwise specified, two equivalent representations will not be thought of as different. The same irreducible representation can then figure several times in the representation $\mathbf{G}$. Denote by

$$\mathbf{G}^{(1)}, \mathbf{G}^{(2)}, \ldots, \mathbf{G}^{(j)}, \ldots$$

the sequence of *irreducible representations of the group* $\mathscr{G}$. According to the uniqueness theorem, any completely reducible representation $\mathbf{G}$ obeys the equivalence law

$$\mathbf{G} \simeq \sum_j n_j \, \mathbf{G}^{(j)} \tag{D.8}$$

and the sequence of integers ($\geqslant 0$) $n_1, n_2, \ldots, n_j, \ldots$ is uniquely-defined. Similarly, the set of characters of $\mathbf{G}$ obeys the equation

$$\chi = \sum_j n_j \, \chi^{(j)}. \tag{D.9}$$

The uniqueness theorem is completed by the two following theorems:

THEOREM II. *If* $\mathbf{G}$ *is completely reducible, so is any component* $\mathbf{G}_1$ *of* $\mathbf{G}$, *and its decomposition in irreducible parts is the sum of a certain number of irreducible components of* $\mathbf{G}$.

Thus, if $\mathbf{G} \simeq \mathbf{G}_1 + \mathbf{G}_2$, and if $\mathbf{G}$ can be decomposed according to (D.8), then

$$\mathbf{G}_1 \simeq \sum_j n_j{}^1 \, \mathbf{G}^{(j)} \quad \text{with} \quad n_j{}^1 \leqslant n_j \qquad (j = 1, 2, \ldots).$$

THEOREM III. *If* $\mathbf{G}$ *is completely reducible and if there exists a homomorphic mapping of its space* $\mathscr{E}$ *onto the space* $\mathscr{E}_1$ *of another representation* $\mathbf{G}_1$ *of the same group, then* $\mathbf{G}_1$ *is a component of* $\mathbf{G}$.

Theorem III applies in particular when to each basis vector $|\varkappa\rangle$ of the space $\mathscr{E}$ we can make correspond a vector $|\hat{\varkappa}\rangle$ of the space $\mathscr{E}_1$, the $|\hat{\varkappa}\rangle$ spanning the whole of $\mathscr{E}_1$ without necessarily being linearly independent, and the $|\hat{\varkappa}\rangle$ transforming linearly one into another by the same matrix formulae as the $|\varkappa\rangle$, i.e.

$$g[|\hat{\varkappa}\rangle] = \sum_\lambda |\hat{\lambda}\rangle \, G_{\lambda\varkappa}(g).$$

In this case, it is obvious that the correspondence $|\varkappa\rangle \rightarrow |\hat{\varkappa}\rangle$ establishes a homomorphic mapping of $\mathscr{E}$ onto $\mathscr{E}_1$.

In particular:

COROLLARY III. *If the spaces spanned by the vectors* $|a\varkappa\rangle$ ($\varkappa$ variable) *and* $|b\mu\rangle$ (μ variable) *are associated respectively with the representations* $\mathbf{G}^a$ *and* $\mathbf{G}^b$, *and if the tensor product* $\mathbf{G}^{ab}$ *of these two representations is completely reducible, then the representation* $\mathbf{G}'$ *defined in the space spanned by the product vectors* $|a\varkappa\rangle\,|b\mu\rangle$ *is a component of* $\mathbf{G}^{ab}$.

N.B. The vectors $|a\varkappa\rangle\,|b\mu\rangle$ are not necessarily linearly independent. If they are, then $\mathbf{G}' \simeq \mathbf{G}^{ab}$.

9. Applications to Quantum Mechanics

The groups that appear in quantum theory are groups of transformations in state-vector space. They are nearly always unitary linear transformations and we limit the discussion to transformations of this type in what follows.

We denote the state-vector space by $\mathscr{E}$ and a set of unitary operators $G_1, G_2, \ldots$ forming a group by $\mathscr{G}$.

Let $|u\rangle$ be a vector of $\mathscr{E}$. $|u\rangle$ and the set of vectors $G_1|u\rangle, G_2|u\rangle, \ldots$, formed by applying the operators of the group to $|u\rangle$ do not necessarily span the whole of $\mathscr{E}$, but a certain subspace $\mathscr{E}_u$ of $\mathscr{E}$. $\mathscr{E}_u$ is an invariant subspace with respect to the transformations of the group, and is associated with a certain unitary (and therefore completely-reducible) representation $\mathbf{G}^u$ of the group $\mathscr{G}$. We say that the vector $|u\rangle$ transforms according to $\mathbf{G}^u$.

Similarly, if Q is a linear operator of $\mathscr{E}$, Q and the set of operators $G_1QG_1^{-1}, G_2QG_2^{-1}, \ldots$, obtained by application of the transformations of the group, span a vector space $\mathscr{E}_Q$ (the vectors of this space are operators) whose elements transform linearly one into another under the operations of the group; $\mathscr{E}_Q$ is associated with a representation $\mathbf{G}^Q$ of $\mathscr{G}$, which, in all the cases to be examined, will be either completely reducible, or else irreducible. By definition, Q transforms according to $\mathbf{G}^Q$.

By definition the operator Q is *invariant with respect to* $\mathscr{G}$ if it transforms according to the identical representation: Q then commutes with all the operators of the group. More generally, the operator Q is a *component of an irreducible tensor operator of the group* $\mathscr{G}$ if it transforms according to an irreducible representation $\mathbf{G}^{(j)}$ of $\mathscr{G}$.

Irreducible subspaces $\mathscr{E}(\tau j)$. Representation suited to the group $\mathscr{G}$

The space $\mathscr{E}$ is the direct sum of irreducible, invariant subspaces $\mathscr{E}(\tau j)$. Each of these is associated with a certain irreducible representation $\mathbf{G}^{(j)}$ of $\mathscr{G}$; the index τ distinguishes between those associated with the same irreducible representation. We denote by d_j the degree of $\mathbf{G}^{(j)}$.

Let $|\tau j\mu\rangle$ (μ variable) be d_j vectors forming a basis in $\mathscr{E}(\tau j)$. Since $\mathbf{G}^{(j)}$ is defined only to within an equivalence, the choice of this basis is completely arbitrary. It is convenient to make a choice once and for all by defining a *standard basis* for $\mathscr{E}(\tau j)$ in which each operation of the group is represented by a well-defined matrix $G^{(j)}_{\lambda\mu}$:

$$G|\tau j\mu\rangle = \sum_{\lambda=1}^{d_j} |\tau j\lambda\rangle\, G^{(j)}_{\lambda\mu}. \tag{D.10}$$

In what follows, we shall suppose that this standard choice has always been made.

The set of all the vectors $|\tau j\mu\rangle$ (τ, j, μ variable) forms a system of basis vectors for the space $\mathscr{E}$. We shall henceforth give the name of *standard representation suited to the group* $\mathscr{G}$ to the representation $\{\tau j\mu\}$. The term representation is here to be taken in its usual quantum mechanical sense. The transformation properties of ket vectors and operators under the operations of the group $\mathscr{G}$ lead to particularly simple properties of their components in this representation. These properties are summarized by the following two theorems.

Components of ket vectors and operators in the $\{\tau j\mu\}$ representation

THEOREM A. *If the vectors* $|u1\rangle, \ldots, |u\nu\rangle, \ldots$ *transform linearly one into another like the basis vectors of the unitary representation* $\mathbf{G}^{a}$, i.e. if

$$G|u\nu\rangle = \sum_{\varrho} |u\varrho\rangle\, G^{a}_{\varrho\nu},$$

then their components $\langle\tau j\mu|u\nu\rangle$ *have the following properties:*

1° If $\mathbf{G}^{(j)}$ DOES NOT APPEAR *in the decomposition*

$$\mathbf{G}^{a} \simeq \sum_{k} n_k\, \mathbf{G}^{(k)} \tag{D.11}$$

of $\mathbf{G}^{a}$ *into irreducible parts, then necessarily* $\langle\tau j\mu|u\nu\rangle = 0$.

2° If $\mathbf{G}^{(j)}$ DOES APPEAR in (D.11), *and if* $\langle a\nu|\sigma k\chi\rangle$ *is the matrix that effects this decomposition, then*

$$\langle\tau j\mu|u\nu\rangle = \sum_{\sigma=1}^{n_j} u^{j}_{\tau\sigma}\, \langle a\nu|\sigma j\mu\rangle^{*}, \tag{D.12}$$

where the $u^{j}_{\tau\sigma}$ *are* n_j *constants independent of* μ *and* ν.

THEOREM B. *If the operators $Q_1, Q_2, \ldots, Q_\nu, \ldots$ transform linearly one into another like the basis vectors of the unitary representation* $\mathbf{G}^a$, i.e. if

$$G\, Q_\nu\, G^{-1} = \sum_\varrho Q_\varrho\, G^a_{\varrho\nu};$$

then the matrix elements $\langle \tau_1 j_1 \mu_1 | Q_\nu | \tau_2 j_2 \mu_2 \rangle$ *have the following properties:*

1° If $\mathbf{G}^{(j_1)}$ DOES NOT APPEAR *in the decomposition*

$$\mathbf{G}^a \otimes \mathbf{G}^{(j_2)} \simeq \sum_k n_k^{aj_2}\, \mathbf{G}^{(k)} \tag{D.13}$$

of the tensor product $\mathbf{G}^a \otimes \mathbf{G}^{(j_2)}$ *into irreducible parts, then necessarily*

$$\langle \tau_1\, j_1\, \mu_1 | Q_\nu | \tau_2\, j_2\, \mu_2 \rangle = 0.$$

2° If $\mathbf{G}^{(j_1)}$ DOES APPEAR, *and if* $\langle a j_2 \nu \mu_2 | \sigma k \chi \rangle$ *is the matrix that effects this decomposition, then*

$$\langle \tau_1\, j_1\, \mu_1 | Q_\nu | \tau_2\, j_2\, \mu_2 \rangle = \sum_{\sigma=1}^{n_{j_1}^{aj_2}} \langle \tau_1\, j_1 \| Q \| \tau_2\, j_2 \rangle_\sigma\, \langle a j_2\, \nu \mu_2 | \sigma j_1\, \mu_1 \rangle^*, \tag{D.14}$$

where the $\langle \tau_1 j_1 \| Q \| \tau_2 j_2 \rangle_\sigma$ *are* $n_{j_1}^{aj_2}$ *constants independent of* μ_1, μ_2 *and* ν.

Important remark:

The elements $\langle a\nu | \sigma k \chi \rangle$, $\langle a j_2 \nu \mu_2 | \sigma k \chi \rangle$ of the unitary matrices involved in these theorems satisfy the defining equations

$$\sum_{\nu\nu'} \langle a\nu | \sigma k \chi \rangle^*\, G^a_{\nu\nu'}\, \langle a\nu' | \sigma' k' \chi' \rangle = \delta_{\sigma\sigma'}\, \delta_{kk'}\, G^{(k)}_{\chi\chi'}, \tag{D.15a}$$

$$\sum_{\substack{\nu\nu' \\ \mu\mu'}} \langle a j \nu \mu | \sigma k \chi \rangle^*\, G^a_{\nu\nu'}\, G^{(j)}_{\mu\mu'}\, \langle a j\, \nu'\, \mu' | \sigma' k' \chi' \rangle = \delta_{\sigma\sigma'}\, \delta_{kk'}\, G^{(k)}_{\chi\chi'}. \tag{D.15b}$$

They are completely determined by giving the representations $\mathbf{G}^a$, $\mathbf{G}^a \otimes \mathbf{G}^{(j)}$. They therefore depend *only* on the way in which the vectors $|u\nu\rangle$ or the operators Q_ν, transform under the operations of the group $\mathscr{G}$.

Proof of Theorem A

Let us apply the unitary transformation $\langle a\nu | \sigma k \chi \rangle$ to the basis vectors $|u1\rangle, |u2\rangle, \ldots, |u\nu\rangle, \ldots$. We thereby obtain a new set of basis vectors for the space spanned by the latter:

$$|u\sigma k \chi\rangle = \sum_\nu |u\nu\rangle\, \langle a\nu | \sigma k \chi \rangle. \tag{D.16}$$

The unitarity relations give

$$|u\nu\rangle = \sum_{\sigma k \chi} |u\sigma k\chi\rangle \langle a\nu|\sigma k\chi\rangle^*. \tag{D.17}$$

It follows from the very definition of this unitary transformation that the d_k vectors $|u\sigma k\chi\rangle$ (σ, k fixed, χ variable) span a certain subspace $\mathscr{E}_u(\sigma k)$ and form a standard basis for the representation $\mathbf{G}^{(k)}$ in this subspace. Expressing them in terms of the vectors of the basis $\{\tau j\mu\}$ we have

$$|u\sigma k\chi\rangle = \sum_{\tau j\mu} |\tau j\mu\rangle \langle \tau j\mu|u\sigma k\chi\rangle.$$

The d_j-line and d_k-column matrix $\langle \tau j\mu|u\sigma k\chi\rangle$ (μ and χ variable, the rest fixed) effects a homomorphic mapping of $\mathscr{E}_u(\sigma k)$ into $\mathscr{E}(\tau j)$. Since the representations of these subspaces are either inequivalent or equal, we have, from Schur's lemma

$$\langle \tau j\mu|u\sigma k\chi\rangle = \delta_{jk}\,\delta_{\mu\chi}\,u^j_{\tau\sigma}, \tag{D.18}$$

where $u^j_{\tau\sigma}$ is a constant independent of μ. With this result, the projection of both sides of Eq. (D.17) onto $|\tau j\mu\rangle$ gives

$$\langle \tau j\mu|u\nu\rangle = \sum_{k\chi} \delta_{jk}\,\delta_{\mu\chi}\,(\sum_{\sigma} u^j_{\tau\sigma}\,\langle a\nu|\sigma k\chi\rangle^*).$$

Both parts of Theorem A are contained in this equation. Q.E.D.

Proof of Theorem B

Consider the vectors $Q_\nu|\tau_2 j_2\mu_2\rangle$ (ν and μ_2 variable, τ_2 and j_2 fixed). They transform linearly one into another like the basis vectors of the $\mathbf{G}^a \otimes \mathbf{G}^{(j_2)}$ representation. It does not necessarily follow that the space they span is associated with this representation, for they are not necessarily linearly independent; however, according to Corollary III, the representation in question, if not $\mathbf{G}^a \otimes \mathbf{G}^{(j_2)}$ itself, is in any case one of its components. In spite of the possibility of a linear dependence among these vectors, we can deal with them in exactly the same way as we dealt with the $|u1\rangle, \ldots, |u\nu\rangle, \ldots$ of theorem A.

We define the vectors

$$|q\tau_2\, j_2\,\sigma\, k\chi\rangle = \sum_{\nu\mu_2} Q_\nu|\tau_2\, j_2\,\mu_2\rangle \langle a j_2\,\nu\,\mu_2|\sigma k\chi\rangle. \tag{D.16'}$$

From the unitarity relations for the matrix $\langle a j_2 \nu\mu_2|\sigma k\chi\rangle$,

$$Q_\nu|\tau_2\, j_2\,\mu_2\rangle = \sum_{\sigma k\chi} |q\,\tau_2\, j_2\,\sigma k\chi\rangle \langle a\, j_2\,\nu\,\mu_2|\sigma k\chi\rangle^*. \tag{D.17'}$$

The d_k vectors $|q\tau_2 j_2 \sigma k\chi\rangle$ (χ variable, the rest fixed), are either all null, or form a standard basis for the representation $\mathbf{G}^{(k)}$. In the latter case, we may apply theorem A. Thus in all circumstances,

$$\langle \tau j \mu | q \, \tau_2 \, j_2 \, \sigma k \chi \rangle = \delta_{jk} \, \delta_{\mu\chi} \, \langle \tau j \| Q \| \tau_2 \, j_2 \rangle_\sigma ,$$

where $\langle \tau j \| Q \| \tau_2 j_2 \rangle_\sigma$ is a constant independent of μ. Hence the projection of both sides of (D.17′) onto $|\tau_1 j_1 \mu_1\rangle$ gives

$$\langle \tau_1 \, j_1 \, \mu_1 | Q_\nu | \tau_2 \, j_2 \, \mu_2 \rangle = \sum_{k\chi} \delta_{j_1 k} \, \delta_{\mu_1 \chi} \, (\sum_\sigma \langle \tau_1 \, j_1 \| Q \| \tau_2 \, j_2 \rangle_\sigma \, \langle a \, j_2 \, \nu \mu_2 | \sigma k \chi \rangle^*),$$

whence theorem B. Q.E.D.

Selection rule

If $|u\rangle$, Q, $|v\rangle$ *transform respectively like* $\mathbf{G}^u$, $\mathbf{G}^Q$, $\mathbf{G}^v$ *and if none of the irreducible components of* $\mathbf{G}^v$ *appear in the decomposition of* $\mathbf{G}^Q \otimes \mathbf{G}^u$, *then necessarily*

$$\langle v | Q | u \rangle = 0.$$

This rule is widely used. When $\mathbf{G}^u$ and $\mathbf{G}^v$ are irreducible representations it follows directly from 1° of theorem B, but it applies equally well when none of $\mathbf{G}^u$, $\mathbf{G}^Q$, $\mathbf{G}^v$ are irreducible. To show this, we note that $Q|u\rangle$ transforms (Corollary III) according to the representation $\mathbf{G}^Q \otimes \mathbf{G}^u$ or one of its components, and we apply theorem A to the vector $Q|u\rangle$.

A particular case: the rotation group

Theorems A and B apply notably to the rotation group.

The problem of the addition of two angular momenta is a particular application of theorem A. The $(2j_1+1)(2j_2+1)$ vectors $|\alpha j_1 j_2 m_1 m_2\rangle$ introduced in § XIII.25 transform like the basis vectors of the representation $\mathbf{D}^{(j_1)} \otimes \mathbf{D}^{(j_2)}$ formed by the tensor product of the irreducible representations $\mathbf{D}^{(j)}$, $\mathbf{D}^{(j_2)}$ of the rotation group [1]). According to the discussion of Section V of Chapter XIII, the decomposition of this representation into irreducible parts is given by:

$$\mathbf{D}^{(j_1)} \otimes \mathbf{D}^{(j_2)} \simeq \sum_{J=|j_1-j_2|}^{j_1+j_2} \mathbf{D}^{(J)} \tag{D.19}$$

1) To speak here of the rotation group $\mathscr{R}_3$ is in fact an abuse of language. What we have, in fact, is the group $\mathscr{U}_2$, "covering group" of $\mathscr{R}_3$.

and the elements of the unitary matrix that realizes this decomposition are the Clebsch–Gordon coefficients $\langle j_1 j_2 m_1 m_2 | JM \rangle$. Since each irreducible representation appears at most once in (D.19), i.e.

$$(n_J^{j_1 j_2} = 1 \text{ for } J = j_1+j_2, j_1+j_2-1, \ldots, |j_1-j_2|),$$

the sum on the right-hand side of (D.12) contains only one term in this case. The components of $|\alpha j_1 j_2 m_1 m_2\rangle$ in each subspace $\mathscr{E}(\tau J)$ are therefore known to within a constant (independent of M).

Similarly, the Wigner–Eckart theorem (§ XIII.32) results from the application of Theorem B to the components $T_q^{(k)}$ of a tensor operator irreducible with respect to rotations, i.e. to $(2k+1)$ operators transforming like the basis vectors of the $\mathbf{D}^{(k)}$ representation.

The matrix element $\langle \tau_1 j_1 m_1 | T_q^{(k)} | \tau_2 j_2 m_2 \rangle$ is given by expression (D.14). Since each component $\mathbf{D}^{(J)}$ of $\mathbf{D}^{(k)} \otimes \mathbf{D}^{(j_2)}$ appears only once in the decomposition of this representation into irreducible parts ($n_J^{kj_2}=1$ for $J=k+j_2, \ldots, |k-j_2|$), the sum on the right-hand side of (D.14) has only one term in this case.

N.B. The definition of the reduced matrix element $\langle \tau_1 j_1 \| \mathbf{T}^{(k)} \| \tau_2 j_2 \rangle$ adopted in Chapter XIII differs by the factor $\sqrt{2j_1+1}$ from that adopted here.

Invariant observables. $\mathscr{G}$ degeneracy

If Q is an *observable invariant* with respect to $\mathscr{G}$:

$$[Q, G] = 0 \text{ for any } g \in \mathscr{G}$$

The d_j vectors $Q|\tau j \mu\rangle$ (τj fixed, μ variable) transform like the basis vectors of the $\mathbf{G}^{(j)}$ representation. Theorem B (or equally theorem A or Schur's lemma) gives in this case

$$\langle \tau j \mu | Q | \tau' j' \mu' \rangle = \delta_{jj'} \delta_{\mu\mu'} Q_{\tau\tau'}^{(j)}. \tag{D.20}$$

Q is thus represented by a particularly simple matrix in a standard representation suited to the group $\mathscr{G}$.

In such a representation, the eigenvalue problem for Q reduces to the diagonalization of the Hermitean matrices $Q^{(j)}$ whose elements $Q_{\tau\tau'}^{(j)}$ depend only on the indices τ and τ'. To each value of j we thus have corresponding a certain number of eigenvalues of Q, namely the eigenvalues $q_1^{(j)}, q_2^{(j)}, \ldots, q_i^{(j)}, \ldots$ of the matrix $Q^{(j)}$; *each non-degenerate eigenvalue of this matrix is a d_j-fold degenerate eigenvalue of Q*; each p-fold degenerate eigenvalue of $Q^{(j)}$ is a pd_j-fold degenerate eigenvalue of Q.

We note in particular the following two properties:

1° If Q is invariant with respect to $\mathscr{G}$, the subspace of each of its eigenvalues is invariant with respect to $\mathscr{G}$.

2° If Q is an observable invariant with respect to $\mathscr{G}$, defined in a *finite* space whose vectors transform into one another according to the $\mathbf{G}$ representation, and if the decomposition of $\mathbf{G}$ into irreducible parts is given by

$$\mathbf{G} \simeq \sum_k n_k \, \mathbf{G}^{(k)},$$

then the number of distinct eigenvalues of Q is *at most* equal to $\sum_k n_k$.

IRREDUCIBLE TENSOR OPERATORS

If an operator Q transforms according to $\mathbf{G}^Q$, it is always possible to put it into the form of a sum in which each term transforms according to one of the irreducible components of $\mathbf{G}^Q$. The irreducible tensor operators merit particular attention.

By definition, the components of an irreducible tensor operator $\mathbf{T}^{(k)}$ of order k transform linearly one into another according to the irreducible representation $\mathbf{G}^{(k)}$. That operator therefore defines a d_k-dimensional representation space for $\mathbf{G}^{(k)}$. In particular it has d_k *standard components* $T_\chi{}^{(k)}$ (k fixed, χ variable) that form a standard basis in this representation space; by definition [cf. relation (D.10)]

$$G\, T_\chi^{(k)}\, G^{-1} = \sum_\varrho T_\varrho^{(k)}\, G_{\varrho\chi}^{(k)}. \tag{D.21}$$

Let

$$\mathbf{G}^{(g)} \otimes \mathbf{G}^{(h)} \simeq \sum_l n_l{}^{gh}\, \mathbf{G}^{(l)} \tag{D.22}$$

be the decomposition into irreducible parts of the tensor product of the irreducible representations $\mathbf{G}^{(g)}$, $\mathbf{G}^{(h)}$ and let $\langle gh\gamma\eta|\sigma l\lambda\rangle$ ($\sigma = 1, \ldots, n_l{}^{gh}$) be the elements of the unitary matrix effecting this decomposition. The standard representation of the components $T_\chi{}^{(k)}$ has, according to theorem B, the noteworthy properties:

$$\langle \tau_1 j_1 \mu_1 | T_\chi^{(k)} | \tau_2 j_2 \mu_2 \rangle = \begin{cases} 0 & \text{if } n_{j_1}^{kj_2} = 0 \\ \displaystyle\sum_{\sigma=1}^{n_{j_1}^{kj_2}} \langle \tau_1 j_1 \| T_\chi^{(k)} \| \tau_2 j_2 \rangle_\sigma \, \langle k j_2 \chi \mu_2 | \sigma j_1 \mu_1 \rangle^* & \text{if } n_{j_1}^{kj_2} \neq 0. \end{cases} \tag{D.23}$$

Conclusion

It results from the above considerations that we can fully exploit the transformation properties of ket vectors and operators of Quantum Mechanics in the operations of a given group $\mathscr{G}$ if we know how to:

(*i*) write down all the irreducible representations of this group (to within an equivalence) and construct the matrices of each of these representations corresponding to a standard choice for the basis vectors of that representation;

(*ii*) decompose tensor products of these representations into irreducible parts and determine the matrix which effects the decomposition of each of these products (i.e. determine the coefficients n_l^{gh} of equation (D.22) and the "Clebsch–Gordon coefficients" $\langle gh\gamma\eta|\sigma l\lambda\rangle$).

III. FINITE GROUPS

Notation

$\mathscr{F}$, finite group considered

N, order of the group.

f, element of the group.

L, number of classes ($L \leqslant N$).

I, identity element.

$\mathscr{C}$, class of the group.

f^a, element of class $\mathscr{C}_a$.

l_a, number of elements in the class $\mathscr{C}_a$.

$k_a \equiv \sum_{i=1}^{l_a} f_i^a$, sum of the elements of $\mathscr{C}_a$.

F, representation of $\mathscr{F}$.

$\boldsymbol{\chi}$, set of characters of **F**.

F, matrix representing f in **F**.

$K_a \equiv \sum_{i=1}^{l_a} F_i^a$.

$\mathbf{F}^r$, regular representation.

$\chi^{(a)} \equiv \operatorname{Tr} F^a = \dfrac{1}{l_a} \operatorname{Tr} K_a$.

$\mathbf{F}^{(j)}$, jth irreducible representation (to within an equivalence).

d_j, degree of $\mathbf{F}^{(j)}$: $d_j = \chi^{(j)}(I)$.

$F^{(j)}$, unitary matrix representing f in $\mathbf{F}^{(j)}$ for a standard choice fixed once and for all for the basis vectors of that representation.

$F^{(j)}_{\alpha\beta} \equiv (f|j\alpha\beta)$ element of the matrix $F^{(j)}$ relative to line α and column β.

$\chi^j(a) \equiv (a|j)$ character of the class $\mathscr{C}_a$ in the representation $\mathbf{F}^{(j)}$.

10. Generalities

Rearrangement lemma

If $f_1, f_2, \ldots, f_N$ are the elements of the group written in a certain order, then each element of the group appears once and only once in the sequence $f_1 f, f_2 f, \ldots, f_N f$ obtained by multiplying each of them by the same element of the group f: it is simply the elements of the group written in a different order.

(All the properties of this paragraph result from this lemma.)

Subgroup of $\mathscr{F}$

If $\mathscr{H}$ is a subgroup of $\mathscr{F}$ of order N_h, N is a multiple of N_h:

$$N = hN_h \qquad (h, \text{ integer} > 0).$$

The integer h is called the *index* of the subgroup.

If $\mathscr{H}$ is an invariant subgroup, its index h is the order of the factor group $\mathscr{G}/\mathscr{H}$.

Classes of $\mathscr{F}$

N is a multiple of the number of elements l_a in any one of its classes

$$N = p_a l_a \qquad (p_a, \text{ integral} > 0)$$

(the elements of $\mathscr{F}$ which commute with a given element f^a of the class $\mathscr{C}_a$ form a subgroup whose index is l_a).

The group algebra. Class sum k_a

The linear combinations of the elements of the group $\sum_{s=1}^{N} x^s f_s$, where $x^1, x^2, \ldots, x^s$ are any complex numbers, form an algebra (of hypercomplex numbers): the group algebra.

The L hypercomplex numbers obtained by summing the elements of each class are called class sums:

$$k_a \equiv \sum_{i=1}^{l_a} f_i{}^a \qquad (a = 1, 2, \ldots, L). \tag{D.24}$$

These L operators commute with all the elements of the group algebra, and any other number having this property is a linear combination of these L operators.

CLASS ALGEBRA

The group algebra is not commutative unless the group is Abelian. However, the linear combinations of the L operators k_a form a commutative algebra, the class algebra, or the centre of the group algebra (if the group is Abelian, the class algebra is identical with the group algebra). One finds:

$$k_a k_b = k_b k_a = \sum_{c=1}^{L} g_{ab}^{c} k_c. \qquad \text{(D.25)}$$

The coefficients g_{ab}^{c} are *integers* $\geqslant 0$.

Although linearly independent, the L class sums are related by relations (D.25) and can therefore all be expressed as functions of a limited number of them.

Each class sum obeys an algebraic equation of degree inferior or equal to L.

11. Representations

REGULAR REPRESENTATION $\mathbf{F}^{r}$

This is the degree-N representation obtained by taking the N elements of the group itself as basis vectors. The vectors of the representation space are therefore the elements of the group algebra.

All but one of the elements of the $N \times N$ matrix representing f in $\mathbf{F}^{r}$ are null. The non-vanishing element is equal to 1.

The principal properties of the representations of the group nearly all follow from the rearrangement lemma, Schur's lemma and the study of the regular representation.

PROPERTIES OF REPRESENTATIONS IN GENERAL

Any representation of a finite group is equivalent to a *unitary* representation of that group.

If two representations have the same set of *characters*, they are equivalent [1]) (the converse is evident).

If $F_1, F_2, \ldots, F_N$ is a set of linear operators forming a finite group $\mathscr{F}$, and if $|u\rangle$ is a given vector in ket space, the representation $\mathbf{F}^{u}$

---

[1]) Consequence of the uniqueness of the decomposition into irreducible parts and of the orthogonality of the characters of the irreducible representations (see below). This property remains when the group is infinite provided that the two representations are completely reducible.

according to which $|u\rangle$ transforms in the operations of the group, is a *component of the regular representation* $\mathbf{F}^{\mathrm{r}}$ (if $\mathbf{F}^{u}$ is of degree N, $\mathbf{F}^{u} \simeq \mathbf{F}^{\mathrm{r}}$).

In a given representation $\mathbf{F}$, $k_1, k_2, \ldots, k_L$ are represented by matrices $K_1, K_2, \ldots, K_L$ that can be *simultaneously diagonalized*, and that commute with any matrix representing an element of the group:

$$[K_a, F] = 0. \tag{D.26}$$

IRREDUCIBLE REPRESENTATIONS

a) *Number.* The number of inequivalent, irreducible representations is equal to the number of classes, L.

b) *Degree.* If d_j is the degree of the jth irreducible representation $\mathbf{F}^{(j)}$ $(j=1, 2, \ldots, L)$

$$N/d_j \text{ is integral} \tag{D.27}$$

$$\sum_{j=1}^{L} (d_j)^2 = N. \tag{D.28}$$

c) *Orthogonality relations.* If the unitary, irreducible representations $\mathbf{F}^{(j)}$, $\mathbf{F}^{(k)}$ are either inequivalent or equal [1]),

$$\boxed{\frac{d_j}{N} \sum_{f=1}^{N} (f|j\,\alpha\,\beta)\,(f|k\,\gamma\,\delta)^* = \delta_{jk}\,\delta_{\alpha\gamma}\,\delta_{\beta\delta}} \tag{D.29}$$

From (D.29) we obtain the orthogonality relation for characters

$$\boxed{\sum_{a=1}^{L} \frac{l_a}{N}\,(a|j)\,(a|k)^* = \delta_{jk}} \tag{D.30}$$

Each representation being unambiguously defined by a standard choice of its basis vectors, the N^2 quantities

$$\sqrt{\frac{d_j}{N}}\,F^{(j)}_{\alpha\beta} \equiv \sqrt{\frac{d_j}{N}}\,(f|j\,\alpha\,\beta)$$

$$(f=1, 2, \ldots, N;\ j=1, 2, \ldots, L;\ \alpha, \beta=1, 2, \ldots, d_j)$$

[1]) Demonstration: if S is a $d_j \times d_j$ matrix, the matrix $T \equiv \sum_{f=1}^{N} F^{(j)} S F^{(k)-1}$ obeys the relation $F^{(j)}T = TF^{(k)}$ for all f (rearrangement lemma). Thus (Schur's lemma), T is either identically null or a multiple of unity according as $\mathbf{F}^{(j)}$ and $\mathbf{F}^{(k)}$ are inequivalent or equal. One obtains relations (D.29) by fixing S in an appropriate fashion.

are the elements of an $N \times N$ unitary matrix. Similarly, the L^2 quantities $\sqrt{l_a/N}\chi^j(a) \equiv \sqrt{l_a/N}(a|j)$ are the elements of a $L \times L$ unitary matrix. From the two unitarity relations (D.29), (D.30) we respectively deduce the two following:

$$\sum_{j=1}^{L} \sum_{\alpha,\beta=1}^{d_j} \frac{d_j}{N} (f|j\,\alpha\,\beta)\,(g|j\,\alpha\,\beta)^* = \delta_{fg} \tag{D.31}$$

$$\frac{l_a}{N} \sum_{j=1}^{L} (a|j)\,(b|j)^* = \delta_{ab}. \tag{D.32}$$

d) Special cases. If $\mathbf{F}^{(k)}$ is the identical representation, $(k=1)$ (D.29) and (D.30) give

$$\sum_{f=1}^{N} (f|j\,\alpha\,\beta) = N\,\delta_{j1} \qquad \sum_{a=1}^{L} l_a(a|j) = N\,\delta_{j1}. \tag{D.33a}$$

If g is the unit element $(g=I)$, (D.31) and (D.32) give

$$\sum_{j\alpha\beta} d_j(f|j\,\alpha\,\beta) = N\,\delta_{fI} \qquad \sum_{j} d_j(a|j) = N\,\delta_{aI}. \tag{D.33b}$$

e) Relation between class sums and characters. The matrices $K_a^{(j)}$ representing the k_a are *multiples of the unit matrix* (Schur's lemma):

$$K_a^{(j)} = k_a^{(j)} 1^{(j)}. \tag{D.34}$$

$$k_a^{(j)} = \frac{1}{d_j} \operatorname{Tr} K_a^{(j)} = \frac{l_a}{d_j} (a|j). \tag{D.35}$$

From (D.25) and (D.35),

$$l_a\, l_b(a|j)\,(b|j) = d_j \sum_{c=1}^{L} g_{ab}^c\, l_c(c|j) \tag{D.36}$$

from which, due to the orthogonality relation (D.32),

$$g_{ab}^c = \frac{l_a\, l_b}{N} \sum_{j=1}^{L} \frac{1}{d_j} (a|j)\,(b|j)\,(c|j)^*. \tag{D.37}$$

12. Irreducible Components of a Representation

General method

In order to obtain the coefficients n_j of the decomposition

$$\mathbf{F} \simeq \sum_{j=1}^{L} n_j\, \mathbf{F}^{(j)} \tag{D.38}$$

of a representation **F** into irreducible components, we need only to know its set of characters $\chi(a)$ and the sets of characters of the L irreducible representations of the group. According to eq. (D.9) and relations (D.30),

$$n_j = \frac{1}{N} \sum_{a=1}^{L} l_a (a|j)^* \, \chi(a). \tag{D.39}$$

N.B. We have:

$$p \equiv \frac{1}{N} \sum_{a=1}^{L} l_a |\chi(a)|^2 = \sum_{j=1}^{L} n_j^2.$$

Thus $p=1$ is a criterion for the irreducibility of **F**.

Regular representation $(\chi^{\mathrm{r}}(a) = N\delta_{aI})$

$$\mathbf{F}^{\mathrm{r}} \simeq \sum_{j=1}^{L} d_j \, \mathbf{F}^{(j)}. \tag{D.40}$$

The regular representation contains each irreducible representation of the group a number of times equal to the degree of that representation [relation (D.28) follows].

Tensor product of irreducible representations

$$\mathbf{F}^{(g)} \otimes \mathbf{F}^{(h)} \simeq \sum_{j=1}^{L} n_j^{gh} \, \mathbf{F}^{(j)}. \tag{D.41}$$

Equation (D.9) reads in this case

$$(a|g)\,(a|h) = \sum_{j=1}^{L} n_j^{gh} (a|j) \tag{D.42}$$

and (D.39) gives

$$n_j^{gh} = \frac{1}{N} \sum_{a=1}^{L} l_a (a|g)\,(a|h)\,(a|j)^*. \tag{D.43}$$

These two relations are to be compared with (D.36) and (D.37).

Lemma:

$\mathbf{F}^{(j)}$ is contained as many times in $\mathbf{F}^{(g)} \otimes \mathbf{F}^{(h)}$ as $\mathbf{F}^{(g)}$ in $\mathbf{F}^{(j)} \otimes \mathbf{F}^{(h)*}$.

(*N.B.* If the irreducible representations are all self-conjugate, n_j^{gh} is symmetrical with respect to its three indices.)

COMPONENTS OF DEGREE 1

The tensor product $F^{(g)} \otimes F^{(h)}$ of two irreducible representations contains at most one component of degree 1; a necessary and sufficient condition for the first-degree representation $\mathbf{F}_1$ to figure in this product is that

$$\mathbf{F}^{(g)} \simeq \mathbf{F}_1 \otimes \mathbf{F}^{(h)*}. \tag{D.44}$$

In particular, the representation space $\mathscr{E}_g \otimes \mathscr{E}_h$ of this product contains *at most one* vector invariant under the transformations of the group; this vector exists if, and only if,

$$\mathbf{F}^{(g)} \simeq \mathbf{F}^{(h)*}. \tag{D.45}$$

13. Construction of the Irreducible Invariant Subspaces

We shall henceforth suppose that a standard choice of the basis vectors has been made for each irreducible representation $\mathbf{F}^{(j)}$. We then say that a vector is of the type $(j\mu)$ if it transforms like the μth vector of a standard basis of $\mathbf{F}^{(j)}$. The unitary matrices $F^{(j)}$ being thereby unambiguously defined, we now wish to construct the vectors of a standard basis suited to the group $\mathscr{F}$ in the space $\mathscr{E}$ of the representation $\mathbf{F}$ introduced at the beginning of § 12. We limit ourselves to the case where $\mathscr{E}$ is generated by application of the operators $F_1, F_2, \ldots, F_N$ of the group to a given vector $|\rangle$ in ket-space $(n_j \leqslant d_j)$. In the applications of Group Theory to Quantum Mechanics we can always reduce the problems to this special case.

BASIS OPERATORS $B^{(j)}_{\mu\nu}$ OF THE REGULAR REPRESENTATION

Let us introduce the N operators

$$B^{(j)}_{\mu\nu} \equiv \frac{d_j}{N} \sum_{f=1}^{N} (f|j\,\mu\,\nu)^*\, F \tag{D.46}$$

$$(j=1, 2, \ldots, L; \quad \mu, \nu = 1, 2, \ldots, d_j).$$

It follows from the orthogonality relations (D.31) that the N operators of the group are linear combinations of these operators:

$$F = \sum_{j=1}^{L} \sum_{\mu,\nu=1}^{d_j} (f|j\,\mu\,\nu)\, B^{(j)}_{\mu\nu}. \tag{D.47}$$

From the unitarity of the F, the rearrangement lemma and relations (D.29), we have the fundamental properties

$$B^{(j)\dagger}_{\mu\nu} = B^{(j)}_{\nu\mu} \tag{D.48}$$

$$F\,B^{(j)}_{\mu\nu} = \sum_{\varkappa} B^{(j)}_{\varkappa\nu}(f|j\varkappa\mu) \tag{D.49}$$

$$B^{(j)}_{\mu\nu}\,B^{(k)}_{\varrho\sigma} = \delta_{jk}\,\delta_{\nu\varrho}\,B^{(j)}_{\mu\sigma}. \tag{D.50}$$

According to (D.49), the N elements of the group algebra that are represented by the $B^{(j)}_{\mu\nu}$ form a standard basis in the regular representation.

CONSTRUCTION OF A STANDARD BASIS WITH THE AID OF THE $B^{(j)}_{\mu\nu}$

If one knows how to construct the operators $B^{(j)}_{\mu\nu}$ – in other words, if one knows the N matrix elements $(f|j\mu\nu)$ – the problem of constructing a standard basis in $\mathscr{E}$ is practically solved.

Indeed

a) If not null, $B^{(j)}_{\mu\nu}|\rangle$ is a vector of type $(j\mu)$ [eq. (D.49)].

b) The N vectors $B^{(j)}_{\mu\nu}|\rangle$ span the whole of the space [eq. (D.47)].

c) The $d_j{}^2$ vectors $B^{(j)}_{\mu\nu}|\rangle$ corresponding to the same value of j have the following properties:

(*i*) the d_j vectors corresponding to the same value of

$$\nu\ (\mu = 1, 2, \ldots, d_j)$$

have the same norm, and form, except for the normalization a standard basis for the representation $\mathbf{F}^{(j)}$;

(*ii*) the d_j vectors corresponding to the same value of

$$\mu\ (\nu = 1, 2, \ldots, d_j)$$

span the n_j-dimensional space $\mathscr{E}_{j\mu}$ of the vectors of type $(j\mu)$; they are related by $(n_j - d_j)$ linear relations whose coefficients are independent of μ (in particular, if $n_j = 1$, these d_j vectors are multiples of each other and the multiplication factors are independent of μ).

Thus to construct a standard basis in $\mathscr{E}$ suited to the group, we need only to choose for each value of j a definite value $\bar{\mu}$ of μ and to construct, by the Schmidt orthogonalization method for example, a set of n_j basis vectors in the space $\mathscr{E}_{j\bar{\mu}}$:

$$|\tau j \bar{\mu}\rangle = \sum_{\nu=1}^{d_j} c^{\tau j}_{\nu}\, B^{(j)}_{\bar{\mu}\nu}|\rangle \qquad (\tau = 1, 2, \ldots, n_j)$$

$$\langle \tau j \bar{\mu} | \tau' j \bar{\mu}\rangle = \delta_{\tau\tau'}.$$

Then the vectors

$$|\tau j \mu\rangle = \sum_{\nu=1}^{d_j} c_\nu^{\tau j} B_{\mu\nu}^{(j)}|\rangle$$

$$(j=1, 2, \dots, L; \quad \mu=1, 2, \dots, d_j; \quad \tau=1, 2, \dots, n_j)$$

form the sought-for standard basis, the d_j vectors $|\tau j \mu\rangle$ (τ and j fixed, $\mu=1, \dots, d_j$) forming a standard basis for the representation $\mathbf{F}^{(j)}$.

OTHER PROPERTIES OF THE $B_{\mu\nu}^{(j)}$. PROJECTORS ONTO THE SPACES $\mathscr{E}_{j\mu}$ AND TRANSFER FROM ONE TO ANOTHER

Let us write

$$\Pi_\mu^{(j)} \equiv B_{\mu\mu}^{(j)} \equiv \frac{d_j}{N} \sum_{f=1}^{N} (f|j\,\mu\,\mu)^* F. \tag{D.51}$$

The operators $\Pi_\mu^{(j)}$ ($j=1, 2, \dots, L$; $\mu=1, 2, \dots, d_j$) form a set of orthogonal projectors whose sum is equal to 1 [1]):

$$\Pi_\mu^{(j)\dagger} = \Pi_\mu^{(j)} \tag{D.52}$$

$$\Pi_\mu^{(j)} \Pi_\varrho^{(k)} = \delta_{jk}\, \delta_{\mu\varrho}\, \Pi_\mu^{(j)} \tag{D.53}$$

$$\sum_{j=1}^{L} \sum_{\mu=1}^{d_j} \Pi_\mu^{(j)} = 1 \tag{D.54}$$

$\Pi_\mu^{(j)}$ is the projector onto the space $\mathscr{E}_{j\mu}$ of the vectors of type $(j\mu)$ [eq. (D.49)]. *The decomposition of unity* (D.54) permits one to express any vector of $\mathscr{E}$ in the form of a sum of vectors each belonging to a particular $\mathscr{E}_{j\mu}$

$$|u\rangle = \sum_{j\mu} \Pi_\mu^{(j)} |u\rangle.$$

If $\mu \neq \nu$, the operator $B_{\mu\nu}^{(j)}$ is the *transfer operator* from the subspace $\mathscr{E}_{j\nu}$ to the subspace $\mathscr{E}_{j\mu}$. The reason for this name is easily seen; from (D.50) and (D.48)

$$\Pi_\gamma^{(g)} B_{\mu\nu}^{(j)} \Pi_\eta^{(h)} = \delta_{gj}\, \delta_{jh}\, \delta_{\gamma\mu}\, \delta_{\nu\eta}\, B_{\mu\nu}^{(j)} \tag{D.55}$$

$$B_{\mu\nu}^{(j)\dagger} B_{\mu\nu}^{(j)} = \Pi_\nu^{(j)}. \tag{D.56}$$

---

1) This is true whatever $\mathbf{F}$, even if this representation is not a component of $\mathbf{F}^r$.

Thus $B^{(j)}_{\mu\nu}$ acting on any vector orthogonal to $\mathscr{E}_{j\nu}$ gives zero, and acting on any vector of $\mathscr{E}_{j\nu}$ transforms it into a vector of $\mathscr{E}_{j\mu}$, the correspondence thereby established between these two spaces being one-to-one and conserving the scalar product.

If $|\sigma j\nu\rangle$ is a vector of type $(j\nu)$, the d_j vectors

$$B^{(j)}_{\mu\nu}|\sigma j\nu\rangle \qquad (\mu = 1, 2, \ldots, d_j)$$

form a standard basis for the $\mathbf{F}^{(j)}$ representation.

Use of the class sums K_a. Projector $P^{(j)}$

If we merely wish to find the irreducible invariant subspaces of $\mathscr{E}$ we do not need to know the N^2 standard matrix elements $F^{(j)}_{\mu\nu} \equiv (f|j\mu\nu)$.

The class sums

$$K_a = \sum_{i=1}^{l_a} F_i{}^a \qquad (a = 1, 2, \ldots, L)$$

have at least one common set of basis vectors. To each vector of this set there corresponds a certain sequence $k \equiv (k_1, k_2, \ldots, k_L)$ of eigenvalues of these operators. There exists in all L series of possible eigenvalues $k^{(1)}, k^{(2)}, \ldots, k^{(L)}$, defined by equation (D.35) and corresponding each to a definite irreducible representation of the group. Consequently, if we simultaneously diagonalize $K_1, K_2, \ldots, K_L$, each series of eigenvalues $k^{(j)}$ is $n_j d_j$-fold degenerate and the corresponding subspace $\mathscr{E}_j$ defines the component $n_j\mathbf{F}^{(j)}$ of $\mathbf{F}$. If the n_j are all equal to 1, the decomposition of $\mathscr{E}$ into irreducible invariant subspaces is thereby automatically realized. If not, it remains to make this decomposition in each of the subspaces $\mathscr{E}_j$ for which $n_j > 1$.

Recall that the L operators K are all functions of a limited number of them; we therefore need only to diagonalize these to diagonalize them all.

The problem of diagonalizing the K operators is practically solved if we know the set of characters for all the irreducible representations of the group (tables of characters exist for most of the groups used in physics; cf. references of note, p. 1079). Indeed, the projector $P^{(j)}$ onto the space $\mathscr{E}_j$ is

$$\begin{aligned} P^{(j)} &\equiv \sum_{\mu=1}^{d_j} \Pi_\mu{}^{(j)} = \frac{d_j}{N} \sum_{f=1}^{N} \chi^{(j)*}(f)\, F \\ &= \frac{d_j}{N} \sum_{a=1}^{L} (a|j)^*\, K_a. \end{aligned} \qquad \text{(D.57)}$$

IV. PERMUTATIONS[1]

(Group $\mathscr{S}_n$)

14. Generalities. Cycles. Classes

Definition

Suppose we have n objects distributed among n "boxes" (ex.: n particles in n quantum states). A permutation of the n objects is a modification of their distribution among these n "boxes". We can label the objects with the integers from 1 to n, and define a particular permutation by the symbol

$$p = \begin{pmatrix} \alpha_1 \, \alpha_2 \dots \alpha_n \\ \beta_1 \, \beta_2 \dots \beta_n \end{pmatrix},$$

where $\alpha_1, \alpha_2, \dots, \alpha_n$ are the n integers written in an arbitrary order and $\beta_1, \beta_2, \dots, \beta_n$ the same integers written in an order such that object β_i occupies in the new distribution the place that α_i occupied in the old. Thus in the permutation of 5 objects:

$$p_a = \begin{pmatrix} 1 & 2 & 3 & 4 & 5 \\ 5 & 3 & 2 & 1 & 4 \end{pmatrix}$$

object 5 takes the place of 1, 3 that of 2, etc. The significance of the symbol is clearly unaltered by a change in the order of its columns.

The successive application of two permutations p_a, p_b is equivalent to the single permutation $p_c \equiv p_b p_a$. The latter can easily be written down if the upper line of the symbol p_b is identical with the lower line of the symbol p_a. If, for example, p_a is the permutation defined above, and if

$$p_b = \begin{pmatrix} 1 & 2 & 3 & 4 & 5 \\ 4 & 3 & 5 & 1 & 2 \end{pmatrix} = \begin{pmatrix} 5 & 3 & 2 & 1 & 4 \\ 2 & 5 & 3 & 4 & 1 \end{pmatrix},$$

$$p_c \equiv p_b \, p_a = \begin{pmatrix} 1 & 2 & 3 & 4 & 5 \\ 2 & 5 & 3 & 4 & 1 \end{pmatrix}.$$

---

[1] A simple and complete discussion of the theory of Young tableaux and its application to the permutation group is given in the book by D. E. Rutherford, *Substitutional Analysis* (University Press, Edinburg, 1948). The essential of the theory of the group $\mathscr{S}_n$ is given by B. L. van de Waerden, *Modern Algebra* (Ungar, Ed., New York, 1950), vol. II, p. 190–193.

In particular, the inverse of p is the permutation whose symbol results from that of p by interchange of the two lines:

$$p^{-1} = \begin{pmatrix} \beta_1\, \beta_2 \,\dots\, \beta_n \\ \alpha_1\, \alpha_2 \,\dots\, \alpha_n \end{pmatrix}.$$

The permutations of n objects form a group of order $n!$.

CIRCULAR PERMUTATIONS. CYCLIC NOTATION

The permutation

$$\begin{pmatrix} \alpha_1\, \alpha_2 \,\dots\, \alpha_{k-1}\, \alpha_k\, \alpha_{k+1} \,\dots\, \alpha_n \\ \alpha_2\, \alpha_3 \,\dots\, \alpha_k \quad \alpha_1\, \alpha_{k+1} \,\dots\, \alpha_n \end{pmatrix},$$

in which α_2 takes the place of α_1, α_3 that of α_2, ..., α_k that of α_{k-1}, α_1 that of α_k and the $(n-k)$ remaining objects α_{k+1}, ..., α_n keep their place, is by definition a *circular permutation, or cycle, of the k objects* $\alpha_1, \alpha_2, \dots, \alpha_k$; k is the *length of the cycle*. A permutation of this type can be represented by the symbol

$$p = (\alpha_1\, \alpha_2 \,\dots\, \alpha_k). \tag{D.58}$$

By convention, the first object in the list, α_1, takes the place of the last, α_k, and each of the others takes the place immediately on its left. With this notation the order of the k elements is defined only to within a circular permutation.

Two cycles having no common element commute.

Any permutation of n objects is a product of commuting cycles (these cycles have no common element) *and this decomposition is unique.*

Thus the permutation p_a defined above is the product of (154) with (23) and is written *in cyclic notation*:

$$p_a = (154)\,(23) = (23)\,(154).$$

Similarly,

$$p_b = (14)\,(235) \qquad p_c = (125)\,(3)\,(4).$$

The cycles of length 1 are equivalent to the identity transformation and may be omitted; we write simply: $p_c = (125)$. If this omission is not made, the sum of the lengths of the cycles of a permutation is equal to n.

A permutation is completely defined by:

(*i*) *its cycle structure*, that is, the number of its cycles, $h\ (\leqslant n)$, and their respective lengths $\lambda_1, \lambda_2, \dots, \lambda_h$ $(\lambda_1 + \lambda_2 + \dots + \lambda_h = n)$;

(*ii*) the numbers that appear in each cycle and their order to within a circular permutation.

If we reverse the order of the numbers in each cycle we get the inverse permutation. Thus

$$p_a^{-1} = (451)\,(32).$$

Classes

Two permutations with the same cycle structure belong to the same class, and conversely.

The cyclic notation for the conjugate element to p, $p' = xpx^{-1}$, is derived by application of the permutation x to the sequence of n numbers figuring in the cyclic notation for p. Example:

$$p_a = \begin{pmatrix} 1 & 5 & 4 & 2 & 3 \\ 5 & 4 & 1 & 3 & 2 \end{pmatrix} = (154)\,(23)$$

$$x = \begin{pmatrix} 1 & 2 & 3 & 4 & 5 \\ 2 & 4 & 1 & 3 & 5 \end{pmatrix} = \begin{pmatrix} 5 & 4 & 1 & 3 & 2 \\ 5 & 3 & 2 & 1 & 4 \end{pmatrix} \qquad x^{-1} = \begin{pmatrix} 2 & 5 & 3 & 4 & 1 \\ 1 & 5 & 4 & 2 & 3 \end{pmatrix}$$

$$p' \equiv x\,p_a\,x^{-1} = \begin{pmatrix} 2 & 5 & 3 & 4 & 1 \\ 5 & 3 & 2 & 1 & 4 \end{pmatrix} = (253)\,(41).$$

Transpositions

A transposition is a permutation of two objects (cycle of length 2). The transpositions form a class of $\mathscr{S}_n$.

Any cycle of a given length k is equal to the product of $k-1$ transpositions:

$$(\alpha_1\alpha_2 \ldots \alpha_k) = (\alpha_1\alpha_2)\,(\alpha_2\alpha_3) \ldots (\alpha_{k-1}\alpha_k).$$

More generally, any permutation p can be written as a product of transpositions. Such a decomposition is not unique but the number of transpositions involved will have a definite parity, either even or odd, which we shall denote by $(-)^p$. By definition, a permutation is *even* or *odd* according as $(-)^p = +1$ or -1.

Subgroups of $\mathscr{S}_n$. The group $\mathscr{A}_n$

$\mathscr{S}_n$ has one, and only one *invariant subgroup*, the group of even permutations $\mathscr{A}_n$. The index of $\mathscr{A}_n$ is equal to 2, its coset is the ensemble of odd permutations and the factor group $\mathscr{S}_n/\mathscr{A}_n$ is Abelian.

Among the other subgroups of $\mathscr{S}_n$ are the groups $\mathscr{S}_m$ of permutations of m objects where $m<n$, the groups $\mathscr{A}_m(m<n)$, etc. The index of $\mathscr{S}_m$ is $(n!/m!)$ and the index of $\mathscr{A}_m$ $2(n!/m!)$.

SYMMETRIZERS AND ANTISYMMETRIZERS OF $\mathscr{S}_n$

Two linear combinations of the operations of $\mathscr{S}_n$ play a special rôle, the symmetrizer s and the antisymmetrizer a:

$$s \equiv \frac{1}{n!} \sum_p p \qquad a \equiv \frac{1}{n!} \sum_p (-)^p p \tag{D.59}$$

(the sums extend over all $n!$ elements of the group $\mathscr{S}_n$). s and a are particular linear combinations of the class sums; they commute with all the operations of the group and also have the following special properties:

$$qs = sq = s \qquad qa = aq = (-)^q a \qquad (q \in \mathscr{S}_n) \tag{D.60}$$

$$s^2 = s \qquad a^2 = a. \tag{D.61}$$

15. Partitions

DEFINITION

A *partition* $\lambda = [\lambda_1\lambda_2 \ldots \lambda_h]$ of the integer n is a sequence of positive integers, arranged in the order $\lambda_1 \geqslant \lambda_2 \geqslant \ldots \geqslant \lambda_h$, whose sum is equal to n:

$$\lambda_1 + \lambda_2 + \ldots + \lambda_h = n.$$

Since the cycle structure of a permutation is defined by a definite partition of n, *each partition of n defines a class of $\mathscr{S}_n$*.

INEQUALITIES

Let $\lambda \equiv [\lambda_1 \ldots \lambda_h]$, $\mu \equiv [\mu_1 \ldots \mu_k]$ be two partitions of n. By definition:

$\lambda = \mu$ if $h = k$ and if $\lambda_1 = \mu_1, \lambda_2 = \mu_2, \ldots, \lambda_k = \mu_k$;

$\lambda > \mu$ if the first nonzero term in the sequence $\lambda_1 - \mu_1, \lambda_2 - \mu_2, \ldots,$ is positive;

$\lambda < \mu$ if the first nonzero term in the sequence $\lambda_1 - \mu_1, \lambda_2 - \mu_2, \ldots,$ is negative.

Example: for $n = 5$ $[5] > [41] > [32] > [31^2]$, etc.

(By convention, $[31^2]$ is an abbreviated notation for $[311]$.)

YOUNG DIAGRAMS Y_λ

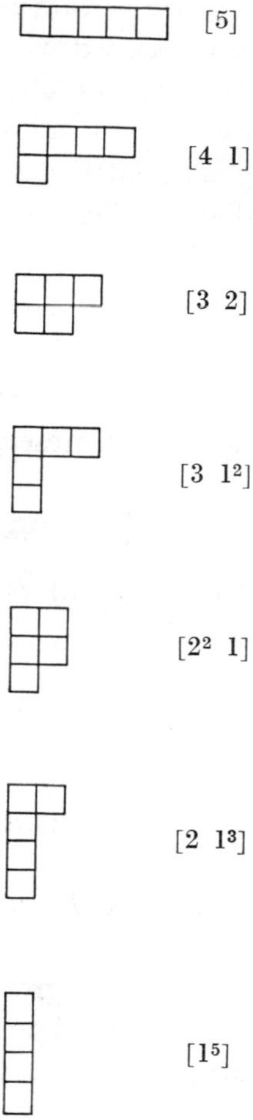

Fig. D.1. The partitions of 5 and their Young diagrams.

A given partition $[\lambda_1 \lambda_2 \dots \lambda_h]$ may be represented by a diagram Y_λ, called a Young diagram, made up of n squares arranged in h lines placed one above the other, the first line having λ_1 squares, the second λ_2 squares, ..., the hth λ_h squares (cf. Fig. D.1).

YOUNG TABLEAUX $\Theta_\lambda{}^p$

With the first n integers we can number the n squares of the diagram Y_λ in $n!$ ways, obtaining each time a certain *Young tableau*.

We shall denote by Θ_λ, and give the name of *normal tableau* to, the tableau in which the numbers 1, 2, ..., are arranged in their normal order: the sequence $1, 2, \dots, \lambda_1$ in the first row, $\lambda_1+1, \lambda_1+2, \dots, \lambda_1+\lambda_2$ in the second, etc. By applying the permutation p

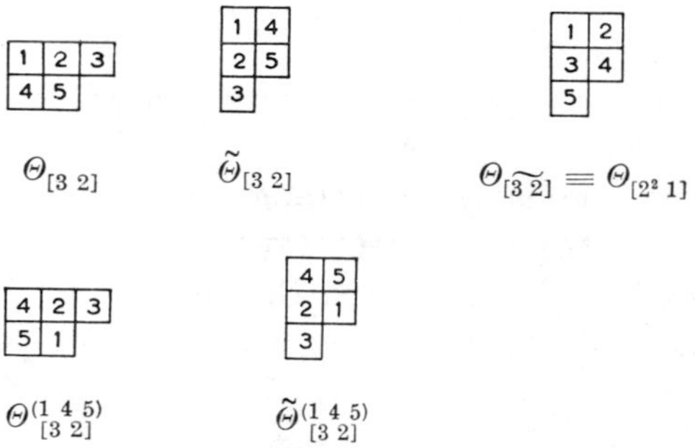

Fig. D.2. Several tableaux corresponding to the partitions $\lambda \equiv [3\,2]$ and $\tilde{\lambda} \equiv [2^2\,1]$ of the number 5.

to the n numbers of Θ_λ we obtain a new tableau $\Theta_\lambda{}^p \equiv p\Theta_\lambda$. Note that $q\Theta_\lambda{}^p \equiv \Theta_\lambda{}^{qp}$ and that there are $n!$ different tableaux for each Young diagram (cf. Fig. D.2).

ASSOCIATED PARTITIONS

Two partitions are associates one of the other if the Young diagram corresponding to one results from interchanging the rows and the columns of that of the other (reflection in the principal diagonal). In what follows we denote this type of correspondence with the symbol $\sim$. Thus $\tilde{\lambda} \equiv [\tilde{\lambda}_1 \dots \tilde{\lambda}_k]$ denotes the partition associated with $\lambda \equiv [\lambda_1 \dots \lambda_h]$. Note that $k = \lambda_1$ and $h = \tilde{\lambda}_1$, and that $\tilde{\lambda}_s$ is the number of elements of the partition λ equal or greater than s and *vice versa*.

We similarly define the Young diagram, $\tilde{Y}_\lambda \equiv Y_{\tilde{\lambda}}$ associated with Y_λ and the tableau $\tilde{\Theta}_\lambda{}^p$ associated with $\Theta_\lambda{}^p$. Note that (cf. Fig. D.2)

$$\tilde{\Theta}_\lambda{}^p = p\tilde{\Theta}_\lambda$$

but that in general

$$\tilde{\Theta}_\lambda \neq \Theta_{\tilde{\lambda}}$$

16. Young "Symmetrizers". Construction of Irreducible Representations

"SYMMETRIZERS" s_λ, a_λ, $\tilde{s}_\lambda$, $\tilde{a}_\lambda$ OF THE LINES AND THE COLUMNS OF Θ_λ

We define the operators s_λ, the symmetrizer of the lines of Θ_λ, and a_λ, the antisymmetrizer of the lines of Θ_λ, as follows

$$s_\lambda \equiv \frac{1}{\lambda_1!\,\lambda_2!\,\dots\,\lambda_h!} \sum_h h_\lambda \tag{D.62}$$

$$a_\lambda \equiv \frac{1}{\lambda_1!\,\lambda_2!\,\dots\,\lambda_h!} \sum_h (-)^h\, h_\lambda \tag{D.63}$$

the summation extending over the $\lambda_1!\,\lambda_2!\,\dots\,\lambda_h!$ permutations h_λ that leave the *lines* of Θ_λ invariant, i.e. those for which the elements of each cycle are all on the same line of Θ_λ. The h_λ form a subgroup $\mathscr{S}_{[\lambda]}$ of $\mathscr{S}_n$; $\mathscr{S}_{\lambda i}$ being the group of permutations of the λ_i objects on the ith line of Θ_λ, $\mathscr{S}_{[\lambda]}$ is the product of the subgroups

$$\mathscr{S}_{\lambda_1}, \mathscr{S}_{\lambda_2}, \dots, \mathscr{S}_{\lambda_h} \text{ of } \mathscr{S}_n;$$

s_λ and a_λ are respectively the products of the symmetrizers and the antisymmetrizers of these h subgroups.

The symmetrizer $\tilde{s}_\lambda$ and the antisymmetrizer $\tilde{a}_\lambda$ of the columns of Θ_λ (i.e. the lines of $\tilde{\Theta}_\lambda$) are similarly defined; they are the operators

$$\tilde{s}_\lambda \equiv \frac{1}{\tilde{\lambda}_1!\,\dots\,\tilde{\lambda}_k!} \sum_v v_\lambda \tag{D.64}$$

$$\tilde{a}_\lambda \equiv \frac{1}{\tilde{\lambda}_1!\,\dots\,\tilde{\lambda}_k!} \sum_v (-)^v\, v_\lambda \tag{D.65}$$

the summation extending over the $\tilde{\lambda}_1! \ldots \tilde{\lambda}_k!$ permutations v_λ leaving invariant the *columns* of Θ_λ.

Principal properties

a) These are products of symmetrizers or of antisymmetrizers, and therefore

$$s_\lambda^2 = s_\lambda \qquad a_\lambda^2 = a_\lambda \qquad \tilde{s}_\lambda^2 = \ldots \tag{D.66}$$

$$h_\lambda\, s_\lambda = s_\lambda\, h_\lambda = s_\lambda \qquad h_\lambda\, a_\lambda = a_\lambda\, h_\lambda = (-)^h\, a_\lambda \qquad v_\lambda\, \tilde{s}_\lambda = \ldots \tag{D.67}$$

b) If $\varpi \equiv \sum_p x_p p$ is an arbitrary linear combination of the elements of $\mathscr{S}_n$ (an element of the group algebra) and if [1])

$$\lambda > \mu \qquad \text{or} \qquad \tilde{\lambda} < \tilde{\mu} \tag{D.68}$$

then

$$\begin{aligned} \tilde{a}_\mu\, \varpi\, s_\lambda = s_\lambda\, \varpi\, \tilde{a}_\mu = 0 \\ \tilde{s}_\mu\, \varpi\, a_\lambda = a_\lambda\, \varpi\, \tilde{s}_\mu = 0. \end{aligned} \tag{D.69}$$

In particular, it results from either of the conditions (D.68) that

$$\tilde{a}_\mu\, s_\lambda = s_\lambda\, \tilde{a}_\mu = \tilde{s}_\mu\, a_\lambda = a_\lambda\, \tilde{s}_\mu = 0. \tag{D.70}$$

"IRREDUCIBLE SYMMETRIZERS" i_λ AND j_λ

$$\begin{aligned} i_\lambda \equiv s_\lambda\, \tilde{a}_\lambda \equiv \sum_{hv} (-)^v\, h_\lambda\, v_\lambda \qquad (i_\lambda \neq 0) \\ j_\lambda \equiv \tilde{a}_\lambda\, s_\lambda \equiv \sum_{hv} (-)^v\, v_\lambda\, h_\lambda \qquad (j_\lambda \neq 0). \end{aligned} \tag{D.71}$$

We call i_λ the "irreducible symmetrizer" and j_λ the "irreducible antisymmetrizer" of Θ_λ. We similarly define the irreducible symmetrizer and antisymmetrizer of $\tilde{\Theta}_\lambda$:

$$\tilde{i}_\lambda \equiv \tilde{s}_\lambda\, a_\lambda \qquad \tilde{j}_\lambda = a_\lambda\, \tilde{s}_\lambda,$$

ϖ being defined as above, one can show that

$$s_\lambda\, \varpi\, \tilde{a}_\lambda = Cst.\ i_\lambda \qquad \tilde{a}_\lambda\, \varpi\, s_\lambda = Cst.\ j_\lambda. \tag{D.72}$$

From (D.69) and (D.72) we easily deduce

$$i_\lambda i_\mu = i_\mu i_\lambda = Cst.\ \delta_{\lambda\mu} i_\lambda \qquad j_\lambda j_\mu = j_\mu j_\lambda = Cst.\ \delta_{\lambda\mu} j_\lambda. \tag{D.73}$$

---

[1]) One of the conditions (D.68) does not necessarily imply the other, *Example*: if $\lambda = [41^2]$ and $\mu = [33]$, we have $\lambda > \mu$; however $\tilde{\lambda} = [31^3]$. $\tilde{\mu} = [2^3]$ and therefore $\tilde{\lambda} > \tilde{\mu}$.

FUNDAMENTAL THEOREM. (*i*) *In the space of the regular representation of the group* $\mathscr{S}_n$, *the vectors* ϖi_λ (ϖ, arbitrary element of the algebra of $\mathscr{S}_n$) *span an irreducible invariant subspace* $\mathscr{E}_\lambda$ *and are therefore associated with a certain irreducible representation* $\mathbf{P}^{(\lambda)}$ *of* $\mathscr{S}_n$.

(*ii*) *The vectors* ϖj_λ *span the same invariant subspace* $\mathscr{E}_\lambda$.

(*iii*) *If* $\lambda \neq \mu$, *the irreducible representations* $\mathbf{P}^{(\lambda)}$ *and* $\mathbf{P}^{(\mu)}$ *are inequivalent.*

Since the number of irreducible representations of $\mathscr{S}_n$ is equal to the number of its classes, and therefore to the number of partitions of n, this theorem permits the construction of them all. Consequently, each irreducible representation of $\mathscr{S}_n$ may be characterized by a well-defined Young diagram.

"SYMMETRIZERS" OF ASSOCIATED TABLEAUX AND ASSOCIATED REPRESENTATIONS

To each element $\varpi = \sum_p x_p p$ of the group algebra, we associate the element $\varpi' = \sum_p (-)^p x_p p$. This correspondence is linear, one-to-one, and has the following properties:

a) if $\eta = p\varpi$, $\eta' = (-)^p p \varpi'$;
b) if $\zeta = \varpi\eta$, $\zeta' = \varpi'\eta'$ (conservation of the product).

One notes that the "symmetrizers" of the associated tableaux Θ_λ, $\tilde{\Theta}_\lambda$ are in one-to-one correspondence in this way, i.e.

$$a_\lambda = s_\lambda' \qquad \tilde{a}_\lambda = \tilde{s}_\lambda'$$

whence

$$\tilde{i}_\lambda \equiv \tilde{s}_\lambda a_\lambda = j_\lambda' \qquad \tilde{j}_\lambda \equiv a_\lambda \tilde{s}_\lambda = i_\lambda'. \tag{D.74}$$

Let $\varpi_1 i_\lambda$, $\varpi_2 i_\lambda$, ..., be a set of basis vectors defining the representation $\mathbf{P}^{(\lambda)}$ in accordance with the Fundamental Theorem; from (D.74) the corresponding vectors are $\varpi_1' \tilde{j}_\lambda$, $\varpi_2' \tilde{j}_\lambda$, ...; they define the representation $\mathbf{P}^{(\tilde{\lambda})}$. With this choice of bases, it is clear that the matrices $P^{(\lambda)}$, $P^{(\tilde{\lambda})}$ representing in each of them a given permutation p are related by

$$P^{(\tilde{\lambda})} = (-)^p P^{(\lambda)}. \tag{D.75}$$

"SYMMETRIZERS" OF $\Theta_\lambda{}^p$

Just as we did for the tableau Θ_λ, we can define with the help of $\Theta_\lambda{}^p$

the permutations $h_\lambda{}^p$, $v_\lambda{}^p$ and the symmetrizers $s_\lambda{}^p, \ldots, i_\lambda{}^p, \ldots$. We note that

$$h_\lambda{}^p = p\,h_\lambda\,p^{-1} \qquad v_\lambda{}^p = p\,v_\lambda\,p^{-1}$$

whence

$$s_\lambda{}^p = p\,s_\lambda\,p^{-1}, \qquad a_\lambda{}^p = \ldots, \text{etc.} \tag{D.76}$$

The "symmetrizers" of $\Theta_\lambda{}^p$ have properties analogous to the properties of the "symmetrizers" of Θ_λ; they can be deduced from the latter with the aid of relations (D.76).

17. Principal Properties of the Irreducible Representations of $\mathscr{S}_n$

Most of the properties of the irreducible representations of $\mathscr{S}_n$ follow from the properties of the "symmetrizers" given in the preceding paragraph.

Each irreducible representation $\mathbf{P}^{(\lambda)}$ of $\mathscr{S}_n$ is characterized by a certain Young diagram and may be constructed with the aid of the irreducible symmetrizer i_λ (or j_λ).

Each of them is *self-conjugate*

$$\mathbf{P}^{(\lambda)*} \simeq \mathbf{P}^{(\lambda)}. \tag{D.77}$$

Representations of degree 1

The *only two* representations of degree 1 are

(*i*) the identical (or symmetrical) representation $\mathbf{S}$;

(*ii*) the antisymmetrical representation $\mathbf{A}$ in which each permutation p is represented by $(-)^p$.

They are respectively generated by s and a [eq. (D.59)].

The Young diagram for $\mathbf{S}$ has a single line and represents the partition $[n]$, that of $\mathbf{A}$ a single column and represents the partition $[1^n]$.

Associated irreducible representations

Two irreducible representations $\mathbf{P}^{(\lambda)}$, $\mathbf{P}^{(\tilde{\lambda})}$ are said to be associates one of the other if their Young diagrams are associates one of the other. It results from eq. (D.75) that:

$$\mathbf{P}^{(\tilde{\lambda})} \simeq \mathbf{A} \otimes \mathbf{P}^{(\lambda)}. \tag{D.78}$$

Components of degree 1 of the tensor product $\mathbf{P}^{(\lambda)} \otimes \mathbf{P}^{(\mu)}$

$\mathbf{P}^{(\lambda)} \otimes \mathbf{P}^{(\mu)}$ has one (and only one) component of degree 1 if, and only if, we have one of the following:

(*i*) $\lambda = \mu$, in which case that component is $\mathbf{S}$;

(*ii*) $\lambda = \tilde{\mu}$, in which case that component is $\mathbf{A}$.

IRREDUCIBLE REPRESENTATIONS OF $\mathscr{S}_{n-1}$ CONTAINED IN $\mathbf{P}^{(\lambda)}$

Any irreducible representation of $\mathscr{S}_n$ is a representation (not necessarily irreducible) of its subgroup $\mathscr{S}_{n-1}$.

Let us denote by the symbol $\mathbf{P}_t{}^{(\lambda)}$ the irreducible representation of the group $\mathscr{S}_t$ corresponding to the partition λ of the integer t. It can be shown that the decomposition of $\mathbf{P}_n{}^{(\lambda)}$ into parts irreducible *with respect to the group* $\mathscr{S}_{n-1}$ is given by:

$$\mathbf{P}_n^{(\lambda)} \simeq \sum_{\mu} \mathbf{P}_{n-1}^{(\mu)}, \tag{D.79}$$

the summation being extended over all partitions μ of the integer $(n-1)$ corresponding to Young diagrams that can be obtained by removing a square from the diagram corresponding to the partition λ of the integer n.

Example:

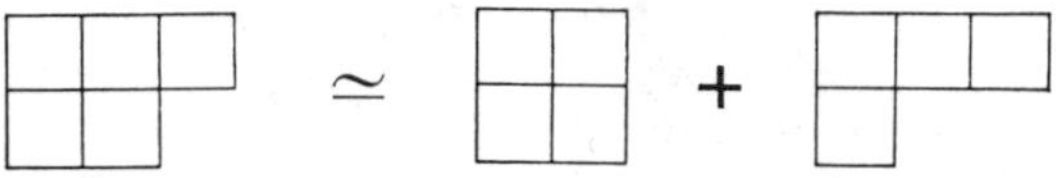

Eq. (D.79) can be used to relate certain characters of $\mathscr{S}_n$ to the characters of $\mathscr{S}_{n-1}$. In particular it can be used to deduce the degrees of the representations of $\mathscr{S}_n$ from the degrees of the irreducible representations of $\mathscr{S}_{n-1}$.

CONSTRUCTION OF THE IRREDUCIBLE INVARIANT SUBSPACES OF A GIVEN REPRESENTATION $\mathbf{P}$

In the representation $\mathbf{P}$, the various "symmetrizers" previously introduced are represented by *linear*, *Hermitean* operators (to within a constant, projectors) which we shall denote by the corresponding capital letter.

The method of constructing the irreducible components of $\mathbf{P}$ follows from the fundamental theorem of § 16. If $|u\rangle$ is an arbitrary vector of the space $\mathscr{E}$ of the representation $\mathbf{P}$, $I_\lambda|u\rangle$, if not null, transforms like $\mathbf{P}^{(\lambda)}$ and its representation space contains the non-null vector $J_\lambda|u\rangle$. The set of vectors $I_\lambda|\rangle$ formed by application of I_λ to the basis vectors of $\mathscr{E}$ spans a subspace $\mathscr{J}_\lambda$ having a number of dimensions equal to the number n_λ of components $\mathbf{P}^{(\lambda)}$ contained in

P. Let $|\sigma\rangle$ be one of the vectors of an orthonormal basis in $\mathscr{J}_\lambda$; the space $\mathscr{E}_{\sigma\lambda}$ formed by application of the operators of the group to $|\sigma\rangle$ is a representation space for $\mathbf{P}^{(\lambda)}$; one obtains n_λ orthogonal representation spaces by effecting this manipulation on the n_λ basis vectors of $\mathscr{J}_\lambda$.

If Q is an operator of $\mathscr{E}$ invariant with respect to $\mathscr{S}_n$, it transforms the vectors of each of the subspaces $\mathscr{J}_\lambda$ linearly one into another. The problem of diagonalizing Q in $\mathscr{E}$ is completely solved once we have diagonalized it in each of the subspaces $\mathscr{J}_\lambda$.

Symmetry properties of the vectors of $\mathbf{P}^{(\lambda)}$

Ket vectors do not in general have well-defined properties of symmetry or antisymmetry. We say that a vector $|\rangle$ is of the well-defined symmetry S_λ if it belongs to the subspace of the projector S_λ: such a vector is symmetrical in any permutation of the elements of a same line of Θ_λ. In the same way a vector is A_λ-antisymmetrical if it belongs to the subspace of the projector A_λ.

Starting from the tableaux $\tilde{\Theta}_\lambda$, $\Theta_\lambda{}^p$, one similarly defines the symmetries of type $\tilde{S}_\lambda$, $S_\lambda{}^p$ and the antisymmetries of type $\tilde{A}_\lambda$, $A_\lambda{}^p$ respectively [1]).

Of the two vectors of well-defined symmetry $S_\lambda{}^p$, $S_\mu{}^q$ the *more symmetrical* is by definition the one that corresponds to the larger of the partitions λ, μ. Of the two vectors of well-defined antisymmetry $A_\lambda{}^p$, $A_\mu{}^q$, the *more antisymmetrical* is the one that corresponds to the larger of the partitions λ, μ.

We can now deduce from (D.69) and the Fundamental Theorem that:

The space of an irreducible representation $\mathbf{P}^{(\lambda)}$ *contains one and only one S_λ-symmetrical vector* (and consequently one, and only one $S_\lambda{}^p$-symmetrical vector, p being any permutation) *and no vector of greater symmetry* [2]).

---

[1]) The permutation P transforms any S_λ-symmetrical vector into a $S_\lambda{}^p$-symmetrical vector and any A_λ-antisymmetrical vector into an $A_\lambda{}^p$-antisymmetrical vector [cf. relations (D.76)].

There is no such correspondence between the symmetries of type S_λ, A_λ and the symmetries of type $\tilde{S}_\lambda$, $\tilde{A}_\lambda$; the latter are equivalent to the symmetries of the type $S_{\tilde{\lambda}}{}^q$, $A_{\tilde{\lambda}}{}^q$ respectively, q being the particular permutation defined by

$$\tilde{\Theta}_\lambda = q\Theta_{\tilde{\lambda}}.$$

[2]) More generally, there exists no S_μ-symmetrical vector corresponding to any partition μ satisfying one or the other of the inequalities

$$\mu > \lambda \qquad \tilde{\mu} < \tilde{\lambda}.$$

It contains one, and only one $A_{\tilde{\lambda}}$-antisymmetrical vector, and no vector of greater antisymmetry.

CLASS SUM OPERATOR FOR TRANSPOSITIONS K_T

To each partition μ there corresponds a certain class and a class sum operator K_μ. The various possible eigenvalues $k_\mu^{(\lambda)}$ of this operator correspond to the different irreducible representations $\mathbf{P}^{(\lambda)}$ of $\mathscr{S}_n$; they are functions of the integers $\lambda_1, \lambda_2, \ldots, \lambda_h$ occurring in the partition λ of n. (*N.B.* If two partitions are different, the corresponding eigenvalues of a particular K_μ are not necessarily different: $\lambda \neq \lambda'$ does not necessarily mean that $k_\mu^{(\lambda)} \neq k_\mu^{(\lambda')}$.) Let us consider in particular the class sum operator K_T for the transpositions:

$$K_T \equiv K_{[2\,1^{n-2}]} \equiv \sum_{i<j} (i\,j).$$

If we note that K_T commutes with all the permutations and that therefore

$$k_T^{(\lambda)}\, I_\lambda = K_T\, I_\lambda = S_\lambda\, K_T\, \tilde{A}_\lambda,$$

and if we take eqs. (D.67) into account, it is easy to show that $k_T^{(\lambda)}$ is equal to the difference between the number of transpositions of type h_λ (symmetrical pairs) and the number of transpositions of type v_λ (antisymmetrical pairs):

$$k_T^{(\lambda)} = \sum_{i=1}^{h} \frac{\lambda_i(\lambda_i - 1)}{2} - \sum_{j=1}^{k} \frac{\tilde{\lambda}_j(\tilde{\lambda}_j - 1)}{2}. \qquad \text{(D.80)}$$

18. System of n Fermions of Spin $\frac{1}{2}$

SYMMETRY OF THE STATES OF n IDENTICAL SPINS $\frac{1}{2}$

THEOREM. *The space spanned by the vectors of total spin (SM) formed by n identical spins $\frac{1}{2}$ is associated with an irreducible representation of $\mathscr{S}_n$, the representation whose Young diagram corresponds to the partition $[\frac{1}{2}n+S, \frac{1}{2}n-S]$ of the integer n* (a Young diagram with at most two lines).

COROLLARY I. If $n=2$, there is one antisymmetrical state, the state $S=0$, and 3 linearly independent symmetrical states, the states $S=1$.

COROLLARY II. If $n>2$, there are no antisymmetrical states; there are in all $n+1$ linearly independent, completely symmetrical states, namely the $2S+1 \equiv n+1$ states for which the total spin is a maximum $(S=\frac{1}{2}n)$.

Proof

The space $\mathscr{E}^{(s)}$ formed of the n spins $\frac{1}{2}$ is of 2^n dimensions. Denote by u_i, v_i the dynamical states of the ith individual spin corresponding respectively to the eigenvalues $+\frac{1}{2}$ and $-\frac{1}{2}$ of s_z. An orthonormal basis in $\mathscr{E}^{(s)}$ is obtained by taking all possible products of n of these u and v vectors. Thus the vector

$$\zeta_M \equiv u_1 u_2 \ldots u_\nu v_{\nu+1} \ldots v_n$$

is a vector of this basis; it is also an eigenvector of the component S_z of the total spin

$$\mathbf{S} = \sum_{i=1}^{n} \mathbf{s}_i,$$

and the corresponding eigenvalue is $M = \nu + \frac{1}{2}n$. By effecting all possible permutations on ζ_M, we form in all

$$\binom{n}{\nu} = [n!/(\tfrac{1}{2}n+M)!\,(\tfrac{1}{2}n-M)!]$$

distinct vectors which span the subspace of the eigenvalue M; each of these vectors contains $\frac{1}{2}n+M$ vectors of type u and $\frac{1}{2}n-M$ vectors of type v.

This subspace can subsequently be subdivided into orthogonal subspaces corresponding to the different possible eigenvalues of $\mathbf{S}^2$; the quantum number S can take the $\frac{1}{2}n-|M|+1$ possible values: $|M|, |M|+1, \ldots, \frac{1}{2}n$. We denote by $\mathscr{E}^{(s)}(SM)$ the subspace formed by the vectors of total spin (SM). Since $\mathbf{S}^2$ and S_z *commute with all of the permutations*, each of these subspaces defines a representation o $\mathscr{S}_n$; moreover, since S_+ and S_- commute with all the permutations, the representations defined by two subspaces corresponding to the same value of S are equivalent.

We shall now prove Corollary II (Corollary I is evident). For this it suffices to consider the projections of the vectors of an orthonormal basis in $\mathscr{E}^{(s)}$ onto the space of symmetrical states and onto the space of antisymmetrical states. This is particularly simple with the basis vectors defined above. Since $n > 2$, any vector ζ of that basis contains at least two individual spins in the same state, u or v; suppose that ζ contains the factor $u_i u_j$; since $A = A\frac{1}{2}(1-(ij))$ and $\frac{1}{2}(1-(ij))\,u_i u_j = 0$, necessarily $A\zeta = 0$. On the other hand there is one, and only one totally symmetrical linear combination of basis vectors belonging to the subspace of the eigenvalue M, namely the sum of these $\binom{n}{\nu}$ basis vectors; since this is true for each possible value of M, this totally symmetrical vector corresponds necessarily to the maximum value $S = \frac{1}{2}n$ of the total spin. This completes the proof of Corollary II.

The demonstration carried out with A may be repeated with the antisymmetrizer $\tilde{A}_\lambda$ with the result that $\tilde{A}_\lambda \zeta = 0$ if the Young diagram Y_λ contains more than two lines. It follows that the Young diagrams for the irreducible components of the representation of $\mathscr{S}_n$ defined in $\mathscr{E}^{(s)}$ have at most two lines.

Let $\lambda = [\lambda_1 \lambda_2]$ be a partition of n that meets this condition. The number of irreducible components $\mathbf{P}^{(\lambda)}$ is equal to the number of linearly independent vectors of the type $I_\lambda|\rangle \equiv S_\lambda \tilde{A}_\lambda|\rangle$ that can be formed. For the enumeration of these we need only to consider the tableau Θ_λ:

1	2		.....	λ_2	λ_2+1	.....	λ_1
λ_1+1	λ_1+2		.....	$\lambda_1+\lambda_2$			

The n spins $\frac{1}{2}$ may be put into two separate sets, the $(\lambda_1 - \lambda_2)$ elements $\lambda_2+1, \lambda_2+2, \ldots, \lambda_1$ of the first line having no partner in the second, and the λ_2 pairs of elements situated in the same column. Let the total spins of these sets be denoted by $\mathbf{S}_1$ and $\mathbf{S}_2$ respectively:

$$\mathbf{S} = \mathbf{S}_1 + \mathbf{S}_2.$$

Denote by $S^{(\lambda_1-\lambda_2)}$ the projector onto the states symmetrical with respect to the $(\lambda_1 - \lambda_2)!$ permutations of the spins of the first set. Clearly

$$I_\lambda = S_\lambda \, S^{(\lambda_1-\lambda_2)} \, \tilde{A}_\lambda.$$

However, from its very definition, $\tilde{A}_\lambda$ is the projector onto the singlet state of each of the pairs of the second set; there is only one vector of this set having this property (Corollary I), it corresponds to the spin $S_2 = 0$. As for $S^{(\lambda_1-\lambda_2)}$, it projects the vectors of the first set onto the $(2S+1)$-dimensional space corresponding to the largest possible value of S_1 (Corollary II), namely $\frac{1}{2}(\lambda_1 - \lambda_2)$. Thus $S^{(\lambda_1-\lambda_2)} \tilde{A}_\lambda$ projects onto a $(2S+1)$-dimensional space corresponding to the value $S = \frac{1}{2}(\lambda_1 - \lambda_2)$ of the total spin. Since the projector S_λ commutes with $\mathbf{S}$, its action on the vectors of this space is either to annul them all or to transform them into vectors of the same total spin. The first possibility is excluded, otherwise it would be impossible to find vectors of total spin $\frac{1}{2}(\lambda_1-\lambda_2)$ in $\mathscr{E}^{(s)}$. Our theorem follows from the second. Q.E.D.

FORMATION OF COMPLETELY ANTISYMMETRICAL VECTORS

The dynamical states of n fermions of spin $\frac{1}{2}$ span a space formed by the tensor product $\mathscr{E}^{(0)} \otimes \mathscr{E}^{(s)}$ of the space $\mathscr{E}^{(s)}$ defined above and the space $\mathscr{E}^{(0)}$ of the orbital variables. $\mathscr{E}^{(0)}$ can be subdivided into mutually orthogonal, irreducible invariant subspaces $\mathscr{E}^{(0)}(\sigma\mu)$ with respect to the group $\mathscr{S}_n$; $\mathscr{E}^{(0)}(\sigma\mu)$ is associated with a certain irreducible representation $\mathbf{P}^{(\mu)}$; the index σ is to distinguish between the spaces associated with the same irreducible representation of $\mathscr{S}_n$. To form a complete set of orthogonal, totally antisymmetrical vectors, we need only to do so in each subspace $\mathscr{E}^{(0)}(\sigma\mu) \otimes \mathscr{E}^{(s)}$. The number of linearly independent, antisymmetrical vectors in such a subspace is equal to the number of times that the component $\mathbf{A}$ figures in the representation defined in this subspace and therefore, (§ 17), to the number of irreducible representations associated with $\mathbf{P}^{(\mu)}$ figuring in the decomposition of the representation defined in $\mathscr{E}^{(s)}$. *If Y_μ has more than two columns there are none. If Y_μ contains at most two columns, and if we put*

$$\mu = [2^{\frac{1}{2}n-S}\ 1^{2S}], \tag{D.81}$$

in accordance with the theorem above, there are $(2S+1)$ of them, and the antisymmetrical vectors that can be formed are the eigenvectors of $\mathbf{S}^2$ *corresponding to the total spin (SM) $(M=-S, -S+1, \ldots, S)$.*

SCALAR OBSERVABLES INDEPENDENT OF THE SPINS. LS COUPLING

If Q is a spin-independent, scalar observable, it may be regarded as an observable of the space $\mathscr{E}^{(0)}$ invariant under rotation and permutation of the orbital variables alone:

$$[Q, L] = 0 \qquad [Q, P^{(0)}] = 0.$$

$\mathscr{E}^{(0)}$ is the direct sum of $(2L+1)d_\mu$-dimensional subspaces $\mathscr{E}^{(0)}(\tau L\mu)$ irreducible with respect to the group of rotations and permutations [1]:

[1] $\mathscr{E}^{(0)}(\tau L\mu)$ is reducible with respect to the rotation group alone; it is the sum of d_μ equivalent irreducible subspaces ($d_\mu =$ degree of the representation $\mathbf{P}^{(\mu)}$). Similarly, it is reducible with respect to the group $\mathscr{S}_n$; it is the sum of $(2L+1)$ equivalent irreducible subspaces.

L is the angular momentum quantum number, μ the partition associated with the representation $\mathbf{P}^{(\mu)}$ of the permutation group, τ an additional quantum number to distinguish between equivalent subspaces. In particular, we can choose $\mathscr{E}^{(0)}(\tau L\mu)$ so as to have Q equal to a certain constant $q_\tau^{(L\mu)}$ in each of them (cf. § D.9).

The eigenvectors of Q corresponding to the eigenvalue $q_\tau^{(L\mu)}$ are the antisymmetrical vectors of the subspace $\mathscr{E}^{(0)}(\tau L\mu) \otimes \mathscr{E}^{(s)}$. According to the above demonstration, these can only be formed if Y_μ has at most two columns; the partition μ is then unambiguously defined by the specification of the quantum number S [eq. (D.81)]. The subspace of the antisymmetrical vectors of $\mathscr{E}^{(0)}(\tau L\mu) \otimes \mathscr{E}^{(s)}$ corresponds to a well-defined value S of the total spin of the particles; it is a certain $(2L+1)(2S+1)$-dimensional subspace $\mathscr{E}(\tau LS)$ in which one can choose eigenvectors of total orbital angular momentum and total spin

$$|\tau L S M_L M_S\rangle \qquad (M_L = -L, \ldots, +L;\ M_S = -S, \ldots, +S)$$

which form a standard basis $\{L^2 S^2 L_z S_z\}$.

GENERAL INDEX

(Page numbers relating to Volume 1 are in *italics*; starred page numbers refer to footnotes)

P

Q

S

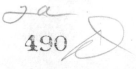